To the reader

This book is about physics. It deals with the forces that shape the world, from the smallest particle to the galaxies of stars that the universe is made of. It also deals with the way that forces and energy are used by all of us – in living and moving, in work and play, in sending messages, in storing information and using it to control so many things in the modern world.

The book is split up into short topics. Each topic includes Activities (with a blue background) – things to do in the lab and at home – and Questions (mauve background). There are also case studies and extension exercises (with a green background) which take some of the ideas a bit further.

You'll notice that there are references to the other two books in the **Nelson Balanced Science** series. Michael Roberts' book **The Living World** is mainly about biology and John Holman's book **The Material World** is mainly about chemistry. By using our books together we hope you will enjoy finding out about science – and that you'll want to study it further.

Ken Dobson

I am grateful to many people who helped to write this book, and I would particularly like to thank John Holman and Michael Roberts. Special thanks are due to Anna Grayson for writing most of the Earth science material. The following people helped by reading and making very useful comments on the early drafts of the book:

Mark Tweedie, Heckmondwike Grammar School

Michael Brimicombe, Cedars Upper School, Leighton Buzzard

Professor E K Walton, Department of Geography and Geology, University of St Andrews

David Fielding, Radley College, Abingdon, Oxon

Joe Jefferies, ASE Lab Safeguards Committee

Charles Tracy, Watford Grammar School

Stephen Pickersgill, Wycombe High School

Contents

Section A Forces and materials		2–23
A1	Squashing, pulling, bending	2
A2	Strong? Tough? Heavy?	6
	Eureka!	11
A3	Forces and structures	12
A4	Machines	18
	Analysing machines	23

Section B Forces and movement		24–57
B1	Speed, time, distance	24
B2	The mathematics of movement	28
B3	Crashes and bangs	32
B4	Gravity	40
B5	The Leaning Tower of Pisa	46
B6	Satellites	50
B7	Newton and Einstein	54

Section C Messages		58–95
C1	Signals and codes	56
C2	Sounds	62
C3	The ear and hearing	66
C4	Waves	70
C5	Controlling light	74
	Fibre optics	79
C6	What is light?	80
C7	Light as a wave	86
C8	Light and colour	90
	Signals from space	94
	Seeing with sound	95

Section D Energy		96–135
D1	Where does energy come from?	96
D2	Measuring energy?	100
D3	Using energy	104
D4	Saving and wasting – the laws of energy	112
D5	Radioactivity	116
	Radioactive dating	119
D6	What happens when atoms decay?	122
D7	Nuclear energy	128
D8	Radiation and life	132
	Good tidings?	134
	A sun-warmed house	135

Section E Electricity and magnetism		136–191
E1	Electric signals	136
E2	Magnets	140
E3	Controlling electricity: current and resistance	144
E4	Using circuits	148
E5	What is electricity?	154
	Static – friend and foe	158

E6 Using electricity: heating and lighting 160
E7 Using electricity safely 164
A steam iron 167
E8 Using electricity: motors and dynamos 168
E9 Electricity from frogs? 172
How does it work? An electric bell 174
E10 Ions and electrolysis 176
E11 The electricity industry 180
E12 Electrons in space 188

Section F Earth and space **192–214**

F1 The dynamic Earth 192
F2 Sky patterns 198
F3 Patterns in space 202
F4 How the Earth was made 206
Planets, atmospheres and life 213
F5 Outer space 214

Appendix: Units, graphs and data **220**

Index **225**

A1 Squashing, pulling, bending

The way materials react to forces often decides how we use them.

The pole vaulter in picture 1 uses a long glass-fibre pole to pull himself 8 m above the ground. The pole has to be strong and light. It also has to be bendy – but not too bendy! When he comes down on the other side he relies on the softness of the foam plastic to cushion his fall.

Making and choosing materials

The materials used in making the pole and the cushion have been carefully chosen for the job they have to do. They behave in the right way when forces are applied to them. In fact, both of these materials are **synthetic**, which means that they have been made in a factory, and don't occur naturally on Earth.

Modern materials like these are designed and made by materials scientists. They need to know what the materials will be used for. They need to know how much force they must be able to withstand, how 'heavy' (dense) they need to be, and how 'bendy' they must be.

Useful materials

Picture 2 shows lots of synthetic materials, as well as some natural ones. Can you tell which are 'natural' and which are synthetic? In some sports grounds even the grass is artificial! The designers and makers of vaulting poles, safety mats – and even the clothes that the athletes wear – have to make a sensible choice of what materials to use.

To help them to design or choose the best materials for a purpose, scientists must test them in a standard way. They must also know if changing the size of the object will make any difference. A thinner vaulting pole will be lighter, cheaper and easier to run with, but might break more easily.

Testing materials

The activities at the end of this topic will give you an idea of how materials are

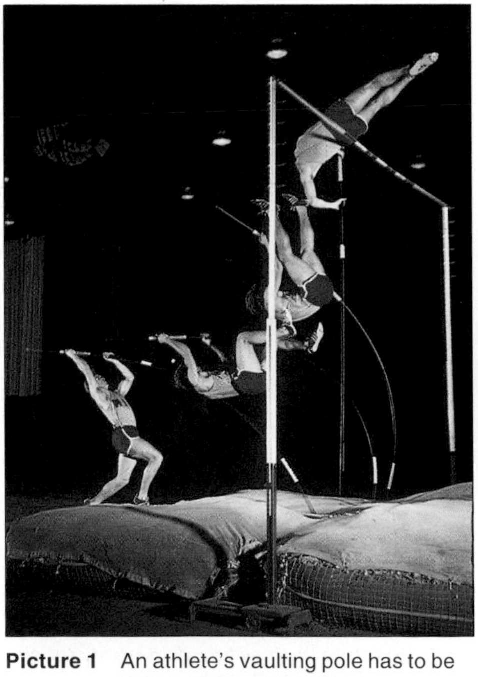

Picture 1 An athlete's vaulting pole has to be strong, light and flexible.

Picture 2 Natural and synthetic materials: can you tell which is which?

tested. The tests have to be 'fair' – for example the samples of different materials must be the same size, and tested under the same conditions. You could do a **flexibility** test as shown in picture 3 (see also activity A). Extra bending force is applied by simply adding weights to the end of the sample. The effect of doing this can be measured by seeing how far down the end of the beam bends.

This kind of test shows that all materials will bend to some extent – but if the sample is too thick the movement will be too small to be seen without special instruments.

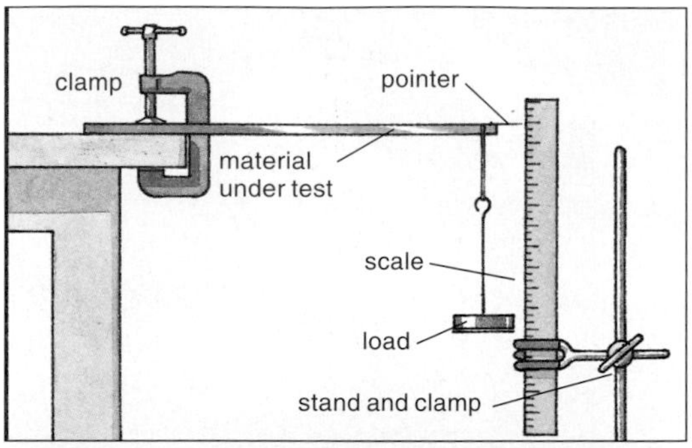

Picture 3 One way of testing materials to compare how flexible they are.

Plastic and elastic

These words have a special meaning in materials science. They describe what a material does when forces are applied to it. Forces tend to change the shape of an object. If the shape stays changed even when the force is taken away the material is called **plastic**.

Mud, Plasticine, clay and putty are good examples of plastic materials.

But if the object returns to its original shape when the force is removed it is called an **elastic** material. Rubber, steel, wood and many other materials behave like this. Both the foam safety mat and the vaulting pole in picture 1 are made of elastic materials.

Picture 4 Steel is elastic – up to a point!

Are plastics plastic?

Most of the materials that we call 'plastics' are synthetic materials that *were* plastic at the time they were made. Then they were heated or chemically treated to make them set hard, and they stopped being plastic.

Over the limit

Many useful materials are only elastic up to a point. If too much force is applied they will not return to their original shape. Steel is quite elastic, but large forces may bend it out of shape permanently, like a car body that has been in an accident (picture 4). At some stage it stopped being elastic, and became plastic. Metals like copper and lead show this effect more easily, with less force needed.

Glass

Surprisingly, glass is also elastic. Thin glass fibres can be bent easily. But if too much force is applied glass will not just **deform plastically**, like steel or copper, but shatter. A material like this is said to be **brittle**.

Testing for elasticity

Activity B is about finding out whether a material is elastic or not, and how much force is needed to make it go beyond its elastic limit. To check if the material is elastic you need to take measurements both when forces are increased and when they are decreased.

Using graphs

Graphs are a useful way of using experimental data to compare one material with another. A graph of force applied (or **load**) plotted against the change it produces will show clearly how the materials behave.

The graphs in picture 5 show how different materials might behave in these tests. The black line shows what happens as the load is increased. The green line shows what happens when they are unloaded.

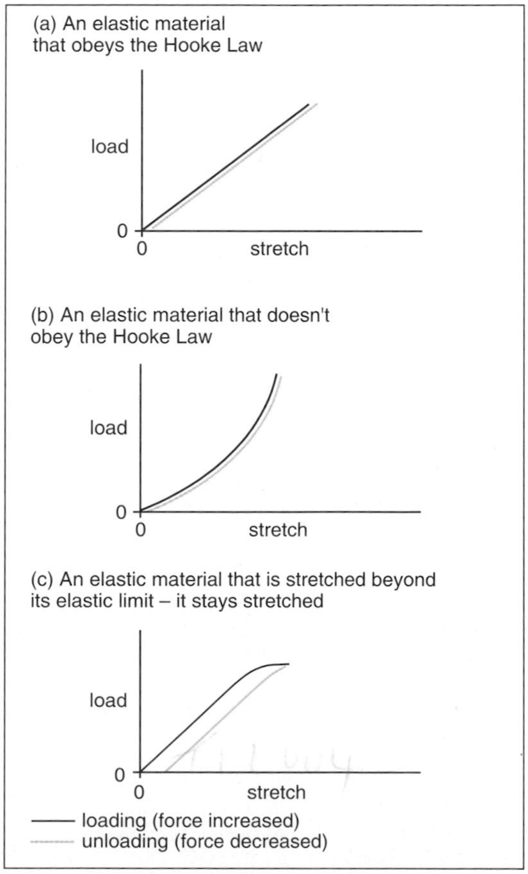

Picture 5 Graphs can show how different materials stretch differently.

The Hooke Law

When objects are stretched or compressed they change their shape. For some materials length changes steadily for a steady change in the applied force. Every extra bit of force produces an equal, extra bit of length. Materials that do

Picture 6 This force measurer relies on the Hooke Law.

this are said to obey the **Hooke Law**.

As in activity B, it makes sense to measure the change in length, or the **extension**, of the sample. A material that obeys the Hooke Law will give a straight line graph. The graph produced by such a material is shown in picture 5(a). The other graphs in the picture show how other materials behave when they are stretched. Of course, the change produced could be a shortening, caused by a compression force, or an angle of bending produced by a sideways force.

Using elasticity to measure forces

Objects that obey the Hooke Law are used in making a spring balance or a newton meter. The marks on its scale show the extension or compression produced by a force. Because the spring inside obeys the Hooke Law the length changes can be marked as **force** changes. Picture 6 shows an example of a force measurer that uses the Hooke Law.

Activities

A Testing for flexibility

Picture 3 shows how to set up a test of flexibility. Make sure that the specimens of the materials you are testing are the same width, thickness and length. The specimens might be plastic, metals (steel, copper, tin) or wood.

Use a clamp to fix one end of a specimen of material firmly to the bench or table. Apply forces at the other end using either a newton meter or by adding masses. Take care to apply these forces at the same distance from the end, for each specimen.

If you load the specimen by adding masses, you need to know that the force exerted when you add a mass of 100 g is just about 1 newton. For each specimen, complete a table of results as shown:

Applied force (N)	Deflection (mm)

Plot graphs of deflection against applied force. Use the same pair of axes for all the materials.

Write a report on your tests, making sure that you:

- describe the differences between the materials,
- note any pattern of behaviour of any of the materials,
- explain any precautions you took to ensure that the tests were fair and accurate.

B Elastic or not?

An elastic material will change its shape when a force is applied and then return to its original shape when the force is removed. In this experiment you will test one or more objects to see if they are elastic or not. In each case use a stretching force, which could be done either by using a newton meter or by hanging weights (masses) on the specimen. See picture 7.

Suitable objects to test are: an elastic band, a steel spring, a 'home-made' spring made by coiling 300 mm of copper wire around a pencil.

If you have special equipment of the kind shown in picture 8 you will be able to test a length of thin copper wire – or a wire made of other metals. This experiment needs special care – check the details with your teacher.

CARE! Wear eye protection if the specimens are likely to snap and fly back, e.g. filaments and wires. Put a box of waste packing material under heavy loads to catch them if they fall and prevent anyone having a foot in the way.

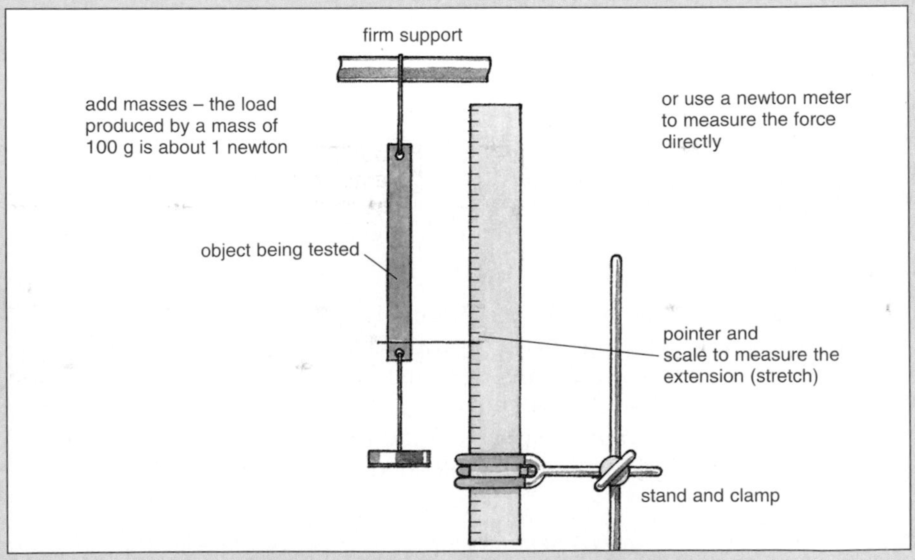

Picture 7 Testing to see if material or objects obey the Hooke Law.

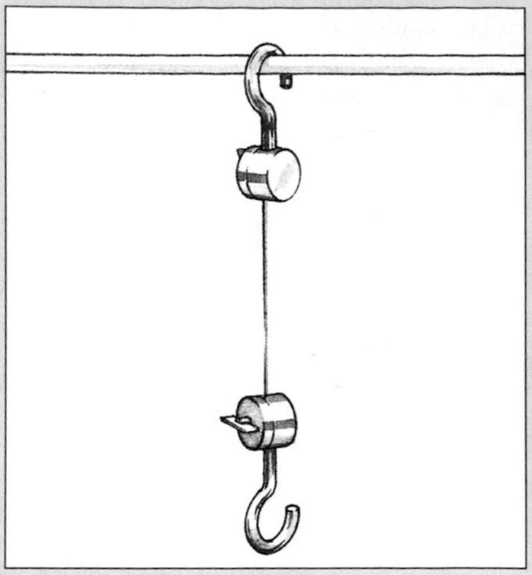

Picture 8 Special apparatus for investigating how metal wire stretches.

You need to measure how much each object **extends** (increases in length) when an extra load is applied. Take measurements while loading and unloading. Set out your measurements for each specimen in a table as shown:

Applied load (N)	
Extension when loading (mm)	
Extension when unloading (mm)	

Plot graphs of extensions, both loading and unloading, for each object tested (as in picture 5 above). Write a short report on your tests:

- describing briefly what you did and measured,
- stating which objects behaved elastically,
- stating which objects obeyed the Hooke Law.

C What makes a good bouncer?

Plan an experiment to compare how good the following materials are at bouncing:

glass (e.g. a marble), steel, lead, wood and rubber.

Check with your teacher that your experiment is workable, then carry it out.

What property of the material is most important in deciding how bouncy it is? For example, density, elasticity, toughness? Use the table of values on page 9 to help you answer this question.

Questions

1 Sort the following materials into two groups:

a elastic, b plastic:
steel, glass, wood, clay, Plasticine, cotton, mud, putty, cardboard, foam plastic, polythene.

2 Use the information given in this topic, plus any ideas you already have, to answer the following questions.

a Why is a pole used by a pole vaulter made of a material which is 'bendy, but not too bendy'?
b Why are most springs made of metal?
c Both steel and foam rubber obey the Hooke Law. Why are the safety mats in the gym made of foam rubber, not steel?

3 Explain as clearly as you can what the following words mean:

a elastic,
b plastic,
c brittle,
d flexible.

4 Which of the graphs in picture 9 of extension plotted against load would you expect to match the following materials:

a rubber,
b copper wire,
c a piece of string,
d Plasticine.

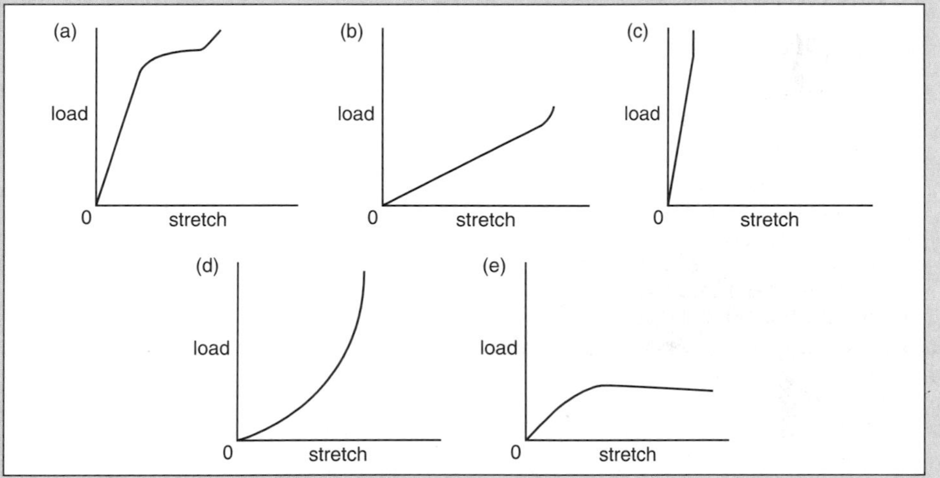

Picture 9

5 Look at picture 2. Write down the names of the synthetic materials you can identify (e.g. glass).

6 Look at a biscuit.

a Use the words you have learned in this topic to describe its properties as a **material**.
b Biscuits come in a variety of different packagings (see picture 10). How do the mechanical properties of the biscuit decide what kind of packaging the biscuit manufacturers need to use?

Picture 10

A2
Strong? Tough? Heavy?

Strong materials may not be tough – and needn't be heavy.

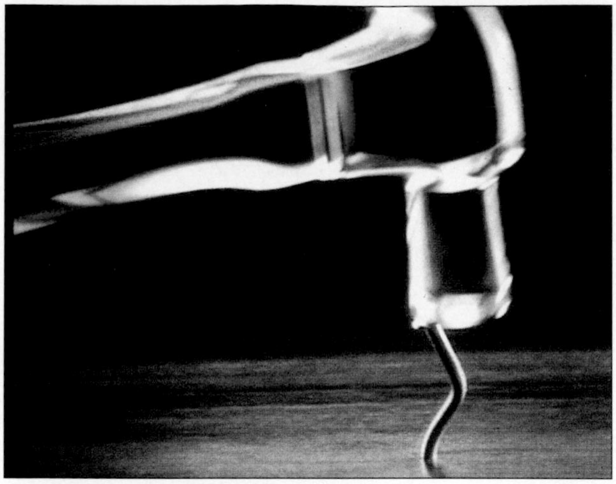

Picture 1 Glass can be very tough. This glass hammer is strong enough to drive in a nail without shattering.

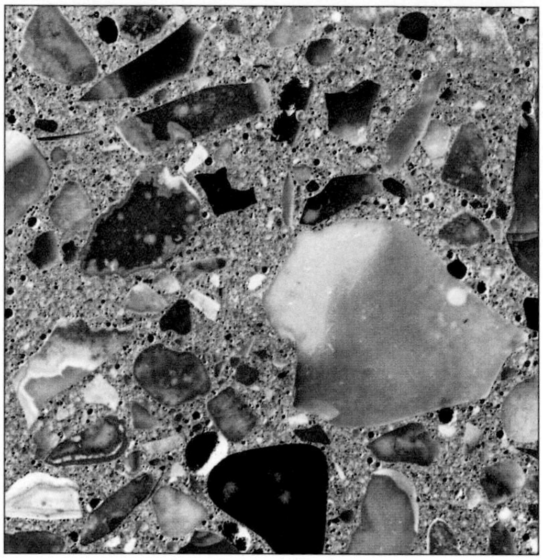

Picture 2 Concrete in close-up.

Steel and glass

A strong material needs a lot of force to break it, compared with a weak material of the same size. Steel is strong – but so is glass. Think of how many milk bottles there are in the world – they get rough treatment but they last quite a long time.

The important practical difference between glass and steel is that steel is also *tough*. That is, it doesn't crack like glass does. Steel milk bottles would last much longer! When too much force is applied to steel it will bend instead of shattering.

Can glass be tough?

A special glass can be made that is very tough – but it is expensive. Picture 1 shows glass that can stand a very large force, and bends rather than breaks. This is the kind of glass that might be used in banks as a protection against thieves.

A weak material can be quite tough, like Plasticine or even cardboard. A biscuit is neither strong nor tough.

Making materials stronger and tougher

Everyday objects aren't usually made of a pure material. More and more, they are made of mixtures of materials. These mixtures are called **composites**. This means that the good properties of one material can be combined with the good properties of another material.

Concrete

Concrete is a good example of a composite material. Ordinary concrete is made from cement, sand and pebbles. Sand and pebbles are very strong materials, and they are hard to break or crack. Unfortunately they aren't much use on their own – the grains or stones are separate and fall apart too easily. But thousands of years ago it was discovered that if they are stuck together by even a fairly weak material the result is a very useful building material – concrete.

A material that sticks particles together is called a **cement** or a **matrix**. The cement used in concrete is made by heating limestone with clay. When cement is mixed with water, it reacts to form a hard, strong solid.

Picture 2 shows what concrete is like inside. You can see the sand grains and parts of the pebbles in the cement that are holding them together.

Concrete does have a problem – it cracks too easily. The cracks start in the cement, grow bigger and move through the cement in the spaces between the grains. But if there are enough grains or pebbles of the right size they stop the cracks getting any bigger – they are too strong and tough for the cracks to get through.

Concrete cracks more easily when it is bent or stretched (in **tension**). The pulling forces make the cracks bigger. But if concrete is always used in **compression** the forces act to close the cracks up. Picture 3 shows how cracks are helped to grow by pulling forces, and may be stopped by pebbles and by compression forces.

On a larger scale, a brick wall is stronger if the bricks are 'bonded' in such a way that a failure in the mortar (making a large 'crack') is stopped by meeting the centre of another brick. Compare the walls in picture 4.

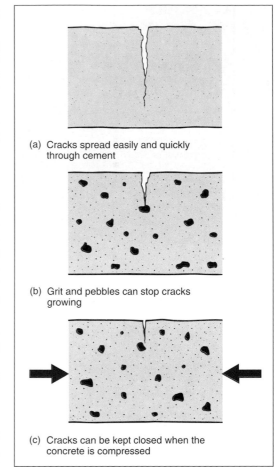

(a) Cracks spread easily and quickly through cement

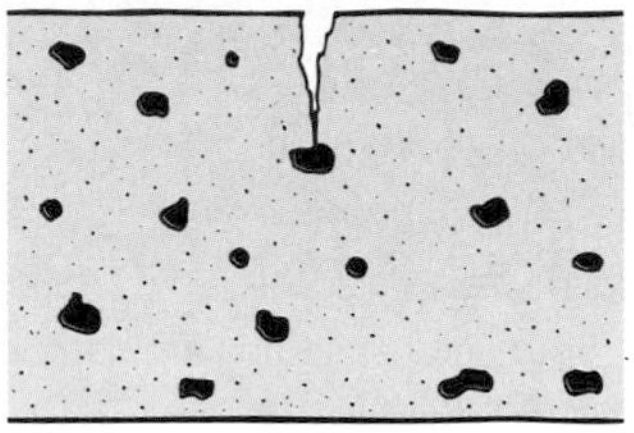

(b) Grit and pebbles can stop cracks growing

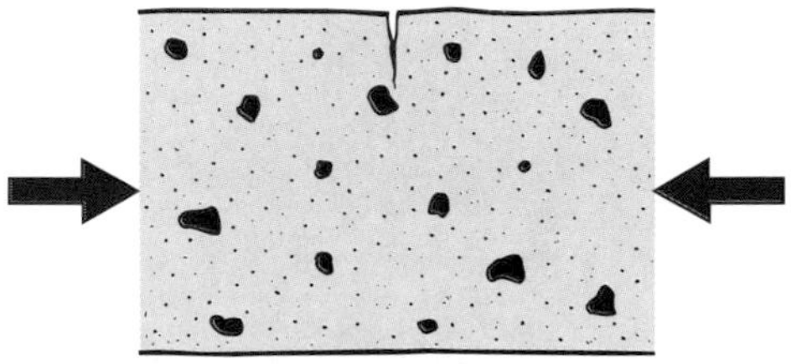

(c) Cracks can be kept closed when the concrete is compressed

Picture 3 Cracks.

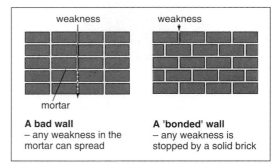

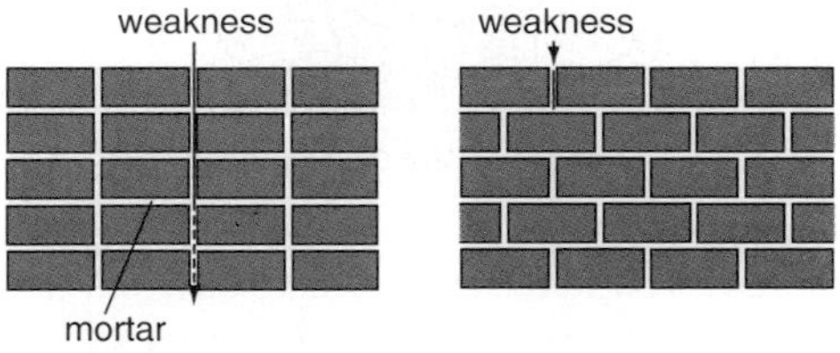

A bad wall – any weakness in the mortar can spread

A 'bonded' wall – any weakness is stopped by a solid brick

Picture 4 Two types of brick bonding in walls.

Using fibres to make materials tougher

Concrete is a rough, heavy kind of material. It is good for making things like buildings and bridges, but is not too pleasant for making, say, indoor furniture. But the principle of using a mix of materials is used in lots of everyday objects.

In general, the idea is that one material (the matrix) gives flexibility and the other, (the reinforcing) gives strength. The combination is a composite material with both strength and toughness. Glass-reinforced plastic is another composite material. It is used to make canoes, yachts, plant containers, baths and many other things.

Glass-reinforced plastic is light, and can be flexible without losing strength. Plain plastic would bend a little and then shatter because of the cracks that develop. The glass fibres stop the cracks growing to danger level.

Carbon fibres do the same job in more expensive objects, like tennis rackets and fishing rods. They can also be used to reinforce metals.

Reinforced concrete

Concrete is best used 'in compression'. This means with forces acting on it which squash it, rather than stretch it. This is because concrete is easy to crack, as explained above. This means that concrete would not be very useful as a building material except in pillars or supports, or as a road material.

But engineers have found a way of keeping concrete in compression all the time, wherever it is used. This is done by pouring the concrete mix over steel wires which are kept stretched by very large forces. When the concrete has set hard the wires are let go. As they try to return to their proper length they keep the concrete under compression (see picture 5).

This is called 'pre-stressed' concrete. The compression forces produced by the steel wires inside the concrete beam are larger than the forces the beam is designed to take in its normal use. So any small cracks that may start cannot grow large enough to split the concrete beam.

Picture 5 (a) Making pre-stressed concrete.

(b) Concrete beams.

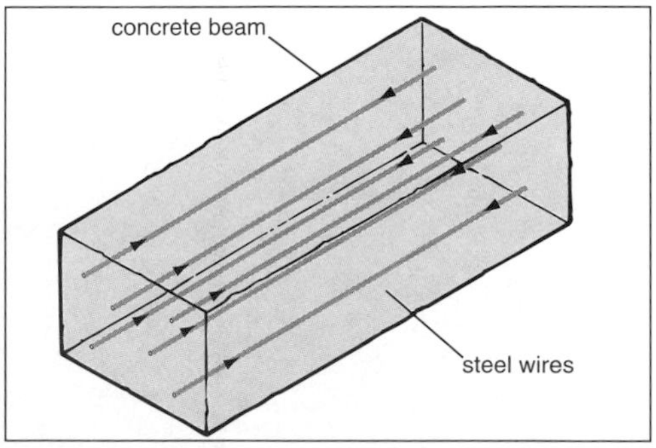

(c) The steel wires are kept pulled tight until the concrete sets hard. When they are let go, the wires pull the concrete together, keeping it in compression.

Picture 6 Both of these lorries are carrying the same weight.

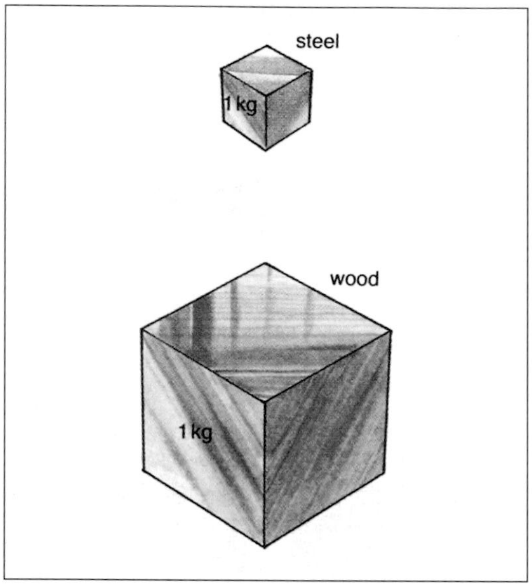

Picture 7 A kilogram of wood takes up nearly ten times as much space as a kilogram of steel.

Picture 8 An airplane under construction showing the open framework.

Density

Both the lorries in picture 6 are carrying the same **load**, but one is a load of wood and the other a load of steel. The lorry with the steel looks almost empty, and it would be easy to put a lot more on it. But to do this would be illegal – and dangerous. The result would be too much force on the wheels and axles of the lorry. If both lorries are loaded to their full legal limits then they are carrying the same load – in other words the steel weighs as much as the wood.

The difference between the two materials is that steel is **denser** than wood. Twenty tonnes of steel take up far less space than twenty tonnes of wood (picture 7).

Measuring density

Density means how much matter there is in a given space. In other words, density is **mass per unit volume**.

As a formula:

$$\text{density} = \frac{\text{mass}}{\text{volume}} \quad \text{or} \quad d = \frac{m}{v}$$

Steel has a density of 7700 kilograms per cubic metre; wood is much less dense, even a 'heavy wood' like oak has a density of only 720 kg/m^3. We can rearrange the formula and use it to calculate how much space (volume) 20 tonnes (20 000 kg) of oak would take up:

$$\text{volume} = \frac{\text{mass}}{\text{density}}$$

$$= \frac{20\,000}{720} \text{ cubic metres}$$

$$= 27.8 \text{ m}^3$$

Use the formula to check that twenty tonnes of steel would only take up 2.6 m^3.

Why is density important?

The density of a material is a very important property. Think of a structure – like a building, a bridge or the skeleton of an animal. If it was made of a dense material it would have the problem of supporting its own weight, as well as any load it had to carry. This might be difficult to do.

Bones have a hollow structure which allows them to be mostly 'empty', so combining lightness with strength. Modern buildings are also designed to combine lightness with strength, using modern low-density materials.

Aircraft have to be strong, but as light as possible. They are built on an open framework, as shown in picture 8. This framework is made from special mixtures of metals (alloys). Scientists called metallurgists have had to develop new strong alloys with very low densities, such as duralumin (aluminium and copper) and magnesium alloys.

Why are some materials denser than others?

The basic reason for some chemical elements being denser than others is that their atoms have more mass (picture 9). An atom of lead is nearly eight times more massive than an atom of aluminium.

But lead is in fact only about four times denser than aluminium. This is because the density of a material is also decided by how crowded together its atoms are. The atoms in lead are 'packed' differently from those in aluminium.

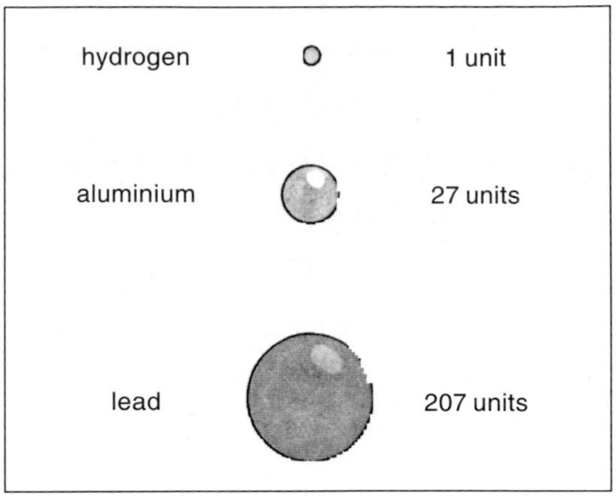

Picture 9 Atoms of different elements have very different masses.

Floating and sinking

The density of a material decides whether it will sink or float. Materials denser than water will sink in it. Less dense materials will float.

The same rule applies to any fluid – helium and hydrogen balloons float in air because these gases are less dense than air. Carbon dioxide balloons fall, sinking through the air.

Of course, you can make a dense material float by giving it a hollow shape. This means that it contains air, and so the average density of the object is less than the density of water.

Table 1 Properties of materials.

Material	Density (kg/m^3)	Elasticity (arbitrary units)	Strength (arbitrary units)
copper	8940	65	10
steel (high-tensile)	7800	100	100
aluminium	2700	35	1.5
aluminium alloy	2800	35–45	10
lead	11350	8	1
wood (oak)	720	5	2
wood (balsa)	200	3	2.5
glass	2500	33	3
glass-reinforced plastic	1850	37	10–70
rubber	2500	0.003	1
bone	1100	10	3
perspex	1200	1.4	12
polythene (high density)	960	0.5	6
concrete ordinary mix	2200	20	cracks
brick	1700	3.5	} depends on joints
breeze block	1400	15	

Notes:

1 Elasticity is measured in terms of how much force is needed to produce a standard percentage extension. The lower the number the easier it is to stretch.

2 Strength is measured as the force needed to break something by stretching it. The bigger the number the harder it is to break it (or deform it permanently).

3 Some materials, like brick, have variable properties. Average values are given.

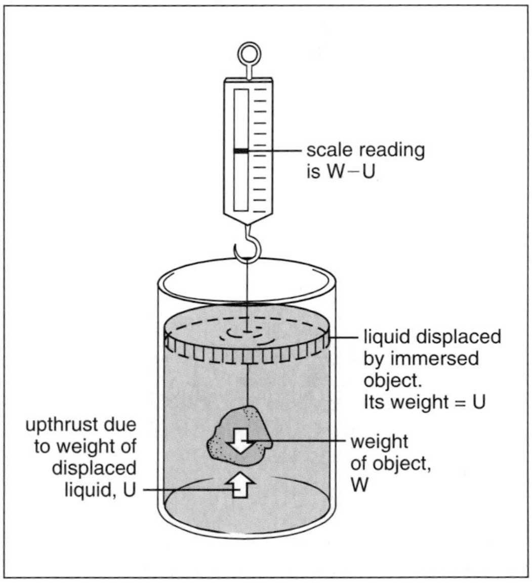

Picture 10

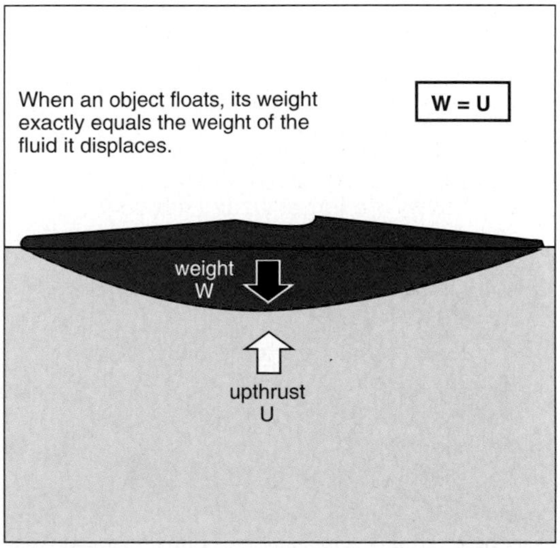

Picture 11

Activities

A Physical properties of materials

There are many possible reasons why a designer chooses to use a particular material to make something with. This topic is about just some of the physical properties of materials.

1 List some other properties that you think might be important.

2 Choose any object that you can see and touch that is made of more than one material. Write down what it is made of and say why you think the designer has chosen those materials.

B Making and testing concrete

What makes the strongest concrete? It might depend on:

- the amount of cement compared with the other ingredients (the aggregate),
- how much water you use,
- the size of the particles in the aggregate (sand, grit, pebbles).

In this activity you will test different concrete mixes. It is best done as a group. Decide what proportions of quantities you want to use. For example, the mix of cement to the other materials (aggregate) could be 1 to 1, 2 to 1, 1 to 2, etc. Make a clear table of the different kinds of mixes and quantities of water that you are going to make samples with.

Your teacher will tell you the size of mould to use – a reasonable size would be a small 'beam' about 20 cm long by 8 cm wide and 5 cm deep. You may have to make the moulds yourselves.

CARE! *Use goggles.* Do not touch the wet mix with your hands. It will damage sensitive skin. Use plastic gloves if possible.

Share the work out amongst the members of the group, so that everybody makes one kind of mix. Use small tins to get the volumes of the different parts of the mix in the right ratios. Put the dry ingredients in a larger tin and mix very well. Add water slowly, mixing it in as you do so. Pour the mix into the moulds and cover it with damp paper so that it doesn't dry out before it sets.

The concrete will take a few days to set properly.

Testing the samples

Picture 12 shows one way of doing this. The aim is to find out how much weight the beam can take without breaking. Make sure that all the beams are tested in the same way. Take care to wear goggles in case the concrete beam shatters with a heavy load.

Put a box of waste packing material underneath to catch the loads if they fall.

Write a report on your results.

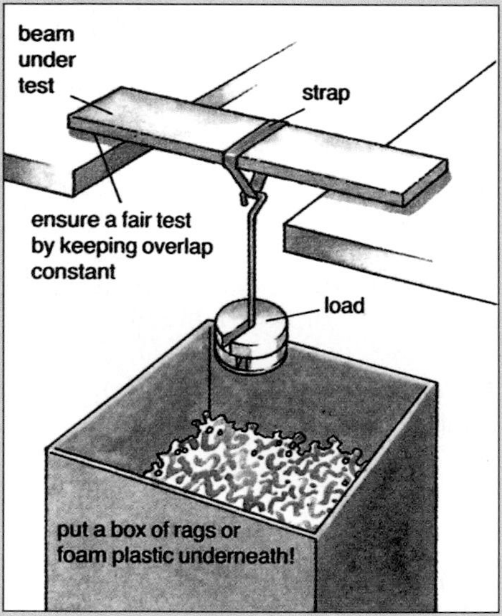

Picture 12

C Measuring density

To find the density of an object you will need to measure two things – its volume and its mass. You then calculate its density by using the formula

$$\text{density} = \frac{\text{mass}}{\text{volume}}$$

The diagrams in picture 13 show three ways for measuring volume.

You will need a suitable balance (lever arm, top-pan, spring) to measure mass.

Choose the best combination of instruments and techniques to measure the densities of some or all of the following materials:

1 a metal block,

2 a wooden block,

3 a specimen of rock,

4 oil,

5 water,

6 sand.

D Finding out about densities

Use a library or a reference book to find out:

1 What is the densest element?

2 What is the least dense element?

3 What is the densest timber?

4 Birds' bones are less dense than, say, human bones. How is this achieved?

E Floating and sinking

1 Use table 1 on page 9 and a reference book to find the densities of the following materials: oak, copper, lead, brick, balsa, candle wax.

2 Sort these materials into two groups, those that sink in water (a) and those that float (b).

3 The density of water is 1000 kg/m^3. Polypropylene is a plastic with a density of 900 kg/m^3. Will it float or sink in water?

4 Alcohol has a density of 800 kg/m^3. Will polypropylene float in alcohol?

5 Ice floats with about 90% of its volume under water. Make a reasonable guess at the density of ice.

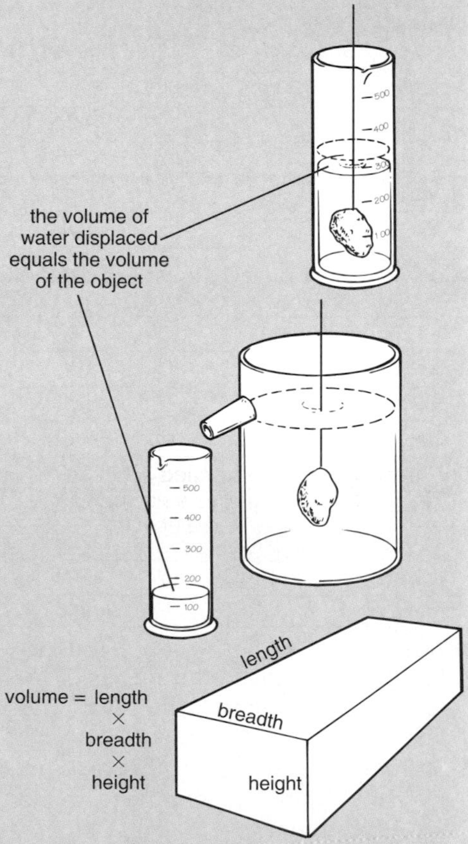

Picture 13

Questions

1 Concrete beams are best used 'in compression'.

a What does 'in compression' mean?
b What happens if the beams are used 'in tension'?
c Why are the concrete beams used in modern buildings usually 'reinforced' with strong steel wires?

2 Why are some materials made of a 'resin' or 'matrix' with fibres inside? (For example, glass fibres in plastic, carbon fibres in metals and plastics.)

3 Make an estimate of how much of the material in your classroom is synthetic ('man-made') compared to the amount that is 'natural' (like wood or stone).

Choose one of the synthetic materials and give one reason (other than cost) why it might have been selected for its purpose.

4 Using your own experience, put the following materials in order of density, the most dense material first:

oak, expanded polystyrene, lead, glass, the human body, water.

5 Some of the key words used in this topic are: strong, tough, brittle, weak, composite, matrix, reinforce, cracks.

Write a sentence about three of the materials listed below, in which at least six of the above key words are used correctly. You don't need to use each word about each material!

Materials: **wood**, **glass**, **concrete**, **polythene**.

6 Wood is a lot less dense than steel, but most ships are made of steel. How can a steel ship float?

7 Copy out and complete the table below by calculating the missing values. You will need to use the formula

$$\text{volume} = \frac{\text{mass}}{\text{density}}$$

8 Engineers often want to use a material that is both strong and light, i.e. a material that has a good 'strength-to-weight ratio'.

a Give two examples of applications where a good strength-to-weight ratio would be useful.
b For the two examples you have given, suggest materials that might be used in practice.
c Use the table of properties on page 9 to calculate the values of strength/density for the following materials:
aluminium, steel, glass, wood, fibreglass.

Write a sentence or two commenting on the results of your calculations.

9 Describe how you might measure the density of the following:

a a metal cube,
b oil,
c a piece of rock with no definite shape,
d air.

Material	Mass	Volume	Density
copper	200 g	22.4 cm^3	
aluminium		400 cm^3	2.7 g/cm^3
lead		0.5 cm^3	11 350 kg/m^3
brick	2000 kg	1.2 m^3	
steel	2000 kg		7700 kg/m^3
wood	2000 kg		600 kg/m^3
concrete		4.5 m^3	2200 kg/m^3

Eureka!

The ancient Greeks were quite broadminded. But the sight of a naked man running through the streets shouting 'I've found it! I've found it!' caused a few heads to turn and probably collected a swarm of children calling out rude words.

The naked man was called Archimedes. He was already famous as a scientist, and he had just solved a physics problem! He had discovered what we now call **Archimedes' Principle**. The local king had asked him to check whether a new crown was made of pure gold or a cheaper mix of gold and silver.

The answer came to him in the bath. It was based on the fact that when you get into a bath the water level rises. Everybody knows this! But Archimedes suddenly realised that the volume of water the body pushes aside must equal the volume of the body.

This breakthrough would allow him to measure the volume of the crown. By weighing it he could work out its density (see page 8). If the crown's density was the same as the density of pure gold the king would be happy. If not, a goldsmith was going to be in serious trouble.

Archimedes went on to work out that an object will appear to lose weight in water. When an object is put into water the water level rises. This creates an extra pressure in the water which squeezes the object and tends to push it upwards. Think of grabbing hold of a piece of soap in the bath. This upward push, or upthrust, makes an object appear to weigh less in water than it did in air (picture 10). The weight loss is equal to the weight of the water displaced. This effect occurs in any substance that can flow (i.e. any **fluid**). So it applies to gases as well as liquids.

Archimedes' Principle: *when an object is wholly or partly immersed in a fluid it will experience an upward force (upthrust) equal to the weight of fluid it displaces.*

An object floats when the upthrust from the fluid is equal to the weight of the object (picture 11).

Suppose a piece of rock weighs 8 N in air and appears to weigh 5 N in water. The weight of water it displaces is thus 3 N. Archimedes realised that it displaces its own volume of water, so he could say

$$\frac{\textit{weight of rock}}{\textit{weight of same volume of water}}$$

$$= 8 / 3 = 2.7$$

Thus the density of the rock must be 2.7 times the density of water (the *relative density* of the rock). The density of water is 1000 kg/m^3, so the rock must have a density of 2700 kg/m^3.

As a general rule

relative density = weight in air/apparent loss of weight in water

Try these questions.

1 Design and carry out an experiment to check Archimedes' ideas.

2 A reel of copper wire weighs 250 g in air. When it is lowered into water it seems to weigh just 222 g. Use these results to calculate the density of copper.

3 Archimedes' rule only works if water has a density of 1 g/cm^3. Why is this?

A3
Forces and structures

Ships, bridges, buildings, animal skeletons and plants are all* structures*. They have to be strong enough to do their job, and must make economical use of materials.

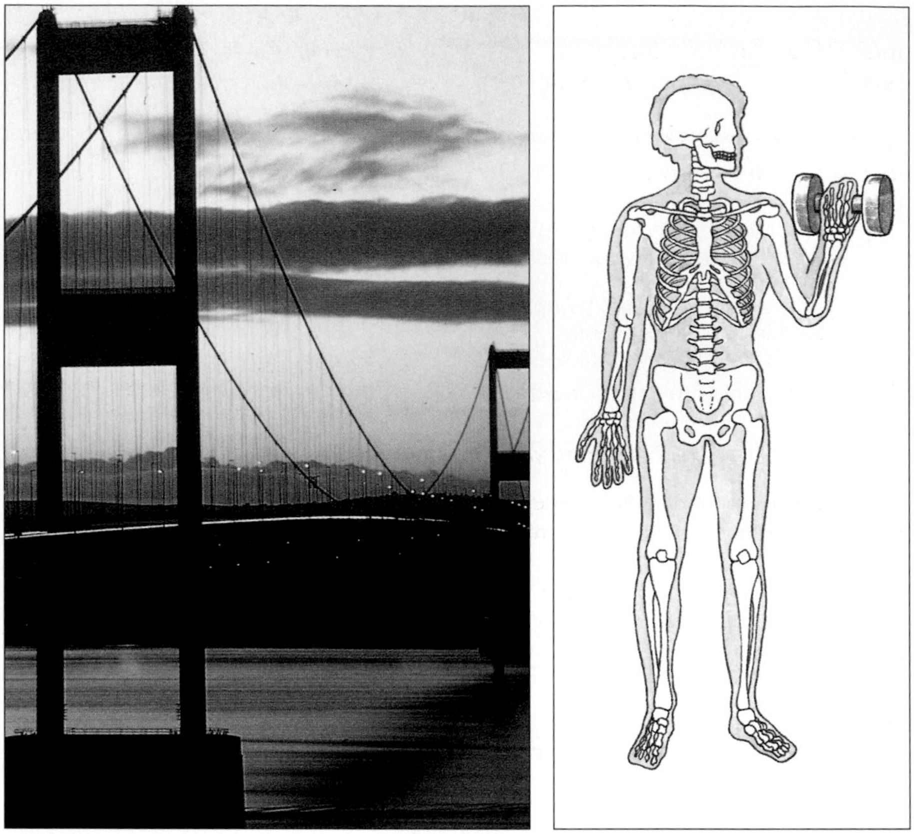

Picture 1 Most things are designed to withstand forces.

Picture 1 shows both natural and synthetic objects that have to withstand forces. Of course, they also have to do other things – like carry traffic, or move at speed. They are known as **structures**.

Strength

A structure can be made strong by

- making it from strong materials,
- good design and arrangement of its components.

A strong material may be **stiff** (like steel) or **brittle** (like glass). A stiff material will stretch or squash a little rather than shatter. Materials that can stretch or be squashed without any permanent damage or change of shape are called **elastic** materials. Rubber is a strong material and is more flexible than steel – this means that for samples of the same size, rubber will stretch more for the same applied force.

Picture 2 Steel is stiff – so keeps its shape even in the thin sheets used to make a car.

Picture 3 The forces that act on objects.

Some materials are easy to squash, and stay squashed. Plasticine and modelling clay are like this. This response to a force is called **plastic** behaviour. There is more about this on page 3.

Surprisingly, metals can sometimes be plastic. A copper wire will stretch slightly when loaded: the bigger the load the more it stretches. But when the load is increased it will reach a point where the wire carries on stretching. At this stage it is behaving plastically. Eventually the wire breaks.

It is this plastic-like property that makes it possible to draw many metals out into thin wires in the first place, or to make shapes by 'stamping' them in powerful presses (picture 2).

Many elastic materials or objects stretch or compress in such a way that the change in size or shape is proportional to the force causing the change. Such materials obey the **Hooke Law** – see pages 3 and 4 for more about this.

The effects of forces on structures

Engineers describe these forces according to the effects they produce, as illustrated in picture 3. These are:

tension forces which stretch an object
compression forces which squash an object
torsion forces which twist an object
bending forces which bend an object
shear forces which tend to tear an object

Coping with forces

What the objects in picture 1 have in common is that they are made of lots of smaller parts which are joined together. The shape of the parts, and the way they are joined together, ensure that they are not damaged by the forces.

A structure may have to cope with more than one kind of deforming force. Pictures 4 and 9 show how this can be.

The building blocks of structures

Most structures are made of lots of different parts designed to cope with the various forces acting on them. The most obvious force is caused by gravity. This acts on the structure because of its own weight, or because of the load it has to carry.

Moving objects also have to cope with acceleration forces, the effects of braking – and even the effects of a collision.

Objects that might get hot have to withstand the very strong forces caused by the material trying to expand.

Strength of materials

Solids like metals and wood are held together not so much by the forces between individual atoms or molecules but by the forces between groups of atoms or molecules in various kinds of microstructures. The microstructure of a carbon steel consists of small crystals of iron pinned together by even smaller carbon crystals (see picture 5). When a steel wire breaks it means that some crystals have pulled apart from each other. The crystals themselves are much stronger – single crystals can be manufactured which are very strong indeed. Single carbon crystals are easier to make than single iron crystals and are used as **carbon fibres** to strengthen alloys and plastics (picture 6). But most metals and alloys are composed of millions of small crystals – they have a polycrystalline structure.

Wood is one of the most useful structural materials – used in furniture as well as the frames of houses. Its strength comes from its long, interlocking fibres which form the grain of the wood (picture 7). Wood is much stronger

Picture 4 A simple plank bridge. Which part is under tension and which part is in compression?

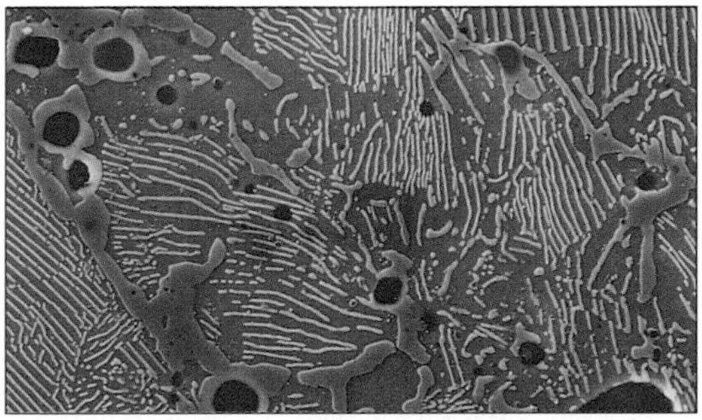

Picture 5 Electron micrograph of carbon steel. The lines are plates, seen end on, of alternating pure iron and iron carbide.

Picture 6 This motorbike is partly made of carbon fibre.

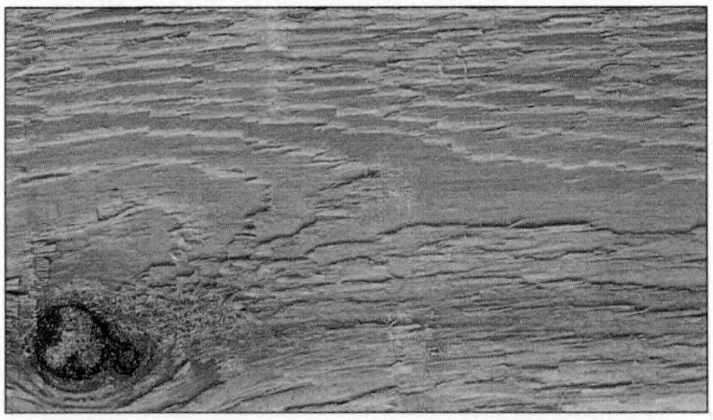

Picture 7 Wood grain.

Picture 8 A cantilever structure: a stand at Watford football ground.

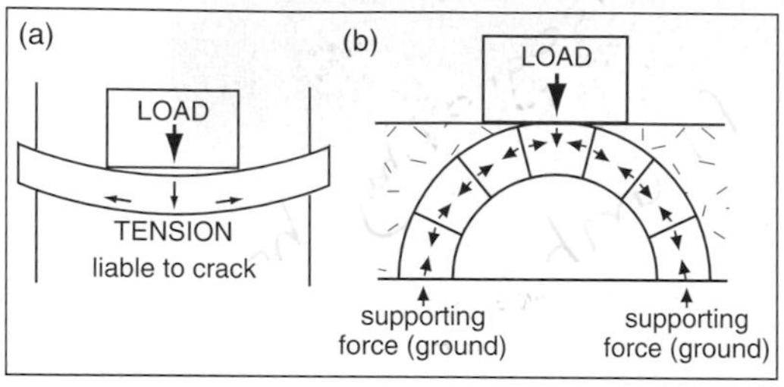

Picture 9 (a) A straight beam is partly in tension – liable to crack. (b) An arch is a curved beam made of smaller wedges. Each wedge is in compression – not likely to crack.

Picture 10 Many structures use triangles to keep themselves rigid.

Picture 11 A Greek temple, over 2000 years old.

when pulled, say, along the grain than across it. Wood is easier to split by separating the fibres than by cutting across them.

Structures are made from smaller structures

Most everyday structures are made up from a small range of 'building blocks'. The most commonly used are beams, triangles, cables (or strings) and pillars (buttresses).

Beams

A beam is simply a piece of strong material used horizontally, like a plank put across a gap. Beams are probably the most commonly used structures.

The beam may be fixed at one end or at both ends. A beam fixed at one end only is called a **cantilever** (picture 8).

A beam will always bend a little, under a load or under its own weight. When this happens one edge of the beam will be stretched (in tension), the other edge will be squashed (in compression). This is shown in picture 4. Beams tend to break by cracking at the tensioned edge, which is being pulled apart, as explained in topic A2 (page 7).

On the other hand an **arch** covering the same space is stronger because the forces acting downward *compress* the material (picture 9).

Triangles

Many structures are made from solid rods fitted together into triangular shapes as shown in picture 10. The rods need to be strong in both tension and compression. This is because some rods are being pulled apart ('ties'), but others are being compressed ('rods'). In a complicated structure, it is sometimes quite tricky to work out which is which.

As long as the ends of the rods are fixed firmly together at the joints the structure will be very strong.

Strings, guys and cables

A piece of string is not much use in compression. It can only withstand a force when it is pulled. Then it can be very strong indeed, for its size. A **cable** is just a very thick 'string', made out of steel or some other strong material.

Cables are used in **tension**, and you will find them in some of the strongest structures in the world – suspension bridges. A suspension bridge (shown in picture 1) uses cables made from a strong material (steel) that is strong in tension. A typical cable for a bridge has to be very strong.

Cables are also used to support tall structures like TV transmitter masts. They do this by pulling down on the mast, rather than holding it up as with a suspension bridge.

Thinner cables made of rope are used to hold down tents and are called **guy ropes**. Old sailing ships used thousands of ropes to keep masts and sails in position.

Pillars

The towers of the bridge in picture 1 may be made of concrete rather than steel. This is because they are designed to withstand mainly compression forces. Concrete is strong in compression but weak in tension.

The roadway of the bridge is a **beam**. It must be heavy and has to carry heavy traffic. It would not be strong enough on its own unless the beam was made very thick. This would be expensive and would look rather ugly.

The bridge designers have used the different materials in the structure to their best advantage. They have shared the forces neatly between the beam, the cable and the pillars.

Of course, the pillars have to carry the total load. They are the strongest and thickest parts of the structure.

A problem with pillars

The pillar has to be very strong, and one way of making it strong is to make it big. This means giving it a large cross section. But this makes it even heavier. In the end most of its bulk is there to support itself rather than the rest of the bridge. Old Greek temples are very beautiful, but there do seem to be a lot of pillars for the load on the roof! (See picture 11.)

Hollow pillars

A hollow pillar can be just as strong as a 'filled-in' one. This fact was a great surprise to the ancient Romans who discovered it, and is still a surprise to most people today. The Romans learned to build pillars for bridges and buildings in which the strength was in a fairly thin shell on the outside of the pillar. The inside was filled in with rubble to stop this outer shell bending.

A modern bridge may have its pillars made of hollow steel tubes, which are just as strong as concrete and weigh far less.

Steel is much denser than concrete, and a lot more expensive, but because the pillar is hollow it uses very little material.

Everyday structures

Many everyday objects make use of this idea to reduce their weight and cost as shown in picture 12. As you can see, some of these structures are biological structures. Nature got there before the Romans!

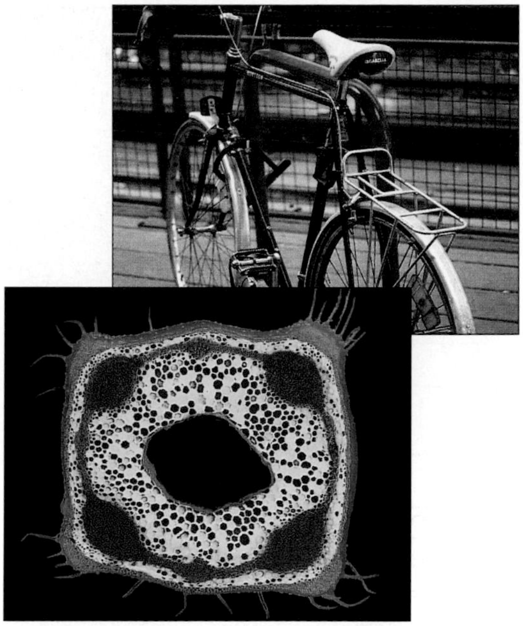

Picture 12 Hollow structures.

Living structures

The human body makes use of strings (tendons) and hollow tubes (bones). The bones are strong and light, making best use of the material they are made from. The tendons carry very large forces produced by the muscles. They apply these forces to the bones, so allowing us to move and to lift things.

Plants make use of hollow stems to support themselves, even if the hollow is often filled with a liquid of some kind. Their roots act as cables, anchoring them firmly in the ground (see picture 13).

Picture 13 Carrots are easier to pull up than grass is!

Bones

The skeleton of an animal uses bones as beams and pillars. Look at picture 1 and see if you can work out which job different bones do.

The internal structure of a bone gives strength by using combinations of triangles in a six-sided 'honeycomb' effect (picture 14). The bones of birds have to be especially light for their strength.

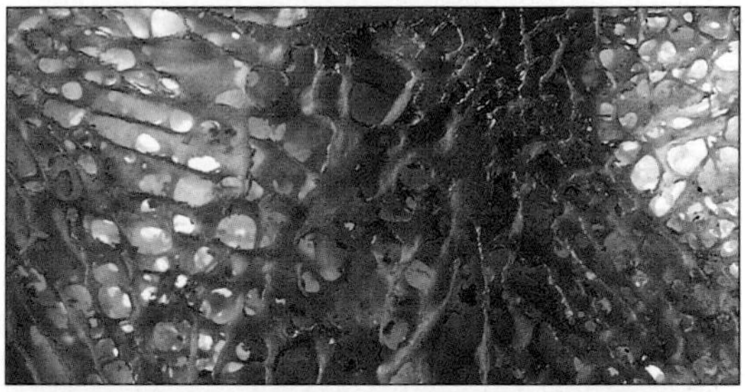

Picture 14 The honeycombed structure of a bone.

Stability

Picture 15 shows a high-speed train. It is designed not only to move along at speeds of up to 250 km/h but also to stay upright and on the track as it goes around bends. It has to be strong enough to withstand the stresses and strains of high-speed motion.

But just as importantly, the train is designed to be as safe as possible in an accident. In a typical accident the passenger sections might leave the track completely. The danger is that the section overturns as it rides over rough ground. If it does the passengers may be injured as the compartment frame collapses or telescopes. Picture 16 shows that it has a low centre of mass. This makes it harder to overturn. It is designed for both **stability** and **strength**. Many everyday objects are designed with the same aims, from teacups and jugs to bridges and the towers that carry television transmitter aerials.

Picture 15

Stability and centre of mass

A stable object is one that doesn't fall over easily when something bumps into it. Think of bumping into a laboratory stool (fairly unstable!) compared with bumping into a kitchen chair at home (fairly stable). Picture 17 shows three simple shapes and it is easy to tell which is the most stable and which is the least stable.

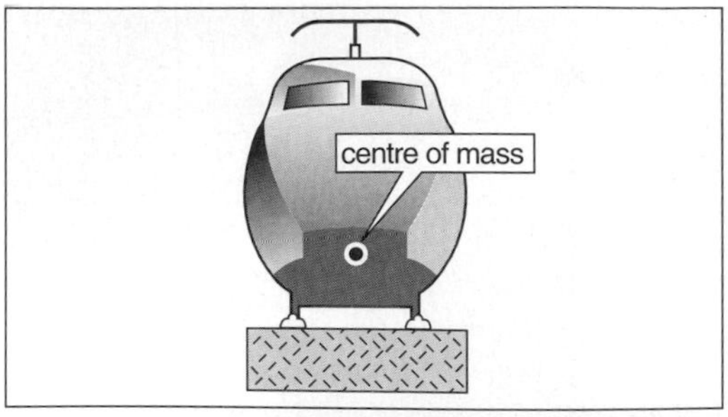

Picture 16

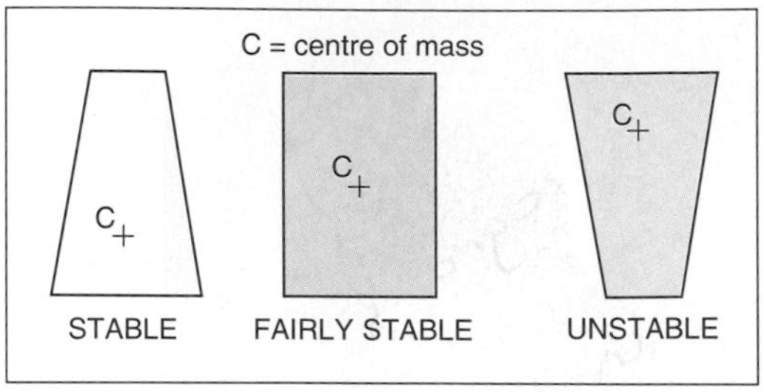

Picture 17 The lower the centre of mass the more stable the object.

The basic physical reason for greater or lesser stability is to do with the position of what is called the **centre of mass** of an object. This is the point where the force of gravity acting on the object appears to act. In a metre stick the centre of mass is in the middle, and you can support the stick by balancing it there on your finger. The centre of mass of a snooker cue is nearer the thick end so you can support it with one finger at that point, as shown in picture 18.

You could *calculate* the position of the centre of mass of a metre stick or plank of wood by using the **lever principle** (see page 19). The moment (turning effect of a force) of gravity pulling down on the left half of the stick is exactly balanced by an equal turning effect pulling down on the right half. But the calculation is hard to do when the shapes are more complicated – as in a bridge, a ship or an aircraft. But it is often possible to guess the position of the centre of mass of a sheet with a symmetrical shape, such as a rectangle or a circle. (See also Activity D.)

Centre of mass relates to stability in the following way: *when an object is tilted so that the centre of mass goes outside its base, the object will topple*. Picture 19 illustrates this, and shows the difference between a shape with high stability and a shape with low stability.

But the shape is only one factor. An object with a possibly unstable shape can be made more stable by making the bottom parts heavier, e.g. by making them thicker or by using a denser material. This is what is done in the high-speed train, a double-decker bus and a glass tumbler (see picture 20), for example.

Activities

A Building a strong structure

Your task is to design and make a structure, and then see which structure can hold up the greatest weight. You will be given:

- some rods (e.g. straws, lengths of dry spaghetti or macaroni, thin card),
- a way of fixing the rods together (glue, sticky tape, bits of wire),
- whatever tools that might be useful.

You will be told the smallest height that your support will have to be above bench or ground level.

Test your structure to see how much of a load it can hold up.

Write a brief, illustrated report explaining how successful your design was, with reasons for choosing that design.

B Studying structures

Choose one of the following:

- a building you know well,
- any kind of transport vehicle,
- any household device,
- any piece of furniture.

1 Look at it very carefully.
2 Write down what materials it is made of.
3 Write down what materials are there to give it strength.
4 Write or draw how it is designed/shaped so that it is strong.
5 The materials in the object may not all have been chosen just to give strength. Can you give one *other* reason, apart from giving it strength, for using any of the materials in the object you are looking at?

C Looking at natural structures

Use a hand lens and a microscope to look at the internal structures of the following:

1 a bone,
2 fresh wood,
3 a holly leaf,
4 an insect wing,
5 a hollow plant stem,
6 the skeleton of a small animal (e.g. a mouse or frog),
7 a seed that is spread by wind (e.g. sycamore, dandelion).

You may be given prepared slides, or you may have to collect the material yourself. Look at them both in cross-section and lengthways, if possible.

There are many other things you could look at as well. For two or three of them draw and describe how the materials and the structure are suited to the job they do.

D Finding the centre of mass

Your teacher will give you some flat sheets in a variety of shapes – both regular and irregular. A flat sheet is called a **lamina**. Start by predicting where you think the centre of mass will be.

Then use a plumb line to find the exact centre of mass as follows.

1 Hang up a lamina, at a point on one edge, from a firm support. The lamina should be able to swing loosely. When it comes to rest the centre of mass will be on a vertical line directly under the point of support, because the weight of the lamina acts through the centre of mass. Use a plumb line to help you draw this vertical line (see picture 21).
2 Now hang the lamina from another point and repeat the experiment. The centre of mass is where the two lines cross. Check this by using a third suspension point.

Use this method to find the centres of mass of a variety of laminae.

Extra
Design an experiment to find the centre of mass of a three-dimensional object, such as a chair.

E Testing structures

Packaging material is often made from thin cardboard. Picture 22 shows some different types of packaging material. Design and carry out tests to find out some or all of the following.

(a) Which type is stronger? (b) How do they respond to tension, compression and bending forces? (c) Are the packaging materials equally strong in all directions?

Summarise your results and explain them by considering the structural shapes used in the different packaging materials. Suggest possible uses for the different materials (e.g. for packaging eggs, books, machinery, glassware, etc.).

Picture 18

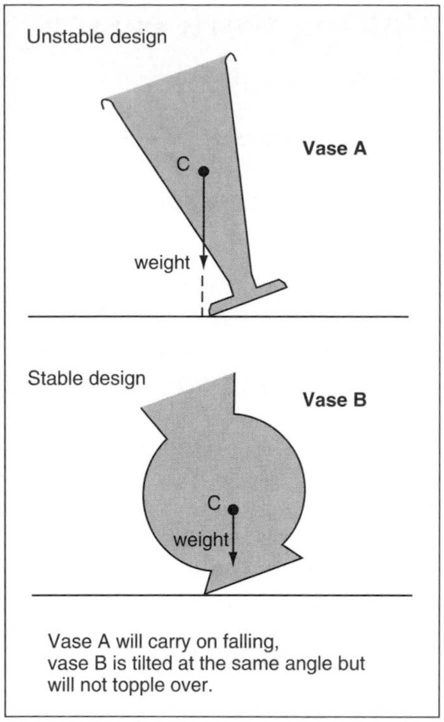

Picture 19

Picture 20

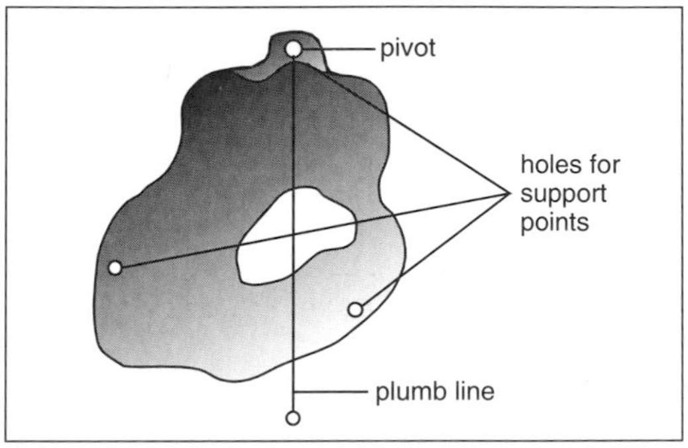

Picture 21

Questions

1 Explain what is meant by the following:

a a tension force,
b a shear force,
c a compression force.

2 What kinds of forces (from the list on page 13) are the structures shown in picture 22 designed to withstand?

3 What kind of force is present:

a in your legs when you are standing up?
b in your arm when you hold a chair with your arm out level?
c in your wrist when you are using a screwdriver?

4 Give two examples of a beam being used as a cantilever in your home or in school.

5 Give an example of the use of triangles in a structure you can see in your home or in school.

6 Explain the following:

a Lightweight tents have poles which are hollow and made of an aluminium alloy.
b Plants with 'fibrous roots' get good support even if their roots don't go very deep into the soil.
c Water plants have stems which are much weaker, in compression, than land plants.
d Electricity pylons (and TV masts) are thinner at the top than at the bottom.

7 Think about three different objects: a biscuit, a plastic ruler, a piece of paper. Describe the materials they are made from using the following terms, as appropriate:

hard, soft, elastic, plastic, strong, weak, brittle, flexible, stiff, dense.

8 a Sketch a cross-section of an oil tanker (viewed from one end). Mark in where you think the centre of mass would be when the ship is (i) fully loaded (ii) empty.

b Suggest why an oil tanker is usually loaded with water (as ballast) when it has delivered its load of oil.

9 An aircraft is kept up by a force called *lift*, which is caused by air flowing over its wings. It is pulled down by the force of gravity, acting through its centre of mass. Why is it a good idea that aircraft are built so that the lift force also acts through the centre of mass?

10 Why is a loaded beam more likely to crack on its underside than on its top?

11 Describe and explain one way of making a structural object less liable to be seriously affected by the growth of cracks.

12 Describe or draw the main features of any bridge that you have seen. Mark on it places that are likely to be in compression (C) or in tension (T). What material is the bridge made from? How has the designer made use of the material to ensure that the bridge is unlikely to fall down?

Picture 22

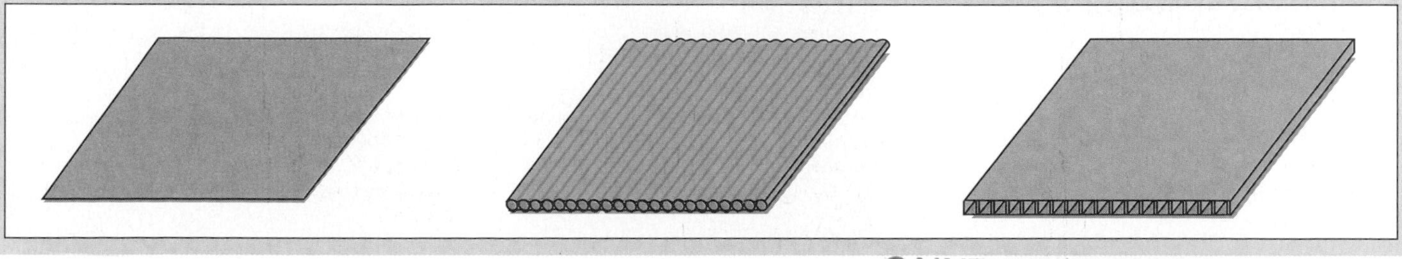

A4 Machines

Human muscles are weak. We can increase their effect by using machines...

Making work easier

Every kitchen and workshop contains tools or implements that make it easier for us to do a job of work. Most of them are used to increase the size of a force. Opening a tin is easy – with a tin opener.

Bottle openers, screwdrivers, scissors – even door handles – are all examples of 'force multipliers': devices which 'multiply forces' (picture 1).

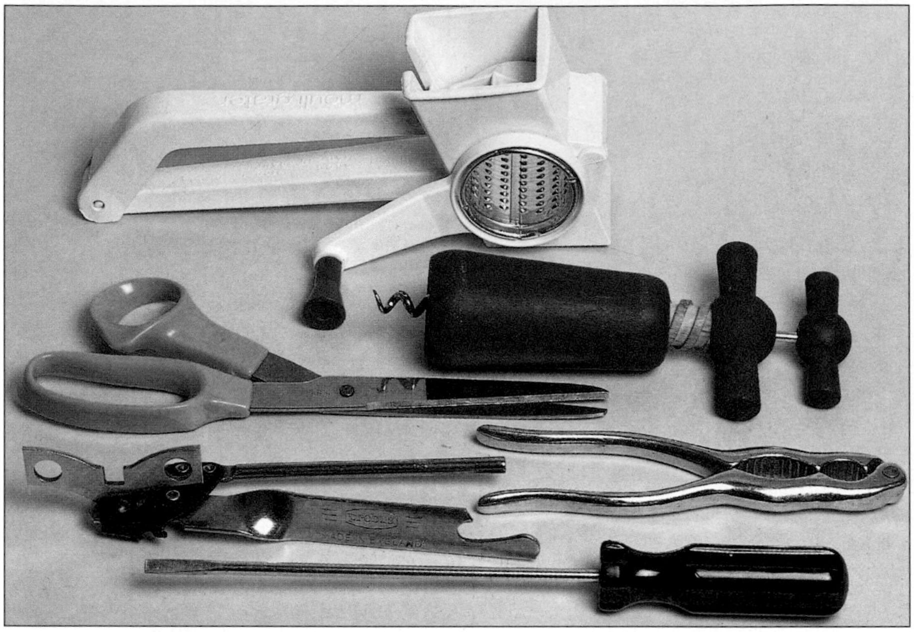

Picture 1 Household machines.

Some machines are very complicated. Just look at a car engine. Even a bicycle has more to it than you might think.

But all these machines are made up of a very few quite simple ones. Some of these are levers, pulleys and sloping planes.

Levers

Picture 2 shows a small child lifting a larger one – by using a seesaw. The large weight is being moved by a smaller one, using the **lever principle**.

When you pull on one end of a pivoted bar it will turn around the pivot. Both children on the seesaw are producing a turning effect. When they are exactly in balance each of them is applying the same size turning effect, but obviously in opposite directions. The turning effect (or **moment**) of their weights is given by multiplying the force by the distance they are from the pivot. Picture 3 shows what we mean by this.

A spanner is a simple machine based on this lever principle. The pivot is

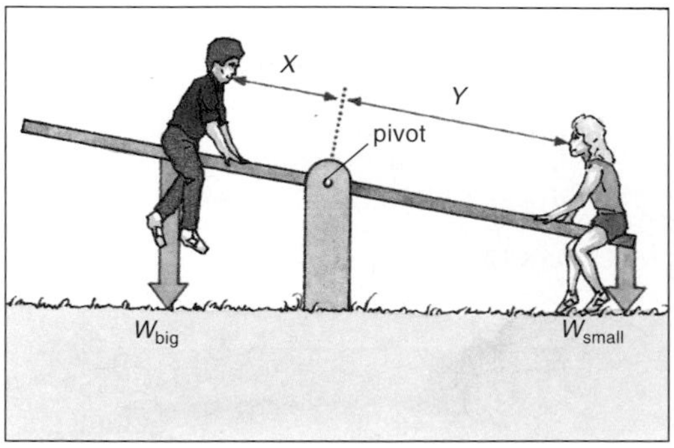

Picture 3 The lever principle: $W_{big} \times X = W_{small} \times Y$.

Picture 2 Seesaws are fun.

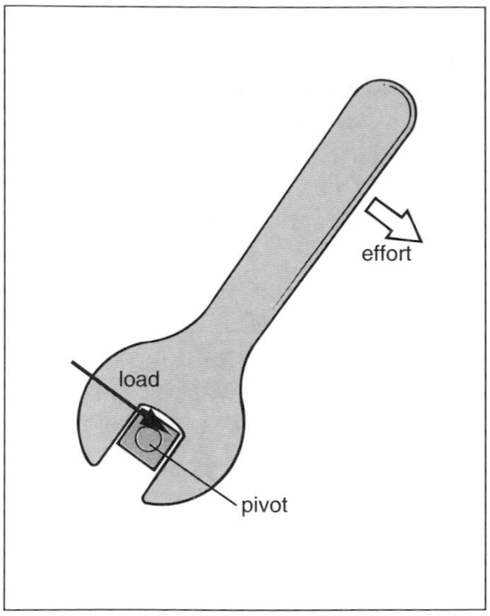

Picture 4 A spanner is a lever.

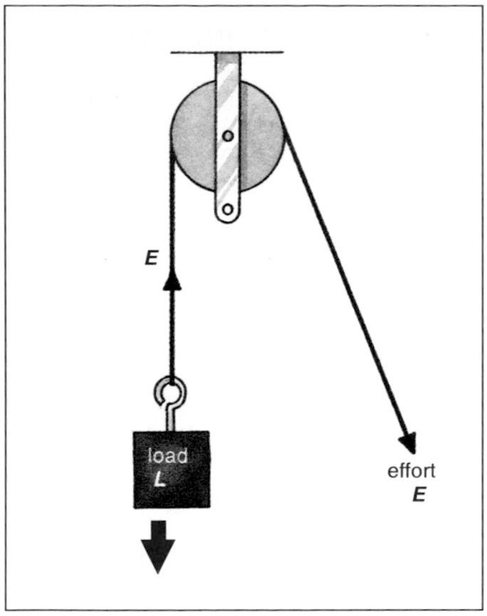

Picture 5 With just one pulley, effort ***E*** just balances load ***L***.

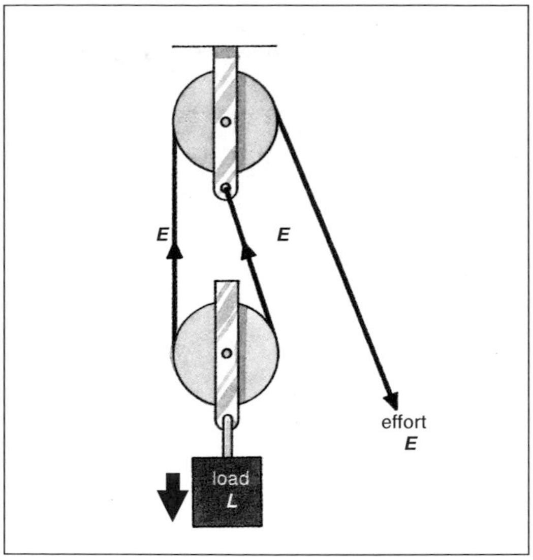

Picture 6 With two pulleys, the effort ***E*** can be about twice as effective.

now the centre of the nut being turned (picture 4). The **effort** force is applied near the end of the handle. The force that is being 'overcome' is called the **load**. In the case of the spanner it is the friction force in the nut being turned.

When the spanner is just turning the nut the lever principle says that:

effort × effort distance = load × load distance

There are very many examples of levers in everyday life. Many of them are 'hidden' as part of more complicated-looking machines. Try counting how many levers there are on a bicycle.

Pulleys

A single pulley is really a kind of moving, circular lever, as shown in picture 5. The wheel is pivoted and so keeps on turning as the load is pulled up. But a single pulley doesn't increase the applied force, because the pivot is exactly in the centre. Pulleys become useful as force multipliers when more than one of them is used.

Picture 6 is a simple two-pulley system. One string goes from the load around both pulleys to where the effort is applied. The load can be nearly twice as large as the effort. This can be explained by the fact that the 'force in the string' is the same all through it. It is E, the effort. The load is supported by a double string, so the upward force is $2 \times E$. This is only exactly true if there is no friction in the system. If there is, some of the effort force has to overcome friction, so less is left to lift the load.

Picture 7 A slope is also a machine.

Sloping planes

These are the largest machines you will ever see. The principle was used by the Ancient Britons to build Stonehenge, and by the Egyptians to build the Pyramids.

Both had the task of lifting very large, heavy stones. They did it by building sloping roads or mounds of earth and sliding the stones up on wooden rollers (picture 7). The force needed to roll something up a slope is much less than the gravity force acting straight down on it.

The less steep the slope the smaller the force you need. Mountain roads are built in a zig-zag to make their steepness less. Other examples of slopes used as force multipliers are: wedges, knife blades, screws and bolts (picture 8).

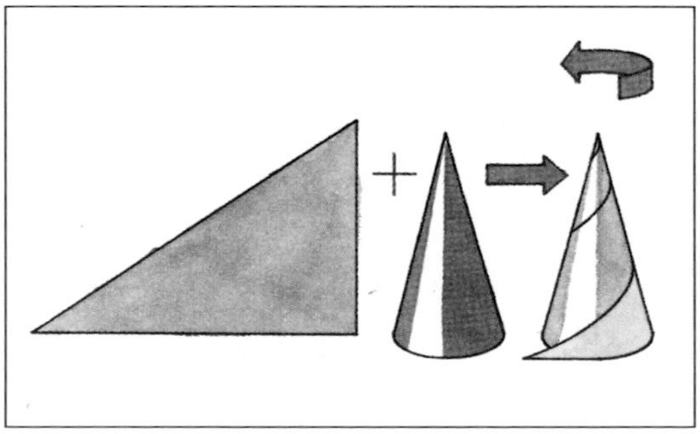

Picture 8 A slope 'fitted' to a cone becomes a screw.

Something for nothing?

The use of machines to multiply forces seems to be against the basic law of energy – see topic D4. Are we really getting something for nothing?

The answer, unfortunately, is no. The energy we put into any machine is always at least equal to, and usually greater than, the energy we get out of it. The simple reason for this is that in every single one of the machines dealt with in this topic, *the effort moves further than the load*.

The energy supplied is equal to the work done by the effort. This is measured by 'applied force × distance moved in the direction of the applied force' (see topic D2). The work done by the effort is likely to be greater than the useful energy obtained by moving the load. At best it will be the same. There is no such thing as a machine which does more work that we put into it!

Efficiency

When you use a machine you usually get less work out than you put in. This is because, for example, you have to lift pieces of rope or pulleys which are not part of the 'payload'. You also have to do work against the forces of friction. Thus we talk about the **efficiency** of a machine, defined as a percentage.

$$\textbf{efficiency} = \frac{\textbf{useful work done}}{\textbf{energy supplied to the machine}} \times \textbf{100\%}$$

There is more about efficiency on page 114.

Hydraulics

Some of the most useful machinery we have uses the principles of **hydraulics**. Instead of using solid materials to transfer energy and forces, hydraulic systems use liquids. They work because of the way a liquid can transfer a pressure. Imagine a rubber bag full of water. When you squash it in one place the extra pressure you exert acts everywhere – if there is a leak in the bag, water will squirt out. It doesn't make any difference where the hole is. In fact the extra pressure in a pressurised liquid not only acts everywhere but is the same everywhere.

This principle is used in many machines: in aircraft to move the wing edges

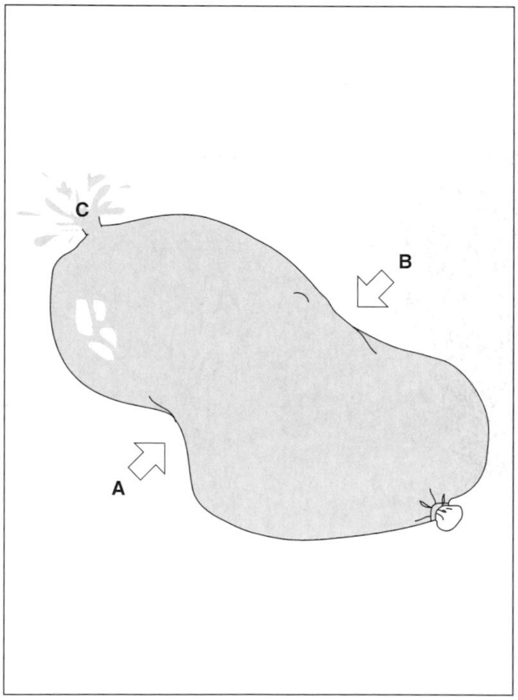

Picture 9 Squash the bag at A and B, the water squirts out at C.

Picture 10 Large machines work by hydraulics; you can see the pistons in this picture.

and control flight, in car brakes, in large earth-moving machines to lift very heavy loads, in garages to lift cars, in factories to squash and stamp metals.

Hydraulics relies on the simple fact that **pressure = force/area**. You can produce a large pressure by using quite a small force – provided it acts over a very small area. It is the difference between sitting on a chair and sitting on a pin! Soft snow can bear your weight if you spread it over a larger area by using skis or snowshoes.

Picture 12 shows the principles as they are used in a hydraulic car lift. A worker exerts quite a small force at a small piston, which produces a pressure in the hydraulic fluid. Suppose the force exerted is 50 N and it acts over an area of 50 square centimetres – which is 5×10^{-3} m^2.

$$\text{pressure } P \text{ in fluid is } P = F/A = 50/(5 \times 10^{-3}) = 10\,000 \text{ N/m}^2$$

The fluid is usually a special oil. The car is placed on a platform above a piston which has a large area in contact with the oil. Suppose this area is 2 square metres. The pressure acts over all this area and we can calculate that since

$$\textbf{pressure} = \frac{\textbf{force}}{\textbf{area}}$$

then $force = pressure \times area = 10\,000 \times 2 = 20\,000$ N.

This force would hold up a 2 tonne vehicle. The force caused like this, by a pressure, is called a **thrust**.

The pressure is the same all through the fluid, i.e.

$$\text{pressure} = E/\text{area } A = L/\text{area } B$$

where, as in picture 12, the effort force is E and the load lifted is L.

Thus the hydraulic car lift has a load to effort ratio $L/E = B/A$. All hydraulic systems rely on having piston surfaces of different areas, A and B. The smaller A is compared to B, the larger the output force that can be produced for a given effort force.

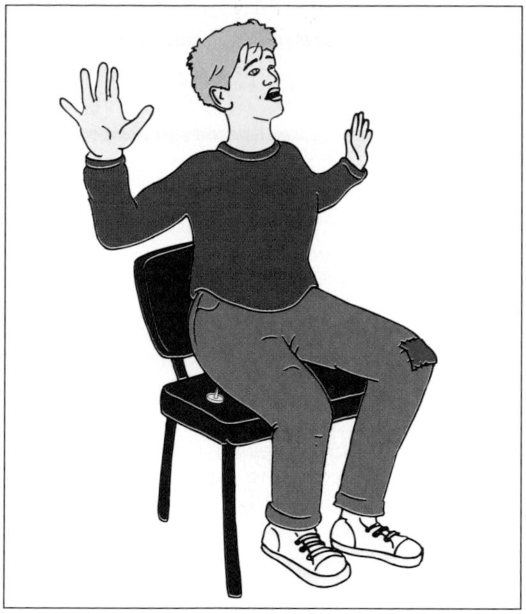

Picture 11 The same force exerts a large or small pressure – depending on the area over which it acts.

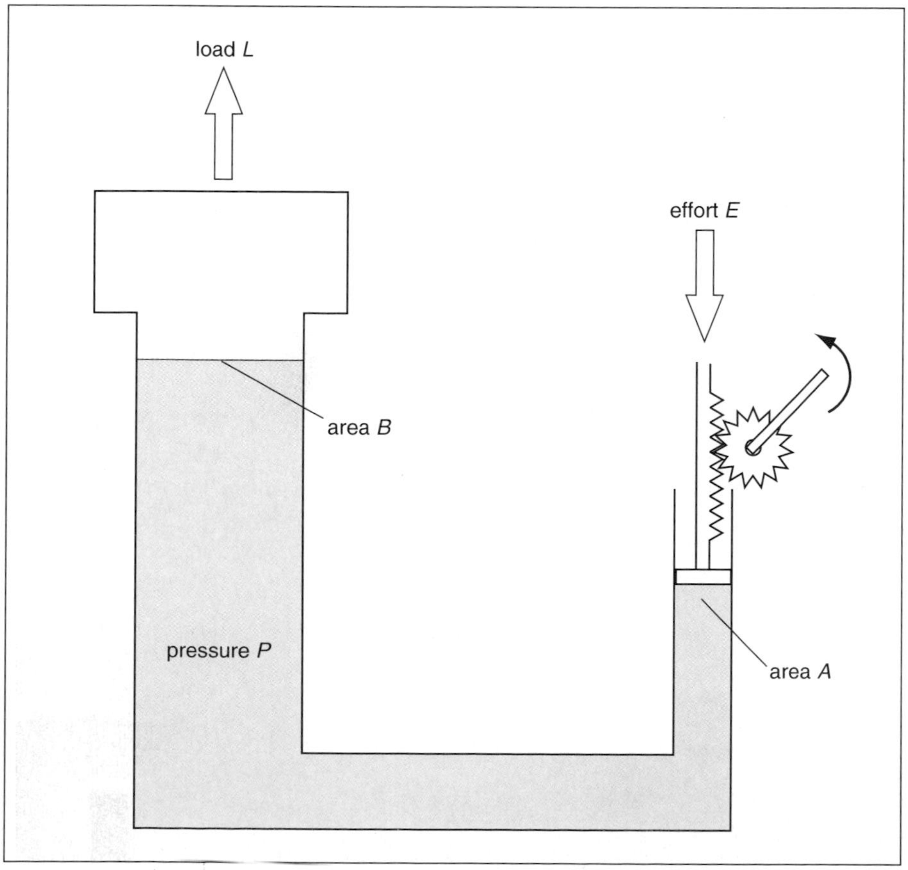

Picture 12 Principle of hydraulic car lift.

Activities

A Investigating machines

You will be given a simple machine, or a working model of one. It could be a pulley system, a simple ramp or a car jack, for example.

1 Measure how much effort force is needed to lift up to five different loads.

Record your results in a table, as above. You can measure the forces involved using a newton meter – or you can assume that the gravity force on 1 kg is approximately 10 N.

	1	2	3	4	5
Effort (N)					
Load (N)					

Choose a range of sensible load values.

Is there a pattern in your results?

2 For one of your load-and-effort combinations measure how the effort moves ('effort distance') when the load moves a certain distance (the 'load distance').

Calculate the work done by the effort, and on the load, by using the formula:
work done (in joules) =
force × distance moved in the direction of action of the force

B Looking at machines

Look at a selection of tools and kitchen utensils. Which of them are machines? Draw two that are and explain how they work, based on the principles of the four basic machines described in this topic.

CARE! Never attempt to lift unsuitable or large loads. Whatever the pulley system is fixed to must be really strong to take the maximum load.

Questions

1 Name ten simple machines that you might find in your home or in the laboratory.

2 Why are machines useful?

Describe one machine and explain how it works.

Why can't you 'get more work out of it' than you put in?

3 Put the following useful things into two headed columns 'machines' and 'non-machines':

a bucket, a knife, an egg whisk, a screwdriver, a door handle, a bookshelf, a spanner, a light switch, a spade, a pen-top.

For one example in each column, give your reasons for putting it there.

4 Name or describe five different levers you could find as part of a bicycle.

5 Picture 13 shows a wheel fixed on an axle. The wheel A has a radius of 50 cm, the axle B a radius of 10 cm.

a What happens to axle B when A turns around once?
b What happens to the bucket on the rope wrapped around B?
c Would this device make it easier to lift the bucket of water?
d This is an old-fashioned kind of machine for lifting water out of a well. Can you think of any modern device that uses the same idea?

6 Estimate (a) your weight in newtons (b) the area of your left foot in square metres. Use these estimates to calculate the pressure you exert on the ground.

7 In a hydraulic ram the area of the effort piston is 4 cm^2 (4×10^{-4} m^2) and the area of the load-carrying pistons is 1 m^2. What force is applied at the load piston when a force of 500 N is applied at the effort piston?

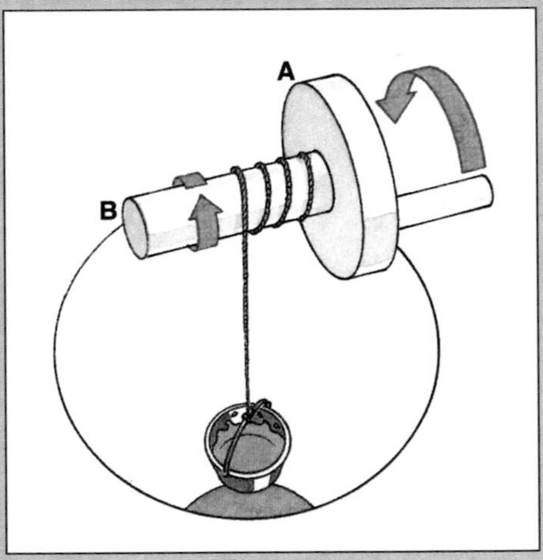

Picture 13 A wheel-and-axle is still useful for getting water from a well.

Analysing machines

Machine	1 Effort (N)	2 Load (N)	3 Distance moved (metres) by *effort*	4 by *load*
1 3-pulley block	20	56	6	2
2 6-pulley block	10	52	12	2
3 sail-lifter on yacht (wheel-and-axle)	25	120	10	2
4 bolt cutter	30	270	0.1	0.01
5 rotary cheese grater	0.6	2	2.4	0.6

Here is some data about different types of machine. It tells you how much effort is needed to lift or move a given load. It also tells you how far the effort force moves for a typical movement of the load. Use this information to answer the questions below. You will need graph paper to answer some of them.

1 In each machine, the effort force has to move quite a lot further than the load. Considering the design of any one machine, explain why this is. (Two of the machines are illustrated in the picture.)

2 Each machine 'multiplies' a small effort force into a larger load force. Use the values in the first two columns to calculate how good each machine is at doing this, by dividing the **load** by the **effort**. The result is called the **mechanical advantage** of the machine. Put the results in a list headed 'mechanical advantage'.

3 Use the data in columns 3 and 4 to calculate, for each machine, how far the effort has to move compared with the load. Do this by dividing 'distance moved by effort' by 'distance moved by load'. The result for each machine is a number that engineers call its **velocity ratio**. Put the results you obtain into a list headed 'velocity ratio'.

4 Look at the values of mechanical advantage (MA) and velocity ratio (VR) you have worked out. It is suggested that there might be a connection between how effective a machine is at moving a load (its MA) and how far the effort has to move compared with the load (its VR).

a Is there any relationship (or pattern) between mechanical advantage and velocity ratio for these five machines? Make a rough guess at what it might be and write it down.

b Now plot the values against each other on a set of graph axes – mechanical advantage up, velocity ratio along.

c Draw the 'best straight line' through these plotted points. Does this confirm your prediction in (a)?

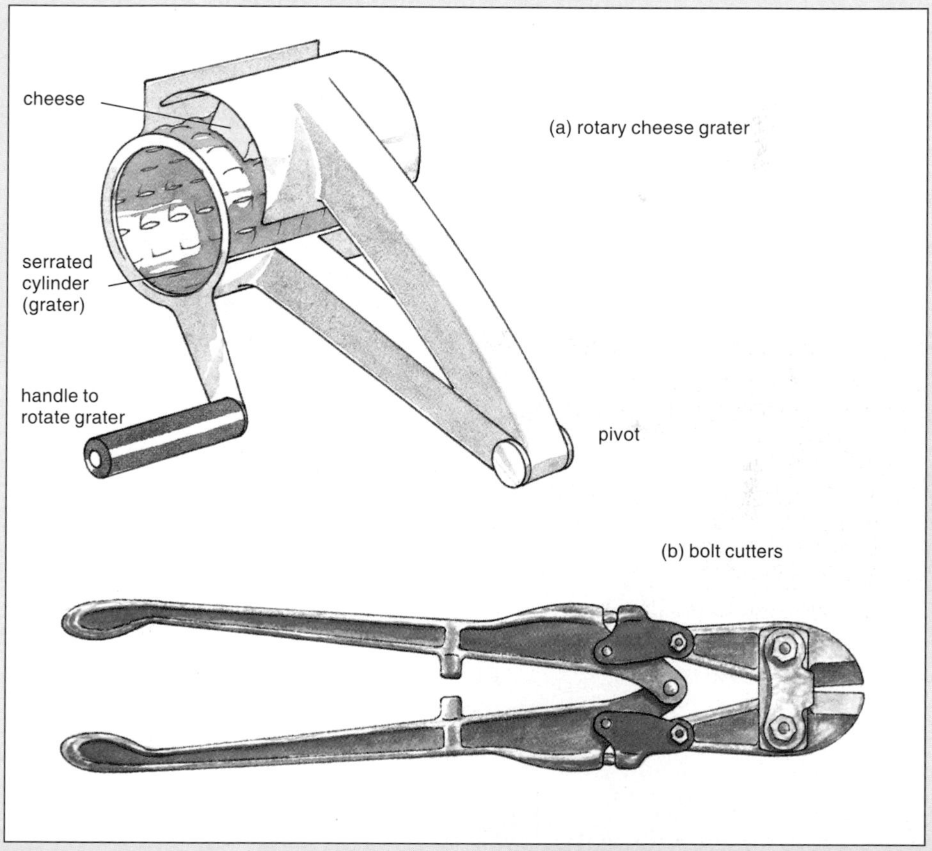

Picture 1 How are these machines adapted to their different jobs?

B1 Speed, time, distance

We live in a world of movement – the flight of birds, high-speed trains, and the high-speed molecules that keep up your bicycle tyres are all examples…

Speed

The **speed** of an object is how far it goes in a unit of time. It is measured in units such as metres per second (m/s), or kilometres per hour (km/h). In Britain you will also see the unit 'miles per hour' (mph), but this is not used in scientific measuring.

Table 1 shows the range of speeds of a number of moving things.

Table 1 Comparison of speeds.

Speeds	m/s	km/h
light speed	300 000 000	1 080 000 000
Earth in orbit	29 790	107 244
typical Earth satellite	7 500	27 000
fast jet aircraft	833	3 000
Concorde (supersonic jet)	648	2 333
average speed of air molecule	500	1 800
sound in air	340	1 224
Boeing 747 Jumbo Jet	270	970
fastest bird (falcon)	97	350
high-speed train (French TGV)	60	216
motorway speed limit (UK 70 mph)	31	112
town speed limit (UK 30 mph)	13.4	48
Olympic sprinter	10.3	37
average walking speed	1.7	6
average speed of a snail	0.006	0.02

Measuring speed

Very many different instruments are used to measure the wide range of speeds shown in the chart. But all of them need to measure just two things: **time** and **distance travelled**.

If you wanted to measure the speed of a sprinter at an athletics track you would measure how long it took the runner to cover the distance of the race. For example, you could use a stop watch, and find that it took the runner 13 seconds to cover a distance of 100 metres. You could calculate the speed (distance covered per second) like this:

$$\text{speed in metres per second} = \frac{\text{distance in metres}}{\text{time in seconds}} = \frac{100 \text{ metres}}{13 \text{ seconds}} = 7.7 \text{ m/s}$$

Picture 1 Racing against the clock.

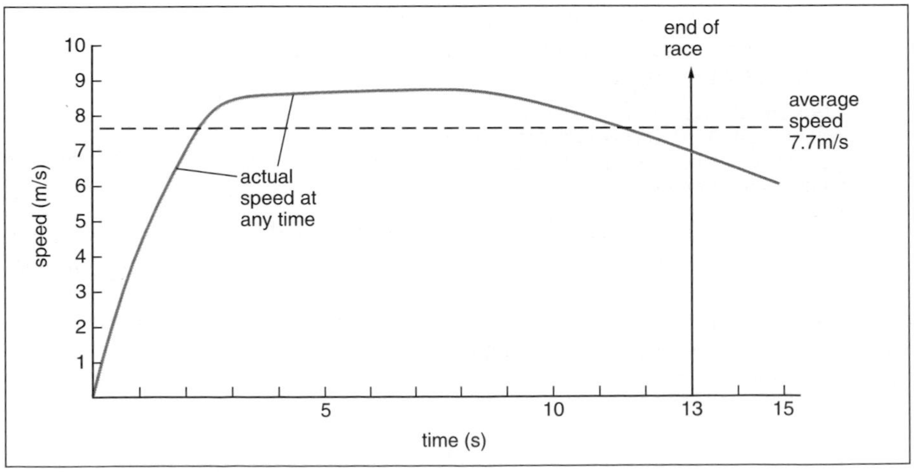

Picture 2 How a runner's speed changes during a race.

Average speed

What we have worked out for the sprinter was the *average* speed over the distance. The runner wouldn't have travelled at this speed steadily for all of the 13 seconds of the race.

A runner starts slowly then accelerates to her fastest speed. She might slow down near the end when her legs get tired. A graph would show this (see picture 2).

In the same way, a car might take four hours to travel a distance of 200 km. Unless it was on a very clear motorway it isn't likely that it would have travelled at the same speed of 50 km/h all the time. It's useful to know the *average* speed of a car on different kinds of roads. When you are planning a journey you can use it to work out how long the journey is likely to take.

We can work out average speeds using a formula:

$$\text{average speed} = \frac{\text{total distance covered}}{\text{time taken for journey}}$$

Written as a formula: $$v = \frac{s}{t}$$

Picture 3 Police can measure the speed of a car using radar.

Instantaneous speed

Sometimes we need to know more about what happens when moving things are changing speed. To do this we need to be able to measure the speed at any given instant. This is not so easy to do. It means that we have to measure the distance an object travels in a very small interval of time, usually much less than a second.

This can be done by using **radar**, as the police are doing in picture 3. The radar 'speed gun' measures the distance the car moves in a time of less than a millionth of a second! A built-in computer works out the result. In school laboratories a useful device called a ticker-timer does the same job (picture 4). It uses a time interval of a fiftieth of a second. See activity C for more details of how to use a ticker-timer.

Your school lab may also have electronic speed measuring devices using interrupted light beams (see picture 5). All these things might look quite complicated, but all they do is what you do with a stop watch and measuring tape. They measure time and distance covered.

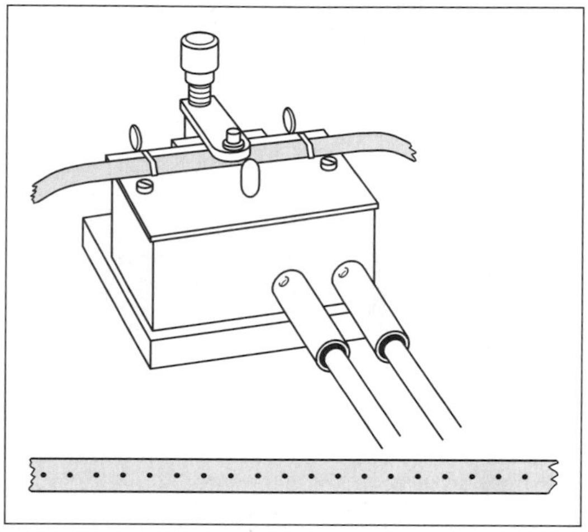

Picture 4 A ticker-timer and a sample of tape: the object was moving with a constant speed. Each ten-tick length shows how far the object travelled in a fifth of a second. A 'ten-tick' length has 10 spaces.

Movement formulae

$$\text{average speed} = \frac{\text{distance covered}}{\text{time taken}} \qquad v = \frac{s}{t}$$

$$\text{distance covered} = \text{average speed} \times \text{time taken} \qquad s = vt$$

$$\text{time taken} = \frac{\text{distance covered}}{\text{average speed}} \qquad t = \frac{s}{v}$$

Working things out

Suppose you wanted to estimate how long it would take to cycle from your home to a holiday area. You might be staying at a camp site or a youth hostel when you get there.

You work out on the map (picture 6) that it is 55 miles away. You now have to decide what your average cycling speed is. A reasonably fit person could cycle at 10 miles an hour on fairly flat roads.

Picture 5 These students are using a computer-assisted speed measuring device.

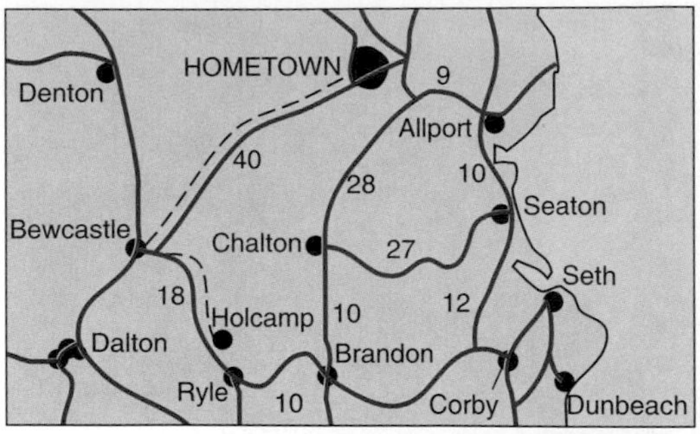

Picture 6 Which is the quickest route from Hometown to Holcamp?

Picture 7 How fast do you walk?

You would use the formula:

$$\text{time taken} = \frac{\text{distance covered}}{\text{speed}}$$

$$\boldsymbol{t} = \frac{\boldsymbol{s}}{\boldsymbol{v}}$$

$$\boldsymbol{t} = \frac{55}{10}\ \text{miles per hour}$$

$$\text{time needed} = 5.5\ \text{hours}$$

This is just an estimate, of course. You might decide to stop for a coffee. The route might be hilly. So you'd allow an extra hour or so to make sure.

Car and lorry drivers have to make the same kind of estimates every time they take a new route. You soon learn that the hardest thing to get right is an estimate of your average speed.

How fast do you walk?

People who do a lot of walking need to have a good estimate of their average walking speed. If you go hiking in the countryside, especially in mountains, you have to make calculations very carefully (picture 7). You may be far from roads and shelter, and mistakes could be dangerous. You wouldn't want to find yourself far from shelter as night falls or the weather turns bad.

Experienced hikers use *Naismith's Rule* to help them calculate timings. This says: *allow 1 hour for every 3 miles (5 km) you measure on the map then add 1 hour for every 2000 ft (600 m) you have to climb*.

This rule works for a fit walker, not carrying a lot of equipment. Question 4 asks you to use this rule to work out some walking times.

Activities

A Timing pendulums

The first accurate clocks were based on the principle of the pendulum. A pendulum is a weight on a cord, made to swing from side to side. Does it swing from side to side in a constant time? What decides how long the weight takes to swing from side to side?

Do an investigation to answer these questions. First list the things that might affect the time of swing. Then think of how you can measure the time of swing accurately. Is it good enough to measure just one swing?

This investigation could take a long time if you tried everything yourself. Organise your group into small teams that can investigate different things. Make sure that they all share their results at the end.

B Measuring average speed

For this investigation you will need a stop watch. You will also need some way of measuring the distances involved. Measure the time taken to cover a measured distance and use the formula:

$$\text{average speed} = \frac{\text{distance covered}}{\text{time taken}}$$

Try some or all of the following measurements:

1 the average speed of a runner,

2 the average speed of a cyclist travelling to school,

3 the average speed of a car passing the school or your home,

4 the average speed of a bird in flight,

5 the average speed of an object falling: (a) from a height of 2 m, (b) from a height of 5 m,

6 the average speed of flow of a river or stream.

C Using ticker-timers

Picture 4 shows a ticker-timer. A length of paper ticker tape is pulled through the timer. It prints a dot on the tape once every fiftieth of a second. It works using electromagnetism and is controlled by the mains ac frequency of 50 Hz. Thus the distance between the dots shows the distance the tape moved in just 1/50 of a second.

Use the timer to investigate one or more of the following:

1 Do you walk at a constant speed?

2 Do objects fall at a constant (steady) speed?

3 How does the speed of the weight at the end of a pendulum change as it swings from side to side?

Hints:

i) Use a fairly short piece of tape (about 1 m long).

ii) Work with 'ten-space' lengths, not one-space lengths. (Ten spaces represent a fifth of a second, which is usually accurate enough.)

iii) You can make your length of tape into a kind of graph showing the motion. Start at the beginning of the tape and count off *ten spaces*. Call this piece of tape (a 'ten-tick') number 1. Count off the next ten spaces and carry on doing this to the end of the tape, numbering each short piece. Cut the tape into your numbered ten-ticks and set them out on a base line as shown in picture 8.

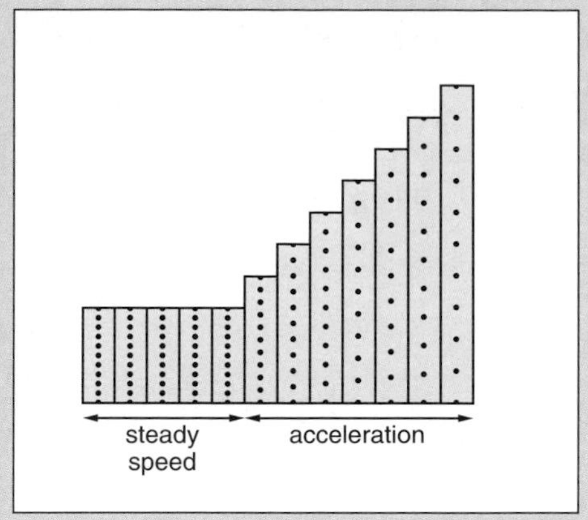

Picture 8

Questions

1 Estimating speed

Look at table 1 (page 24) showing the speeds of a number of well-known objects. Use it, and any other information you might have, to make a sensible guess at the likely (average) speeds of the following:

a a cyclist in a long-distance road race,
b a tennis ball during a serve,
c the signal from a TV transmitter,
d a marathon runner,
e the growth of grass.

2 Using formulae

Use the formulae given on page 25 to calculate the following.

a The speed of a train that covers 300 km in two hours.
b The speed of a walker who covers 24 km in five hours.
c How far a cyclist would travel in five hours at an average speed of 12 km/h.
d How far a car would travel in eight hours at an average speed of 70 km/h.
e How long it would take a ship to travel a distance of 400 km at an average speed of 25 km/h.
f How long it takes light to travel the distance of 149 600 000 km from the Sun to the Earth, at a speed of 300 000 kilometres per second. Give the answer in minutes and seconds.

3 a Name *four* different ways of measuring time.

b All timing devices make use of some kind of regular repetitive movement (e.g. a pendulum). What, do you think, are the things that do this job in the examples you have given in a?

4 Jane, Sally and Salman need to travel from the bridge in the village of Dent (see the map in picture 9) to meet their friends who are staying in Chapel-le-Dale. They plan to travel by the route shown.

a Use the scale of the map (and a piece of cotton, say) to work out how far they have to walk.
b How many feet do they have to climb?
c They are fit and not carrying a load. Use Naismith's Rule (page 26) to work out how long it should take them.

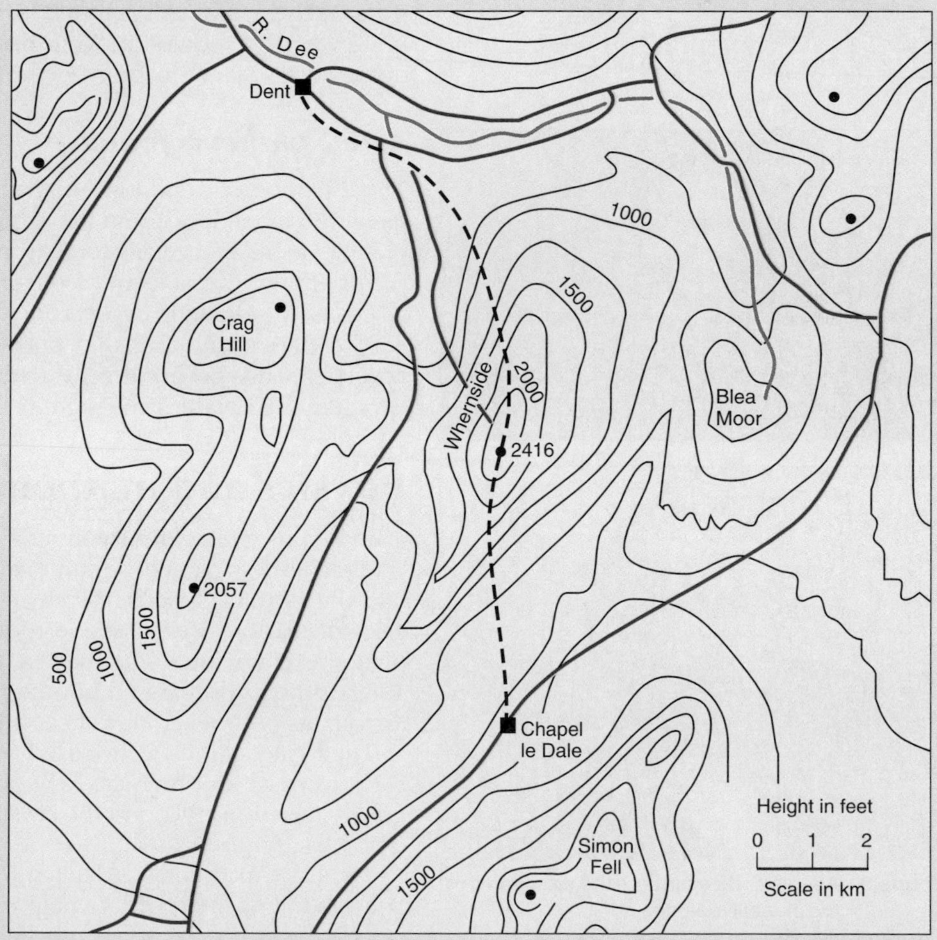

Picture 9

B2
The mathematics of movement

Physics and mathematics go hand in hand. The great value of physics is that it can use mathematics to make very accurate predictions.

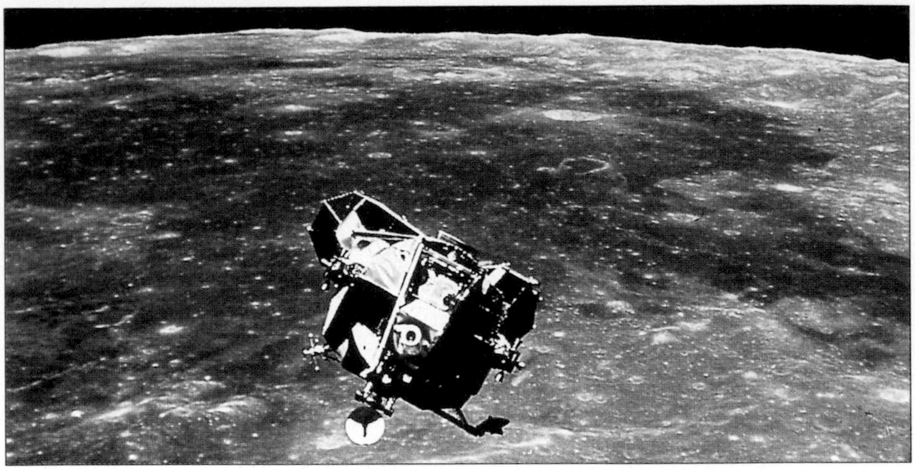

Picture 1 Accurate scientific calculations have enabled us to send capsules and satellites into space – and keep them there.

Moving in space

1969. A space craft is orbiting the Moon. At exactly the right moment, to the nearest hundredth of a second, the rockets are fired. They produce a very precise force, in exactly the right direction. They are on for a precisely calculated time. The capsule, and the precious human cargo it contains, land safely on the lunar surface.

1840. The planet Uranus, orbiting the Sun moves slowly against the background of the fixed stars. Astronomers plot its path, and calculate exactly where it should be in a week's, a month's, a year's time. Then they notice that it is not quite where it should be. What has gone wrong? Perhaps the laws of physics don't work so far away from Earth? Did they do the sums correctly?

A new planet is found

Two astronomers, unknown to each other and working in different countries, have the same idea. Could there be another planet out there in space that no one has seen? The gravity force from the unknown planet could be pulling the planet Uranus out of its plotted path.

One astronomer, Jean Leverrier, is French; the other, John Adams, is English. Unknown to each other, they both work out where the new planet should be. Leverrier sends his predictions to the German astronomers in Berlin, and they spot it in the sky the same night.

Picture 2 Adams and Leverrier – the discoverers of the planet Neptune.

Physics and mathematics working together

John Adams needed four years to make his calculations, using pen and paper. The planet was named Neptune, and was discovered in 1846. The astronauts had their orbits, speeds, forces and times controlled by on-board computer. The calculations were done in thousandths of a second. Picture 3 shows the planet as it was photographed by the Voyager Space Probe as it flew past in 1989. Although separated in time by over a hundred years, astronomers and astronauts both relied on very accurate mathematical calculations.

Their calculations were based on the same simple rules of physics. These rules were set out by Isaac Newton in the 17th century. They are the laws of gravity (see topic B4), and the laws obeyed by objects moving under the action of forces *(dynamics)*.

The basic mathematics dealing with moving objects is summarised opposite. You can follow the proofs to help you understand what the formulae mean.

In this section we use the following symbols for the quantities we measure:

time	t	force	F
distance	s	acceleration and deceleration	a
speed at start	u	mass	m
speed at end	v		

Picture 3 The planet Neptune.

The equations of movement: speed, distance, acceleration and time

To help you keep track, each formula is numbered.

Average speed

We have already seen in topic B1 that

$$\text{average speed} = \frac{\text{total distance covered}}{\text{total time taken}}$$

Or $\quad v = s / t \qquad (1)$

Acceleration

Something that speeds up is **accelerating**. If it is increasing its speed steadily we say that it has a steady **acceleration, *a***. For straight line movement, this is defined as **change in speed per second**. To measure acceleration we need to measure not only the change in speed of an object but also the time it takes to change its speed (see picture 4).

That is:

$$\text{acceleration} = \frac{\text{change in speed}}{\text{time taken for the change}}$$

$$\text{Or, acceleration} = \frac{\text{speed at end of timing} - \text{speed at start}}{\text{time interval}}$$

As a formula: $a = \dfrac{v - u}{t} \qquad (2)$

The unit is $\dfrac{\text{metres per second}}{\text{seconds}}$ or m/s^2

The formula (2) can be rearranged as $v = u + at$ (3)

Picture 4 How acceleration is calculated.

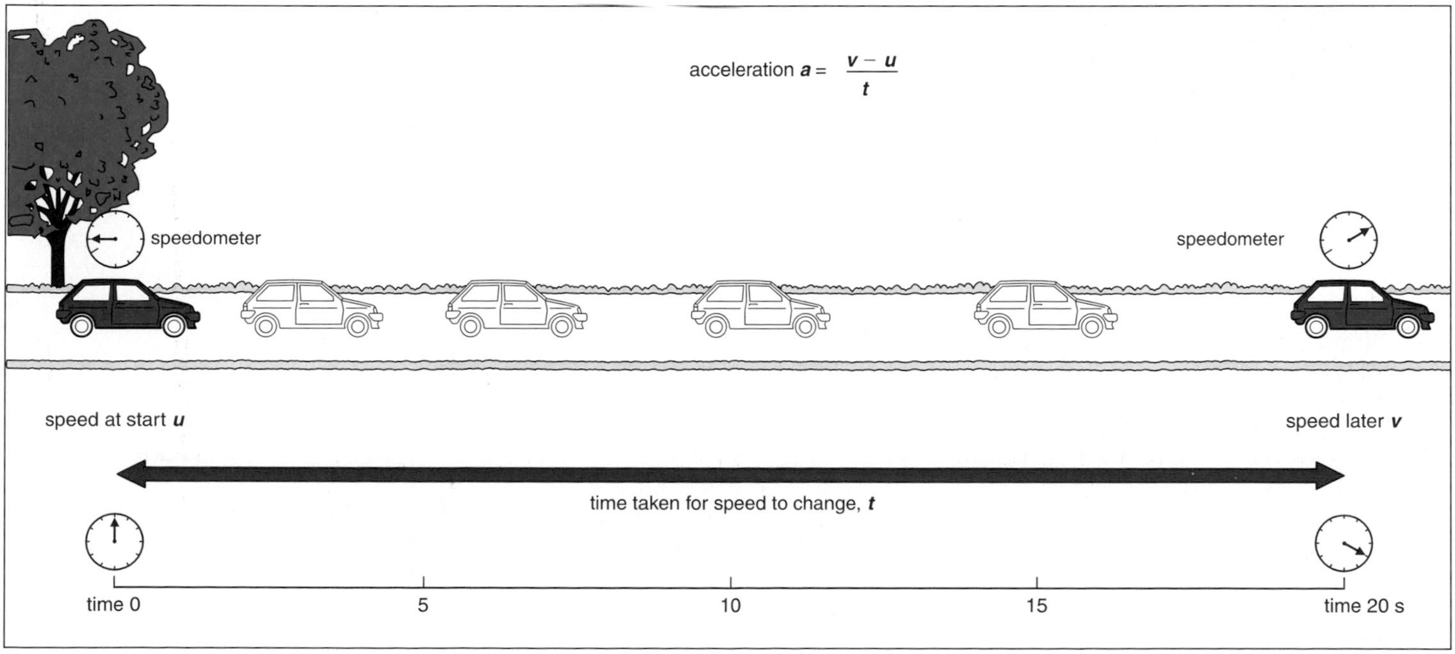

Equations and formulae of motion

$$\text{average speed} = \frac{\text{distance covered}}{\text{time taken}}$$

$$a = \frac{v - u}{t}$$

$$v = u + at$$

$$s = \tfrac{1}{2}(u+v)\,t$$

Also: $F = ma$

Finding the distance travelled

Equation (1) can be rearranged as $s = vt$. Picture 5(a) shows that vt is also the shaded area under the graph. **In fact, whatever the shape of the graph the area between it and the time axis represents the distance travelled.** This area is hard to measure if the graph has a complicated shape as in the picture 5(d).

Moving with an initial speed

Picture 5(b) shows the speed–time graph of an object that is already moving at a speed u when timing starts. It is accelerating steadily, so the graph is a straight line and its speed reaches a value v after a time t.

This means that its average speed is the mean of u and v.

$$\textbf{average speed over time } t = \frac{(u + v)}{2}$$

From equation (1) distance covered = average speed × time, or:

$$s = \frac{(u + v)}{2}\,t \qquad (4)$$

The dotted line in picture 5(b) shows this average speed.

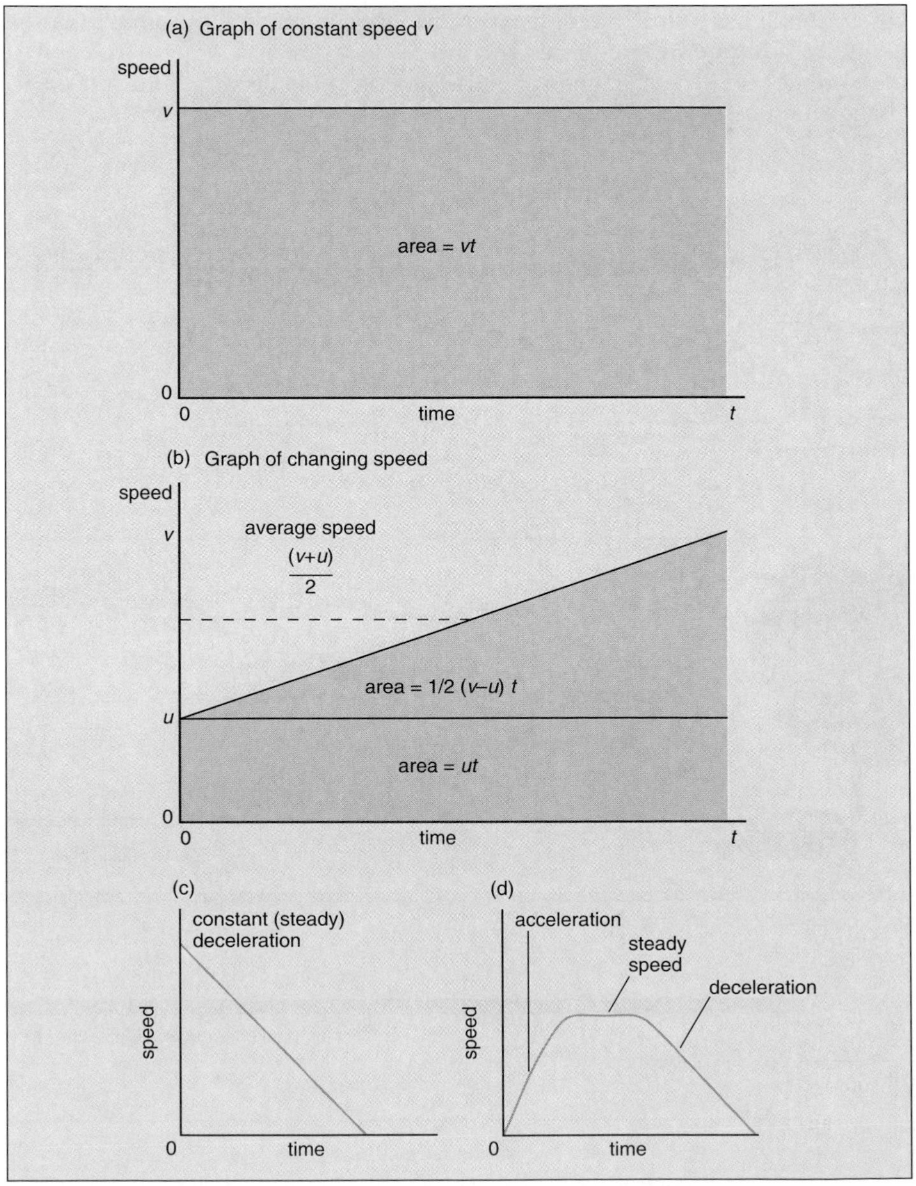

Picture 5 Graphs of motion.

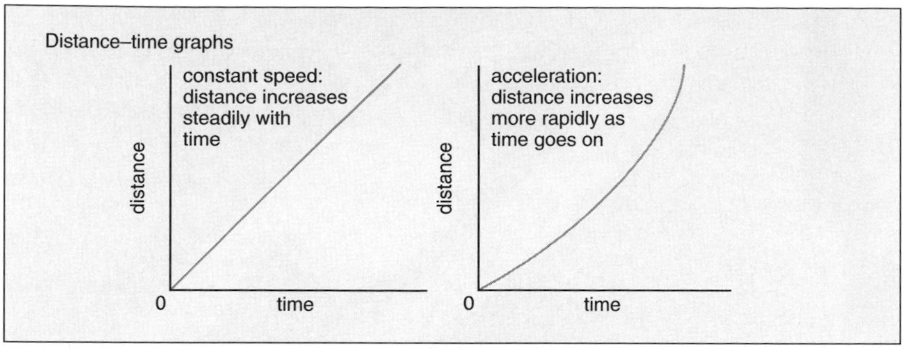

Picture 6 Graphs showing different kinds of movement.

Activities

A

Use a library, CD-ROM or encyclopaedia to find out what you can about:

1 the Apollo space flights and Moon landings,

2 the discovery of Neptune.

B

This is an activity about collecting data about some everday movements and then analysing them using graphs. All you need is a tape measure, a metre rule, a sloping track and a stopwatch

1 work in a group to collect distance–time data for a person who is told to walk at least 10 m at a steady speed. (*Hint*: You could measure the time at every 2 m, say.) Use the data to plot a distance–time graph. How can you tell that the person walked at a steady speed? Which member of the group is best at keeping up a steady speed?

2 Now for something more difficult – this experiment was first done by the famous Italian physicist Galileo (see page 46) in the 17th century. Collect data, using a stopwatch and a metre rule, to investigate the motion of a ball or trolley rolling down a slope. Part 1 should have helped you design a method for doing this quite accurately, but think of ways of getting more reliable results. Plot a graph of your data as in part 1. Explain the features of your graph using the terms *acceleration, constant acceleration, speed, steady speed.*

3 Investigate what happens when you change the angle of the slope.

Questions

To answer these questions you may need to use the formulae given in this section or to draw graphs.

1 a A cyclist travelled 25 km in two hours. What was the average speed of the cyclist?

b How far would a car travel in 5 hours at an average speed of 80 km per hour?

c How long would it take an athlete running at an average speed of 5 m/s to cover a distance of 2000 m?

2 Calculate the following:

a the change in speed produced when a car accelerates at 2 m/s^2 for a time of 15 seconds,

b the acceleration required to speed up an aircraft from a speed of 100 m/s to 500 m/s in 40 seconds,

c the speed change produced in a ship when it is decelerated at a rate of 0.2 m/s^2 for 100 seconds,

d how long it would take a car travelling at 30 m/s (about 70 mph) to stop, at a deceleration of 4 m/s^2.

3 A free-fall parachutist jumps out of an aeroplane. At first she accelerates downwards at 10 m/s^2, but as the air resistance builds up the acceleration gets less. After about 5 seconds her downward acceleration is zero and she is falling at a steady speed of 30 m/s. She keeps falling at this speed for another 20 seconds and then opens her parachute.

a What happens to her speed when she opens the parachute?

b Sketch a graph of the parachutist's speed plotted against time for the first 60 seconds of her fall, putting in as much detail as you can.

c After falling for 1 minute, she is 1,200 m above the ground and her parachute has reduced her downward speed to 8 m/s. How long will she take to reach the ground?

d Would it make any difference to your answer to part c if there was a wind blowing horizontally at 5 m/s? Explain you answer and say how you would expect the wind to affect her motion.

4 A car travelling in a limited speed zone travels at the speed limit of 36 km per hour.

a What is this speed in metres per second?

b The car leaves the speed limit zone and accelerates to a speed of 25 m/s, taking 30 seconds to do so. What was the acceleration of the car (in m/s^2) in that 30 seconds?

c How far did the car travel during the 30 seconds it was accelerating?

time after start (s)	0	2	4	6	8	10	12	14	16	18	20
speed (m/s)	0	3	6	9	12	15	18	20	21	21	21

B3
Crashes and bangs

Stopping and starting can be gentle – but what about when they are not? The key idea is momentum.

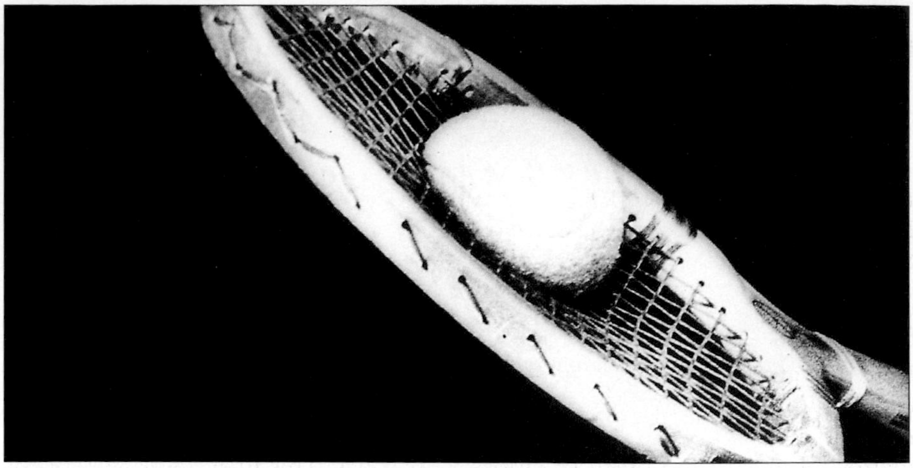

Picture 1 Hitting a tennis ball.

Hitting things

The photograph in picture 1 shows a tennis ball just as it is being hit by the racket. You can see why they change the balls so often, and why rackets have to be made so very strong. The forces on both are very large.

Both the ball and the racket are distorted by the impact. The ball is squashed almost flat, and the racket strings are stretched. This is a good example of one of the basic laws of forces and movement.

The law of action and reaction

This was first discovered by the great scientist Isaac Newton over 300 years ago. He said that action and reaction are equal and opposite. This means simply that the force exerted on the ball by the racket – the 'action force' is the same in size as the force exerted on the racket by the ball – the 'reaction'. The forces are acting in opposite directions.

Twin forces

This law of Newton's is one of those laws of nature that always applies. Another way of looking at it is to assume that forces occur in pairs.

Blow up a balloon and let it go. The balloon rushes forwards and the air in it rushes out backwards. In a rocket or jet the force produced by the engine acts just as much on the vehicle as on the hot gases rushing out at the back (picture 2). This means that the forces involved are equal in size and opposite in direction.

Even when you walk, your foot pushing back on the ground causes a reaction that pushes you forward. When a magnet attracts a piece of iron, there is an equal and opposite force pulling the magnet towards the iron. If you try this you can feel both forces.

Picture 2 Forces occur in pairs: the upward push on the rocket equals the downward push on the exhaust gases.

Collisions

In a collision, forces act for a very short time. The forces are often quite large and the objects that collide run a risk of being damaged. This is what happens in traffic accidents.

In ball games the equipment is designed to avoid damage, although cricketers might not agree! (Picture 3.)

But apart from any damage that might happen in a collision, there is also a change in movement. Objects speed up or slow down. Large objects seem to be harder to speed up and slow down than smaller ones. Think of the difference between tennis and table tennis, or between pushing a pram and pushing a car.

It was again Isaac Newton who realised that there are just two things that are important when collisions happen.

According to Newton, these are:

- the **speed** and its **direction**,
- the **masses** of the colliding objects.

In any collision, the more massive the object and the faster it is going the more effect it will have. The combination is a quantity called **momentum. Momentum is mass (*m*) multiplied by speed in a given direction**. Speed in a given direction is called **velocity *(v)***. So **momentum** = ***mv***.

Picture 3 This sportsman is prepared to withstand unwanted forces.

Mass

Mass was a very new and strange idea in 1680, and it's not that easy to grasp even now. We can think of it as a measure of how hard it is to make an object move, even when it is perfectly free to do so, like an object in space. The more matter there is in an object, the more mass it has. This idea helps to explain why table tennis bats aren't much use on a tennis court. The property of mass that makes it hard to move is called **inertia**.

Force and momentum

The effect of a force is to change the momentum of an object. The change is bigger when the force is *larger*, or when the force *acts for a longer time*.

So what exactly happens in a collision?

Let's start by thinking about an easy example.

A simple collision

The simplest collision is when a moving ball collides centre to centre with another, identical, ball which is perfectly still ('at rest'). As they make an impact, the forces between them are the same all the time. The moving ball stops dead and the other one moves off with the same speed and in the same direction. In terms of momentum, all the momentum of the first ball has been given to the second one.

The law of momentum

Collision experiments produce the result that whenever a collision happens the total momentum of the colliding objects stay the same. The key formula is:

total momentum before collision = total momentum after collision

Picture 4 shows this. Try it with two coins.

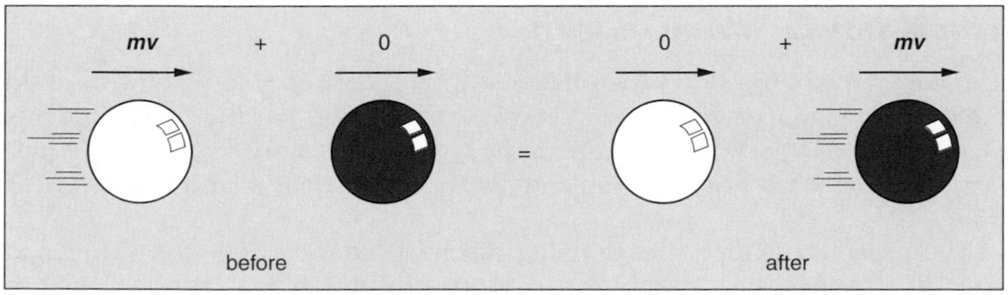

Picture 4 In collisions, momentum stays the same.

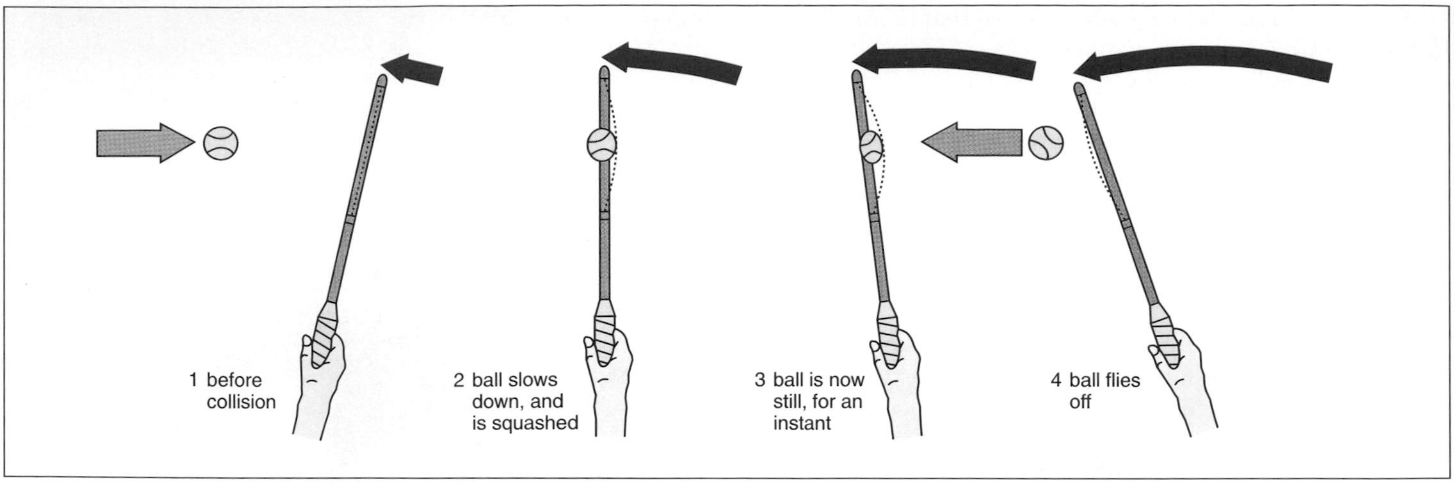

2 ball slows down, and is squashed
3 ball is now still, for an instant

Picture 5 Forces and movement in tennis.

Tricky collisions

Let's consider a slow motion action replay of what happens when a tennis ball is hit by a tennis racket. As the ball touches the strings of the racket the action–reaction forces begin to act. The ball is crushed, and the strings are pushed back. The forces increase and at some stage the ball is stopped, probably when the forces are greatest.

The racket is only slowed down a little. This is because it is so much more massive than the ball, while the force on it is the same as the force on the ball.

But this is only half the story. The forces are still acting, even if they are getting less. The ball regains its normal shape and the strings go back to being straight. The forces are now pushing the ball forward very quickly, faster than the racket in its 'follow through'. So the ball flies away from the racket. The drawings in picture 5 summarise this.

But what has all this to do with real life? Think about safety on the road and other places where collision accidents can happen.

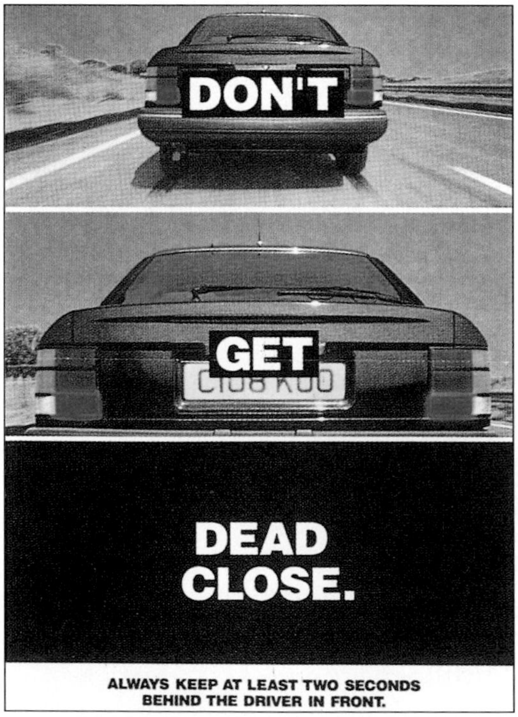

DON'T
GET
DEAD CLOSE.
ALWAYS KEEP AT LEAST TWO SECONDS BEHIND THE DRIVER IN FRONT.

Picture 6 Do posters help to save lives?

Stopping safely

To stop a moving object you have to take away its momentum. The only way to do this is to provide a force. Think of stopping a car. It can be done using a large force or a short time – as in a collision. Or it can be done with a small force over a longer time – by using brakes. Brakes use the force of **friction** to slow the wheels down. There must also be good friction between the tyres and the road, otherwise the car may skid.

A safe design allows fast-moving objects to give up their momentum slowly. Cars are designed with 'crumple zones'. The front of the car is deliberately made 'softer' than it could be, so that it crumples slowly in a collision.

Travel slowly – think quickly

The chart in table 1 shows the official stopping distances for cars with good tyres and good brakes. It has been worked out by the government's Department of Transport. The faster a car is going, the more momentum it has, so it takes longer to stop. The 'braking distance' is how far the car travels in this time.

The chart also shows the 'thinking distance'. It takes time for a driver to react to an emergency. The thinking distance is how far the car travels before the driver reacts by stepping on the brake pedal.

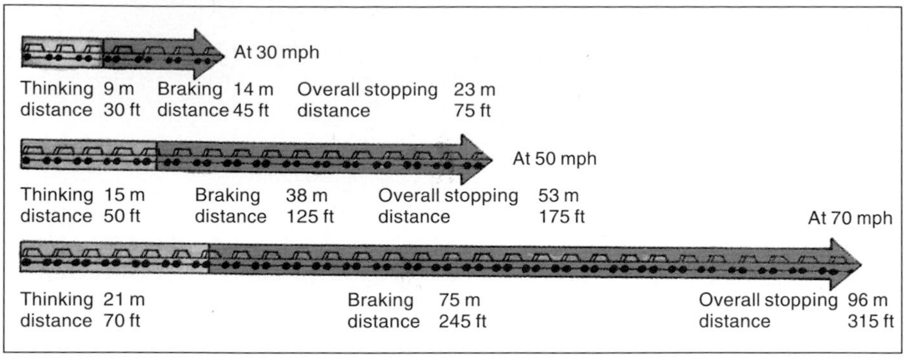

Table 1 Official stopping distances.

Speed limits

The physics of this topic should help you understand the reasons for speed limits on the road. At high speeds both thinking distance and braking distance are increased. In fact the braking distance is quadrupled for a doubling in speed (table 1).

Also, the force of a collision is greater at a greater speed, so that most damage is done. In fact, the damage also more than doubles when the speed doubles. This is because a bigger force acts for a longer time.

Momentum and impulse

Momentum is one of the most important ideas in physics – and is especially important when it comes to collisions. We know that forces make things speed up or slow down, that is, forces make things change their velocity. A change in velocity means a change in momentum, because *momentum* = *mass* × *velocity*. The bigger the force, the bigger its effect on momentum. And the longer a force acts, the bigger its effect. We can combine these two ideas into a rule:

force × time = change in momentum produced

As a formula:

$$Ft = \text{change in } (mv).$$

In simple cases, when things are moving in a straight line, the change in momentum is simply *mass* × *change in speed*, i.e.

Ft = (momentum with ending speed) – (momentum with starting speed)

Or

$$Ft = mv - mu)$$

and so

$$Ft = m(v - u)$$

The quantity Ft is so important that it is given a special name: **impulse**.

We can rearrange this formula as:

$$\boldsymbol{F = m\frac{(v-u)}{t}}$$

Now $\boldsymbol{(v - u)/t}$ looks familiar. It is what we defined in the last topic as **acceleration,** $\boldsymbol{a}$. The formula becomes simpler:

$$\boldsymbol{F = ma}$$

In words: **force** = **mass** × **acceleration**.

This is one of the most important formulae in physics. It is the basis of space flight, astronomy, car performance and indeed any kind of animal and human movement.

It would be a good idea to do some of the activities at the end of the topic so that you get a feel for what all this mathematics means in real life situations.

Picture 7 Why safety belts and crumple zones are helping to save lives.

The newton

It is the last formula above that is used to define the unit of force used in science and engineering. A **newton** is the size of the force that can give a mass of 1 kg an acceleration of 1 m/s^2.

$$1\ N = 1\ kg \times 1\ m/s^2$$

Newton's Laws of Motion

Newton wrote down three simple laws to describe how and why objects move. They summarise the ideas we have already met.

Newton 1: An object will keep still or carry on moving at a steady speed in a straight line unless a **force** acts on it.

Newton 2: The effect of a force on an object free to move is to change its momentum such that force × time equals the momentum change produced.

Newton 3: Forces are always found in **pairs**, equal in size but acting in opposite directions.

Newton's Laws are very reliable in everyday life and in astronomy. But in this century we have found that they break down at very high speeds and we have to use Einstein's ideas instead.

Newton's Laws are very important in physics, and they will be used a lot in the next sections. As you use them you will learn to understand them better.

Impulse – and staying alive

Think about stopping a car. F is now the braking force. When it stops, the momentum is zero because speed is zero. The change in momentum is mv: so we can say

$$Ft = mv$$

If we want to stop a car quickly, so that t is small, then F must be large. But the bigger the braking force the more likely the car is to skid – the same applies to a bicycle, as you might have already found out from your own experience! The Highway Code chart of stopping distances assumes not only good brakes but also that the tyres get a good grip on the road (table 1). This grip – a friction force – gets less when tyres are worn or the road is wet or icy.

When a car is stopped by a collision, in an accident, it stops very quickly. Time t is very small – perhaps just a few thousandths of a second. This means that the force F is very large, and so will damage the car.

The stopping force on the people in the car will also be large if they stop quickly – and they will be injured. **Seat belts** work by holding the body to the car frame so that the body doesn't shoot forward to hit the windscreen (picture 7). The belt also stretches a little, so that the body actually takes longer to slow down than the car does. The change in momentum is just the same but takes place more slowly. This reduces the force on the body and helps stop or reduce injury.

Air bags are also designed to ensure that in a collision the body takes longer to slow down than the car. A small microchip senses a sudden deceleration by the force on a small piece of plastic. It then triggers a release of liquid nitrogen which blows up the airbag microseconds before the body moves towards the steering wheel.

Cars are designed with a solid central 'cage' surrounded by a much weaker **crumple zone**. In a collision the front (or back) of the car will be weak enough to collapse but strong enough to do so slowly. This again increases the stopping time and so reduces the force involved.

This basic principle is also used to stop high jumpers and pole vaulters breaking their legs. They fall onto beds of soft foam rubber.

Gases and pressure

Gas pressure is useful. It inflates balloons and it holds up tyres. Gas pressure can be gentle and almost unnoticeable – we hardly notice the changes in atmospheric pressure that happen when the weather changes. But high pressure gases make their presence felt – think how hard an inflated tyre feels.

What causes pressure in gases?

You have already learned that matter is made up of small particles which are arranged in different ways to form solids, liquids and gases. In solids they are close together and fixed in place, although they can vibrate. In liquids they are still close together but are free to move around. In gases the particles are much further apart. All this is described by the **kinetic theory** of matter, which explains the nature of solids, liquids and gases in terms of how much the particles of matter move.

We can use the kinetic theory to explain gas pressure. Think of gas inside a balloon. The gas particles move around at random. They constantly collide with each other, and with the walls of the balloon. Every square millimetre of the balloon is battered by millions and millions of tiny particles every second (picture 8).

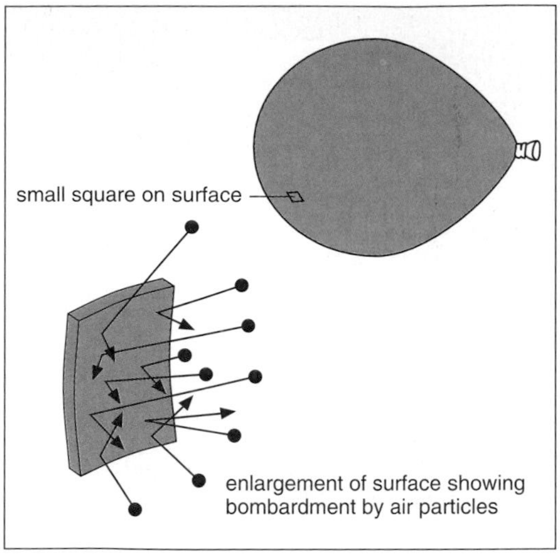

Picture 8 How a gas exerts pressure.

Each particle is too small to have much of an effect on the balloon wall by itself. But the constant battering by millions of particles adds up to a steady force on each square millimetre, and this is what we call pressure. Pressure is simply force per unit area:

$$P = \frac{F}{A}$$ where F is in newtons and A in square metres. P is in pascals (Pa).

See topic A4 for more about pressure.

In fact the balloon has pressure on it from both inside and outside. Outside, it is battered by particles of air from the atmosphere – this is atmospheric pressure. There is also atmospheric pressure inside – plus a bit more, due to the extra air that was blown in. It's this extra pressure that keeps the balloon inflated.

What affects the pressure of a gas?

Volume and pressure

Try a simple experiment with a bicycle pump. Hold your finger over the hole and push in the handle of the pump. You can feel the increasing pressure of gas on your finger. By pushing in the handle you have decreased the volume of the gas inside the pump. This increases its pressure. **When the volume of a gas decreases, its pressure increases.**

We can explain this using our idea that a gas is made of high speed particles. If you halve the volume of the gas, the same number of particles get pushed into half the space. This means that they hit the walls more often. With more particles hitting the walls per second, the pressure increases.

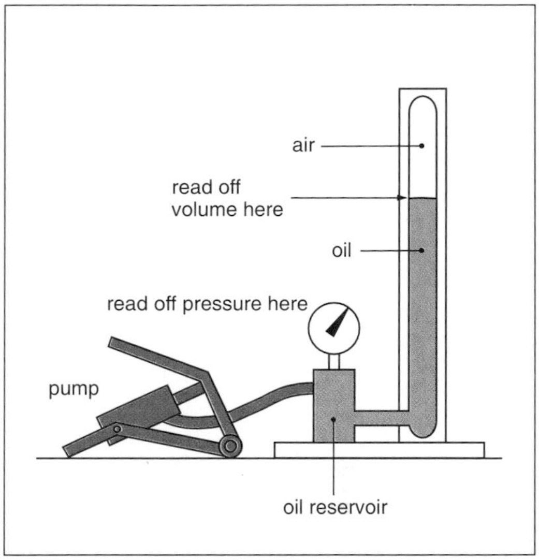

Picture 9 Investigating how the volume of a gas depends on pressure.

Picture 9 shows the apparatus we can use to see how the volume of a gas depends on the pressure. The gas being tested is air, trapped in the vertical glass tube. The temperature is kept constant during the experiment.

The pump is used to increase the pressure of the air in the tube. You can read off the pressure from the pressure gauge. The volume of the air is read off from the graduations on the side of the tube.

Pressure/kPA	Volume/cm^3
100	48
120	40
140	34
160	30
180	26
200	24
220	22
240	20
260	18
280	17
300	16

Table 2 Results obtained using the apparatus in picture 9 to investigate the relationship between P and V for a gas. The pressure is measured in kilopascals, kPa. Normal atmospheric pressure is 100 kPa.

Table 2 shows some results obtained using this apparatus. What happens when the pressure is doubled from 100 kPa to 200 kPa? The volume is halved, from 48 cm^3 to 24 cm^3. When the pressure is multiplied by three, from 100 kPa to 300 kPa, the volume goes from 48 to 16 – it's divided by three.

Picture 10 A car air bag in action.

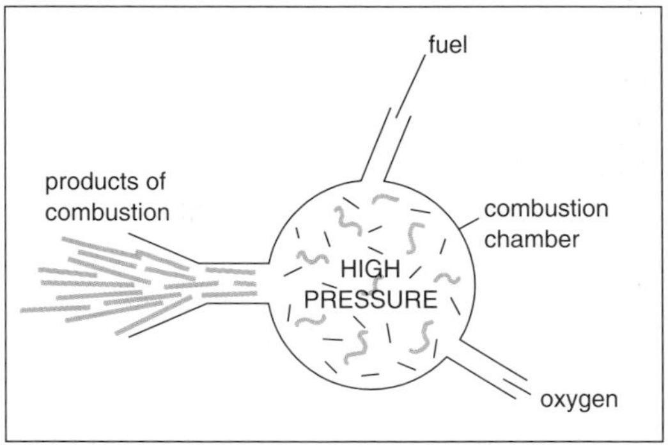

Picture 11 Diagram of a rocket motor.

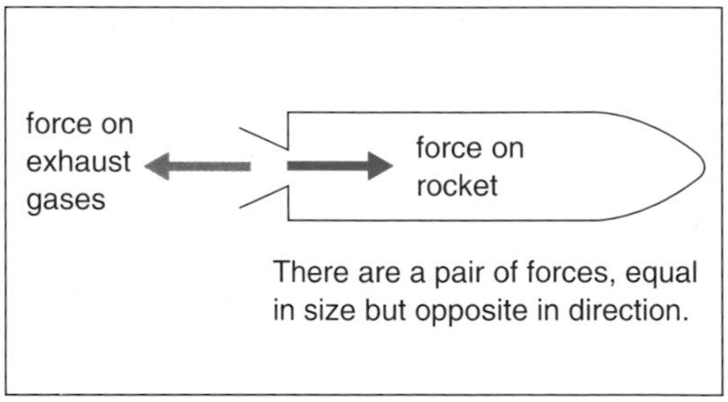

Picture 12 Forces in the rocket system.

This is an inverse relationship: the volume is inversely proportional to the pressure. This can be written mathematically as

$$V \propto \frac{1}{P} \quad \text{or} \quad V = \frac{\text{constant}}{P} \quad \text{or} \quad PV = \text{constant}$$

In Question 4 you can show that the results in table 1 obey these mathematical relationships. Remember, they only work if the temperature is kept constant.

This relationship between P and V is known as **Boyle's Law**, after Robert Boyle, the British scientist who first stated the law in 1662. In words, Boyle's Law says **the volume of a fixed mass of gas is inversely proportional to its pressure, if the temperature is kept constant.**

Most gases obey Boyle's Law pretty well, but no gas obeys it perfectly. Life's like that. An imaginary gas which would obey the law perfectly is called a **perfect gas.**

Boyle's Law saves lives

Most new cars are now fitted with an **airbag**. This stops the driver's body hitting the inside of the car at high speed in a collision. Even with a seat belt the driver's body keeps moving forwards for some distance when the car comes to a very sudden stop. The airbag works like this. It is a strong plastic bag containing a very small flask of nitrogen under a very high pressure. The bag is folded so that it fits into a small space inside the shaft holding the steering wheel. In a collision the car slows down very quickly, and the sudden deceleration moves a plug and the gas is released into the plastic bag.

The gas now obeys Boyle's Law. It is no longer trapped in a very small space under high pressure so it expands to fill the plastic bag which fills the space between the driver and the front of the steering wheel. It happens so quickly – in a thousandth of a second or so – that the driver's chest and head don't have time to move forward into the steering wheel, the fascia or the windscreen.

Rockets

The only way that humans can leave the Earth's surface and move into space is to use **rockets**. Rocket engines are usually very large – but they are also very simple. All you need is to mix a fuel with some oxygen in a combustion chamber and set them alight. The gases burn, get very hot and expand through a small nozzle (picture 11). The gases expand so much that they are forced through the nozzle at a very high speed. Then Newton's rule about forces comes into play:

forces always occur in opposite pairs
(or *action and reaction are equal and opposite*)

The force pushing the hot gases through the nozzle is matched by an equal-sized force pushing the opposite way on the combustion chamber. This of course is fixed to the rocket body and so the whole system is accelerated by this force (picture 12). For a simple rocket engine the pair of forces are always the same size. The rocket accelerates in accordance with

$$\text{force} = \text{mass} \times \text{acceleration}$$

But the rocket is getting lighter because it is losing fuel as the burnt gases stream away. So what do you think happens to the acceleration of the rocket?

Activities

A

Think up a way for producing a steady (constant) force on an object that is free to move. Discuss your idea with your friends and your teacher and agree on a good, workable method.

Plan an experiment which uses your constant force system to find out if larger masses are harder to accelerate than smaller ones. Be clear about what you need to measure.

B

Extend the investigations in activity B to make measurements as accurately as you can to check the following.

(Note: you will need now to have a good method for measuring or comparing accelerations, such as a ticker-timer.)

1 For a constant mass, the acceleration is proportional to the force applied.

2 If you double the mass and halve the force, you get the same acceleration.

3 If you increase the mass, you have to increase the force in proportion if you want to get the same acceleration.

In each case explain what these statements have to do with the key formula **force = mass × acceleration**.

C Thinking about road safety

You will need a collection of road safety pamphlets and slogans, and a copy of the Highway Code. List some key road safety factors, such as seat belts, drunken driving, the clothing that motor cyclists wear and so on. How many of the factors are needed because of the law of physics that says:

force × time = change of momentum

Produce a poster linking as many road safety ideas as you can with this law.

Questions

1 Predict and try to explain what happens when:

a a car travelling at 30 mph on an icy road comes to a sharp bend,
b a cyclist travelling downhill at 40 mph puts on the front brake.

2 Why do heavy container lorries need stronger, more powerful brakes than an ordinary passenger car?

3 a How do they stop ships (like tankers or liners)?

b How do they slow aircraft down while they are in the air?
c How do you slow down, when you are running fast?
d Why do jumbo jet aircraft need longer airport runways than ordinary jets?

4 How does a 'crumple zone' help to protect the passengers in a car?

5 Design an experiment you could do to test a playground surface to see if it was a 'safety surface' or not.

6 In the Highway Code it says that a car should be able to brake to a stop from a speed of 14 m/s (about the speed limit in towns) in a distance of 15 m.

a What is its deceleration in m/s^2?
b A typical car has a mass of 1500 kg. What force must the brakes exert to stop it in this distance?
c How long will the car take to stop?

7 Describe what you would expect to happen to the speeds of the moving objects as a result of the following collisions.

a A small boy running along a corridor bumps into a very large man.
b A large oil tanker moving at speed collides with a small yacht.
c Two equal sized cars travelling at 80 km/h in opposite directions collide with each other head on.

8 Give simple explanations of the following, using the ideas of momentum and/or of 'action' and 'reaction'.

a A moving snooker ball moves another one when it hits it, but doesn't seem to move the table when it hits the side.
b One way to get off a perfectly smooth surface, such as a sheet of very slippery ice, would be to take off a boot and throw it along the ice.
c Sprinters use spiked shoes.
d When a gun fires a shell, the gun 'recoils'.
e Kicking a football is quite easy, but kicking a stone cannonball of the same size could seriously damage your foot.

9 When a gun is fired the bullet leaves it at a very high speed. It is driven out by the force of expanding gases. This force acts on both the gun and the bullet (by Newton's Law 3). Why doesn't the gun move backwards at the same speed as the bullet goes forward?

10 Use the theory of moving molecules (the kinetic theory) to explain why it is hard to squash a pumped up bicycle tyre, even though the air in it is a gas – and doesn't weigh very much.

11 Describe any everyday application of Boyle's Law you know about.

12 a Describe an experiment you have done or seen to prove Boyle's Law. What important safety precautions should you take with this experiment?

b The table gives some measurements that were made in an experiment to test Boyle's Law. Explain and carry out *two* tests on the data to show that the Law was in fact obeyed.

Volume of trapped gas (cm^3)	Pressure (Pa)
84	1.0
75	1.1
64	1.3
50	1.7
42	2.0
32	2.6
35	3.4

B4
Gravity

Gravity is one of the great forces of nature. It makes things fall, and keeps the planets in their orbits.

Gravity is everywhere

Everything we do is affected by gravity. Running, jumping, swimming or just standing still, our bodies are affected by the force that pulls us towards the centre of the Earth. We are so used to it that our very bones grow weaker without it. This happens to astronauts who spend a long time in 'free-fall' (see below).

We can't switch gravity off, the way we can switch off an electromagnet. We can't neutralise it, like we can the forces of static electricity. We have to live with the fact that everything on the surface of the Earth is in a strong gravity field.

The design of roads, railways, buildings, aircraft and even the bodies of living things has to take gravity into account. The study of movement under gravity is vital in physics and engineering, as well as in ball games like tennis and football.

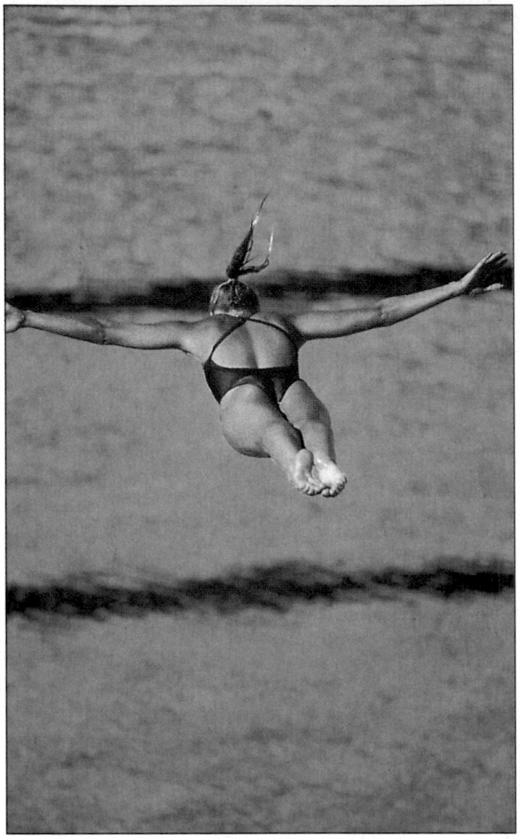

Picture 1 Playing with gravity.

The gravity force field

Every object attracts every other object with a gravity force. The gravity force between you and the person sitting next to you is very small. You attract each other with a force of about a millionth of a newton. You will not notice this.

Gravity forces become important when at least one of the objects is very massive. The earth has a mass of about six million million million million kilograms, so its gravity field is quite strong.

The Earth's gravity field

The strength of a gravity field is measured in terms of how much force it exerts on a 1 kg mass.

On Earth, the force of gravity on an object of mass of 1 kg is about 10 N – or 9.8 N to be more exact. So the strength of the Earth's gravity field, $\boldsymbol{g}$, is 9.8 N/kg.

If we put a more massive object in the gravity field it will have a bigger gravity force acting on it. A piece of iron with mass 2 kg has twice as much iron in it as a piece of iron with a mass of only 1 kg, so it will be pulled towards the Earth with twice the force.

A 2 kg mass feels heavier than a 1 kg mass because it is being pulled down by a force of about 20 N, compared with only about 10 N for the 1 kg mass. The force caused by gravity on a mass is called its **weight**.

We can get a rough measure of weight by just holding the object up. To measure it more accurately we need a newton meter. This is usually a spring balance marked off in newtons.

The weight of an object of mass $\boldsymbol{m}$ – the force $\boldsymbol{F}$ due to gravity on it – is given by the formula $\boldsymbol{F = mg}$.

gravity force (weight) = mass × field strength

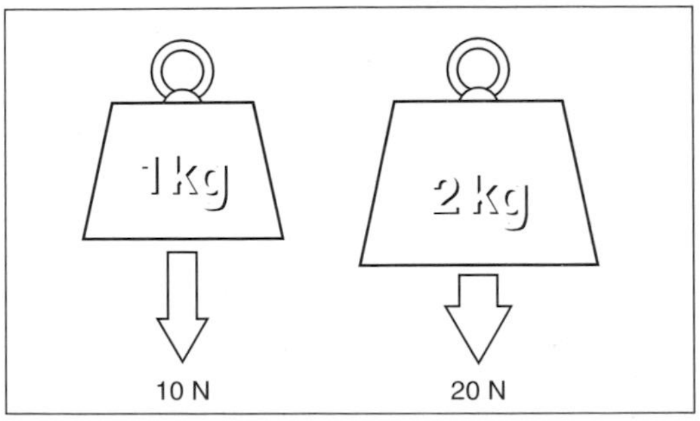

Picture 2 Gravity fields pull harder on a greater mass.

The strength of the Earth's gravity field is defined as the force it exerts on a kilogram of matter. The easy way to measure it would be to use a newton meter as a force measurer and hang a mass of 1 kg on it (picture 3). But this would be cheating! The newton meter has been made at a factory and tested for accuracy by seeing if it gave the right reading when a mass was hung on it. It has been marked off on the assumption that the Earth's gravity field at the surface is 9.8 N/kg.

A better way is to measure the *acceleration of free fall*, **g**. As explained below, the acceleration of free fall is numerically the same as the field strength, i.e. 9.8 m/s^2. Activity B gives ideas for doing this.

Because its gravity field is so weak the Moon doesn't have an atmosphere. Air has weight, and it is the force of gravity that holds it on the Earth. But there is more to this than just the weight of the air.

Air molecules move very fast – on Earth they move at an average speed of about 500 m/s. Some molecules move a lot faster than the average, of course. Now to escape from the Earth, they would need to move at the speed of an Earth satellite – over 11 000 m/s. This is called the escape speed for the Earth.

Hardly any molecules move this fast so air stays on Earth.

On the Moon the escape speed is much less, because of its weaker gravity field. It is only 2400 m/s. The fastest molecules travel faster than this, so any atmosphere on the Moon would have gradually leaked away.

Picture 4(a) shows a ball falling freely towards the Earth. It has been taken using a flashing light that lit the ball every tenth of a second. As you can see, the ball travels a greater and greater distance in each tenth of a second. It is *accelerating*.

This is because it is being pulled down with a steady force, and this produces a constant acceleration (see topic B3). It is called the **acceleration of free fall**.

Picture 4(b) shows the ball again. This time it has been thrown sideways. But gravity still acts, and the ball is pulled downwards exactly as before. This will happen however fast the ball is thrown sideways.

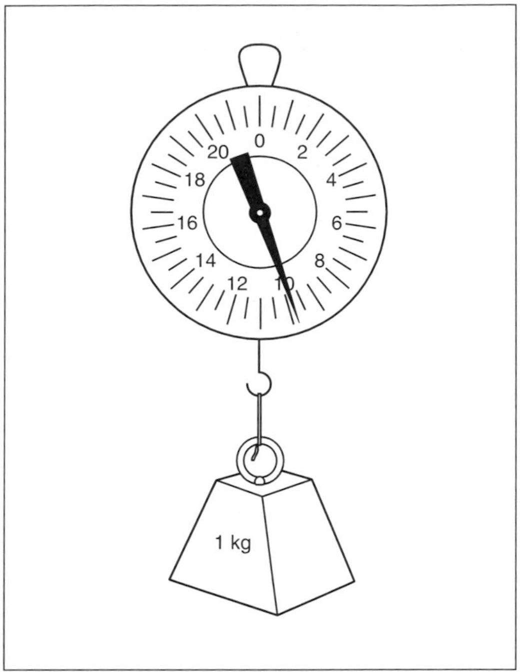

Picture 3 Measuring the strength of the gravity field.

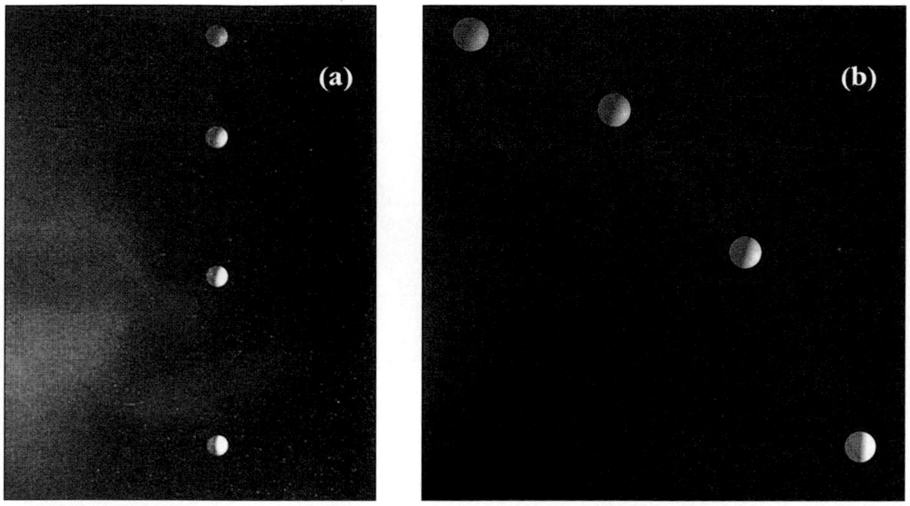

Picture 4 A freely falling object accelerates.

Do heavy objects fall faster than light ones?

No – but keep on reading.

An object is **heavy**, and feels heavy, because gravity is pulling on it with a large force. This is because a heavy object has more mass than a light object.

But because it has more mass it is harder to accelerate! The extra gravity force on the heavy object exactly compensates for the extra mass. So the acceleration of free fall is exactly the same, whatever the mass of the object – see picture 5. This is shown below mathematically.

> Topic B3 has shown that a force causes an acceleration according to the rule
>
> force = mass × acceleration or $\boldsymbol{F = ma}$ (1)
>
> The gravity force on an object in a field of strength $\boldsymbol{g}$ is
>
> force = mass × field strength or $\boldsymbol{F = mg}$ (2)
>
> Putting these two ideas together (1) and (2) tell us that if the accelerating force is gravity, then
>
> $\boldsymbol{F = ma = mg}$ and this can only be true if $\boldsymbol{a = g}$.
>
> *The size of the acceleration of free fall in a gravity field is equal to the size of the field strength.*

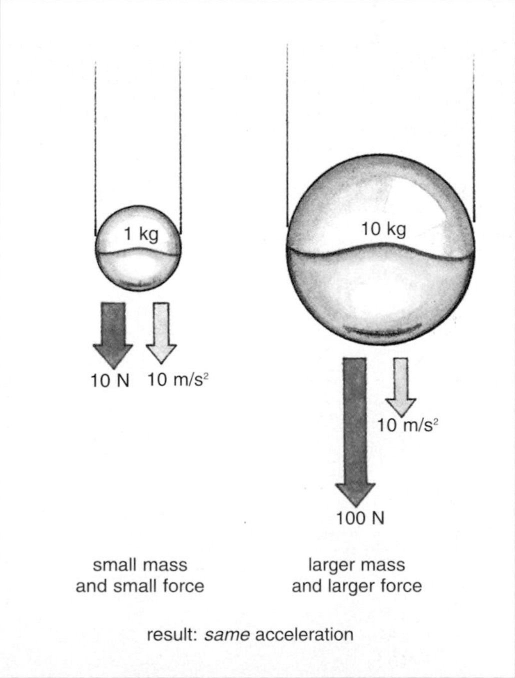

Picture 5 Freely falling objects accelerate at the same rate.

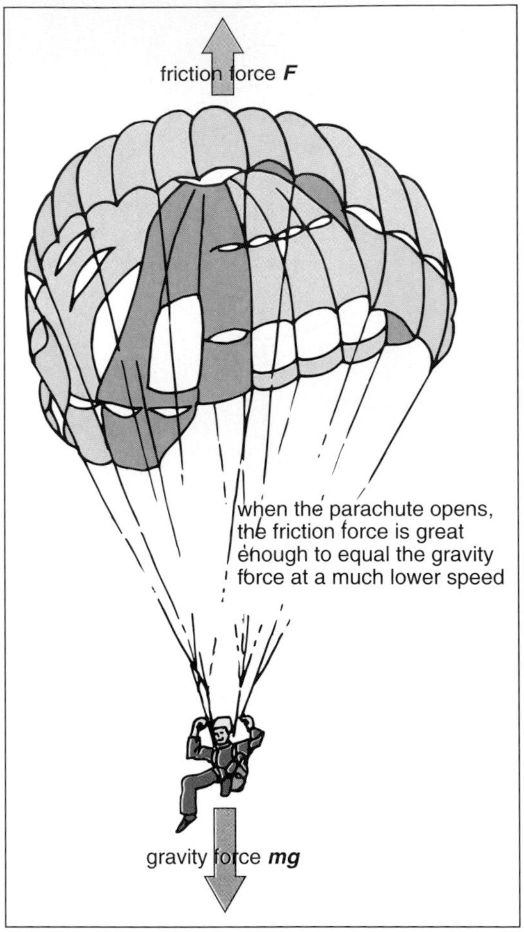
friction force F
when the parachute opens, the friction force is great enough to equal the gravity force at a much lower speed
gravity force mg

Picture 7 Parachutes greatly increase the force of air resistance.

How free is free fall?

There is another force that acts on a falling object, on Earth at least. This is the force of **friction** caused by the object moving through the air. This force depends on the size and shape of the falling object. People falling from an aeroplane accelerate quite rapidly to a high speed – unless they are using a parachute. The shape of the parachute increases the air friction, so they slow down once the parachute is opened.

But whether they wear a parachute or not the falling people eventually reach a steady speed, when they are not accelerating any more. This happens because the force of air resistance acts on them in the opposite direction to the gravity force – see picture 6.

The force caused by air resistance gets bigger the faster you go. (You can feel this when you travel fast on a bicycle.) When the air resistance becomes equal to the gravity force a falling object stops accelerating. It has reached what is called its **terminal** speed.

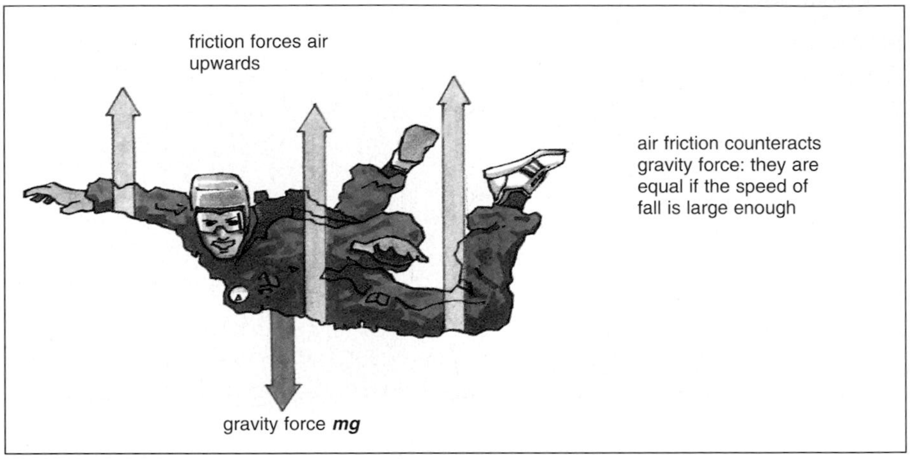
friction forces air upwards
air friction counteracts gravity force: they are equal if the speed of fall is large enough
gravity force mg

Picture 6 A free-fall parachutist – but they don't fall freely!

Working against gravity

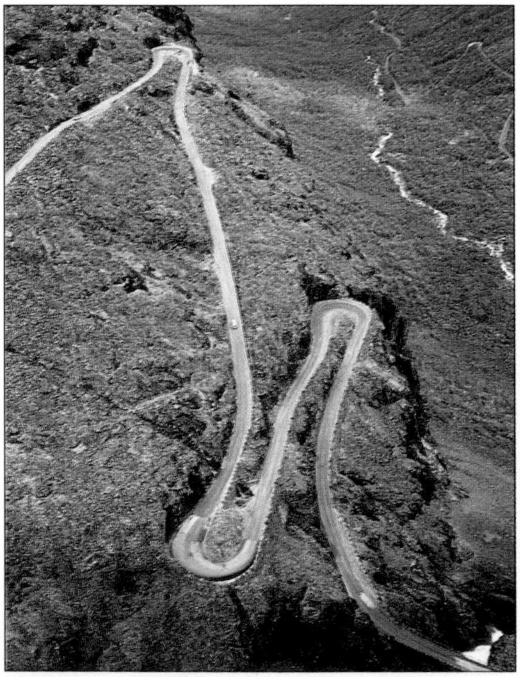

Picture 8 An Alpine road.

Climbing up a hill is usually hard work, whether we walk or ride a bicycle. We are doing work by using muscular force to lift ourselves against the force of gravity. Mountain roads and paths are built in zig-zags to make this job easier (see picture 8).

This makes the way less steep, so that we gain height more slowly, using less force at each step.

We can do this work by using part of the 'energy store' in our bodies, obtained from the food we eat. But not all of the energy is used to lift us uphill against the gravity force. We still have to keep our bodies alive, and doing such hard work makes us feel much hotter. Our bodies are quite good at getting rid of this waste heating energy. But quite a lot of the work we did hasn't been wasted. It has been transferred into a mysterious kind of energy called **gravitational potential energy**.

Potential energy

This potential energy can be a rather dangerous kind of energy for someone high up on a mountain. You can't see it and you can't feel it. But mountain climbers have more than enough of it to kill themselves, if they don't control it properly.

The reason for this is that this potential energy can be changed to movement energy, which is usually called **kinetic energy**. If you fall off a mountain the gravity force pulls you down and you move faster and faster. The energy that you put into climbing the mountain is being given back to you as you fall!

Energy can't just disappear or appear from nowhere (see topic D4). It makes sense to think of work you do as go uphill as being stored as hidden or 'potential' energy. This turns into kinetic energy as you fall.

Of course, potential energy does you no harm at all. Neither does the kinetic energy. It is what happens when you hit the ground that causes the damage.

Picture 9 illustrates the kind of energy transfers that happen when we climb up a hill and come down again.

Don't let energy kill you!

People coming down from the mountains have to get rid of their potential energy safely, a little bit at a time. Climbers and walkers come down carefully – never running! Cyclists need to keep braking, moving the potential energy safely into the surroundings by heating the wheels and brake blocks. This is much better than storing it as more and more kinetic energy!

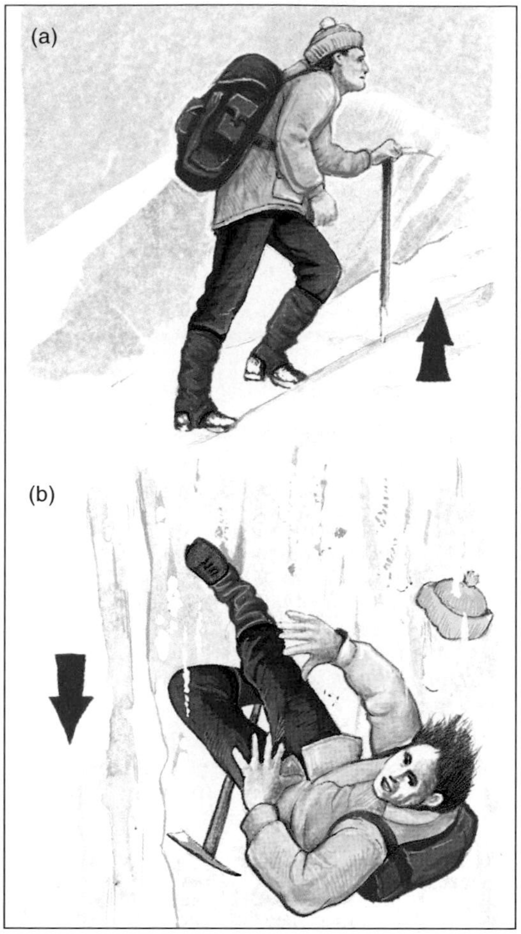

Picture 9 (a) Climbing a mountain is hot work. The climber warms up the surroundings – but also gains potential energy. (b) If the climber fell, the change of potential energy to kinetic energy would happen much too quickly.

Measuring potential energy

Whenever we do work against the force of gravity there will be an increase in potential energy. Lifting a can of beans on to a high shelf gives them extra potential energy. You can't eat this extra energy, but it will give you a nasty bump if the can falls on your head.

Topic D2 explains how energy is measured and how the formula for calculating potential energy is obtained.

The formula is:

$$\textbf{potential energy} = \boldsymbol{mgh}$$

$\boldsymbol{m}$ is the mass of an object, $\boldsymbol{g}$ the strength of the gravity field and $\boldsymbol{h}$ the height through which the object has been lifted, or can fall.

When you lift a can of baked beans on to a shelf a metre above the ground you have given it some extra potential energy. If the can weighs 0.5 kg you increase its potential energy by

$$mgh = (0.5\ \text{kg} \times 10\ \text{N/kg} \times 1\ \text{m})$$
$$= 5\ \text{J}$$

This is not very much, considering that the beans in the can have over **1 million** joules of 'food energy'!

Potential energy to kinetic energy

The energy in a moving object depends on how massive it is and how fast it is going. It is calculated using the formula:

$$\text{kinetic energy, } \boldsymbol{E} = \tfrac{1}{2}\boldsymbol{mv}^2$$

($\boldsymbol{m}$ is the mass of the object, $\boldsymbol{v}$ is its speed).

When an object falls freely in a gravity field its potential energy is getting less and its kinetic energy is increasing.

Its loss in potential energy equals its gain in kinetic energy.

So if our can of beans fell off the shelf, its kinetic energy would be 5 J just before it hit the ground (picture 10). Its potential energy would now be zero.

How fast would it be going just before it hit the ground? We can use these two formulae to work this out:

$$\text{kinetic energy gained} = \text{potential energy lost}$$
$$\tfrac{1}{2}\boldsymbol{mv}^2 = \boldsymbol{mgh}$$
$$\text{or } \boldsymbol{v}^2 = 2\boldsymbol{gh}$$
$$\text{i.e. } \boldsymbol{v}^2 = 2 \times 10 \times 1$$
$$\text{giving speed } \boldsymbol{v} = \sqrt{20} = 4.5\ \text{m/s}$$

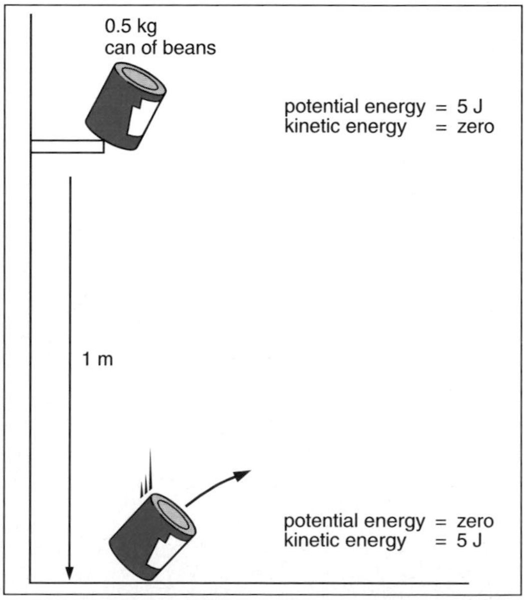

Picture 10 Potential energy changing to kinetic energy.

Kinetic energy and road safety – speed kills

The formula for kinetic energy tells us that the energy increases as the square of the speed. This means that doubling the speed increases the energy by 2^2. It becomes four times as much.

In a road collision, or in a fall, doubling speed means that four times as much energy is available for causing damage. If the speed is tripled, e.g. from 30 mph to 90 mph, the energy becomes *nine times as much*.

Topic D2 also deals with aspects of kinetic energy.

Activities

A Studying movement using diluted gravity

You can 'dilute' gravity by letting something roll down a sloping board instead of letting it fall straight down. Use a sloping board and a stopwatch to find out if heavier things roll down the board faster, slower or take the same time as lighter ones.

Use model cars or lorries, or special 'dynamics trolleys' of differing masses to roll down the slope. Make a careful record of your measurements and explain how they back up your conclusion.

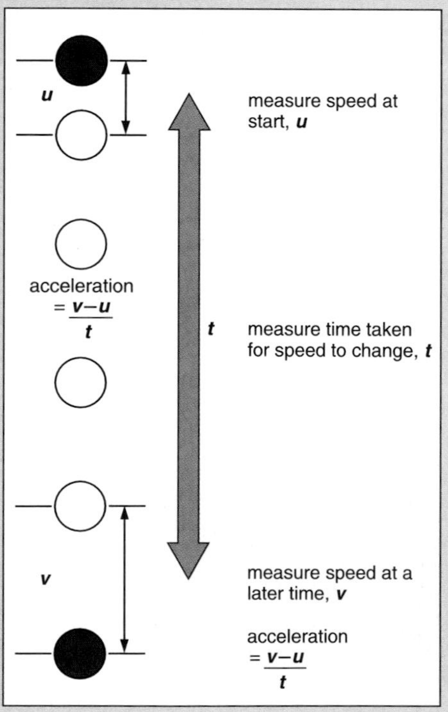

Picture 11

B Measuring the acceleration of free fall

There are lots of ways of doing this, and the details will depend upon what kind of equipment your school can give you. There are two main methods.

Method 1

In this method you measure the speed near the start of the fall and then near the end. The difference between them is the **change** in speed.

You also measure the **time taken** for the speed to change. See picture 11.

You calculate the acceleration as

$$\frac{\text{change in speed}}{\text{time taken}}$$

You can make these measurements using a ticker-timer and tape, or electronically.

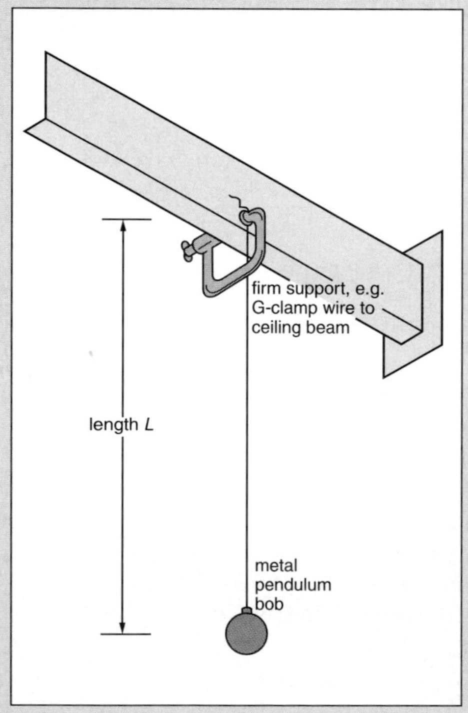

Picture 12

Method 2

In this method you have to measure the distance an object (e.g. a metal ball) falls and the time it takes to fall that distance. The object has to fall from rest. You then calculate the acceleration by a formula:

acceleration of free fall,

$$g = \frac{2 \times \text{distance fallen}}{(\text{time})^2}$$

For a rough measurement you can use a fairly tall building and a stop watch. You can make more accurate measurements using electronic timing, triggered when the ball starts and stops.

C Measuring the Earth's gravity field

Some of the most accurate measurements of the strength of the Earth's gravity field made last century used a **simple pendulum**. This was a heavy ball suspended, very firmly, on a long wire string.

1. Set up a pendulum as shown in the diagram (Picture 12); measure the length L of the string from the point of support to the middle of the ball.
2. Set the ball swinging through an arc of about 5 degrees.
3. Time 50 swings. Call the time t seconds. A swing is counted each time the ball goes through the middle of its swing going from left to right.
4. Divide the time t above by 50 to calculate the time, T, for just one swing.

   Use the formula to calculate the value of g, the strength of the Earth's gravity field.

$$g = \frac{4\pi^2 L}{T^2}$$

D Giving things gravitational energy

For this activity you will need: spring balances, bathroom scales, a metre rule and/or a tape measure, a calculator.

Use the formula:

gravitational potential energy = mass x gravity field strength (g) x height moved

Take $g = 10$ N/kg

1 Take measurements to allow you to work out how much extra potential energy:

a you get when you climb up a flight of stairs in your school,

b you give this book when you lift it from the floor to the bench or desk top,

c you give to a stool or chair when you lift it on to the bench or desk.

2 *Some harder tasks:*

How much kinetic energy do you give a ball when you throw it straight upwards as high as you can?

If you live in a hilly area you can work out how much gravity energy you might gain (and lose) as you travel to school. You will need a map with contours or heights marked on it in metres.

What happens to all the gravitational energy you gain as you climb the hills?

Questions

1 Which of the drawings in picture 13 gives the best idea of how a ball moves when it is thrown?

2 a Why does a parachute slow down the rate of someone falling from an aircraft?

b Why does a person falling without a parachute eventually reach a steady speed? (If they fall far enough!)

c Why do you think airline passengers are never issued with parachutes?

3 In theory all objects fall at the same rate, owing to gravity. So why does a coin fall to the ground faster than a feather?

4 When you throw a ball across a field it eventually comes down to the ground again, however fast you throw it.

a Draw a sketch showing the path taken by the ball as it goes from your hand to the other side of the field.

b Draw the forces acting on the ball: (i) just as it leaves your hand, (ii) half way across and (iii) just before it hits the ground. Show the forces with labelled arrows and label them with their correct names.

Take $g = 10$ N/kg for these questions

5 The formula

$$s = \tfrac{1}{2}gt^2.$$

can be used to work out how far an object goes when it is let go and then falls freely. In this formula s is the distance fallen and t is the time it takes to fall that distance.

a What is g?

b A girl dropped a coin down a well and timed how long it took before she heard the splash as the coin hit the water. The coin took 2 seconds to reach the water. How far down was the water?

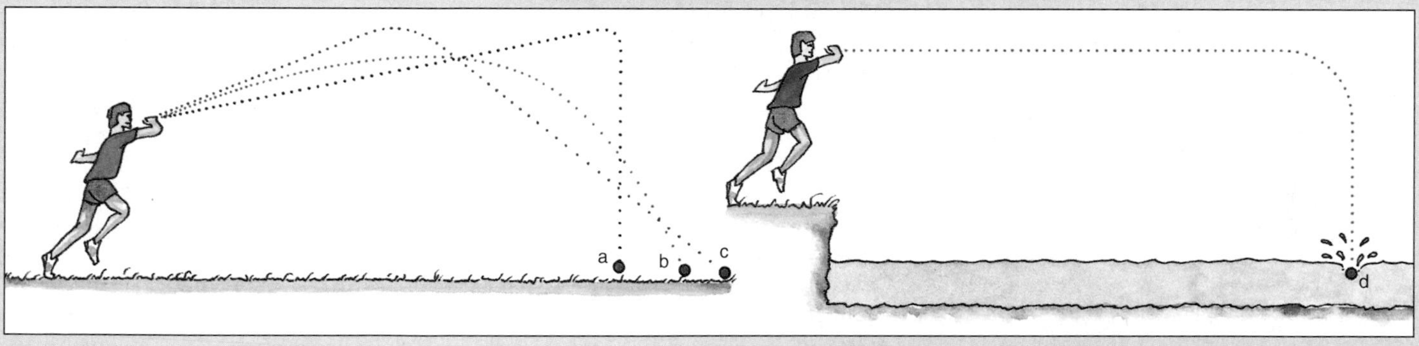

Picture 13

6 Name one situation in each case where gravitational potential energy might be:

a dangerous,

b useful.

7 Hydroelectric power stations need lots of water stored in dams. Why are these dams usually high up in the mountains?

8 Explain the difference between potential energy and kinetic energy.

9 Copy the diagram in picture 14. It shows the path of a car as it goes from A to E. It stops at E. What kind(s) of energy does the car have at each of the points A to E? Write your answers on your diagram.

10 Calculate the change in gravitational potential energy when:

a a car of mass 500 kg climbs a hill 400 m high,

b a climber of mass 65 kg climbs a rock face 200 m high,

c a bird of mass 0.5 kg flies from the ground to a height of 500 m.

11 Do you do any work when you stand still with a 10 kg mass in each hand?

12 A stone of mass 5 kg falls from a cliff 25 m high to the beach.

a How much potential energy did it have before it fell? Use the formula: potential energy = mgh.

b What was happening to this potential energy as the stone fell?

c How much kinetic energy had the stone gained, just as it was about to hit the beach?

d Use the formula $E = \tfrac{1}{2}mv^2$ to calculate the speed with which the stone hit the beach.

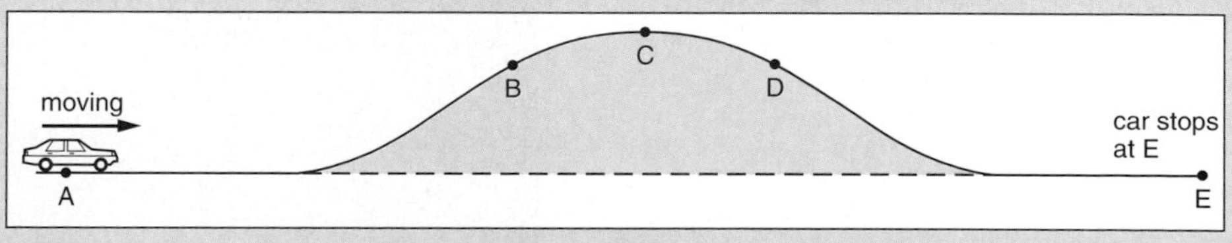

Picture 14

B5
The Leaning Tower of Pisa

This is about a very famous experiment that never actually happened...

Picture 1 shows the famous Leaning Tower of Pisa, which has been defying gravity for 600 years. But it is also famous in the history of science – for an experiment about gravity that may never have actually been done!

This strange non-event was supposed to be the work of a man called Galileo. Galileo Galilei was an Italian astronomer and physicist who lived from 1564 to 1642 (picture 2). Along with Newton and Einstein he ranks as one of the most famous scientists who ever lived.

Don't rock the boat!

In his day, science was something to be learned out of books, written by the old Greek philosophers two thousand years earlier. Experiments and investigations were rarely done, because educated people thought that all the answers were already known. It was considered impolite to challenge this ancient wisdom.

But Galileo was quite a rude man. He didn't believe anything unless he could see it with his own eyes or prove it by experiment or by clear mathematics. He didn't have much patience with important people who weren't very clever. He was also very witty, and this mixture of rudeness and wit made him many enemies.

In his day, important books were written in Latin, which was a language that most people couldn't understand. But Galileo wrote in Italian (picture 3), the language of ordinary people. So more people could understand his attacks on other scholars.

The dangers of making a new science

Galileo's ability to challenge old ideas and replace them with exciting new ones made him a great scientist. But it also meant that he spent the last ten years of his life under arrest, and he nearly got himself sentenced to death.

The old science

The Greek philosopher Aristotle (384 BC to 322 BC) had laid down the rules of physics. For the 4th century BC they were pretty good, but modern scientists like Galileo had started to question them. For example, Aristotle had said that when you throw an object it will carry on, in a straight line, until it runs out of 'force'. Then it does what comes naturally, and falls down (picture 4).

He also said that when they do fall, heavy objects fall faster than light ones.

Tom and Jerry physics

But the ideas are completely wrong, even though many people still actually believe them. Watch a Tom and Jerry or Road Runner cartoon! They only fall

Picture 1 The Leaning Tower of Pisa.

Picture 2 Galileo, who challenged Aristotle.

DIALOGO
DI
GALILEO GALILEI LINCEO
MATEMATICO SOPRAORDINARIO
DELLO STVDIO DI PISA.
E Filosofo, e Matematico primario del
SERENISSIMO
GR.DVCA DI TOSCANA
Doue ne i congressi di quattro giornate si discorre sopra i due
MASSIMI SISTEMI DEL MONDO
TOLEMAICO, E COPERNICANO;
Proponendo indeterminatamente le ragioni Filosofiche, e Naturali tanto per l'vna, quanto per l'altra parte.
CON PRI VILEGI.

Picture 3 Galileo wrote in Italian.

when they 'run out of speed'! There were no cartoons like this in 16th century Italy: life was more serious. Galileo, indeed, wasn't just a 'theoretical' scientist. He was employed by the state of Venice as a military consultant. He had in fact invented a device which he called a telescope, which the Venetian navy found very useful. It allowed them to see and recognise distant ships before the other ships saw them.

Picture 4 This is what should happen when a cannon is fired – according to Aristotle.

Galileo gets the right answers

But Aristotle's theory of movement was not giving the right answers. This was also important in the battles of that time. Cannon balls weren't going where they were supposed to! This was really serious at a time when many cities in Italy were at war with other cities. Galileo's experiments gave him a new theory, and his skill at mathematics allowed him to make much better predictions of where cannon balls were likely to end up (see picture 5).

Professor Galileo became more famous, and his salary was increased.

A famous non-experiment

Take two cannonballs, a 1 kg ball and a 10 kg ball. Carry them to the top of the Leaning Tower of Pisa. Go to the overhanging side and let them both go at the same time. (Warn the people underneath first.)

If Aristotle is right, the 10 kg ball will hit the ground first. If Galileo is right both balls will hit the ground at the same time.

Galileo was right. It's a great pity that we have no evidence that he actually did this experiment. But millions of people, watching on television, saw an astronaut carry out a version of the experiment on the Moon, in 1972. He did not drop two cannonballs, but a hammer and a feather. Both hit the ground at the same time. Galileo would have been clever enough not to use a feather in his experiment, of course!

Don't rock the earth!

Galileo was getting too big for his boots. It was one thing to challenge Aristotle about cannon balls, especially if you had the military on your side. But Aristotle, and the other ancient Greeks, had also said what the Earth and the heavens were like. What they said fitted in with 16th century Christian religious ideas. The Earth was the centre of the universe, and heaven was up there in the sky. The Earth was still, and the Sun, Moon and stars moved around it. (They were right about the Moon.)

Galileo said no. The Sun was still, and the Earth moved around that. So did the planets. His naval telescope could be pointed at the heavens, and there you could see a little model of his ideas. You could see the moons of Jupiter going around the planet, just like the Earth and other planets went around the Sun.

Picture 5 But this is what does happen, as worked out by Galileo.

This was heresy! It contradicted what people thought the Bible said. Galileo was put on trial and condemned as a heretic. The punishment was to be burned at the stake. Galileo was no hero. He 'changed his mind' and denounced his ideas.

But he was still thought to be a dangerous thinker, and had to spend the rest of his life in 'internal exile', in his house in a small town in Italy.

But Galileo was right about the Sun and the planets, and his ideas were proved beyond any shadow of doubt by a man who was born in the very year that Galileo, now old and blind, died. This man was Isaac Newton (see topic B7).

Activities

A Trying Galileo's ideas

1 Plan and carry out your own 'Leaning Tower of Pisa' experiment.

CARE! Make sure no-one can be hit by falling objects.

2 Drop a feather and a coin at the same time. Do they reach the ground at the same time? Why not? Was Galileo wrong after all? Ask your teacher to show you how to devise an experiment in which both a coin and a feather do fall at the same rate.

B Finding out about Galileo and Italy

Use a library to find out more about what Italy was like at the time of Galileo. Why did people think that his scientific ideas were so important? Why did other people disagree with him so strongly that they would have put him to death?

Questions

1 People said to Galileo: 'The Earth can't be moving! If it did, we would all be left behind! There'd be chaos!' How would you answer these critics, using modern science? Galileo didn't know about gravity. How could you answer these critics without using the idea of gravity pulling down on everything on Earth? (Hint: think of dropping something on a train.)

2 The diagram in picture 6 shows a cannon about to be fired at a target hidden behind a city wall. On a simple copy of this diagram draw:

a the angle of the cannon and the path a cannonball would take on Aristotle's theories.

b the angle and path assuming Galileo's (Newton's) theories.

c Why do you think that the military supported Galileo's ideas?

3 What was the key piece of evidence that Galileo used to prove that it was at least possible that the Earth and planets went round the Sun?

4 'Of course the Sun goes round the Earth! You can see it moving, every day!' How can you explain the apparent movement of the Sun through the sky, from dawn to sunset?

5 Galileo's ideas about the Sun and the Earth were thought at the time to contradict the Bible. The Church in Italy thought that this would confuse ordinary people and make them lose their faith in God. Other scientific ideas such as Darwin's Theory of Evolution might have the same effect.

a Can you think of any modern examples of such 'dangerous' ideas?

b Should such ideas only be learned by people who are intelligent enough not to be confused by them?

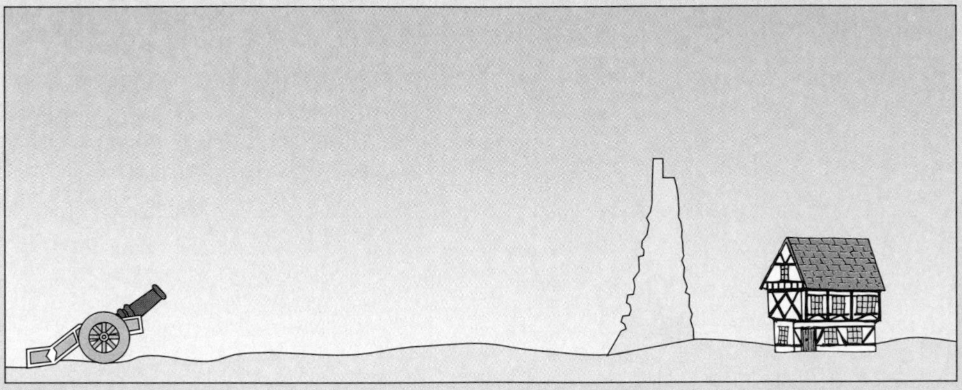

Picture 6

Weighing the Earth

How do scientists know how much the Earth weighs? Strictly speaking, the Earth doesn't weigh anything, of course…

When we 'weigh' something we are really trying to find out what its **mass** is. The mass of an object is a measure of how much matter it contains. **Weight** is a measure of the gravity force on a piece of matter in a gravitational field. As the Earth is in its own gravity field it doesn't make much sense to talk of its 'weight'.

Also, as the Earth is in free fall orbit around the Sun it is 'weightless' even as far as the Sun's gravitational field is concerned.

The laws of gravity were discovered by Sir Isaac Newton (see page 55). He realised that gravity is caused by mass. The bigger the mass, the bigger is the gravity force it can exert. Two masses (of size M and m, say) exert an equal gravity force (F) on each other, given by a formula:

$$F = G\frac{Mm}{r^2}$$

r is their distance apart, in metres. G is a constant, called the **universal constant of gravitation** (see picture 1). This formula could be used to measure the mass of the Earth – M, say – if the other values are known.

Newton could measure the force on a mass m in the Earth's gravity field. In modern units it is well known to be 9.8 N for a 1 kg mass. He also had a good idea of the radius of the Earth. This had been calculated quite accurately in 1684 by the French astronomer Jean Picard. Its modern value is 64 000 000 m (6.4×10^6 m)

But at that time no one knew the value of the constant G. Indeed, Newton died before it was measured. So he never knew the mass of the Earth that his theories had made it possible to measure. It is hard to measure G because gravity is such a weak force. The gravity force between you and the person sitting next to you, for example, is about one ten-millionth of your weight.

The first fairly accurate measurement of G was done in 1774, nearly 70 years after Newton's death. It was done by a Scot, Nevil Maskelyne. He used a simple pendulum which he set up near a cone-shaped mountain in Scotland (see picture 2). The mass of the mountain caused a small gravity force which pulled the pendulum sideways. It was a very tiny effect, but he was able to measure it.

He then worked out the volume of the mountain and measured the density of the rocks it was made of. He then calculated the mass of the mountain using the formula:

mass = density × volume.

He now knew enough to put into Newton's formula to get a value for G. A modern experiment which measures the force between two gold spheres a small distance apart, gives a value of:

$$G = 6.7 \times 10^{-11}\ \text{N m}^2/\text{kg}^2$$

This is the force in newtons between two 1 kg masses a metre apart. It is just 670 billionths of a newton!

The result of such experiments allows us to calculate the mass of the Earth, the Sun and the other planets. We also use it to calculate the masses of distant stars and galaxies.

1 'Gravity is a weak force'. Yet it seems to be quite a large force when you lift up a loaded suitcase, or try to cycle up a steep hill. Why is this?

2 Why is it so hard to measure the value of G?

3 A kilogram mass on the Earth's surface has a gravity force of 9.8 N on it. The mass of the Earth acts as if it was all at the centre, as far as gravity is concerned. The centre of the Earth is 6 400 000 m from the surface.

Use a scientific calculator to check that the mass of the Earth is about

$$6 \times 10^{24}\ \text{kg}.$$

Use Newton's formula, with the values:

$F = 9.8$ N $m = 1$ kg $r = 6\,400\,000$ m
$G = 6.7 \times 10^{-11}$ Nm²/kg²

4 The volume of the Earth is

$$1.1 \times 10^{21}\ \text{m}^3.$$

a Use the formula

$$\text{density} = \frac{\text{mass}}{\text{volume}}$$

to calculate the density of the Earth.

b You should have got an answer of about 5500 kg/m³ for the density of the Earth. But the density of nearly all the rocks we find on the Earth's surface is about 2500 kg/m³. How can this be explained? (See topic F1.)

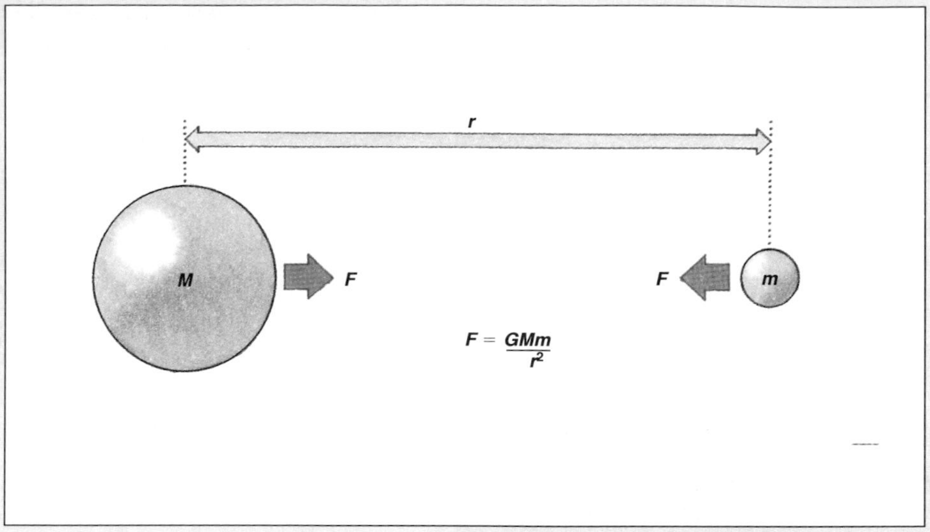

Picture 2 Maskelyne's experiment.

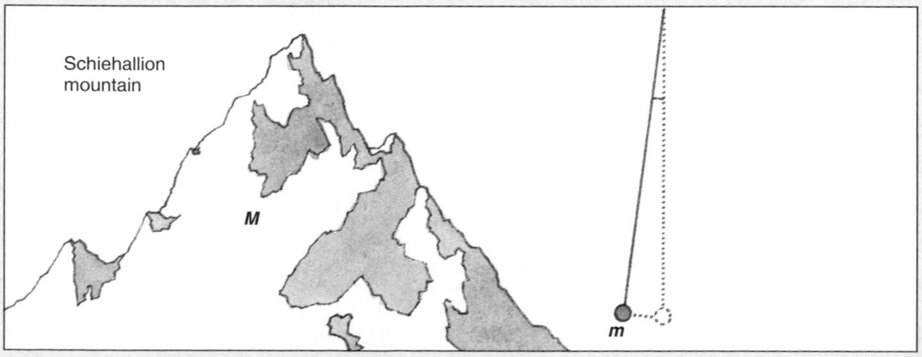

Picture 1 The bigger the mass, the bigger the gravity force it exerts.

B6
Satellites

No engines. No wings. What keeps satellites up there?

Picture 1 Sputnik – the first artificial satellite.

Picture 2 Modern communication satellite.

'I just don't believe it!'

The first artificial satellite to orbit the Earth was launched in 1957. It was a Russian satellite, named **Sputnik**, shown in picture 1. It had a mass of 84 kg and it moved in an orbit between 217 km and 944 km above the Earth's surface.

The Astronomer Royal at the time didn't believe it! He didn't think that a rocket engine could provide enough energy to lift any object that far above the Earth. Since then many thousands of satellites have been launched, some as big and as heavy as a bus. Picture 2 shows a typical modern Earth satellite.

Newton again

Earth satellites had been predicted by Isaac Newton in 1666. The way he thought of getting them into orbit was not very practical, as he well knew. Picture 3 shows his idea. But we can learn from this how actual satellites do in fact stay in orbit.

Any object fired sideways (horizontally) from a tall mountain will not only move sideways but also fall towards the centre of the Earth. It is pulled there by

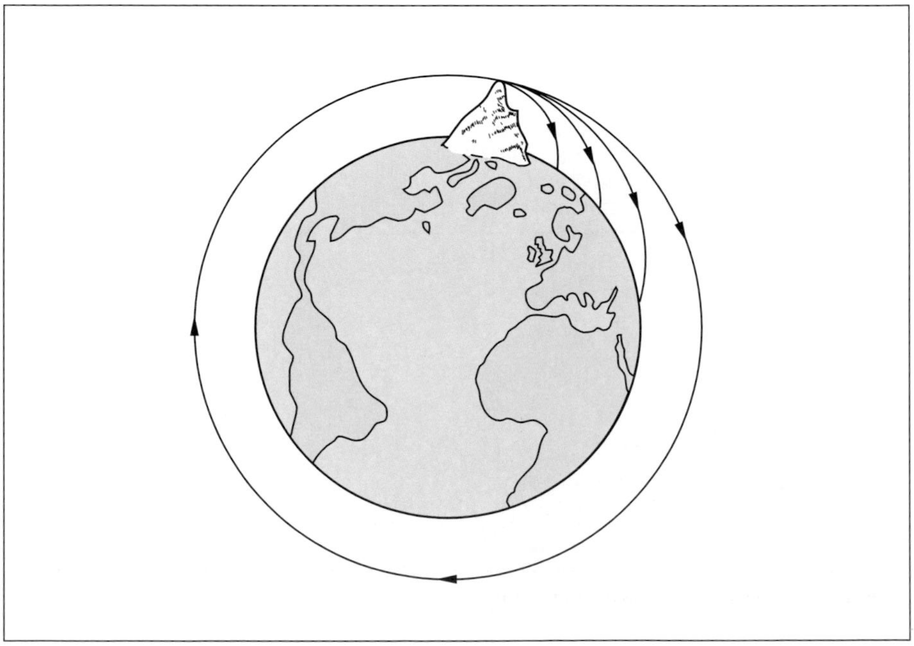

Picture 3 Newton imagined firing a cannon ball from the top of a high mountain. The faster it went, the further the cannon ball would travel before it hit the ground. At a high enough speed, it wouldn't hit the ground at all!.

the force of gravity (see topic B4). The faster it is fired the further it will get before reaching the ground. Newton realised that at a certain speed it will never reach the ground, simply because the Earth itself is curved. At this speed the curved path of the falling satellite would exactly match the curve of the Earth.

How are satellites launched?

No mountain on Earth is high enough for Newton's method to work. There is no gun powerful enough to fire a satellite at the speed needed to stay in orbit. And if there were, the force needed to accelerate the satellite inside the gun barrel would squash it flat!

Instead a rocket system is used to lift the satellite to the top of an 'invisible mountain'. This is called the **injection point**, and it is at least 200 km high (see picture 5).

Picture 4 shows the rocket system used to launch the American Space Shuttle. Most of what you see of the rocket is simply a hollow tank filled with fuel. Most of this fuel is used to lift itself through the atmosphere. There is just enough spare fuel to accelerate the shuttle sideways when it gets high enough to be put into orbit.

The rocket system has three stages, each with its own engine and fuel supply. The first stage contains the most fuel and has the biggest engine. It lifts itself and the next two stages as high as it can. Then it falls off. Stages two and three take over, in turn, and in their turn are thrown away. The Space Shuttle is left travelling in orbit at the speed required to stop it falling closer to the Earth (see picture 5).

Why do some satellites fall down?

Newton explained why satellites stay up – but they don't stay up for ever. The main reason for this is air friction. The Earth's atmosphere gets thinner and thinner the higher you go, but it never thins away to nothing. Even at a height of 1000 km there is enough air left to cause a drag on a satellite which slows it down. Eventually it is travelling too slowly to stay in orbit. It re-enters the thicker part of the atmosphere where friction becomes so great that the satellite 'burns up'.

The energy transferred from movement energy by this air friction heats up the satellite until it melts and burns away.

Picture 4 The rocket system used to launch the Space Shuttle.

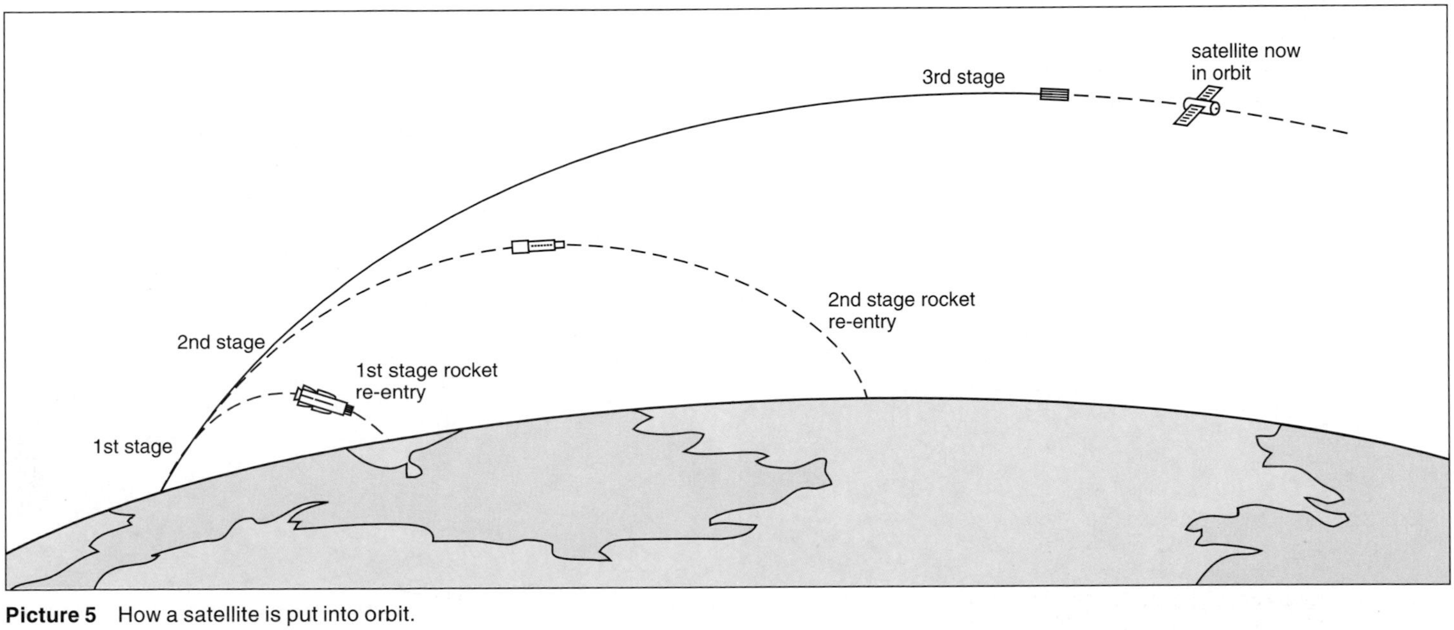

Picture 5 How a satellite is put into orbit.

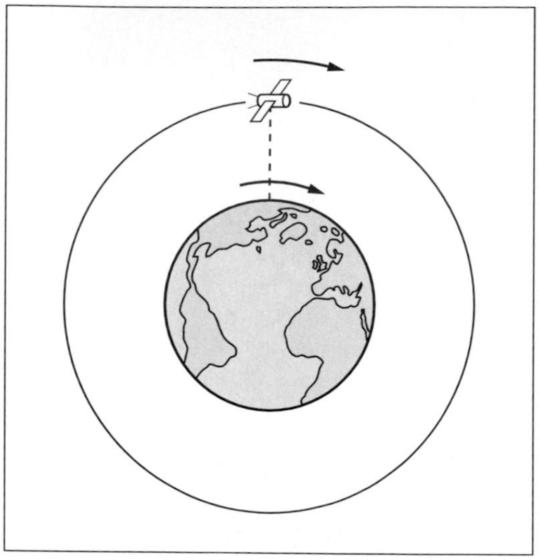

Picture 6 Geostationary orbit: the Earth turns at the same rate as the satellite. This means that the satellite is always positioned over the same point on Earth.

Geostationary orbits

Sputnik went around the Earth once every 90 minutes. This would have made it useless as a TV satellite. It would be in view at any one place on Earth for only a few minutes in each orbit. The TV aerial would need to be motor-driven to follow it. A neat solution would be to have a satellite which always seems to be in the same place in the sky. This in fact is what is done.

The satellite is put into a very high orbit. It still moves, but its speed is just enough to follow the movement of the spinning Earth (see picture 6). This means that it is always over the same place on Earth.

What are satellites used for?

Most Earth satellites are used for military purposes. Different military powers keep an eye on each other's movements using space satellites which can pick up radio and other signals. They have special cameras that can take very clear pictures. They can photograph things as small as a human being from hundreds of kilometres up in space.

But other satellites can photograph clouds – and see through clouds. They can show us what the great air streams of the Earth are doing, and so help forecast the weather. Picture 7 shows a typical weather picture that you can see every day on TV. Satellites can carry sensors that detect infra-red radiation. This makes it possible to measure the temperature of the soil and of vegetation. They can find places where crops may be unhealthy or short of water and nutrients (see picture 8).

Other satellites can sense small changes in gravity forces that might show where the deep-lying rocks are different. This might help us to discover oil or other minerals.

Picture 7 A satellite weather picture.

Picture 8 A satellite picture of the Nile Delta and the Red Sea. The red shows where crops are growing.

Communication satellites

Communication satellites are the ones most people know about. They are put into geostationary orbits and are used to collect and re-transmit TV and radio signals to give us instant world-wide communication.

There are also scientific satellites, which are used to pick up radiations from space – light, X-rays, ultra-violet and infra-red – which are teaching us more about the planets, stars and galaxies.

Activities

A Computing your way into orbit

You might be able to get a computer simulation of satellite launching. If you can, try using different speeds and 'angles of launch' to see what happens.

B Have you ever seen a satellite in orbit?

Some newspapers list the times when important satellites cross overhead at night. Use this information to try and spot a satellite. Explain why you can see it as a shiny spot, although the satellite does not carry any lights of its own.

C Some things to find out

Use a library or any other source of information to answer the following questions.

1 What satellite has travelled furthest from Earth? What task did it have to do?

2 How are messages sent to and from satellites?

3 When did humans first land on the moon? Do you think it was worth sending them there?

D Space travel

Copy out the following passage about travelling in space, filling in the missing words.

Satellites have not escaped the pull of Earth's __________. This is in fact the force that keeps them in __________ around the Earth. But the astronauts do not feel this force. This is because they are in a state of __________—__________.

This makes life difficult. The astronauts, and every loose object, will __________ about in the satellite. If astronauts had to be in space for a long time, it would be a good idea to have some artificial __________. This could be obtained by __________ the satellite around its own axis. The faster it __________, the bigger the __________ force they would feel.

The main problem about space travel is that space is so huge that it would take four years to travel to the nearest __________, even if we could travel at the speed of light. At best, spacecraft could travel at about a tenth light speed, so it would take at least __________ years to get there. A return trip would be impossible. Also, think of the supplies they would need. They would have to recycle __________ and __________, and try to grow their own __________. They would also need a good supply of __________ so that they could manoeuvre the spacecraft when they arrived. A starship, with a crew of 16, would need 300 tonnes of consumables, and another 3000 tonnes for the ship itself.

You can read more about the problems of space travel in a science fiction paperback by Robert L Forward, *Dragonfly* (New English Library, 1985). It's a good read!

Questions

1 Why wouldn't Newton's 'big gun' idea for getting a satellite into orbit work?

2 a Why do many satellites eventually fall back to Earth?
b Why do we not need to worry about being hit on the head by a satellite when it does fall?
c Give five uses of Earth satellites.

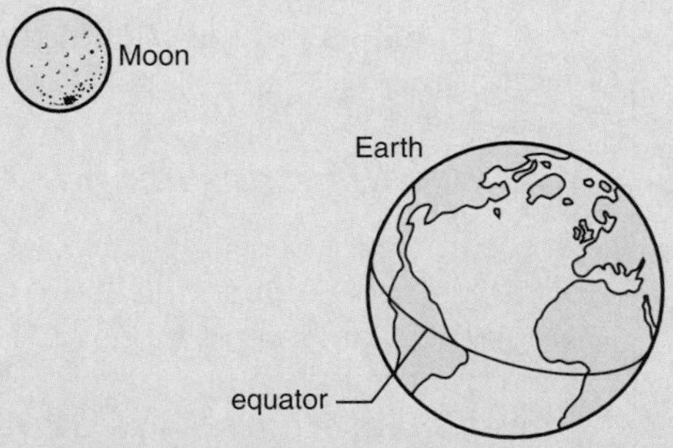

Picture 9

3 Copy the diagrams which show the Earth and the Moon in space (picture 9). On your copy, draw your idea of:
a the likely orbit of a 'spy satellite',
b the likely orbit of a TV broadcast satellite,
c the path that a rocket might take to get into orbit around the Moon.

B7
Newton and Einstein

Two men who changed our view of the universe.

Picture 1 Time and the stars.

Humans are very curious

As far as we can tell, human beings have always wondered about the Sun, the Moon and the stars. They have built temples, pyramids and great circles of standing stones. They have lined them up with the main stars, or the rising and setting of the Sun at important times like spring and harvest. They have worshipped the Sun and the Moon, and put their heroes and heroines into the star patterns. They have used them to make clocks and calendars, and to find their way across seas and deserts.

Making theories

And from the time of Ancient Greeks, over two thousand years ago, they have made theories about what these heavenly objects really are. The Sun is hot, the giver of life, a great ball of fire. The Moon is cold and pale, and just a little dangerous. Stars are tiny sparks, of different colours, in sky patterns that are always the same.

But there are also wandering stars, the planets, which travel through the star patterns, sometimes bright, sometimes pale. Sometimes they disappear altogether, only to return, months later. How can this be explained?

What makes a good theory good?

It isn't too hard to think up a theory for something. The hard bit is to prove it to other people. One way of doing this is to use the theory to predict what is going to happen.

Astrology is a theory that makes predictions. You can look up 'what the stars foretell' in magazines and newspapers. Do they get it right? Do astrologers always win the football pools?

The job of **astronomy** was also to make some predictions: 'If you follow this star you will get to Damascus'. Or 'If you plant your crops when a certain star is just setting at dawn the crops will grow well'. Astronomy always gave better results than astrology, even if it was less fun. But the next step was to find out *why* the stars moved so regularly, and why the wandering stars (called **planets**) were different. In other words, could you *predict* what the stars and planets were going to do?

To do this people needed a theory about what stars and planets actually were.

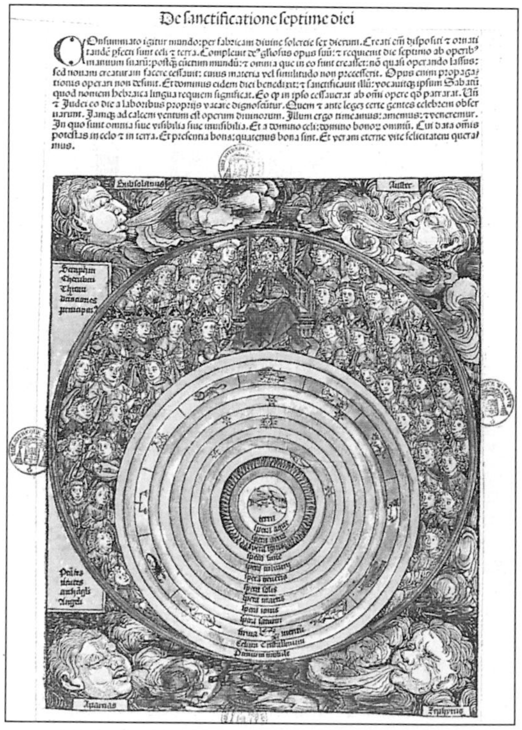

Picture 2 People used to think that the Earth was at the centre of the Universe.

Why are the stars useful?

Over the many thousands of years that people watched the skies, the patterns of movements became well known (picture 2). Astronomers taught sailors how to use the changing positions of Sun, stars and planets to find their way across seas out of sight of land.

By the 15th century, ships and the skills of navigation became good enough for traders to travel further than they had ever done before. The Arabs and the Chinese sailed across the Indian Ocean and the West Pacific, bringing rich trade to and from the islands of the 'Indies'.

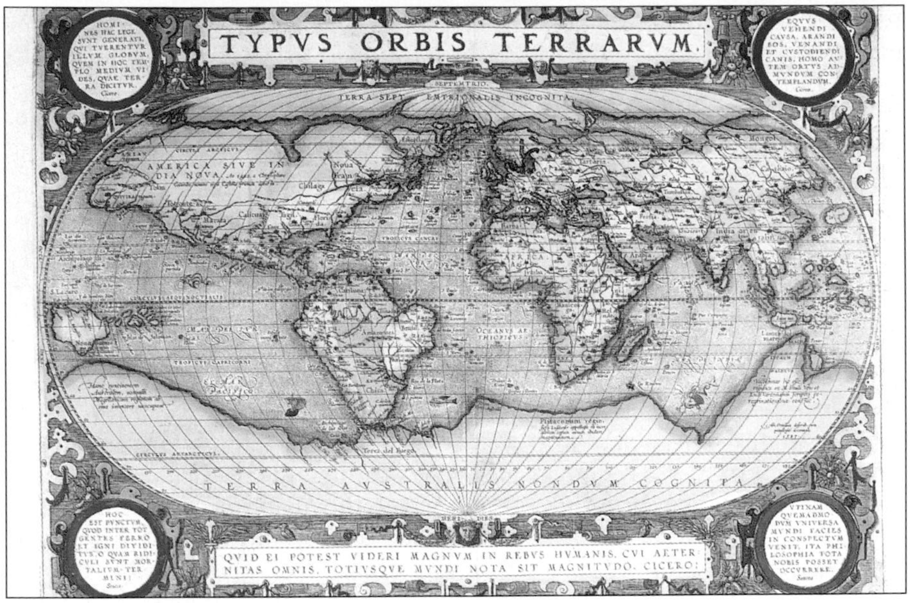

Picture 3 An old map of the world.

The age of discoveries

Then Europeans ventured around the great barrier of Africa to join in this trade. The Portuguese were the first great navigators and the first Europeans to sail around Africa into the Indian Ocean.

Some of these Portuguese sailors were swept off course by wind and current and 'discovered a new land', which we now call Brazil. But they didn't know where they had been, and lost it again (picture 3).

Christopher Columbus

It wasn't until the end of the 15th century, in the year 1492, that a good navigator called Christopher Columbus found South America again, or at least the islands where the tribe called the Caribs lived. However, he thought that he had in fact reached India. He called these islands of the Caribs the 'West Indies'. But India was a good 4000 miles further on, across the huge Pacific Ocean.

Money in the stars

By the middle of the 16th century great fleets of Spanish galleons were carrying tonnes of gold and silver from South America to the King of Spain. The Spanish investment in Christopher Columbus had paid off handsomely.

All this hope for trade and wealth made the study of astronomy even more valuable. It became more than a hobby or a way of 'seeing your future in the stars'. Kings and emperors employed astronomers to work out more carefully the positions and movements of stars and planets useful for navigation (picture 4).

Isaac Newton (1642–1727)

Isaac Newton was born in 1642, exactly a hundred and fifty years after Columbus bumped into the West Indies. Knowledge of stars and planets had improved in that time, but no one knew what they were, or how and why they moved or stayed still.

Navigation was better, but was still more of an art than a science. Many ships were still lost, their sailors and cargoes never to be seen again.

The young Isaac Newton was very bright. He was taught at home until he was twelve, when he was sent away from his family farm in Woolsthorp,

Picture 4 It was here in Tycho Brahe's observatory in Prague, Czechoslovakia, that the astronomer Kepler first proved that the Earth and planets went around the Sun.

Picture 5 Isaac Newton.

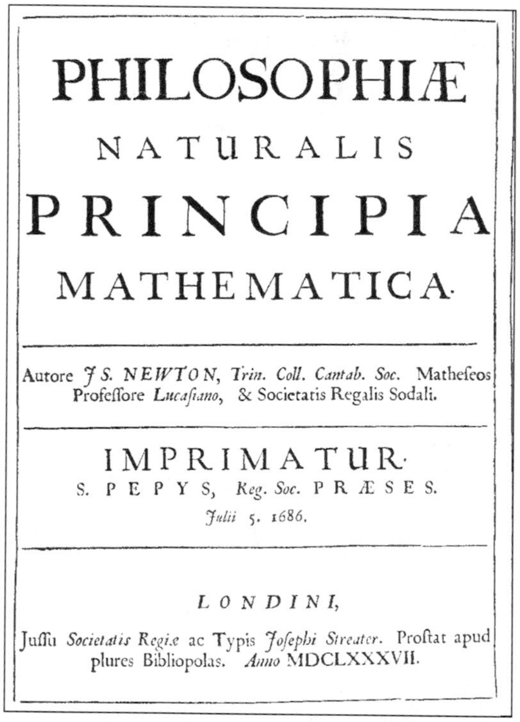

PHILOSOPHIÆ
NATURALIS
PRINCIPIA
MATHEMATICA.

Autore *J S. NEWTON*, *Trin. Coll. Cantab. Soc.* Matheseos Professore *Lucasiano*, & Societatis Regalis Sodali.

IMPRIMATUR.
S. PEPYS, *Reg. Soc.* PRÆSES.
Julii 5. 1686.

LONDINI,

Jussu *Societatis Regiæ* ac Typis *Josephi Streater*. Prostat apud plures Bibliopolas. *Anno* MDCLXXXVII.

Picture 6 Newton had to invent new mathematics, the calculus, to go with his new physics.

Picture 7 The world's largest telescope at Zelenchuk, Caucasus, is based on Newton's design.

Lincolnshire, to the local grammar school. He had to learn Latin, Greek and mathematics, but he became well known for the toys and working models he made. He was as good with his hands as with his brain.

At the age of eighteen he went to the University of Cambridge, and was made professor of mathematics when he was only 27 (picture 5).

Newton's year of discoveries – 1665

As a young man, before he even got a degree or became a professor, Newton made so many discoveries that we still marvel at him. In 1665 the University was closed down because of the Great Plague and he spent a year at home. It was then, the story goes, that he first thought about the force that made an apple fall off a tree. He thought it might also reach as far as the Moon, and keep it in orbit. In a few months he had worked out his first ideas about the Law of Gravity and his Laws of Motion.

During the next years he had to invent completely new mathematics (the **calculus**) which he needed to prove and check his results (picture 6).

All mysteries solved?

The mystery of the solar system was solved. Scientists now knew why and where the planets moved in their orbits (see topics B6 and F3). They were able to work out where the planets would be in the future, and when eclipses of planets, Sun and Moon would occur. Sailors could use these calculations to navigate across the widest seas with great accuracy.

More discoveries

Newton also invented a new kind of telescope, which is still the one most used by astronomers today (picture 7). He discovered the spectrum and so explained how rainbows are formed. He produced new theories of light and heat. He became very famous, and his ideas changed the way people thought about the world.

Scientists began to believe that the world – even the whole universe – must be very simple. Everything must obey simple, clear laws of nature – although they hadn't all been discovered yet. Everything, they thought, could then be predicted.

But at the height of his fame, Newton lost interest in science. He left the University and was given the job of looking after the Royal Mint, where the coinage of Britain is made.

It wasn't a very difficult job, and he had plenty of spare time for his new interest in life, which was working out the dates of when things happened in the Old Testament of the Bible. He was made *Sir* Isaac.

Newton had always been very shy and lonely. He had quarrelled with most of the other scientists he knew, and his friends found it very hard to get him to publish the books he had written about his great discoveries. He worried that he might have made mistakes and he did not like to be proved wrong!

Einstein's new universe

Albert Einstein (picture 8) was one of the few scientists to become as famous as Newton. At the height of his fame thousands of people would crowd into theatres to hear him explain his theories. He knew that most of them didn't understand a word of what he was saying, so he used to play them a couple of tunes on his violin to make up for it.

Try harder, Einstein!

Like Newton, Einstein was very bright. But he was easily bored.

He was born in Germany (in 1879), and went to school there. He didn't do too well at school at subjects he didn't like, and was unpopular with his teachers. He left school at fifteen without proper qualifications and taught himself, while he spent a year hiking and climbing in the mountains of Italy.

Then at sixteen he failed the entrance exam to get into the university in Switzerland where he was now living. But he did so well at maths that the professor invited him to join the class anyway. A year later he had swotted up enough of the boring subjects to pass the exam.

But even university was boring – especially the physics lectures! He nearly failed his exams again, and couldn't get a job. After two years he succeeded and became a civil servant, an examiner of inventions for the Swiss Government.

It was a nice easy job, and he was good at it. In his spare time he was a genius. Like Newton, he taught himself because there was no one else who had thought about things as hard as he had.

Picture 8 Albert Einstein, aged 25.

Einstein's year of discoveries – 1905

At the age of 25, still a civil servant, he wrote three scientific papers which changed the world of physics. The ideas that had been worked out by Newton, and by generations of physicists since, had to be looked at in a new light.

Like Newton's great works, they dealt with space and time, light and heat. In one, he showed that light was not only a wave (see topic C7) but also a particle. In another, he produced his first 'Theory of Relativity'. In the third, he worked out from something as simple as the way smoke spreads out, or sugar dissolves in tea, that atoms must really exist.

Relativity

Einstein is most famous for his two theories of relativity, which have changed the way we look at the universe. For Newton, matter was 'mass', the unchangeable cause of gravity. For Einstein, matter can be changed into energy – and back again – in accordance with the formula $E = mc^2$. For Newton, time rolled on at the same rate everywhere. For Einstein, how long something takes to happen depends on how fast you are travelling. At the speed of light, time stands still.

For Newton, gravity was a **force**: for Einstein, it is a **curve** of 4-dimensional space-time.

The new universe of modern physics

The universe described by physics has always been hard to understand, and probably always will be. After Einstein, we can't even imagine it, even when we understand it. Newton's ideas made possible the improved navigation of the 18th and 19th centuries. They gave us an understanding of the engineering needed to make and use aircraft, rockets and space satellites. Einstein's ideas have led to our modern world. His theories have given us the engineering underlying nuclear energy – and the nuclear bomb. They have led to the ideas needed for lasers, the understanding of the genetic code, the strange world of sub-atomic particles, the reason why the Sun is hot, why black holes exist, and why the Universe is expanding.

Picture 9 The laser, nuclear bombs and what happens when sub-atomic particles collide can only be explained by Einstein's work.

C1 Signals and codes

Human beings need information. We also send out information. This topic is about how information is coded, carried and controlled.

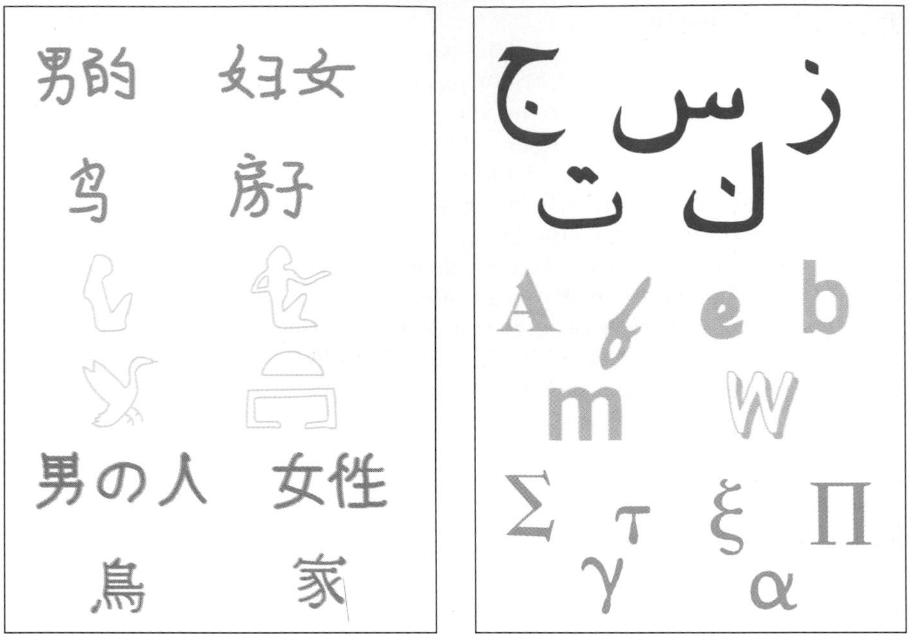

Picture 1 Codes for ideas.

Codes

The language you speak is a code, and not everybody in the world understands it! Writing is a code. Picture 1 shows how different languages have tackled the problem of putting sounds into 'pictures'. The very oldest, like Ancient Egyptian, used drawings of what the sounds meant. The word for 'house' was drawn to look like a house. But this means having a different symbol for each word. It is hard to learn, slow to write and to read, and needs thousands of different code symbols.

It is easier to break the words up into their different sound parts, and have a symbol for each of these. In English we can just about manage with 26 of these symbols – the letters of the alphabet. Of course, we do use more than 26 sounds, but we can combine letters (ee, sh, etc.) to help us cope with the extra sounds. Picture 2 shows some of the codes used in the world today.

When we learn to read we are learning which sounds go with which symbols. In Western languages we 'scan' the letters from left to right. In Arabic, Hebrew and some other languages the symbols are scanned from right to left.

The earliest written books from Ancient Greece show that they were read from right to left on one line and then left to right on the next, and so on. To save time, computer printers print in this way, every other line being printed backwards.

électron	French	电(電)子	Chinese
electrón	Spanish	elektron	Dutch
Elektron	German	электрóн	Russian
elettrone	Italian	elektrono	Esperanto
ηλετρόνιο	Greek	èlĕctrŏn	phonetic
eletron	Portugese	ইলেকট্রন:	Bengali
אֶלֶקְטְרוֹן	Hebrew		

Picture 2 Different codes for the same word.

Carrying messages

Before writing was invented messengers needed very good memories.

Even after the invention of writing they also needed strong legs, like the messenger who carried the news of the battle of Marathon to Athens in 49 BC. He ran so hard that he died after delivering the news, and so never knew that he had just invented marathon running. But sending a messenger was a slow way of carrying information.

Light travels a lot more quickly – at 300 million metres a second. The ancient Romans used light to send messages very long distances. The Roman army built a network of signal stations criss-crossing Europe. Each station had large wooden 'flags' to send messages many kilometres across country (see picture 3).

To make use of 'light messages' new codes had to be invented. To have a different flag movement for each letter of the alphabet would have been a very slow way of doing it. Standard messages, like HELP!, would be given one flag movement. But even so, messages had to be kept very simple. Long, chatty letters were still sent by messengers on ship or horseback.

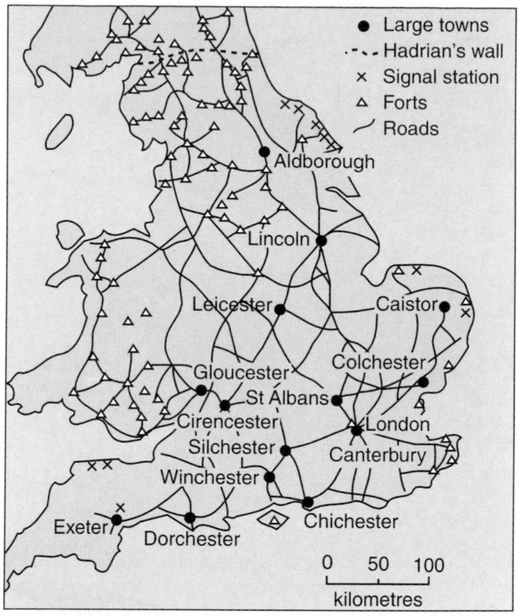

Picture 3 The Romans sent messages using light, over 2000 years ago.

Electric messages

Electric current was discovered at the beginning of the 19th century. It was soon used as a message carrier. In fact that was its first main use, in the form of the **electric telegraph**. A new code – the **Morse Code** – was invented for this kind of message carrier (see picture 4).

Then in 1876 a Scotsman, Alexander Graham Bell, invented the first artificial **transducers**, which allowed speech to be transmitted over long distances. He had invented the **telephone**.

A transducer is a device that transfers signals from one energy system to another. For example, our ears change sound waves into electric signals that the brain can understand. Bell had found another way of changing sound signals into electric signals – the **microphone**. He also had to invent the transducer at the other end to change the electric signals back into sound – a **receiver** or **loudspeaker**.

Even after the telephone was invented, light was still one of the main means of sending messages long distances. Armies and navies used flags, lamps and flashing mirrors (heliographs). They were cheap, quiet and didn't need a network of wires to carry the message.

Then a young Italian called Guglielmo Marconi (picture 5) took up an idea that university physicists had already been experimenting with, and made it practical. He invented a message carrying system that didn't need wires – a '**wireless' telegraph**. To carry messages, this system used what we now call radio waves. These are an invisible part of the **electromagnetic spectrum**, the family of waves (see topic C6), which also includes light.

Picture 5 Guglielmo Marconi.

A	•—	J	•———	S	•••	2	••———
B	—•••	K	—•—	T	—	3	•••——
C	—•—•	L	•—••	U	••—	4	••••—
D	—••	M	——	V	•••—	5	•••••
E	•	N	—•	W	•——	6	—••••
F	••—•	O	———	X	—••—	7	——•••
G	——•	P	•——•	Y	—•——	8	———••
H	••••	Q	——•—	Z	——••	9	————•
I	••	R	•—•	1	•————	0	—————

Picture 4 The earliest electric message carrier and the code it used.

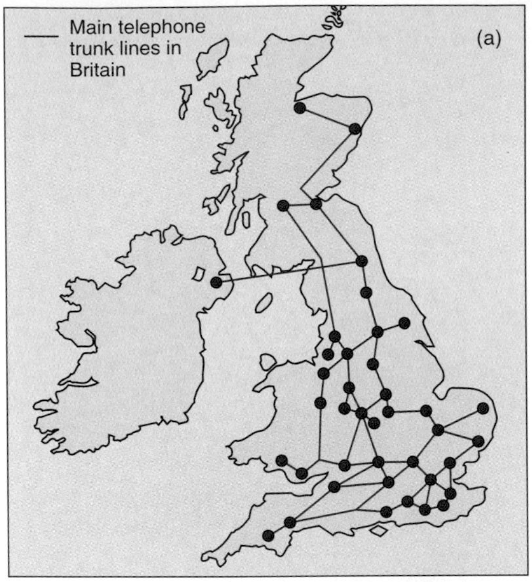

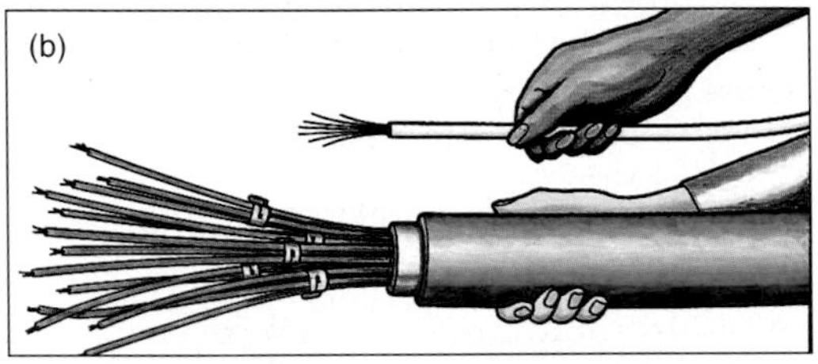

Picture 6 Modern communications are going back to using light – for very good reasons. Each fibre in the top picture of part (b) carries more signals than the whole copper cable in the lower part of (b).

This was one of the most important inventions of the 20th century. It led to the development of radio, radar and TV, and the discovery of new facts about the universe as scientists began picking up radiations from outer space.

Back to light

So much information is now being sent from place to place that it is hard to find room for it. The world is getting more and more crowded with radio and TV signals, criss-crossing each other and getting in each other's way. Telephone lines can only carry so many conversations at once, even when they are specially coded.

This has forced scientists to think of other ways of sending messages. Their solution to the problem is to use light, but light sent down 'wires'. The 'wires' are made of glass drawn out into very thin fibres – **optical fibres** (see topic C5). The main 'trunk' telephone lines in the UK, which carry messages between the main cities, now carry the signals coded into pulses of light instead of electric currents (see picture 6(a)).

A standard copper cable can carry up to a thousand coded conversations at the same time. The optical fibre that replaces it can carry 11 000 conversations, using present coding systems. These can be improved to allow the cable to carry five times as many, if necessary. Using optical systems also improves the quality of the signals, so that they can carry complicated 'computer data' without losing its accuracy. The optical fibre system is also lighter and smaller (see picture 6(b)).

Digital codes

Most modern communication systems use the same code. Information, like speech, music, data from experiments, pictures and computer files, can all be put into numbers, using a simple binary (two-number) **digital code**. These numbers are sent through a medium (wire, optical cable, the air, empty space)

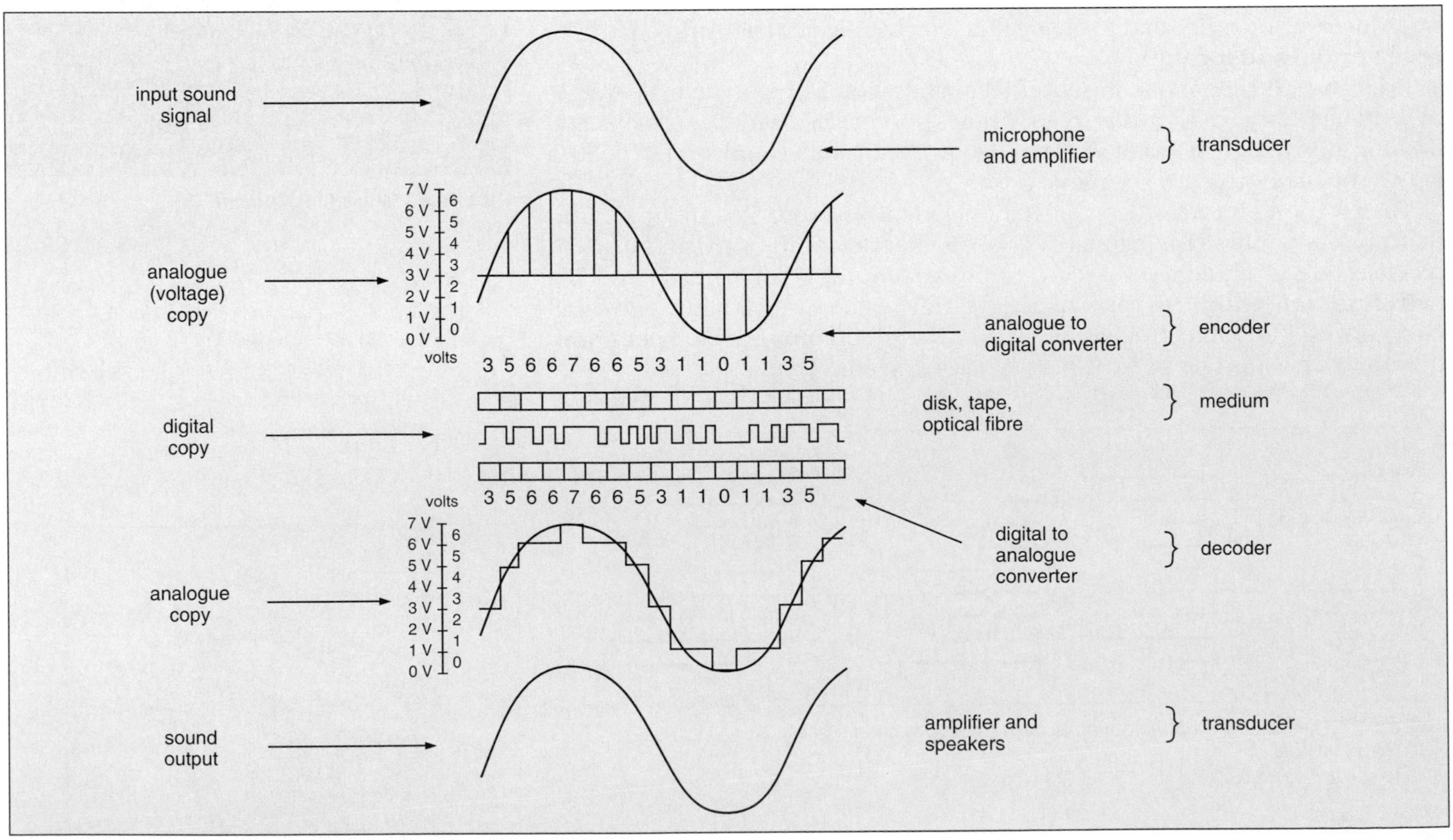

Picture 7 How sound is 'digitised' and then changed back again.

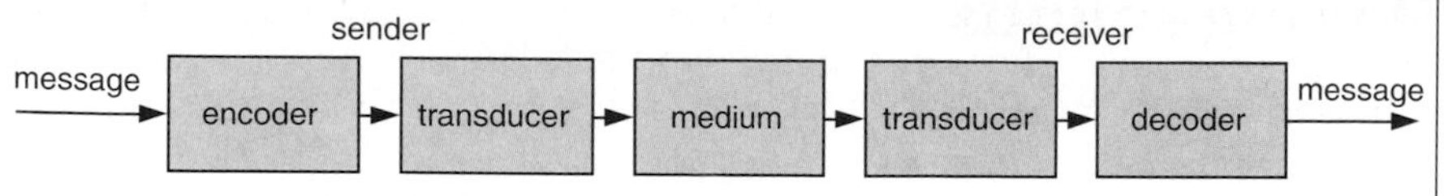

Examples

speech	brain	tongue etc.	air	ear	brain
CD system (part)	analogue-to-digital converter	ultra-violet laser	compact disk	laser	digital-to-analogue converter
TV broadcast	transmitter circuit	aerial (at transmitter)	electro-magnetic waves (UHF)	aerial (at receiver)	TV set

Picture 8 The main parts of an information transmission system.

using some form of carrier. The carrier could be an electric current, or light, radio or TV waves.

The signals are picked up by some kind of receiver. How digital coding works is shown in picture 7.

A block diagram of a typical information transmission system is shown in picture 8.

All information transmission systems need the same basic parts, they are detailed in table 1.

Table 1 Parts of an information transmission system.

Part	Example
an *encoder* to translate data, ideas, words etc. into a suitable form of message (information)	*brain and tongue* to change words into spoken sounds
a *sending transducer* to change the message into something the medium can carry	*microphone* to change sounds into a changing electric current
a *medium* to carry the message from one place to another	*copper wire* to carry the electric current
a *receiving transducer* to change the form of the carried message into a form in which it can be decoded	*telephone earpiece* to change the current back into sounds
a *decoder* to translate the message into a form that can be understood or used	*ear and brain* to change sounds into words you can make sense of

Physics and information

This topic has given you an overview of how information is transmitted. How the various parts of the different kinds of systems actually work will be explained in the rest of the topics in this section.

Activities

A How much information do we need?

We use writing as a code to carry a message to someone who can't hear us. Try this activity to find out about writing as a *code*.

Your group must make up a number of messages. They could be something like:

'I will meet you at Andy's Cafe at 6 pm on Wednesday', or anything else that you can think of.

Work with another group which doesn't know what your messages are. Investigate the following:

1 How many letters can you leave out of your message without making it impossible to understand?

2 What happens when you leave out all the vowels?

3 What happens if you leave out all the consonants?

4 What happens if you only let them see the bottom half of the letters?

B Finding out about codes

You can do this on your own, or as a group. Find out all you can about one of the following topics and give a short 10 minute presentation to your class about it.

1 The Pony Express.

2 The invention of writing.

3 Spy codes – trying to send secret messages.

4 Choose an animal you know something about. How does it communicate? To which other animals does it need to send messages?

5 The invention of 'wireless' – did Marconi know what he was doing?

6 How did Alexander Graham Bell come to invent the telephone?

7 Can plants send messages?

Questions

1 Name *two* devices used in your home that contain information transducers.

2 A TV set is part of an information transmission system. Look at the parts of such a system in picture 8. What jobs do these elements perform:

a the screen,
b the loudspeaker,
c the aerial of a TV set?

3 Picture 8 shows the main parts of an information transmission system. Copy it out and write underneath each box what you would put in it to illustrate:

a sending a letter,
b how a six-month-old baby communicates with its mother.

C2
Sounds

This topic is about how sounds are made and how they travel as waves.

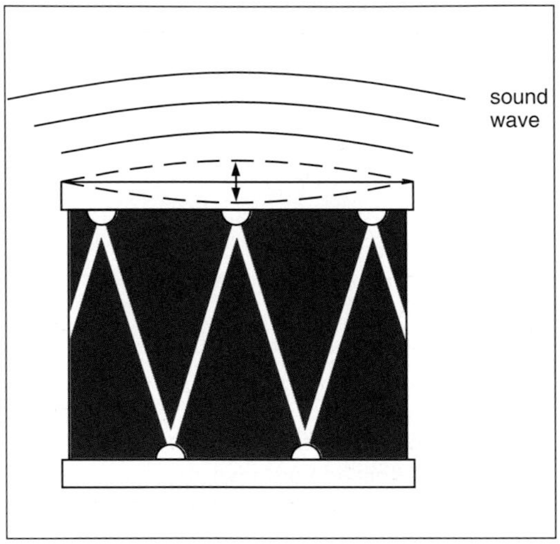

Picture 1 As the drum skin moves up and down, the air above it is squashed, then expanded.

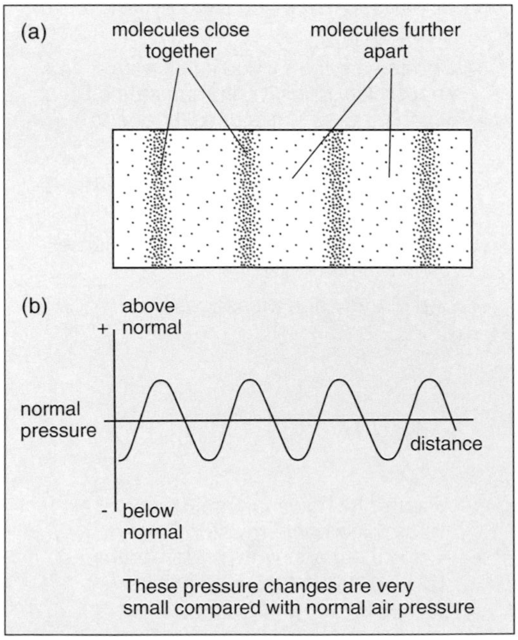

Picture 2 (a) A sound wave in air.
(b) A graph of the pressure of the air looks like this.

Making sounds

Sounds are made when objects vibrate. As the skin of the drum in picture 1 moves up and down it also moves the air next to it. When the drum skin moves up it squashes the air in front of it. When it moves back it leaves an empty space, so that the air has to expand. The result is a **sound wave** that travels through the air away from the drum.

The sound wave produced by the vibrating drum skin is a series of compressions (squashed air) and expansions. These move away from the drum, as each layer of air squashes the one next to it. Picture 2 shows what we imagine a sound wave in air to be like.

The speed at which these alternate layers of compressed and expanded air move away from the drum is the **speed of sound**. This is 331 m/s for normal air.

Sound can also travel through other materials. It moves best when the material is very stiff, for example in metals. The speed of sound in different materials is given in table 1.

Table 1 The speed of sound in different materials.

Material (medium)	Speed in (m/s) (at room temperature and pressure)
air	331
hydrogen	1286
carbon dioxide	260
wood	4200 (variable)
copper	3813
iron	5000
rubber	1600 (variable)
cork	500
water	1480

How sounds are different

We soon learn to recognise different people's voices, the sounds of moving water, the wind in the trees. Most people like music, and can easily tell the difference between one note and another, and one instrument from another. All these sounds are very different, but the differences are based on three things. What we hear is decided by:

- pitch (how high or low?): the number of vibrations the sound made per second (its frequency),
- loudness: the energy carried by the sound wave,
- quality (e.g. from different instruments): the shape of the sound wave.

Of course, what the wave is like is decided at the start by the type of object that is vibrating – the musical instrument, the engine of a car, etc.

Frequency and pitch

Musicians use the word **pitch** to describe how 'high' or 'low' a note is. A high-pitched note is made by something vibrating very quickly. Something vibrating slowly produces a low-pitched note. We use the word **frequency** to describe the rate at which something vibrates. It measures the number vibrations per second, in a unit called the **hertz (Hz)**.

The human ear can hear sounds from sources which vibrate from as low as about twenty vibrations per second (20 Hz) to as high as over 20 000 Hz. Activity A is about measuring your range of hearing.

Wave shapes – amplitude and quality

But there are other differences between sounds. They can be loud or quiet. They can also be different in **quality** – which means we can tell the difference between a note played on a guitar and the same note played on a flute.

Loudness is decided by the energy in the wave. In turn, this is decided by how strongly the source of the sound compresses the air. Sound waves are pressure waves in the air. One way to show a sound wave is to draw a graph of the *change* in the air pressure caused by the wave.

Picture 3 shows some of these graphs. They show how the pressure changes with time at one point in the air for different sounds. The first two (a) and (b) show the same note, but (b) is louder than (a). The *pressure changes* in (b) are greater. This means that they have a greater effect on the ear, so we sense it as a louder sound. The amount that the pressure changes above or below normal is called the **amplitude** of the change. The bigger the amplitude the louder the sound.

Graphs (c) and (d) show notes of the same loudness and pitch made on different instruments. The waves carry the same energy, and they would be 'in tune'. But their *shapes are different*, and we hear these differences as differences in quality. Activity B is about looking at sound waves made by different instruments.

The energy in a sound comes from the vibrating object that makes the sound. The greater the energy that can be delivered by the vibrator the louder the sound can be (picture 4). Big drums are louder than small drums!

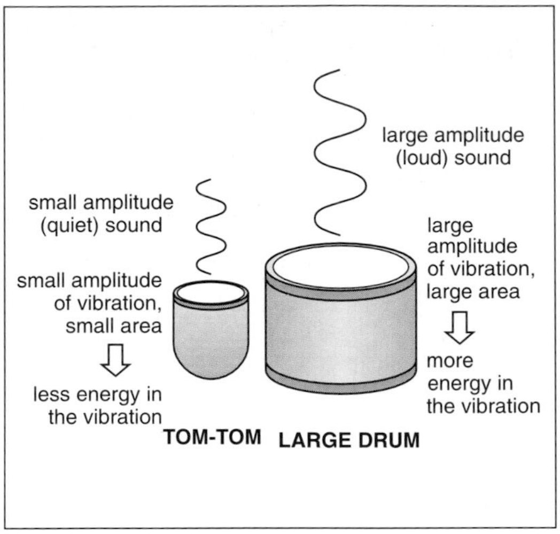

Picture 4

Wave shape and pitch

The shape of the wave can also show the frequency of the sound. Graphs (e) and (f) (see page 64) show notes of the same loudness but of different frequency. Note (f) has a higher pitch than note (e). You can see that there are more waves arriving per second in (f) than in (e). The instrument must have been vibrating quicker. *The more waves there are per second (frequency) the higher the pitch.*

Picture 3 These graphs show how air pressure varies with different types of sound: (a) small amplitude, (b) large amplitude, (sine wave, same frequency), (c) violin note, (d) clarinet note (same pitch and amplitude).

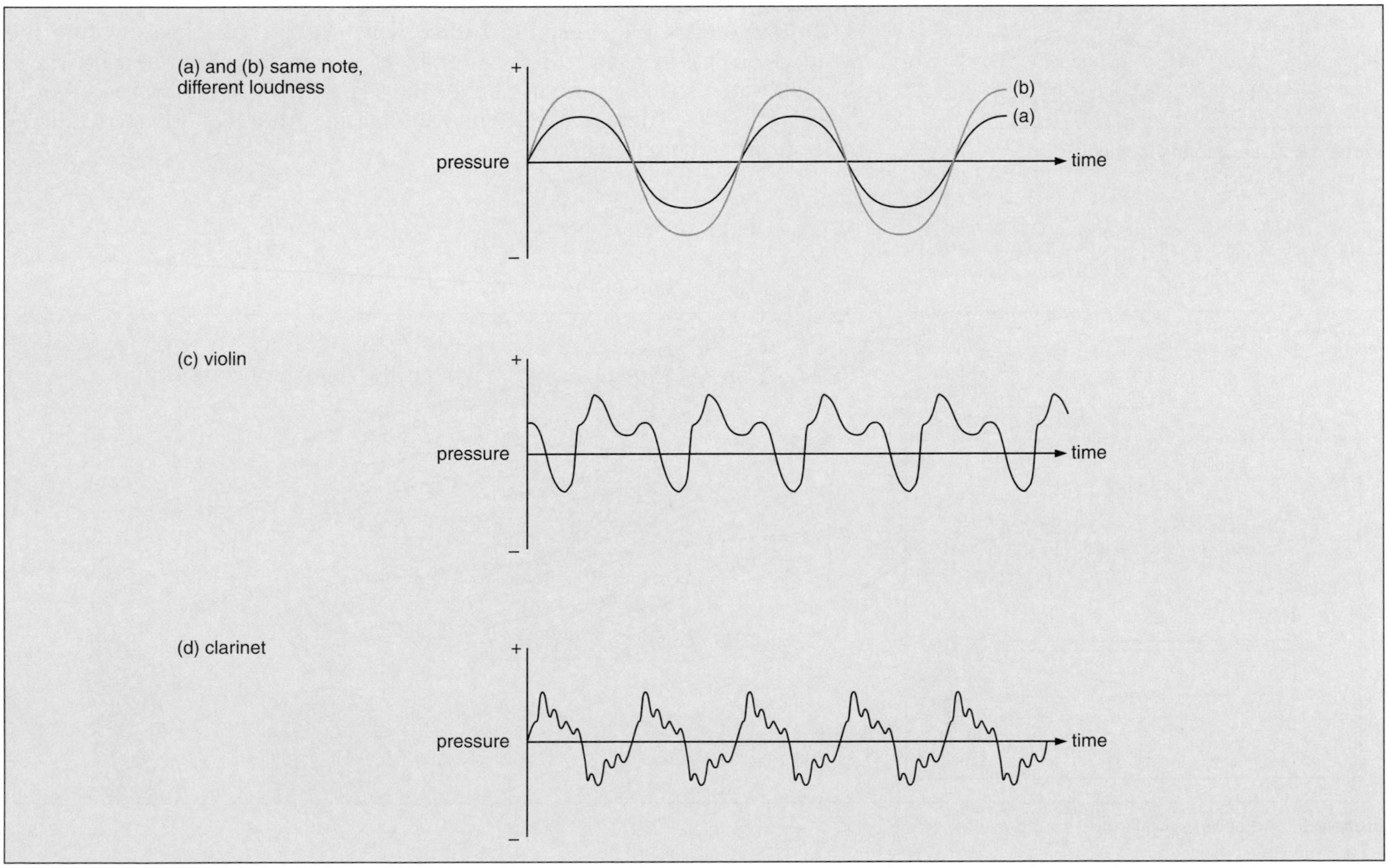

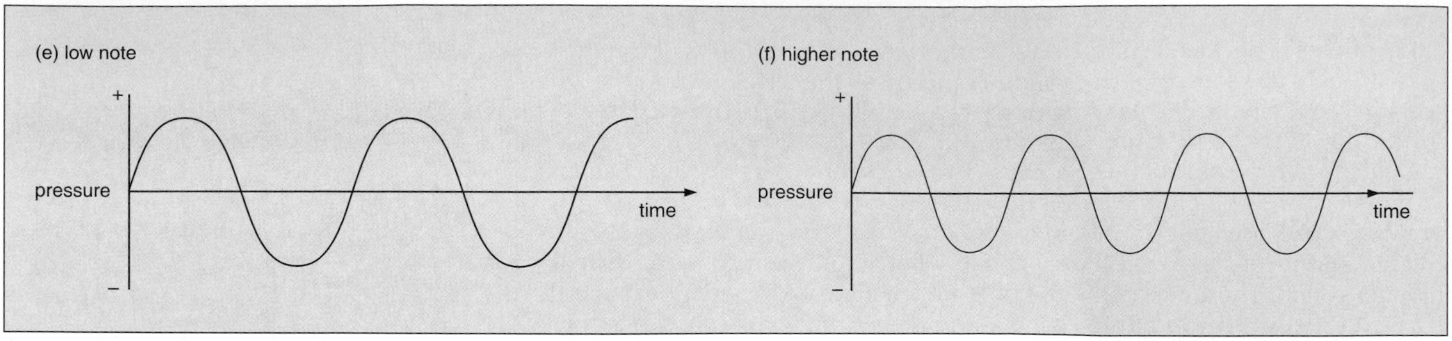

Picture 3

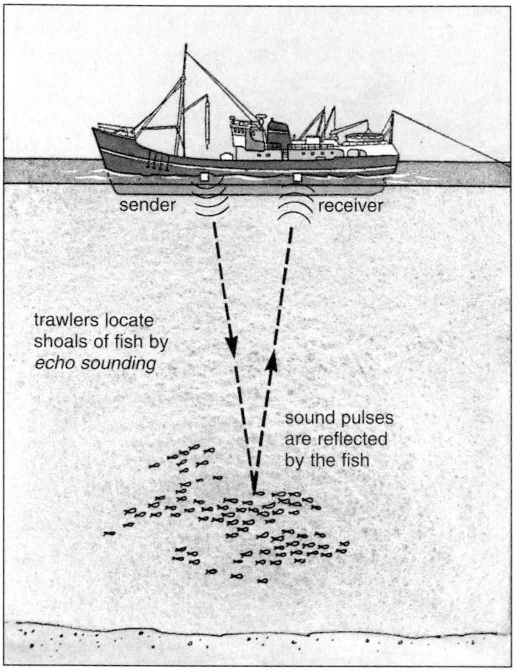

Picture 6 Using sound to find fish.

Echoes

Like other waves, sound can be reflected. We don't usually notice this, but we would find listening to music and speech in rooms and concert halls very strange if the walls didn't reflect sound.

Echoes are very obvious examples of sound being reflected. To hear a good echo, we must stand a few hundred metres from a cliff or hillside. When we shout, the sound travels to the reflector and bounces back (picture 5). If we are far enough away it means that you can finish a short sentence before the echo returns to us.

Echo ranging

If we make a short sharp sound we can time how long it takes for the sound to get to the cliff and come back again. We know that the speed of sound is 340 m/s, so we can work out how far away the cliff is. Suppose it took 2 seconds for the sound to go there and back. This means it took 1 second to get there, so the cliff must be 340 m away.

The same principle is used in **radar**, which uses radio waves to find the position of distant aircraft, for example. However, radio waves can't travel through water, so radar is no use under the sea. Instead, sound waves are used in **sonar** devices. They are used to find submarines, shoals of fish and to survey the bottom of the sea (picture 6).

The echo travels *twice* the distance between you and the cliff.
HELLO
HELLO

Picture 5 An echo is a reflected sound wave.

Activities

A High and low

For this activity you need a cathode ray oscilloscope (CRO), a sound generator and a loudspeaker or headphones. It will need to be set up by your teacher. You can use the controls of the sound generator to change the pitch and the loudness of the notes produced. As well as hearing them, you can see their wave patterns on the screen of the CRO.

Use this equipment to do the following.

1 a See what happens when you make a given note louder and quieter.

Draw some typical results.

b See what happens when you change the pitch of the note.

2 Measure the frequencies of the lowest pitch sounds and the highest pitch sounds that you can hear – i.e. the **frequency range** of your ears. You should start with the sound generator working at a very low frequency – this could be just one 'wave' per second and you should be able to hear the separate pulses. Increase the frequency slowly and note what happens. You will need to adjust the volume control as well!

a At what frequency do the pulses stop being heard separately and start to make a definite 'note'?

b At what frequency do you stop being able to hear the sound?

c Collect together the results of your class or group. Compare them with each other and with the results from your teacher and any other adults you can persuade to be tested. Comment on the results of this survey.

B Looking at sounds

For this activity you need a cathode ray oscilloscope (CRO), a microphone and as many musical instruments as you can borrow. Play each instrument into the microphone with a very steady note. You may need to adjust the CRO controls to get a good steady trace. Compare different instruments playing the same note.

Compare different notes on the same instrument. See the difference between loud and soft notes played on the same instrument. Draw some of the traces that you see.

C Measuring the speed of sound in air

There are lots of ways of measuring the speed of sound. Here are some ideas:

1 Stand in front of a large wall (e.g. the wall of the gym) and clap your hands. You should hear an echo. Now clap your hands at a steady rate. Time it so that the clap occurs at the same time as the echo reaches you. Get a friend to time 20 claps. Divide this time by 20. This is the time it takes for sound to go from you to the wall and back again.

Measure the distance from the wall to you and calculate the speed of sound:

$$\text{speed} = \frac{2 \times \text{distance to wall}}{\text{time taken}}$$

2 Get a friend to stand a long way from you, e.g. the far side of the playing fields or playground. Your friend should have two blocks of wood and hit them together to make a sharp sound. When you *see* the two blocks hit each other start a stop watch. Stop it when you hear the sound. This is the time it takes for the sound to travel the distance between you. Measure this distance and calculate the speed of sound from:

$$\text{speed} = \frac{\text{distance apart}}{\text{time taken}}$$

3 Using electronic timing. Methods (1) and (2) are cheap but rely on human reactions in stopping and starting a watch. Electronic timers have quicker reactions and can measure much shorter times with good accuracy. They can be stopped and started when a sound pulse reaches two microphones just a few metres apart. In this way you can measure the time it takes sound to travel that distance.

Check with your teacher if you have such equipment available. If you have, plan an experiment to use it to measure the speed of sound in your laboratory.

Questions

1 a What is the quietest sound you can hear?

b Why can very loud sounds damage your ear drum?

2 What are the three main ways in which sounds can be different from each other? What are the physical causes of these differences?

3 (For musicians) How are the three differences in question 2 shown on a musical score?

4 a What is an echo? How is it produced?

b Echo sounders are used to find shoals of fish. How do you think they work?

5 A mountain walker notices that when she shouts she hears an echo from a distant cliff. She times it and finds that it takes 2.5 seconds for her shout to be returned as an echo. How far away is the cliff? (Speed of sound in air: 340 m/s.)

6 You can work out how far away you are from a thunderstorm by measuring the time between seeing the lightning flash and hearing the thunder it makes. This works because light travels so much more quickly than sound. A worried boy counted off 5 seconds (by saying 'alpha one, alpha two …') between the flash and the thunder. How far away was the thunderstorm?

7 The diagram below (picture 7) shows three traces of sounds, shown by a cathode ray oscilloscope. Which of them: (a) would be the loudest, (b) would be the highest or lowest in pitch, (c) is likely to be made by a flute?

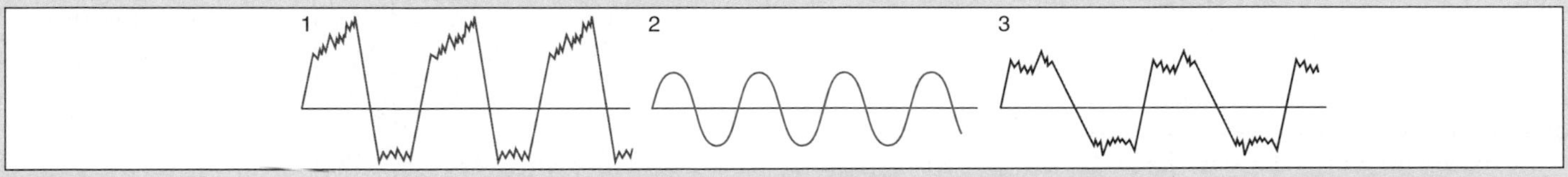

Picture 7

C3 The ear and hearing

Block your ears with your fingers and imagine what it's like to live in silence.

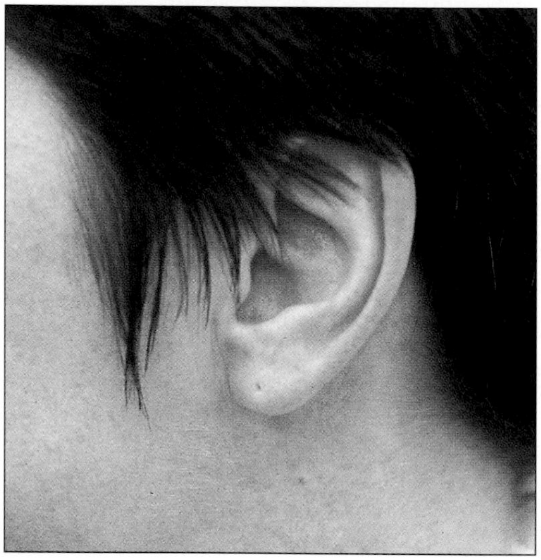

Picture 1 Our ears tell us a lot about what's going on around us.

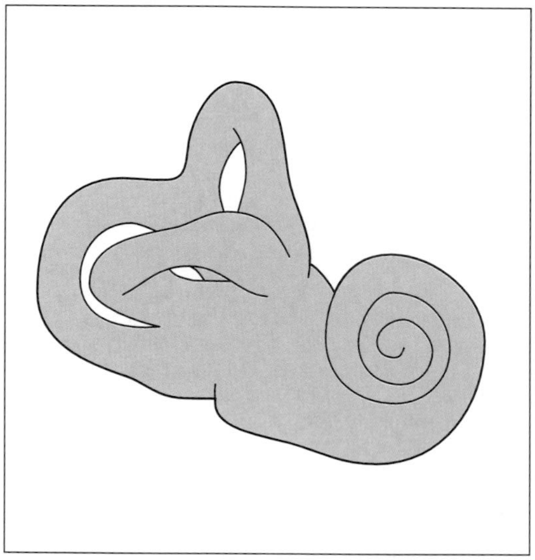

Picture 2 Imagine that the inner ear was taken out of your head. This is what it would look like.

The outside of the ear

Most people think of the ear as just a flap on the side of the head. But there is much more to it than that. The flap is simply a device for catching sounds and directing them into the **ear hole** in front. The flap is called the **pinna** and it contains gristle to keep it stiff.

Inside the ear

The 'business' part of the ear is embedded in the side of the head. Picture 2 shows it on its own outside the head. It is made up of two parts which do quite different jobs. One part helps us to keep our balance – we shall return to that later. The other part enables us to hear. The hearing part consists of a coiled tube rather like a snail's shell. It is called the **cochlea**. The ear hole is connected to the cochlea by a series of channels and chambers which are shown in picture 3.

Let's go on a guided tour of the ear, using picture 3 to help us. The hole leads into a short tube called the **outer ear channel**. The skin lining the first part of the channel secretes wax which catches germs and dust, preventing them from getting into the ear.

Stretched across the inner end of the channel is a tough membrane, the **ear drum**. On the other side of the ear drum is a chamber filled with air. It is called the **middle ear chamber**, and it contains three tiny bones. They are the smallest bones in the body. Because of their shape, they are called the **hammer, anvil** and **stirrup**. They run from the ear drum to a small hole on the other side of the middle ear chamber. This is called the **oval window**, and it leads to the cochlea which is part of the **inner ear**.

The cochlea contains receptor cells which are connected to the brain by the **auditory nerve**. The cochlea is full of fluid, and this plays an important part in the way we hear.

How does the ear hear?

It's Guy Fawkes night and there's a loud bang. The noise sets off **sound waves** which travel through the air (see page 62). Within a fraction of a second the sound waves reach your ear, and the pinna directs them into the outer ear channel.

The sound waves pass along the channel to the ear drum. When they hit the ear drum, the drum vibrates. This moves the ear bones backwards and forwards, causing the foot of the stirrup in the oval window to vibrate. The vibrations of the stirrup then move the fluid in the cochlea.

What happens in the cochlea?

Inside the cochlea there are two membranes stretched across from one side to the other. These membranes run the full length of the cochlea. You can see them in picture 3. The lower one has receptor cells attached to it.

Vibrations of the cochlea fluid make the cochlea membranes vibrate. When the lower membrane vibrates, it stimulates the receptor cells. The receptor cells then send off impulses in the auditory nerve. When the impulses reach the brain, we hear the sound.

That's not quite the end of the story. Look once more at picture 3. You'll see that between the middle ear chamber and the cochlea there is a hole called the **round window**. You may have wondered what it's for. Obviously the pressure which develops in the cochlea fluid has got to be taken up by something. It's taken up by the membrane covering this hole.

We can sum up by saying that the sound waves make the ear membranes vibrate, and the movements are then changed, i.e. transduced, into electrical signals which are sent to the brain.

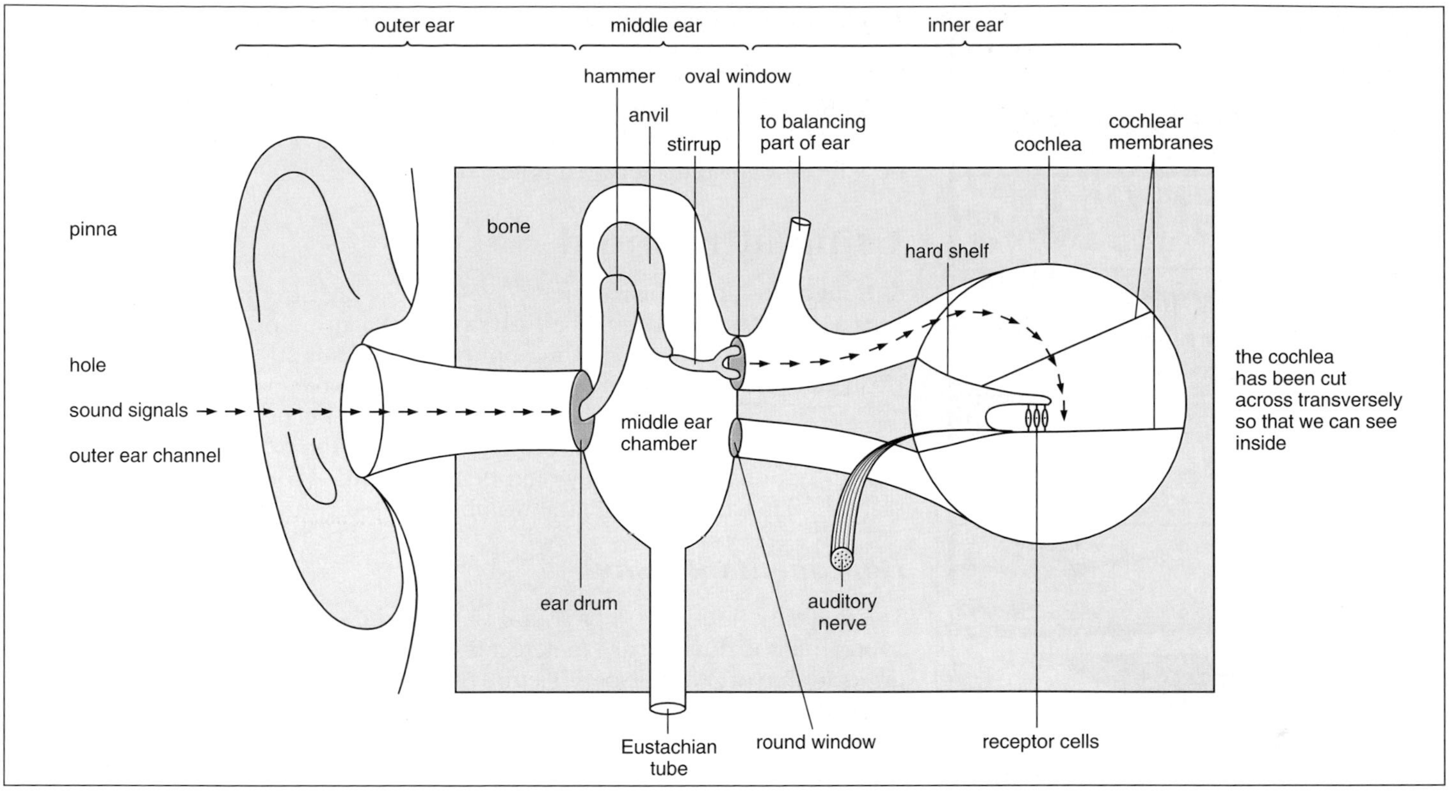

Picture 3 Inside the human ear. The arrows show how sound waves are transmitted to the receptor cells in the cochlea.

Telling the difference between loud and soft sounds

If you play a note on a guitar, its loudness depends on how hard you pluck the wire. The harder you pluck, the greater is the distance through which the wire vibrates and the louder is the sound.

The loudness of a sound is registered by the ear in the same way. Soft sounds cause small vibrations of the cochlea membranes. Louder sounds cause larger vibrations.

Telling the difference between high and low notes

With a guitar, the note depends on how rapidly the wire vibrates – in other words, the frequency. High frequency vibrations give high notes, whereas low frequency vibrations give low notes.

Although the details are different, the ear works in the same kind of way. The membrane to which the receptor cells are attached vibrates at different frequencies in different parts of the cochlea. In other words, the membrane **resonates**, and this enables different notes to be heard.

How can you tell where a sound comes from?

Normally when you hear a sound, you know where it comes from. This is because you have two ears, one on each side of the head. Suppose you hear a sound from the right. Sound waves reach the right ear a fraction of a second before they reach the left ear (picture 4). The result is that nerve impulses are sent to the brain from the right ear slightly before they are sent from the left ear. From this the brain knows that the sound must have come from the right. Although other effects play a part, this is the basis of how we tell where sounds come from, and how we appreciate stereo music.

Picture 4 Where did that bang come from?

The audible range

The frequency (pitch) of a sound is measured in cycles per second or hertz (Hz). The human ear can detect frequencies from about 20 Hz (very low notes) to about 20 000 Hz (very high notes). This is called the **audible range**.

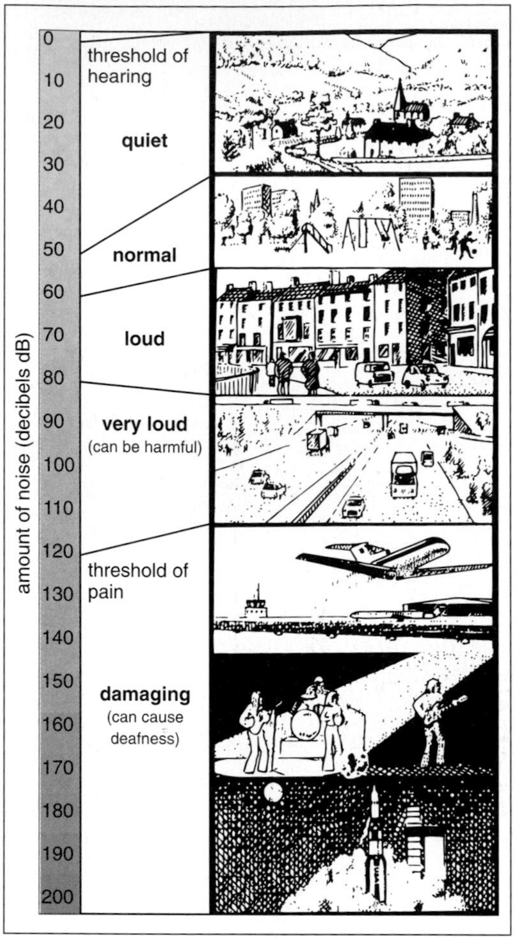

Picture 5 This illustration shows the noise scale as expressed in decibels, the standard unit of noise as measured with a sound meter.

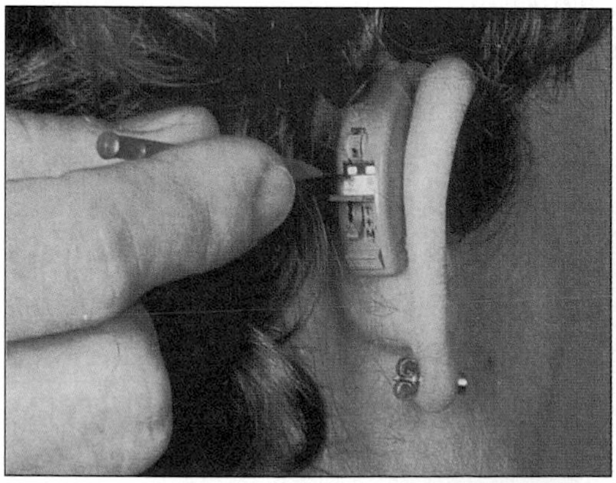

Picture 6 A hearing aid. The case contains a microphone, battery and earphone. The case fits neatly behind the ear. Sound waves are transmitted through a plastic tube to a mould which is placed over the opening of the ear.

Animals such as dogs and cats can hear higher notes than we can, and bats can hear sounds at a frequency of 100 000 Hz! You can hear high notes best when you are young. Elderly people lose this ability.

Within the audible range an average person can distinguish between about 2000 different notes, though a trained musician can do better than this. We are best at distinguishing between notes in the 1000 to 4000 Hz range.

Using ultrasound

Although we cannot hear sound waves of very high frequency they are in fact very useful. These waves, called **ultrasound**, can be produced electronically and are detected by special microphones. Ultrasound is used in industry to clean delicate objects. The vibrations simply shake particles of dirt off the object. The microphones are also used in a kind of echo ranging (see page 64) to find flaws in metal objects. Ultrasound is now the main way of looking into human bodies when X-rays would be dangerous – for example, in antenatal scans, looking at embryos in the womb (see the feature on page 95).

How about intensity?

The intensity (loudness) of a sound is measured in decibels (dB). The quietest sound that the human ear can detect is called the **threshold of hearing** and is given a value of zero decibels. Picture 5 shows the range of intensities from the threshold to the loudest sounds that the human ear can bear. Notice that a sound of 120 dB is on the **threshold of pain**. Sounds louder than this can actually hurt your ears and give you a headache. Prolonged noise above 150 dB can cause permanent deafness. The reason is explained below.

Because of its harmful effects, it is important for noise in the environment to be controlled. Sound levels above 90 dB are not normally allowed in factories, but many of the noises which we hear in our everyday lives are much louder than this. Can you think of examples? People who work close to noisy machinery wear ear plugs. Perhaps we should all wear ear plugs!

What causes deafness?

There are several types of deafness, depending on which part of the ear is affected.

Lots of people become slightly deaf from time to time because the outer ear channel gets blocked with hard wax. This is easily removed by a doctor syringing out the ears with warm water. It helps if the wax is first softened by putting a few drops of olive oil into the ear several days beforehand.

An explosion, or a blow on the side of the head, may rupture the ear drum, causing partial or complete deafness. However, the ear drum usually heals quite quickly and then hearing returns.

More serious deafness is caused by bone tissue growing round the stirrup in the middle ear chamber. This can prevent the stirrup moving, in much the same way as a piston may seize up with rust. If nothing is done about it, this can lead to permanent deafness. However, the person's hearing may be improved by wearing a hearing aid which amplifies the sound waves (picture 6). In severe cases the stirrup may be replaced by an artificial one made of plastic. This type of deafness runs in families,and it can begin when you are quite young.

Sometimes deafness is caused by the cochlea not working properly. For example, suppose you listen to a very loud sound of a particular pitch for a long time. The cochlea membrane vibrates so much that eventually the receptor cells which detect that particular frequency get damaged. The result is that you become deaf to that particular note. Some pop singers have become deaf to certain notes because of this; so have young people who listen to very loud music through headphones. There is no cure for this kind of deafness.

People often get deaf as they grow old. This is usually caused by the auditory nerve failing to carry impulses to the brain in the usual way.

Activities

A Experiments on hearing

This experiment involves using a signal generator.

1 Your teacher will use a signal generator to compare the audible ranges of people in your class. How do people differ in their ranges, and why? Do you think it matters?

2 Plan an experiment to find out if a person's threshold of hearing (i.e. the quietest sound which he or she can hear) depends on the frequency of the sound? If facilities permit, your teacher will help you to carry out the experiment.

3 It is said that females can hear higher notes than males. With the help of your teacher, test this idea on your class.

B Comparing the noise levels in different places

Using a sound meter, find the maximum amount of noise above the hearing threshold in different places such as a street corner, railway station, airport, children's playground, school dining hall, reference library, motorway, factory, park, disco.

Compare your results with picture 5, and decide whether each place is quiet, normal, loud, very loud or damaging. Do you have any difficulty in deciding? If so, why?

C Looking at sounds

For this activity you need a cathode ray oscilloscope (CRO), a microphone and as many musical instruments as you can borrow. Play each instrument into the microphone with a very steady note. You may need to adjust the CRO controls to get a good steady trace. Compare different instruments playing the same note.

Compare different notes on the same instrument. See the difference between loud and soft notes played on the same instrument. Draw some of the traces that you see.

D Measuring the speed of sound in air

There are lots of ways of measuring the speed of sound. Here are some ideas:

1 Stand in front of a large wall (e.g. the wall of the gym) and clap your hands. You should hear an echo. Now clap your hands at a steady rate. Time it so that the clap occurs at the same time as the echo reaches you. Get a friend to time 20 claps. Divide this time by 20. This is the time it takes for sound to go from you to the wall and back again.

Measure the distance from the wall to you and calculate the speed of sound:

$$\text{speed} = \frac{2 \times \text{distance to wall}}{\text{time taken}}$$

2 Get a friend to stand a long way from you, e.g. the far side of the playing fields or playground. Your friend should have two blocks of wood and hit them together to make a sharp sound. When you *see* the two blocks hit each other start a stop watch. Stop it when you hear the sound. This is the time it takes for the sound to travel the distance between you. Measure this distance and calculate the speed of sound from:

$$\text{speed} = \frac{\text{distance apart}}{\text{time taken}}$$

3 Methods (a) and (b) are cheap but rely on human reactions in stopping and starting a watch. Electronic timers have quicker reactions and can measure much shorter times with good accuracy. They can be stopped and started when a sound pulse reaches two microphones just a few metres apart. In this way you can measure the time it takes sound to travel that distance.

Check with your teacher if you have such equipment available. If you have, plan an experiment to use it to measure the speed of sound in your laboratory.

Questions

1 What jobs are done by each of these: the ear drum, the oval window, the receptor cells in the cochlea, the auditory nerve?

2 What is the pinna, and what job does it do? The pinna of an Alsatian dog is more efficient than the pinna of a human. What makes it more efficient?

3 People who drill holes in the road or work in very noisy factories, should wear ear muffs. Why?

4 Suppose someone became deaf to low notes but not to high notes.

a This is unlikely to have been caused by a ruptured ear drum? Why?

b What would be the most likely cause? Explain your answer.

C4
Waves

Sound isn't the only thing that moves as waves. There are waves on water, light waves and earthquake waves.

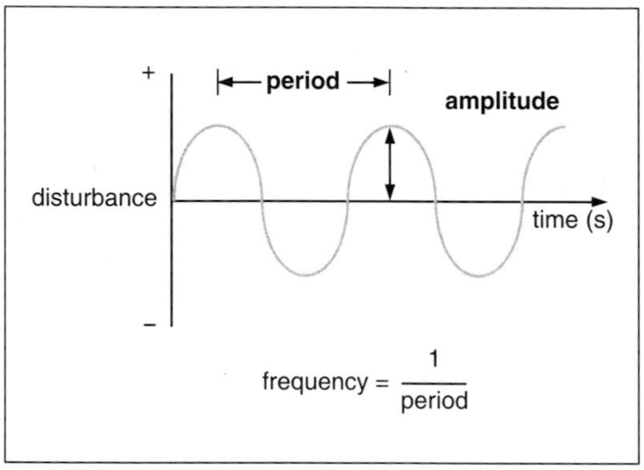

Picture 1 Amplitude and period – (disturbance *v* time).

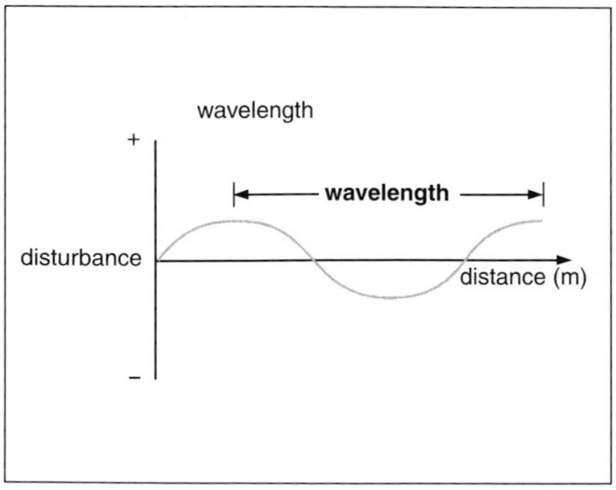

Picture 2 Wavelength and amplitude (disturbance *v* distance).

Waves in space

Light, and the whole electromagnetic spectrum of which it is a small part, travel through space as waves. Earthquakes set up waves which can cause great damage. They also travel right through the Earth, and scientists use them to find out what the inside of the Earth is like. Topic F1 deals more fully with these types of wave.

But whatever kind of waves they are, they are similar to each other. They all *move, carrying energy*. They all have a *pattern*, which repeats *itself*.

Picture 1 is a graph of a typical wave. It could be a water wave, a sound wave or a light wave. We can use it to explain the meaning of the key words we use to describe wave motion.

First, its **amplitude**. This is a measure of how much the wave vibrates the medium it passes through. It could be the height of a water wave, or the pressure of a sound wave.

Next we have the wave's **period**. This is the time it takes for the wave to repeat its pattern. It is the time for one **vibration** of the source of the wave.

The frequency of a wave is related to its period. The more vibrations are made in a second, the shorter is the time that each one takes. Thus, if a wave has a period of 1/100th of a second it repeats itself 100 times a second, so has a frequency of 100 Hz. That is:

$$\text{period} = 1/\text{frequency}$$

Wavelength

The graph in picture 1 was of the wave changes plotted against time. If we plot these against distance instead we get an idea of the size of the wave. This is done in picture 2. The marked distance is the **wavelength** – the distance between equivalent points on the wave pattern. This could be from peak to peak, or from trough to trough.

The wavelength of a typical sound (say middle C) is about 133 cm. The wavelength of light is very much smaller. For yellow light it is about 600 billionths of a metre. Long wave radio broadcasts use a wavelength of over 1000 m.

The wave speed formula

If a source of sound is vibrating sixteen times a second it is producing sixteen waves every second. At the end of that second the first wave has travelled sixteen wavelengths away from the source. The wave speed is simply how far the waves move in a second. In this case it is obviously just 16 wavelengths. Picture 3 illustrates this.

If the sound source vibrated at 20 Hz, it would produce twenty wavelengths in a second. But sound travels at the same speed in air, whatever its frequency, so the waves are more squashed up – the wavelength is smaller. This is also shown in picture 3.

Thus, because the speed of sound is the same, however many waves are made each second they all have to fit into the same distance. This distance is 340 m, in air. Looking at it mathematically:

$$\text{length of a sound wave} = \frac{\text{distance sound travels in a second}}{\text{number of waves made per second}}$$

$$\text{or:} \qquad \text{wavelength} = \frac{\text{speed}}{\text{frequency}}$$

This is usually written more neatly as:

$$\textbf{wave speed} = \textbf{frequency} \times \textbf{wavelength}$$

$$v = f\lambda$$

This formula applies to all waves.

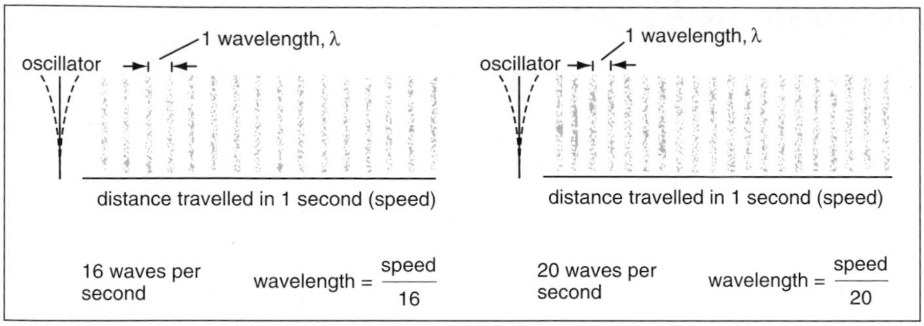

Picture 3 The speed stays the same, so wavelength gets less when frequency increases.

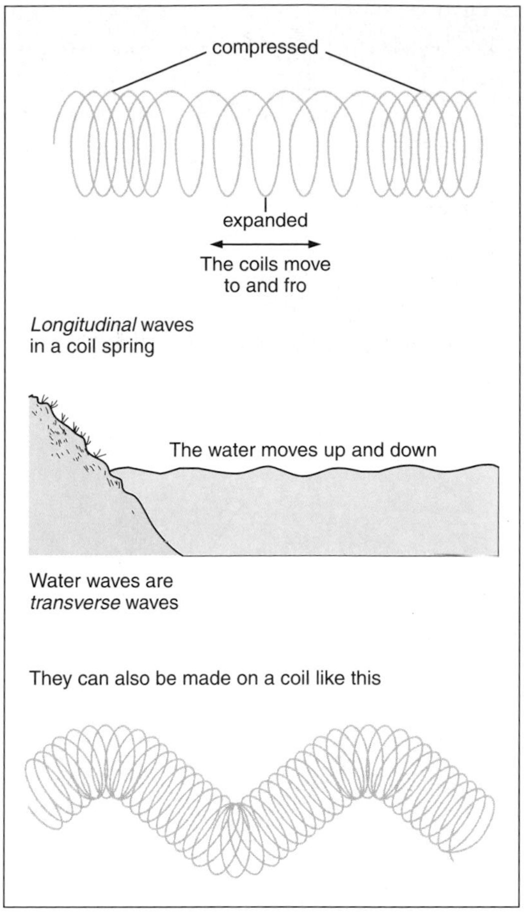

Picture 4 Longitudinal and transverse waves.

To and fro, up and down

Sound waves compress and expand the air. The particles of air move backwards and forwards in line with the direction the sound travels. Waves on a large-coil spring can also do this. These kinds of waves are called **longitudinal** waves.

When sea waves move, the water surface moves up and down as the wave moves along. Waves on a rope or a guitar string are also like this. Waves in which the carrier (medium) moves at right angles to the direction of wave movement are called **transverse** waves. Picture 4 shows these differences.

Waves through liquids

Sound waves travel well through water. Dolphins use sound waves as a sonar to hunt their prey. Sound travels through water because sound is a longitudinal wave. Transverse waves can travel along the surface of water but not through water. This is the case for all liquids. This fact has been used to prove that the core of the Earth is liquid, because the transverse earthquakes waves don't get across to the opposite side of the Earth. (See topic F1.)

Waves can carry energy

Picture 5 shows the coast of Norfolk at a place where the sea cliff is slowly disappearing. The energy for this has been carried by the sea waves continually beating on the base of the cliff. The worst damage is done in storms, when the sea waves are many metres high and carry a great deal of energy.

The bigger the amplitude of a wave the more energy it carries. In fact, the energy carried is proportional to the square of the amplitude. So doubling the wave height increases the energy carried four times. See picture 6.

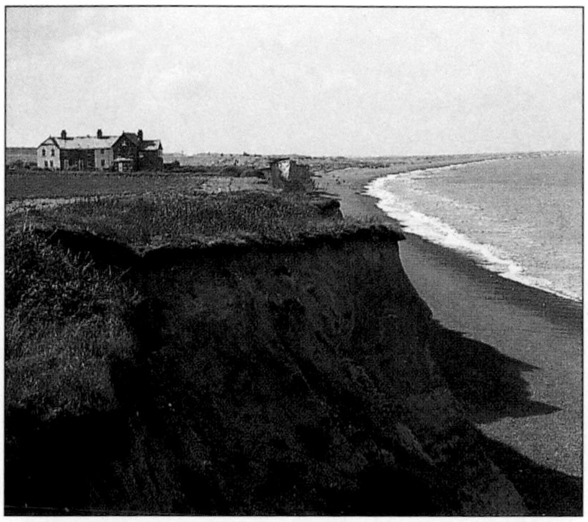

Picture 5

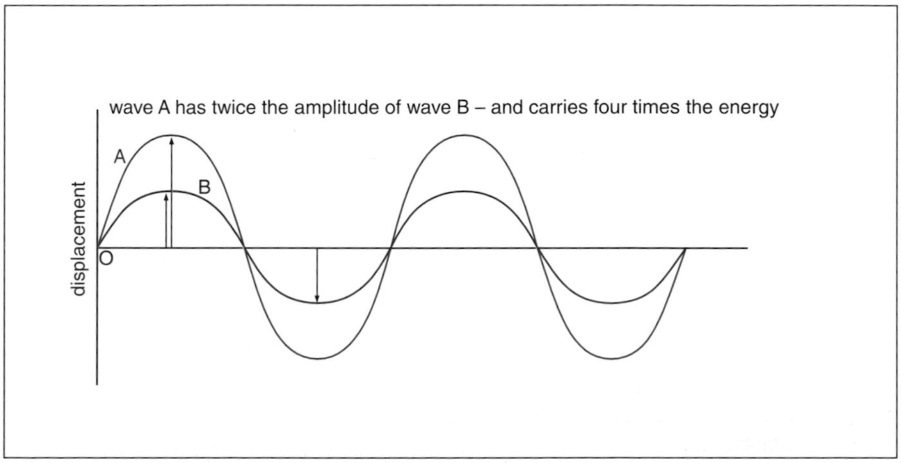

Picture 6 Energy and amplitude for a wave.

Picture 7

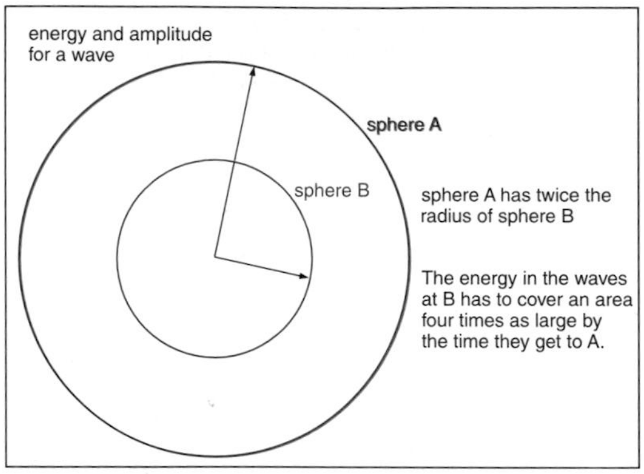

Picture 8 Sphere A has twice the radius of sphere B.

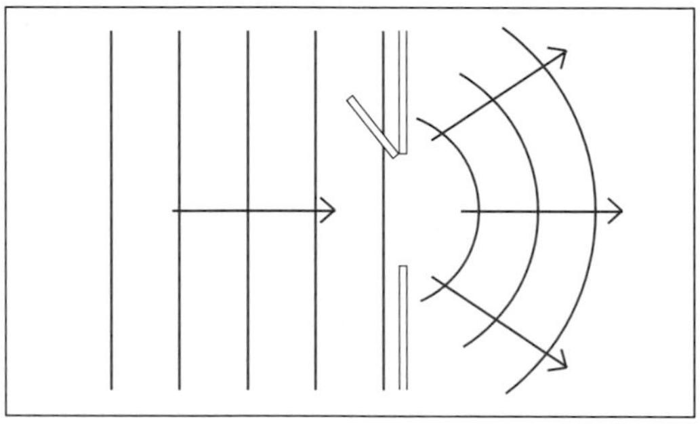

Picture 9 Diffraction means that sound can spread out of an open door in all directions.

Like ripples on a pond

Imagine a stone thrown into the middle of a pond. When it hits the water it makes a small group of water waves that move outwards from the centre (picture 7). Some of the kinetic energy lost by the stone is being carried away by the waves. As the waves spread out into an ever-widening circle the energy has to be shared over a bigger and bigger length of wave. The energy per metre length gets less and less. The same thing happens to a sound wave as it spreads out. The further away it gets from the source of sound, the less energy it carries. Its amplitude gets less and the sound becomes quieter. Exactly the same rules apply to light waves (see topic C6). The further away the source of light is, the fainter it appears to the eye.

A loud sound can break your ear drum, a very bright light like the beam from an industrial laser can carry enough energy to cut through steel. When light and sound waves spread out freely the energy carried per unit area decreases according to an **inverse square law.** As they travel, the same total quantity of energy has to spread out over a bigger area (see picture 8).

This is the reason that you need to have large amplifiers and loudspeakers to fill a concert hall at a pop concert, while the same music can sound just as loud on a walkman with very small headphone speakers. And the sound from the headphones can be just as damaging to the ear!

Hearing around corners: diffraction

Sounds spread out in all directions, and because they move as waves they can bend around corners. Sounds can also 'escape' from a room through an open door. This effect is called **diffraction** – see picture 9. There is more about diffraction in topic C7.

The refraction of sound

Sound waves can change direction when they travel from one medium to another. This is because they travel at different speeds in different media. This effect is called **refraction** and is more useful in application of light than for sound (see topic C6 which describes how a change in speed makes waves refract). Picture 10 shows how you could show the refraction of sound. Sound travels more slowly in carbon dioxide than in air, and so you can make a sound

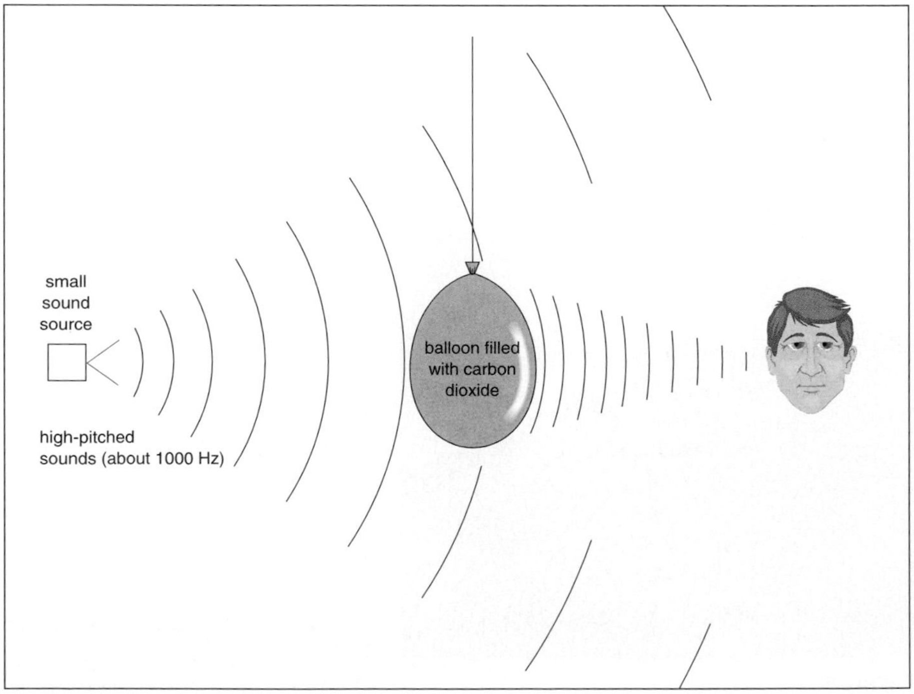

Picture 10 Sound can be refracted. You can use a balloon filled with carbon dioxide as a lens.

'lens' with a ballon filled with carbon dioxide. Sound travels more quickly in hydrogen. What would happen to sound passing through a hydrogen-filled ballon?

Acoustics

Acoustics is the science of sound as an energy carrier. A concert hall needs to have 'good acoustics'. This means that wherever people sit in the hall they can hear the music or speech equally well. The problem that has to be solved by the architect who designs the hall is mostly due to **echoes**.

Most solid surfaces reflect sound. A good reflector bounces back the sound without taking much energy from it. A good absorber will take away most of the energy. Hard, shiny surfaces are usually good reflectors of sound; soft surfaces – like cloth and human bodies – are good absorbers. If a concert hall is full of good reflectors, the sound bounces around from wall to wall and from ceiling to floor and the listener will hear the same note, for example, many times. The result is confusion: the music or speech is muddy and unclear (see picture 11). The hall is too **reverberant**: each sound produces an echo which takes a long time to die away.

But the opposite design is almost as bad. If the walls and ceiling do not reflect sound at all, the sound seems to vanish. It is like hearing a concert in the open air. Music and musicians sound best when there is some reflection; the small echoes add 'life' to the music – it all sounds more natural.

Picture 12 shows the interior of the new Concert Hall in the city of Birmingham. There is little echo delay, and the sound just appears louder. The walls and ceiling are made of a mixture of surfaces which reflect and absorb just the right amount of energy. The seats are made of materials which reflect and absorb sound in just the same proportions as a human body sitting in the seat would. Thus the acoustics are the same however large the audience.

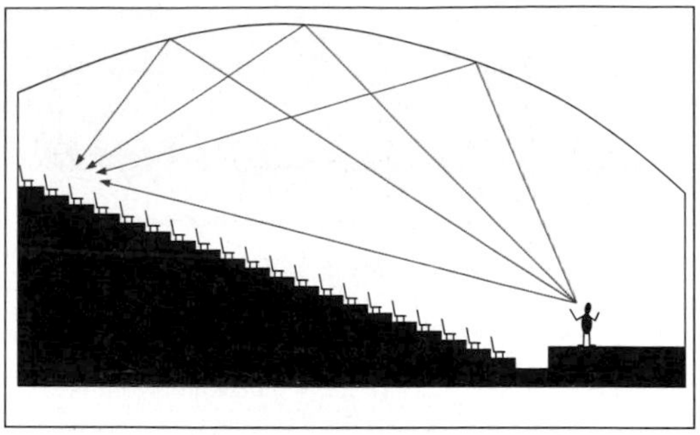

Picture 11 Sound reaches a seat in the hall via several routes. This can cause a muddled sound if there is a long delay between reflections.

Picture 12 Interior of Birmingham City Concert Hall.

Activities

A

You will need a strong, heavy rope and a long coil spring. You will also need a fairly long smooth floor, like a school corridor. You can make wave pulses in the rope by shaking it from side to side for a short time – making one or two 'wavelets'. These are transverse waves.

You can do the same with the coil, but you can also make longitudinal waves.

Investigate the properties of waves, and try answering these questions:

1 Can the waves be reflected?

2 What is the speed of the wave? Does the amplitude of the wave affect its speed? Does the frequency?

3 What happens when two waves pass through each other?

4 Can you alter the speed of waves in the rope? How?

5 Can you alter the speed of waves in the coil spring? How?

B Waves on water

Your school might have some ripple tanks which allow you to explore two-dimensional waves on water. There are lots of experiments that can be done. To begin with, try answering the questions 1, 2 and 3 in activity A for water waves. You can then go on to investigate:

4 What happens when waves are reflected by curved barriers?

5 What happens when waves go through a gap?

6 What happens when they go through two gaps, side by side?

Questions

1 Explain the difference between frequency and period for a wave.

2 Give a brief outline of an experiment you could do show:

a that sound waves can pass through each other,

b that water waves can pass through each other.

3 You should have learned that when light is reflected, 'the angle of incidence is equal to the angle of reflection'. Explain what this means. How could you test to see if sound waves obey the same rule?

4 Use the formula *wavelength = speed/frequency*, and the data in table 1 in topic C2, to calculate the following:

a the wavelength of a 500 Hz note in air,

b the wavelength of a 1000 Hz note in air,

c the speed of a note of 500 Hz which is measured to have a wavelength of 0.5 m in carbon dioxide.

5 The speed of radio waves is 300 000 000 m/s. What is the frequency of the UK Radio 4 programme which has a wavelength of 1500 m?

C5 Controlling light

Light is very useful! This topic is about how we can control it.

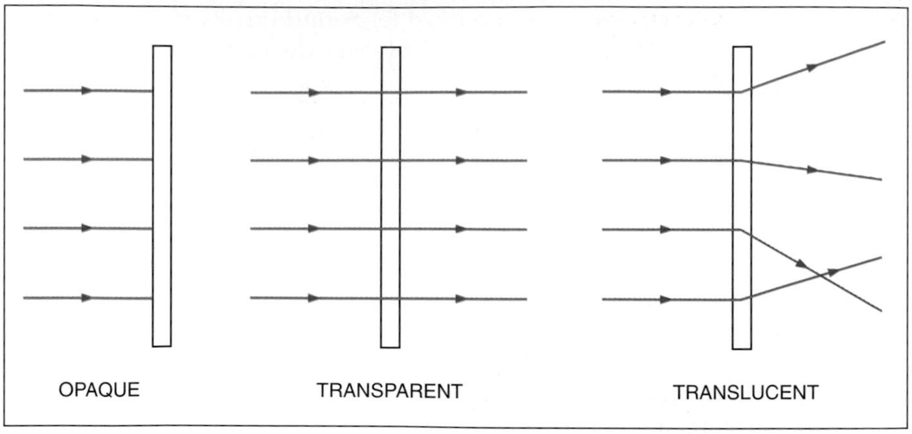

Picture 1 What happens to light in opaque, transparent and translucent materials.

Keeping light in – or out

There are some materials that light cannot pass through. They are **opaque**. We stop light getting into a camera by using a metal or plastic material that is opaque to light.

Curtains and blinds do the same thing. A material that lets light go through it is either **transparent** or **translucent** (see picture 1). A transparent material, like glass, air, water and some plastics, lets light through in straight lines. We can see things clearly through them.

A translucent material breaks up the light so that we don't get a picture of the object sending out the light. Finely scratched glass, or 'ground' glass, is like this. We use translucent materials in some light bulbs and bathroom windows.

White painted materials can reflect light so that more of it goes where want it to, but without a glare. The insides of lampshades are sometimes painted white for this reason (see picture 2).

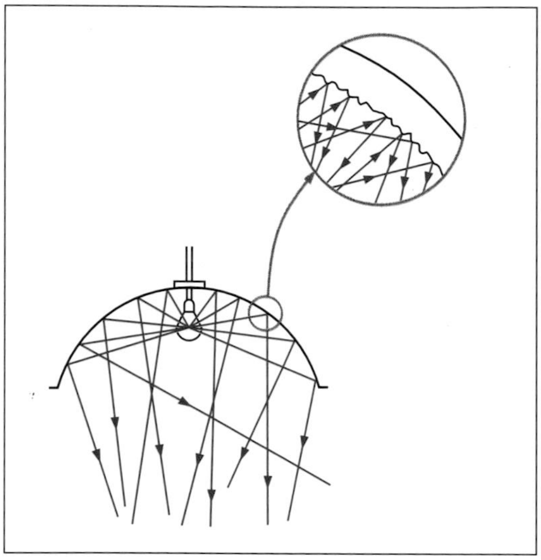

Picture 2 Diffuse reflection – light goes off in all directions.

Mirrors

Mirrors reflect light in a regular way (see picture 3 and compare it with picture 2). The light is reflected according to the rule:

the angle of incidence equals the angle of reflection.

In other words, the light rays make the same angle to the mirror going in as they do when they come away from it. We normally measure these angles between the light rays and a line at right angles to the mirror (called the **normal** line).

This means that flat (**plane**) mirrors reflect light to give a clear image. But it is a 'mirror image', in which left hands turn into right hands, and vice versa (picture 4).

We can work all this out using the idea that light travels in straight lines. Picture 5 shows how this idea explains why an object in front of a mirror produces an image that is as far behind the mirror as the object is in front of it.

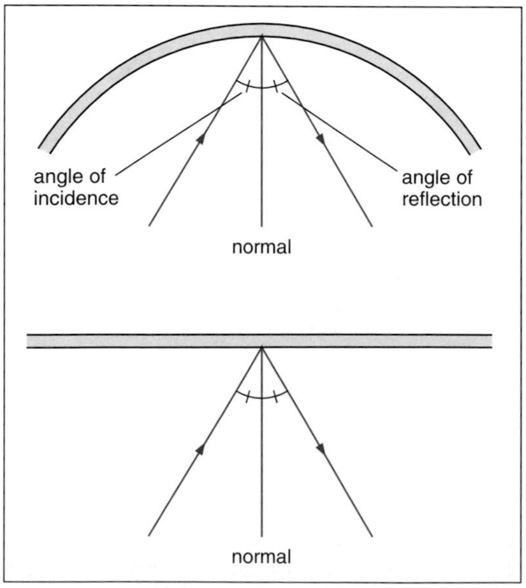

Picture 3 The law of reflection.

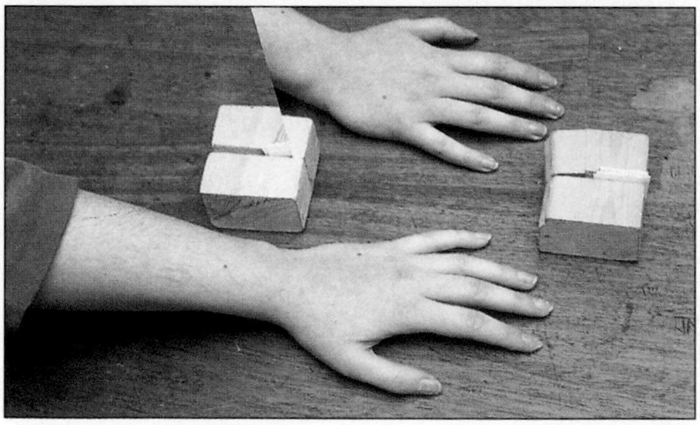

Picture 4 An image in a plane mirror. A left hand becomes a right hand.

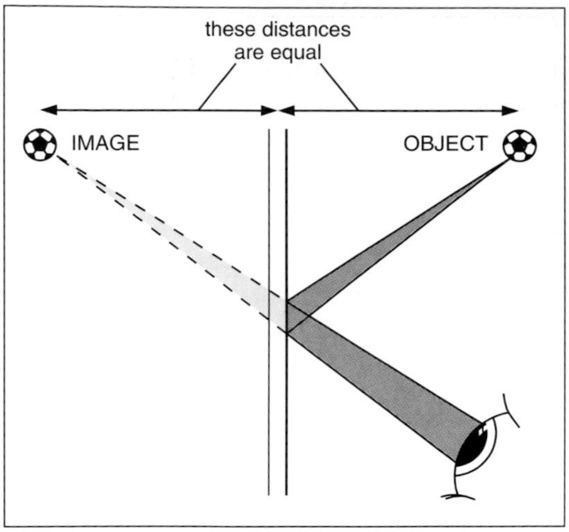

Picture 5 The image that appears in a flat mirror seems as far behind it as the object is in front.

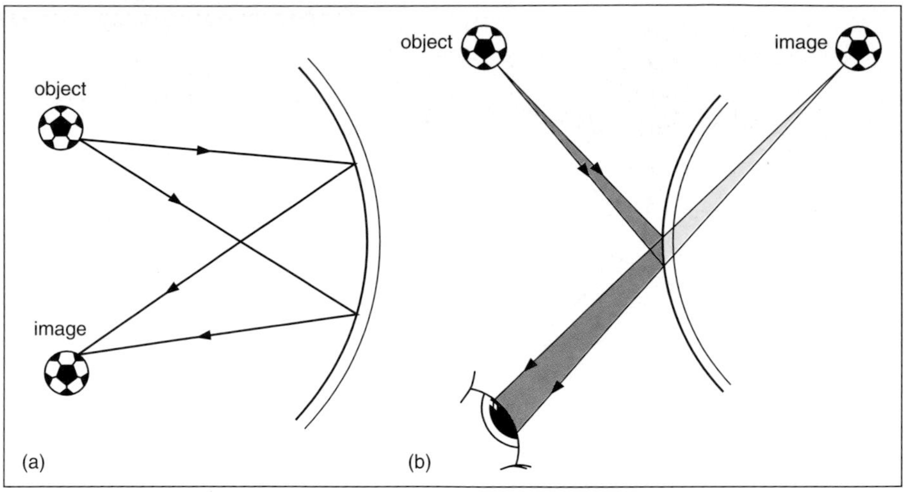

Picture 6 Curved mirrors and their effects on light.

Curved mirrors

Curved mirrors produce interesting effects. They can magnify and make smaller, depending on which way they curve and how far away the object is (see picture 6). If the shiny (reflecting) side curves inward, it is a **concave** mirror. If the reflecting surface curves outwards, it is a **convex** mirror.

Concave mirrors are easy to find in everyday life. They are most often used just to straighten up beams of light, as shown in picture 7. Torches, searchlights and car headlights use mirrors in this way.

They work as they do because of the basic law of reflection, given above. The curved shape of the concave mirror changes the direction of the rays in such a way that parallel light rays coming towards the mirror are all reflected to pass through the same point. This is the **principal focus**. Light leaving the focus retraces the same path and leaves the mirror as a parallel beam. This is shown in picture 7, where the lamp filament is placed at the focus of the mirror.

You will often find convex mirrors in shops, or at the corner of the stairs in a double-decker bus. They are used to give the shopkeeper or bus conductor a **wider field of view**. This helps to stop theft or fare-dodging. This time the shape of the mirror allows light to be collected from a wide angle and reflected towards the observer (see picture 8).

Picture 8 Convex mirrors give a wide field of view.

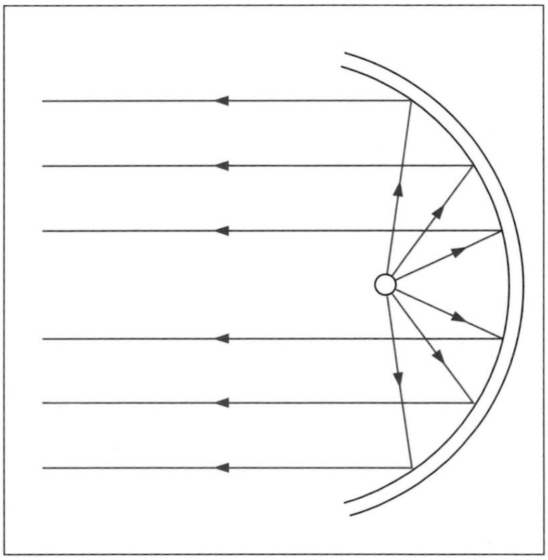

Picture 7 A curved mirror can make a parallel beam of light – as in a searchlight.

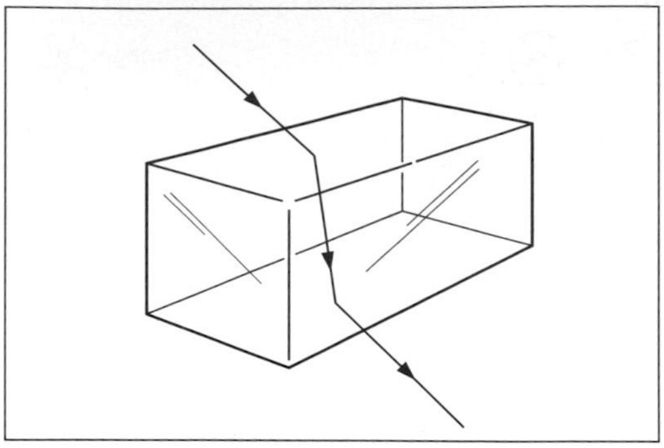

Picture 9 Refraction in a glass block.

Using transparent materials

When light passes at an angle from one transparent material into another it changes direction. This is called **refraction**, and is caused by the fact that light travels at different speeds in the different materials. This effect is used in lenses and optical fibres.

Refraction

Picture 9 shows what happens to a ray of light as it goes from air into glass, and from glass back into air. As it goes into the denser material, it changes direction to make a bigger angle with the surface. The opposite happens on the way out.

Refraction can cause some optical illusions. For example, a pond or swimming pool always looks a lot shallower than it really is. Picture 10 shows why. The light from a fish near the bottom is refracted, and the light *appears* to come from somewhere else, nearer the surface. This is why a straight stick looks bent when you put it in water (picture 11).

A **prism** is a block of glass or plastic with straight sides. It is usually triangular in shape. Light that enters the prism at right angles to a surface carries on unchanged. But if it goes in at an angle it changes direction due to refraction (picture 12).

But prisms are not used to change the direction of light by refraction. The reason is that white light would come out coloured. Prisms produce a spectrum of the light. How they do this is explained in topic C6.

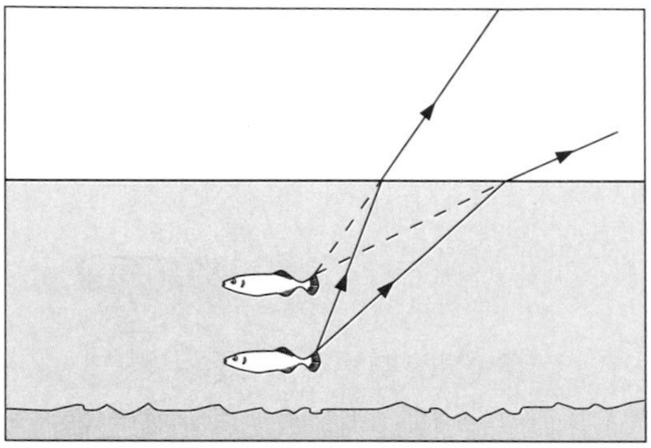

Picture 10 Why pools look shallower than they really are.

Picture 11 A straight stick looks bent in water. Why?

Trapped light – total internal reflection

Picture 13 shows light travelling out of water. See what happens as the angle the light makes with the surface is reduced.

At a certain angle the light doesn't get out at all. It is trapped inside, or **totally internally reflected**. The same thing can happen with glass.

This effect is used, in prisms, to make very good mirrors. It is also used to send light down long thin fibres of glass – **optical fibres**. Picture 14 shows total internal reflection in action in a prism and a glass fibre – see page 79 for descriptions of how they are used in practice.

Focusing and making images

One of the most useful applications of refraction is in **lenses**. Lenses are curved pieces of very clear glass. When a parallel beam of light reaches them the outer part of the beam is bent inwards by refraction at both surfaces of the lens (picture 15).

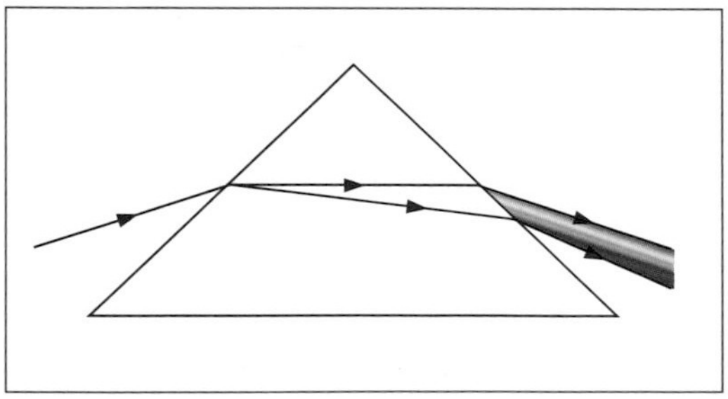

Picture 12 Light passing through a prism.

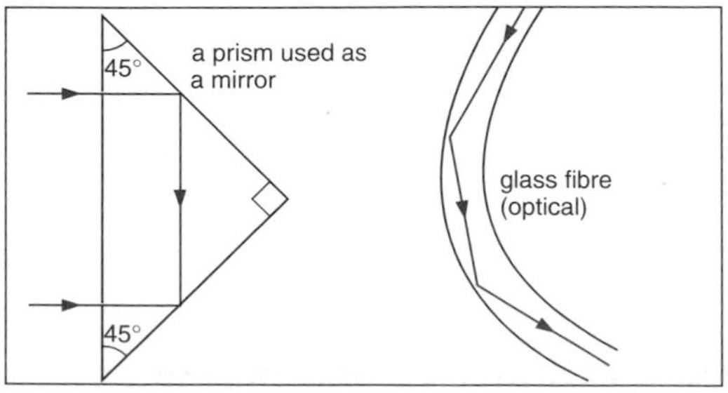

Picture 14 Total internal reflection in action.

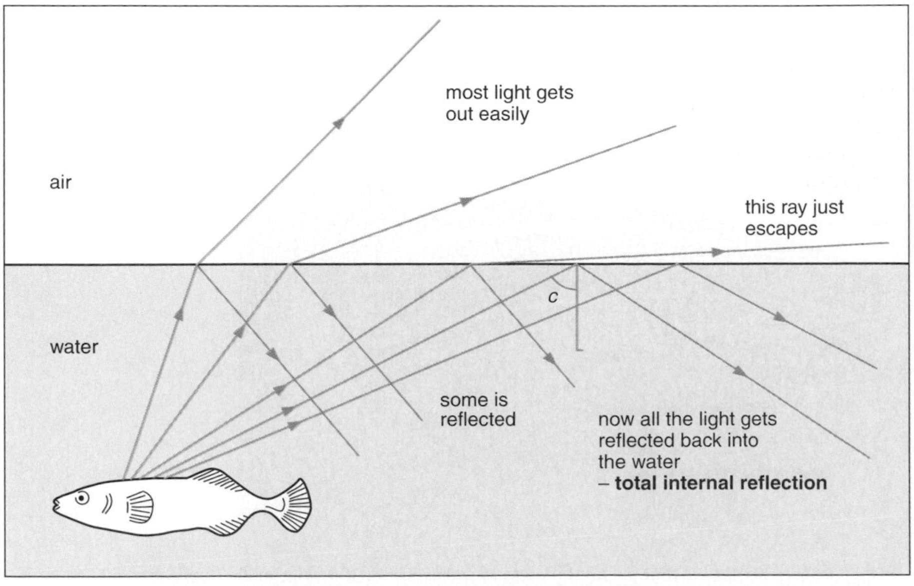

Picture 13 Total internal reflection happens when light reaches the surface at angles greater than a **critical** angle (*c*).

This happens because the light reaches the glass surfaces at an angle. The further out from the centre of the lens the bigger the angle is. So the outer part of the beam is bent inwards more than the inner parts. The beam comes to a point (converges) before spreading out again. This effect is called **focusing**.

The lens in picture 15 is a **positive** or **converging** lens. A lens shaped 'the other way', as in picture 16, makes the light beam spread out (diverge). It is a **negative** or **diverging** lens.

The more curved the lens surfaces are, the more powerful is the lens. Picture 17 shows this.

Lenses are used to make images in various kinds of optical instruments.

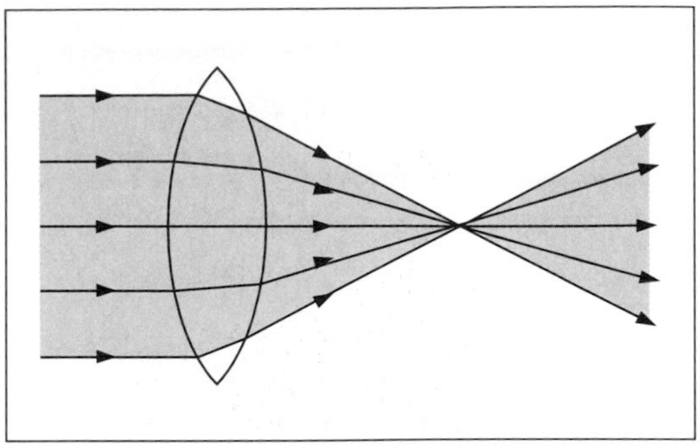

Picture 15 What a positive lens does to light.

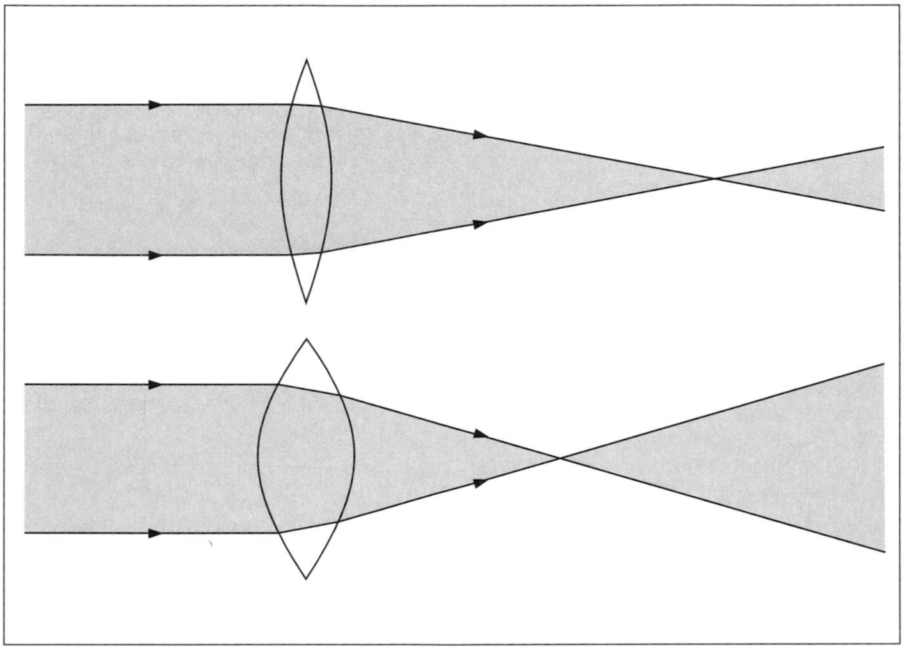

Picture 17 The more curved the lens the more powerful it is.

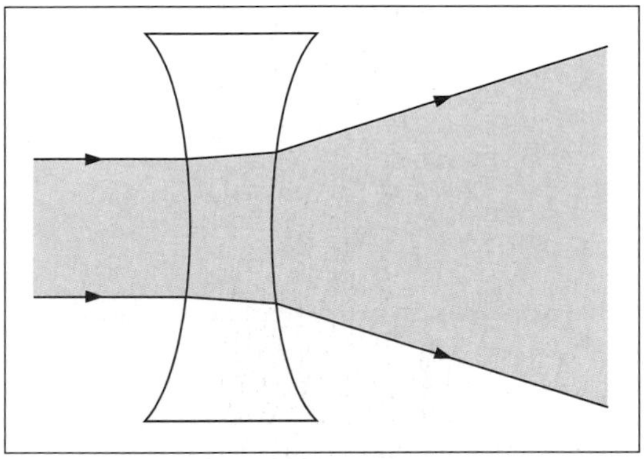

Picture 16 A negative lens makes the light spread out – or diverge.

Seeing inside

Thin glass fibres can be used to carry a beam of light so that the light cannot escape. This is due to **total internal reflection**. A bundle of very thin fibres is used in medical research and in hospitals to look deep inside the human body. Picture 18 shows how the fibres are arranged.

One set of fibres carry light down into the body. The others carry reflected light back – the image of the part of the body that is illuminated.

This useful device is called an **endoscope**. They can be made small enough to slip down a vein and bring pictures back from inside a living heart or other organ. Picture 19 shows the inside of the human gut.

Picture 18 Fibres in an endoscope.

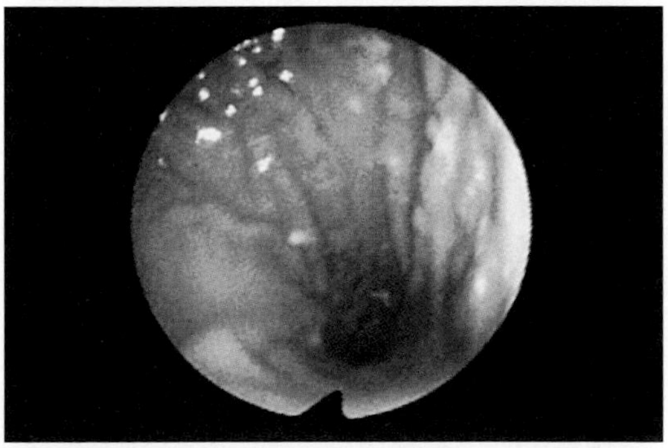

Picture 19 The human gut seen through the endoscope.

Communications

As explained in topic C1, thin glass fibres carrying 'light' signals are much better for carrying information than almost any other medium.

Activities

A Using mirrors

Devise a way of getting a beam of light (from a torch or ray box) from one side of the room to the other, starting with the beam at floor level and finishing with the beam 2 m above ground.

Rules: **1** You aren't allowed to move any furniture.

2 The beam has to change direction five times.

B Where are mirrors used?

Find as many everyday applications of mirrors as you can. You should find at least five. List them all and state whether they use plane or curved mirrors. Describe as exactly as you can how one of them works.

C Making images

Use a small lamp and a positive lens. You will need a card screen – and maybe a white wall will come in handy. By trial and error you should be able to get a clear image of the lamp filament on the screen.

1 Investigate:

a where the lamp and lens have to be to get an image *smaller* than the lamp filament,
b how to get a *magnified* image,
c how to get a really *huge* image.

2 Take measurements to test the prediction that:

size of image × distance of lamp from lens = size of filament × distance of image screen from lens

3 Design and carry out experiments to find out if:

a the rule of reflection (page 74) applies to curved mirrors as well as plane ones,
b the image in a plane mirror is really as far behind the mirror as the object is in front of it.

D Reflecting safety

Get some **reflective paint** or some material that cyclists use on a reflective belt. How do these substances work? (Look at a sample under a microscope. Investigate what it does to light.)

Questions

1 Copy the diagrams in picture 20 and complete them to show what happens to the rays or beam of light, for:

(a) a strong lens,
(b) a weak lens,
(c) a glass block,
(d) a curved mirror.

2 A positive lens can be used to start a fire.

a Explain how it can do this.
b Why is it dangerous to leave empty glass bottles in a wood?

3 'When you look into a river or lake and see a fish, it isn't where you think it is.' Draw a diagram to justify this statement (with you standing on the river bank and rays of light coming to you from a fish in the water).

4 What is the difference between a *transparent* material and a *translucent* material?

5 Why are 'fat' lenses more powerful than 'thin' ones?

6 Compare the human eye with a simple camera. In what ways are they similar, and in what ways are they different?

7 a Explain what is meant by total internal reflection.
b Give three uses for total internal reflection.
c Describe how one of the uses you have named works.

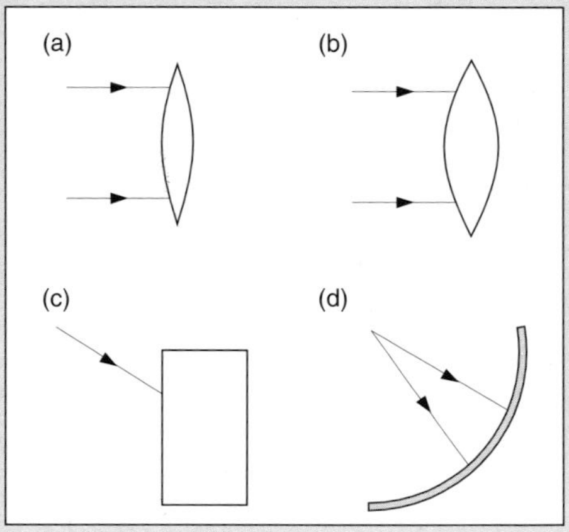

Picture 20

Fibre optics

As explained in topic C1, thin glass fibres carrying 'light' signals are much better for carrying information than almost any other medium. The messages are digitally coded (see topic C1, where digital coding is explained).

The 'light' used is normally invisible – it is a form of infra-red radiation. This radiation travels at the same high speed as light, but travels better through glass than visible light does. It is produced by a laser, which gives a very pure form of radiation.

The radiation is coded electronically. When you speak into a telephone the sounds you make are first changed into a varying electric current. This is a copy (analogue) of the sounds you make. An analogue-to-digital converter changes the signal to a set of binary pulses. In turn these are used to modulate the laser beam in the same digital pattern.

At the listener's end the infra-red pulses are changed to an electric signal again. This can be put back into analogue form electronically and used to make the earpiece work.

Optical fibres are very thin, and are made of very pure and transparent glass. Infra-red 'light' is fed in at one end and cannot escape. This is because of **total internal reflection**. A simple fibre works as shown in picture 1(a). The light bounces off the inside of the fibre. But this produces a distorted signal after the signal has travelled a few kilometres down the fibre.

A better design uses glass in which the speed of the light changes gradually from the inside out. This means that the light path curves gently as shown in picture 1(b).

Even so, the signal gets distorted sooner or later. **Repeater stations** are built into the line to reshape and amplify the signals, as shown in picture 2. In a modern telecommunications system using fibre optics the repeater stations can be 40 km apart. This compares with having them just 8 km apart when copper wires are used to carry messages electrically.

Another advantage is that optical fibres can carry many conversations at the same time. This needs quite complicated electronics, but a typical optical fibre system can allow 11 000 pairs of people to talk to each other simultaneously. The old copper wire system could only carry about 1000 conversations at once.

Optical networks can also carry TV signals and computer data more cheaply and accurately than wire systems can. Thus useful things like home shopping and banking can be much more practicable. But to give everyone an optical fibre connection to their homes is expensive. It isn't cost-effective unless the network is also allowed to carry telephone messages.

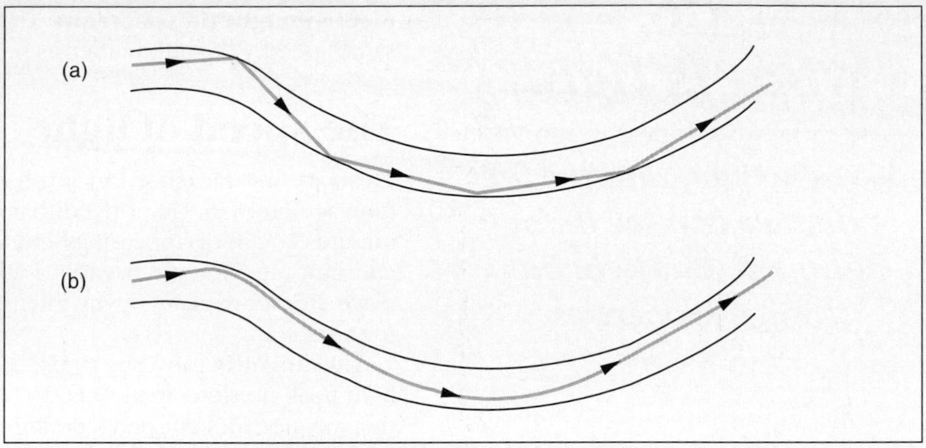

Picture 1 (a) A simple optical fibre.
(b) A more sophisticated fibre.

Now answer these questions.

1 What other uses are there for total internal reflection?

2 What is the difference between **analogue** and **digital**? Explain briefly why using digital code is more reliable than an analogue system.

3 What does a repeater station do?

4 What kind of light is produced by a laser?

5 Give two advantages of fibre optics compared with metal wires as information carriers.

6 What is **infra-red radiation**?

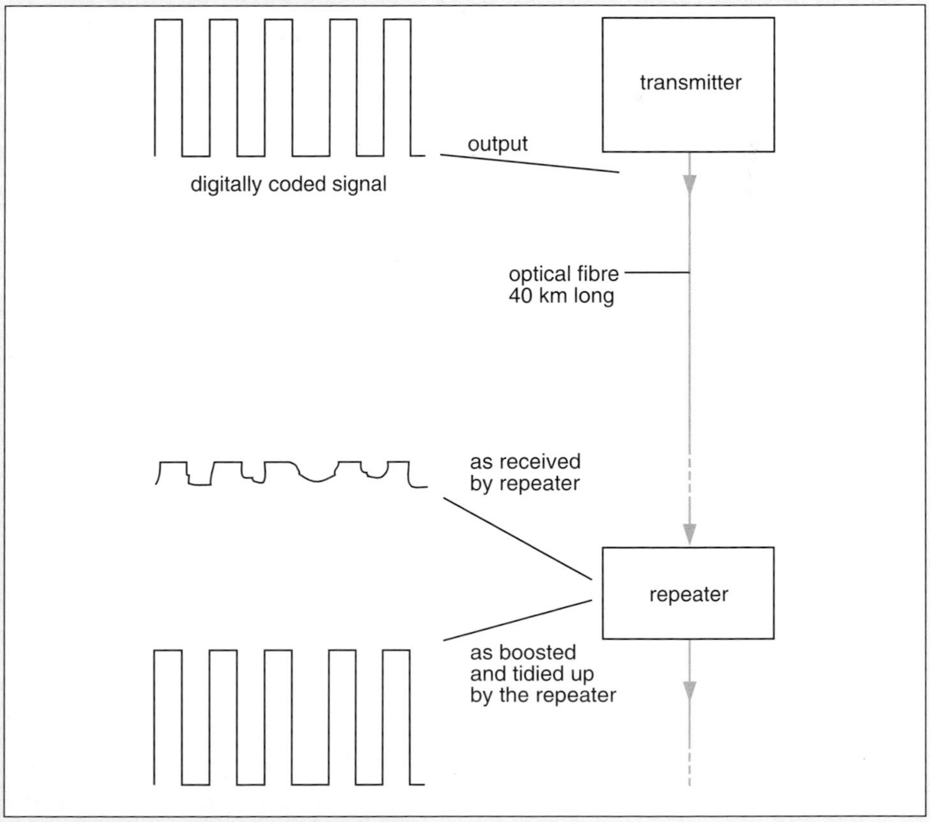

Picture 2 Repeater stations reshape and amplify the signals.

C6
What is light?

We take light, and the fact that we can see it, for granted. But light has strange properties...

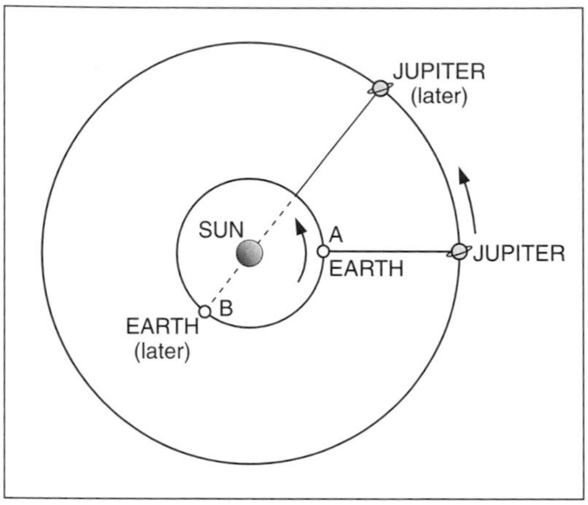

Picture 1 How Römer measured the speed of light.

Light is just the *visible* part of a whole family of 'radiations' that we call the **electromagnetic spectrum**. These radiations all travel through space at the same speed, 300 million metres per second (3×10^8 m/s).

The speed of light

This was first measured by a tidy-minded Danish astronomer, Olaf Römer, as long ago as 1676. He noticed that the moons of Jupiter were sometimes a few minutes late in disappearing behind the planet. The moons of Jupiter orbit at a constant rate, and it was easy to calculate when this disappearance should take place. Römer explained why the moons were late by saying that light took time to travel.

This might be obvious to us, but at that time many scientists believed that light took no time at all to go from one place to another. But Romer said that this was not so: light had a definite speed. He said that light took longer to get to the Earth from Jupiter when the two planets were further apart.

As picture 1 shows, at its furthest point from Earth the light from Jupiter has to cross an extra distance equal to the diameter of the Earth's orbit. He measured the time difference this extra distance caused. The size of the Earth's orbit around the Sun was known fairly accurately in 1676, and so Römer was able to calculate a value for the speed of light.

His measurements of the times were not very accurate, however. His measurements gave the speed of light as only two-thirds of the modern value. But it was a start. The speed of light is now very accurately measured, and is so reliable that we use it to measure distance. Accurate surveying is done by measuring the time it takes for laser beams to travel a particular distance. The times are then converted to distances:

distance = light speed × time of travel.

All electromagnetic waves travel at the same speed in a vacuum. Short radio waves are used in **radar** systems to measure the distances of aircraft in air traffic control.

Radar has been used to measure the distances of planets from Earth. This has given us an accurate measurement of the scale of the Solar System (see

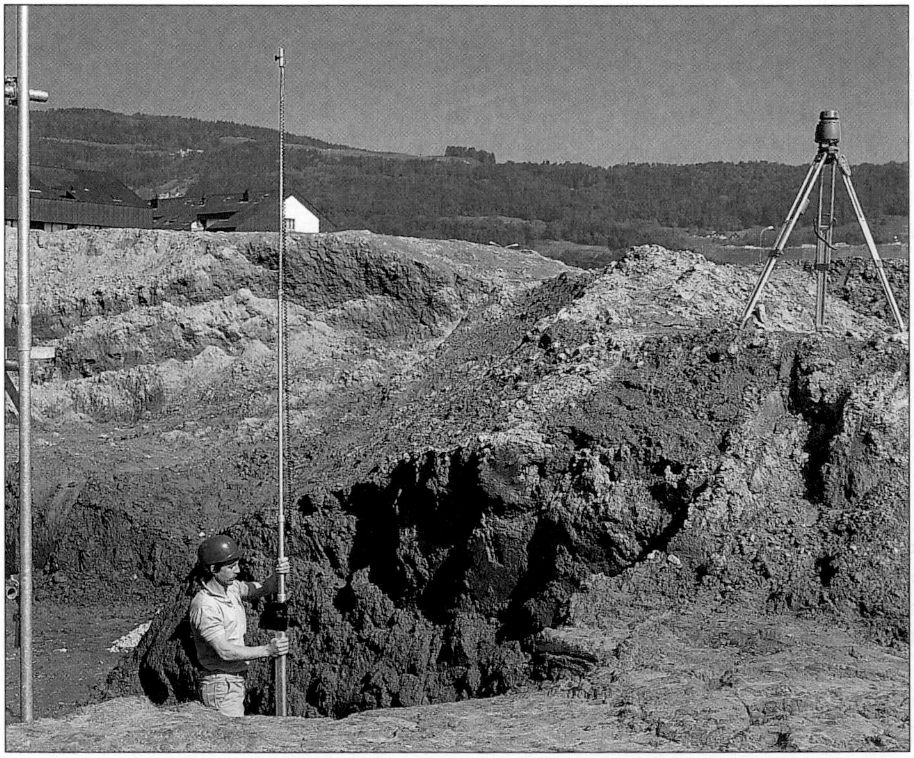

Picture 2 Modern laser surveying instrument in use.

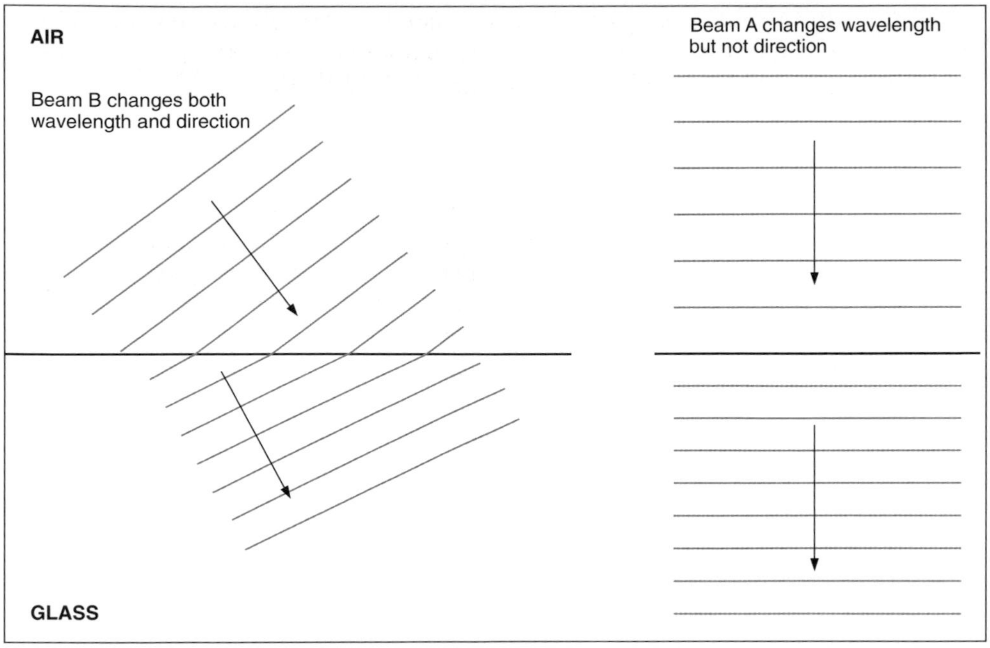

Picture 3 What happens when light moves into a different medium.

topic F3). The distance of the Earth from the Sun is the baseline used to measure the distances of stars. The distances of stars and galaxies are so great that we measure them in **light years** – the distance travelled by light in a year.

Changing the speed of light

When light leaves a vacuum and enters a transparent medium, like glass, it slows down. The most important effect produced by this change of speed is something that you have already studied: **refraction** (see topic C5). Picture 3 shows what happens as a set of waves reaches a glass surface, travelling from air. When the wave hits the surface at right angles (Beam A) the wavelength changes, but there is no change in direction. Beam B reaches the surface at an angle, and as the leading edge slows down the rest of the wave catches up with it. The result is the change of direction called refraction.

Why a prism makes a spectrum

In a vacuum all frequencies of light travel at the same speed. But in a medium like glass high frequency light (which we see as blue) travels more slowly than lower frequency light (such as yellow and red). Thus blue light has a higher refractive index than red light, and is bent through a greater angle. A beam of white light is thus spread out by refraction so that we can see the different colours as a **spectrum**. There is more about colour in topic C8.

Making light

Light usually comes from very hot objects – flames, the Sun, hot filaments. But it can also come from insects (fireflies, glow worms), from the fluorescent paint in TV tubes and some lamps, and from the glowing gases in advertising lights ('neon lights'). But all these sources produce light in the same basic way – by giving energy to atoms to make them unstable.

Picture 4 reminds you what an atom is like – a positive nucleus with some electrons around it. If an atom is given the right amount of energy, the outermost electron jumps up to a slightly higher energy level. It stays there for a while and then falls back to its normal level. When it falls back it gives back the extra energy as light.

The atoms of different elements have their electrons in different levels. Thus the light they give out is different in colour. This means we can tell what kind of element it is from its spectrum (see *Signals from Space*, page 94).

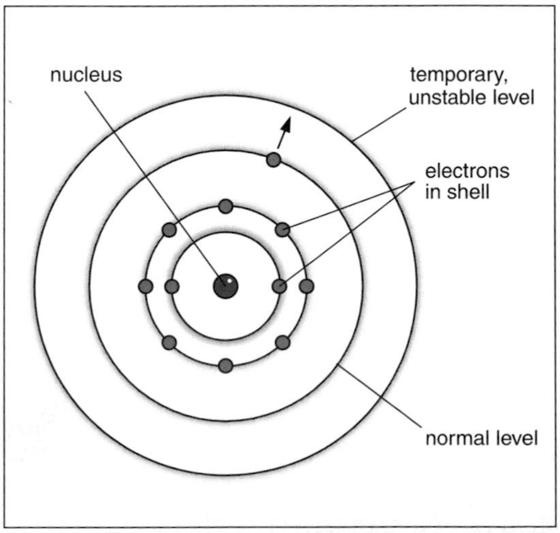

Picture 4 A simple model of the atom.

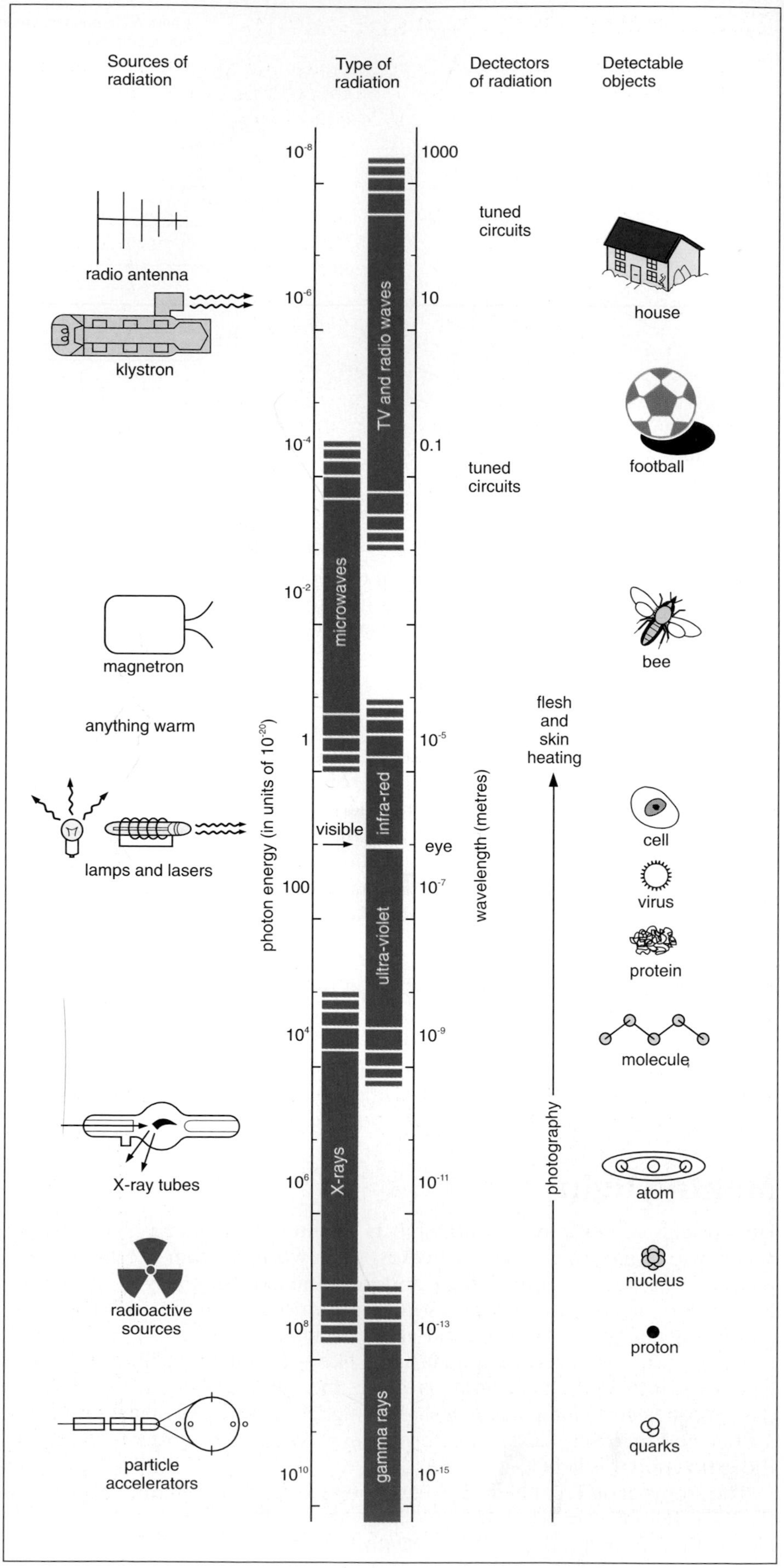

Picture 5 The main parts of the electromagnetic spectrum.

The electromagnetic spectrum

Picture 5 shows the main parts of the electromagnetic spectrum. It summarises how the radiations are made and how they are detected. In one way or another, all ways of making the radiations involve the movement of charged particles.

Electromagnetic waves

Electromagnetic radiations travel as **waves**. They are called electromagnetic because when electric charges move (i.e., there is an electric **current**) they always produce a magnetic field. This is covered in topic E8. An electron is a charged particle. Thus it has an electric field surrounding it.

When electrons move to and fro or go around in circles they produce changing electric and magnetic fields. This is what the **electromagnetic radiations** are – a set of constantly changing, combined electric and magnetic fields that travel through space at 300 million metres a second.

This also means that they don't need anything to 'carry' them. 'Normal waves, like water waves or sound waves, need a **medium**. Water waves need water! Sound needs air, or a liquid or solid. Sound cannot travel through a vacuum because there is nothing there 'to be waved'.

Electromagnetic waves carry their own 'waviness' with them, so they can travel through the vacuum of empty space.

The range of electromagnetic waves is shown in picture 5.

The discovery of radio waves

The electromagnetic theory of light was first put forward by a great Scots physicist, James Clerk Maxwell, in 1873. It was a good theory because it not only explained what scientists knew about light, it also made **predictions**.

Maxwell predicted that there ought to be other radiations which travelled through space at the same speed as light. These waves were not discovered until fifteen years later, in 1888. They were discovered by the German scientist Heinrich Hertz, who detected what we now call radio waves. Although they had been predicted, they were discovered by accident! Radio waves can be made by electric sparks. You may have noticed this when you play a radio close to a car engine.

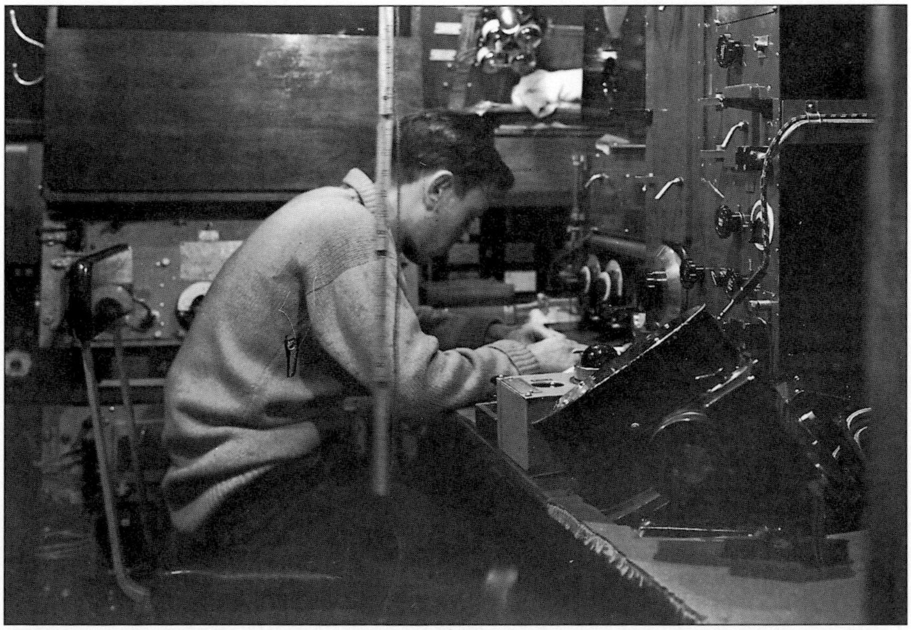

Picture 6 One of the earliest 'Marconi transmitters' used by the Royal Navy.

Hertz was working with a machine used for making static electricity. He noticed that whenever the static machine made a spark, so did a small coil of wire on the other side of the room. Energy was travelling from one side of the room to the other as radio waves. We name the unit of frequency the hertz after Heinrich Hertz.

The whole of the radio and television industry is based on these discoveries. The first radio transmitters were 'spark transmitters' and they were in use, in ships at sea, by 1902 (see picture 6).

The next topic deals with the evidence for the wave nature of light.

Making use of the electromagnetic spectrum

Radio waves are used to carry TV as well as 'sound radio'. The waves travel in straight lines, like light. This means that they don't curve around the Earth so the transmitting aerials can't be too far away from the receiver (picture 7).

To send TV signals across the Atlantic we have to use broadcast satellites to pick up the waves and send them on to their destinations. But radio waves, which are longer, can travel around the Earth because there is a reflecting layer about 100 km above the Earth. This layer has a lot of charged particles, and so acts like a sheet of metal, which contains a lot of free electrons. Metals are shiny because they reflect light. They also reflect radio waves. Physicists didn't know about this reflecting layer and told Marconi that he was an ignorant fool to try and send radio signals to America. Luckily he took no notice of them!

Microwaves have wavelengths much shorter than radio and TV signals, ranging from a few millimetres to tens of centimetres. We also use **microwaves** to send messages, but the wavelengths have to be chosen carefully to make sure that they aren't absorbed in the air. You can see microwave aerials, shaped like satellite dishes, on many public buildings and office blocks. Microwaves that are easily absorbed by water molecules are very useful for **cooking**, because the energy they carry heats up food.

Radar also uses very short radio waves – from about 1 cm to 1 m long. Radar works because metal objects like ships and aircraft reflect the waves.

Light is visible electromagnetic radiation at wavelengths that pass most easily through the atmosphere. This means that it is the strongest radiation on the Earth – and animals and humans have evolved sense organs to make use of it.

Infra-red radiation is invisible but we can sense it because it warms the skin. This radiation has become very important during the past few years – it is used to carry the coded signals in fibre-optic telephone cables (see page 79) and we use it to control TV sets and video recorders. Hot objects give out infra-red

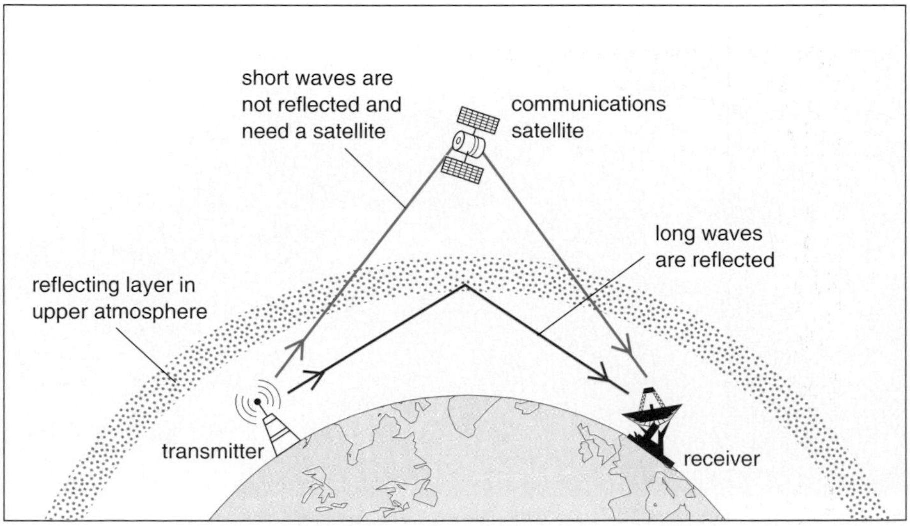

Picture 7 Sending radio and TV signals long distances.

radiation and we use them for cooking food (in gas or electric grills and toasters) and radiant heaters (electric fires).

On the other side of the visible band in the electromagnetic spectrum we have **ultra-violet** (UV) radiation. This has a shorter wavelength than light, and like all very short-wave radiation is dangerous to living cells. Bright sunlight contains a lot of UV and causes sunburn. White skin produces a dark pigment (melanin) to cut down this radiation, but in strong summer sunlight the damage occurs very quickly. The ozone layer in the upper atmosphere cuts out the most dangerous UV, but some still gets through – and the ozone layer is itself at risk from polluting chemicals released into the atmosphere.

But UV can be useful. In controlled doses it can help treat skin disease. Ordinary fluorescent lamps use ultra-violet light made by low pressure mercury gas to make a phosphor glow and emit white light.

At the very short-wave end of the spectrum we have **x-rays** and **gamma rays**. Both are very penetrating and can get deep into the body. This makes them dangerous, as they may not just kill living cells but turn them into cancer cells. But this is also what makes X-rays and gamma rays useful – they can be used to treat cancer tumours by killing the diseased cells. We also use the penetrating power of X-rays to make pictures of internal organs and broken limbs.

Gamma radiation is powerful enough to kill bacteria, which makes them useful for sterilising surgical instruments, especially objects that would be damaged by heating. Gamma rays are sometimes used to kill bacteria and even insects in food, but many people disagree with using them for this purpose.

Activities

A The uses of electromagnetic waves

The chart of the electromagnetic spectrum (picture 5) shows the main uses of the different parts of the electromagnetic spectrum. Use reference books to find other uses for any section of the spectrum that interests you.

B Make a radio!

Picture 8 shows the components you need to make a simple radio. You can connect them together using crocodile clips. To make sure it works you need to have a good long aerial wire and a good connection to earth.

Use a book on radio to find out how the circuit works.

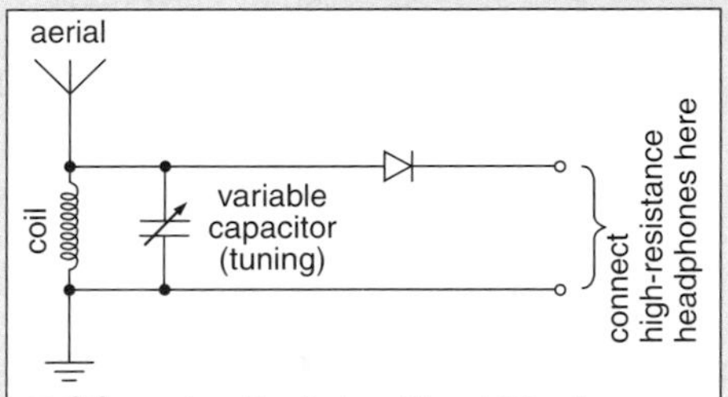

aerial – a length of wire at least 10 m long
earth – connect to a metal tap
coil – buy a special one or wrap 2 m of wire around on empty toilet roll

diode, variable capacitor } ask your teacher!

Picture 8

Questions

1 The famous scientist Galileo tried to measure the speed of light using two people with lanterns, standing about a mile apart from each other. One person was supposed to send a light signal back when he saw the light sent to him by the first person. Galileo tried to measure the time this took. The experiment was a complete failure. Suggest one or two reasons why it failed.

2 Design an experiment to show that infra-red (heating) rays travel at the same speed as visible light.

3 Which parts of the electromagnetic spectrum

a can be used for heating?
b cause skin tanning?
c can pass through flesh but are partly stopped by bones?
d can cause cancer?
e are stopped by the ozone layer in the atmosphere?
f are used to find the positions of distant aircraft?

4 The speed of light is 300 000 000 metres per second (3×10^8 m/s). Use the wave formula **speed = frequency × wavelength** to calculate the following:

a the wavelength of MW radio waves that are broadcast at 1500 kHz.
b the frequency of BBC Radio 4 which is broadcast on a 'long wave' of 1500 m.
c the wavelength of the waves in a microwave oven which works on a frequency of 2450 000 000 Hz (2.45×10^9 Hz).

C7
Light as a wave

How do we know that light is a wave? How can we use its 'waviness'?

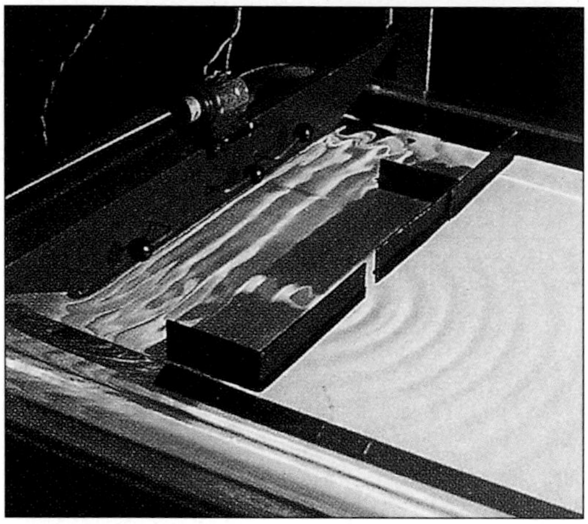

Picture 1 Waves spread out when they go through a gap.

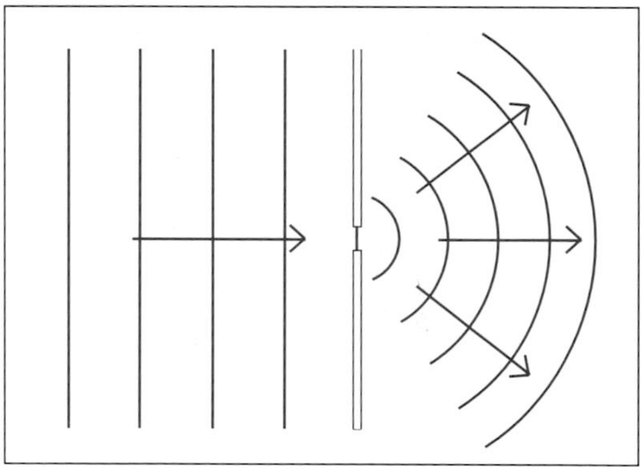

Picture 2 This effect is called diffraction.

Waves

Topic C4 deals with some of the main properties of waves. Water waves and waves on ropes and springs are easy to see. We can show sound waves on an oscilloscope, and investigate how the **frequency** and **amplitude** of the waves change when we alter pitch and loudness.

Light waves are harder to investigate. Their wavelength is so small. But all waves behave in much the same way, in that they can show **diffraction** and **interference** effects. We use these effects to investigate light. They are explained below.

Diffraction

Picture 1 shows water waves moving through a gap in a barrier. When they reach the gap the waves spread out. This effect is called **diffraction**. Picture 3 shows what would happen if particles, like bullets, were fired at a barrier with a gap in it. The bullets that go through the gap carry on in a straight line.

When light is shone through a narrow gap it actually spreads out. This is shown in picture 4. This means that light is behaving like a wave, and not like a particle. If light travelled in straight lines, like a stream of particles, it would make a sharp shadow as shown in picture 3.

But as picture 4 also shows, light makes a more complicated pattern than you might expect. There are zones of light and dark outside the main spread of light. This effect is due to another property of waves – **interference**. This picture was made by shining light through a narrow slit.

Interference

Picture 5 shows what happens when waves meet. Two pulses travelling in opposite directions on a rope can pass through each other. When they meet the waves just 'add up'. Two 'up' parts of a wave (the crests) add up to make a larger crest. Two 'down' parts (the troughs) add up to make an even bigger trough. This is what you would expect.

But it might be surprising to see that when a crest meets a trough the result is a 'zero'. It is even more surprising that this also happens with light. Two light waves can meet – and the result is darkness! But this is what has happened in picture 4. The dark places are where two sets of light waves have met and cancelled each other out.

We say that when two waves meet they **interfere**. They can add up to make a bigger wave – or cancel each other out (picture 5).

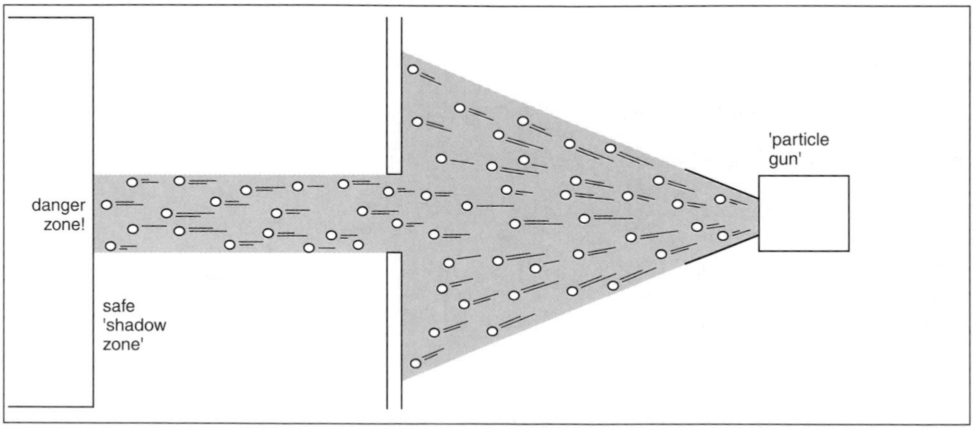

Picture 3 Particles don't diffract but travel in straight lines.

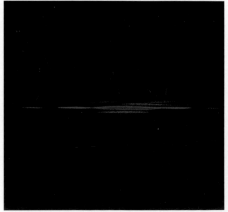

Picture 4 Light spreads out – like a wave.

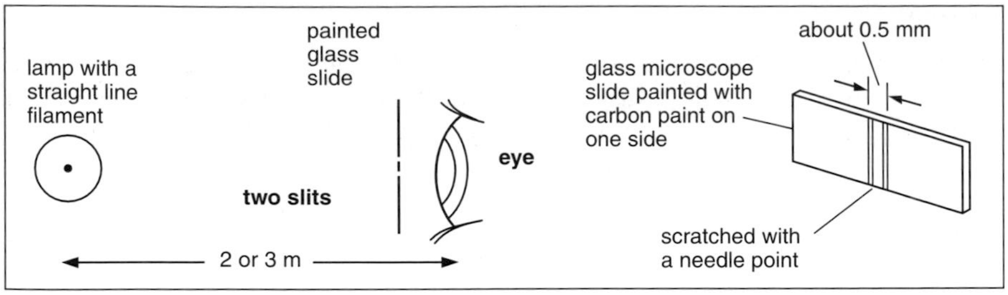

Picture 6 How to see 'Young's fringes'.

The two-slit experiment

This experiment was first done by a doctor, Thomas Young, in the early part of the 19th century. It was the first clear proof that light travelled as a wave. At that time scientists believed that light was made of particles, like tiny bullets. They believed this so strongly that Young's work was accused of being 'absurd and illogical'. It was completely ignored for twenty years.

Picture 6 shows how you could set it up to do it yourself. When you look through the two narrow slits on the painted glass slide you will see an **interference pattern** like the one shown in picture 7. Picture 8 shows how the waves from the two slits combine. At some places they meet so that crests always meet with crests. The following troughs always meet with troughs. The result is a light patch.

At other places, the crest of wave from one slit always meets with a trough from the other slit. The result is darkness. The activities at the end of the topic are about investigating these effects with light and radio waves.

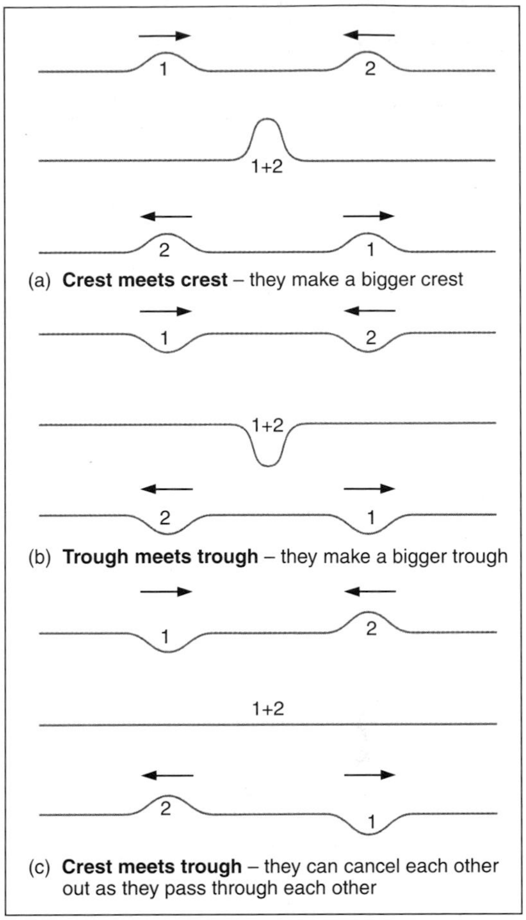

1
2
1+2
(a) **Crest meets crest** – they make a bigger crest
(b) **Trough meets trough** – they make a bigger trough
(c) **Crest meets trough** – they can cancel each other out as they pass through each other

Picture 5 What happens when waves meet.

Picture 7 This is what we see in Young's two-slit experiment

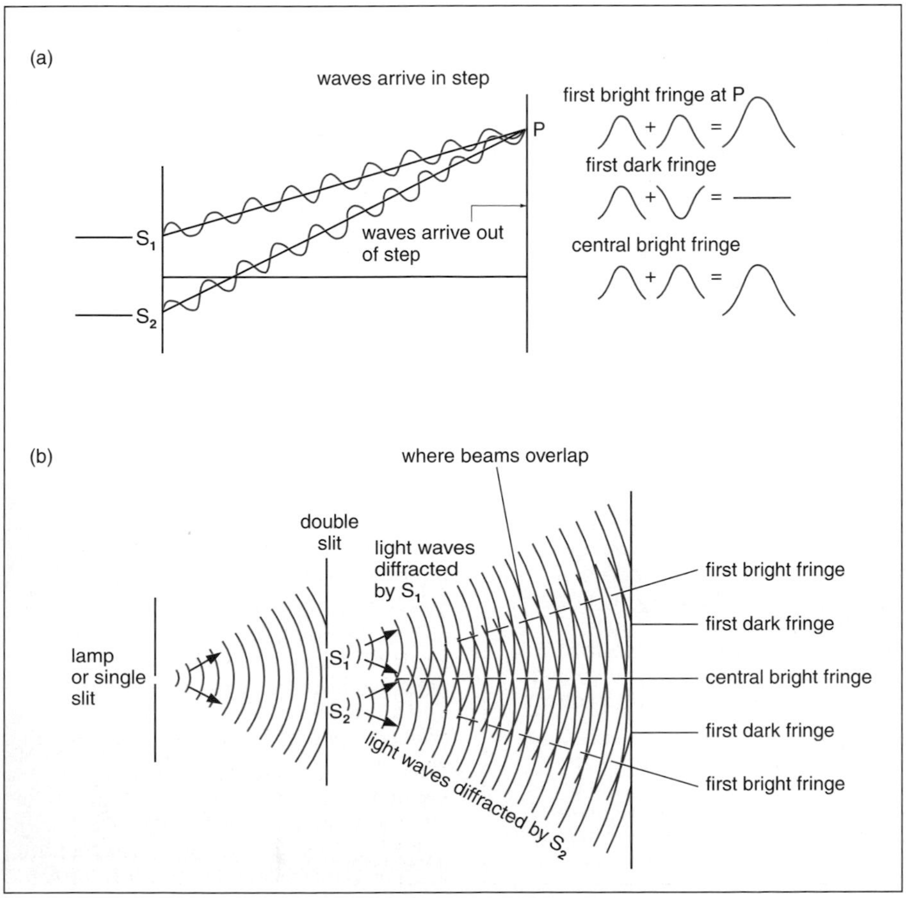

Picture 8 What happens in Young's two-slit experiment.

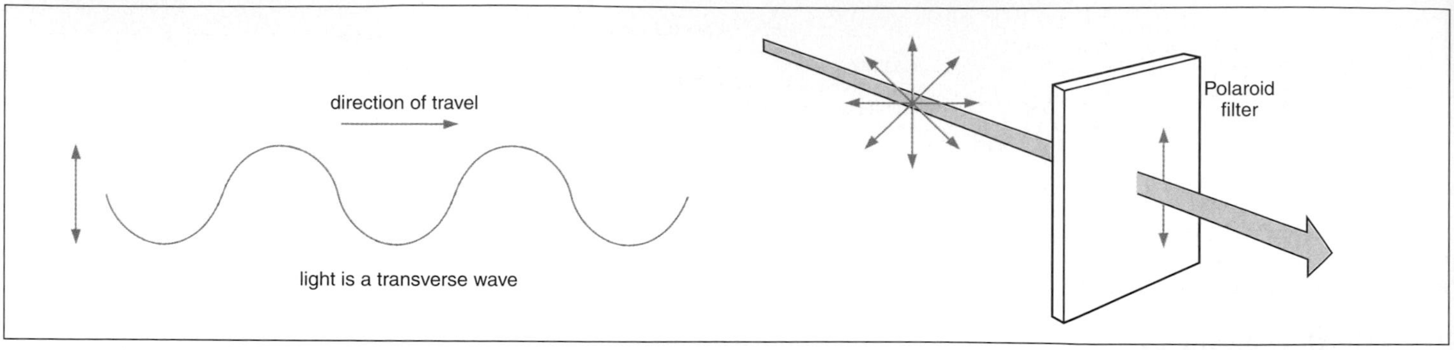

Picture 9 Light can be polarised because it is a transverse wave.

Polarised light

Light is a **transverse** wave, which means that it vibrates at right angles to the direction in which it travels (see page 71). Normally, a ray of light is a mixture of waves, all vibrating at different angles to each other, as shown in picture 9. A filter made from a special substance called **Polaroid** only lets through the waves which vibrate in one direction. The light that comes through is said to be **polarised**.

If you hold another piece of polaroid film in the path of the polarised light it will let it through – but only if the film is aligned the right way. If you turn it through 90 degrees it cuts out all the light. This effect is shown in picture 10.

Polaroid **sunglasses** work because light reflected from shiny surfaces, like water or glass, is partly polarised. The glasses are made of polaroid film. They cut out the polarised light. Thus they cut down 'glare' from shiny surfaces – which in summer is usually strong reflected sunlight (picture 10).

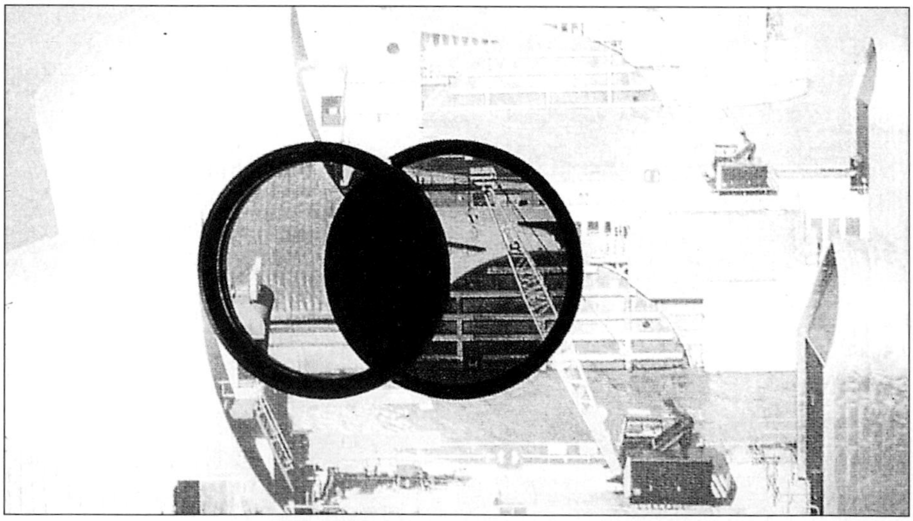

Picture 10 Polaroid filters can cut out glare. When they are 'crossed' they cut out all the light.

Activities

A Looking through holes

These are experiments about the wave nature of light that you can do at home.

You will need a distant street lamp, or at least a bright torch placed about 50 m away. You can also do this in the laboratory, by looking at a small hole lit by a bright lamp.

1 Face the spot of light and look at it through the gap between two fingers (e.g. the first and second fingers of one hand). Gradually bring the fingers closer together to make an ever narrowing slit. Just before the light from the lamp disappears you should see it broaden out. This is **diffraction**.

2 Get a piece of kitchen foil about 10 cm long by 5 cm wide. The exact size doesn't matter. With a sharp pin or needle, make a small hole in the foil. When you look through the pinhole at the light source you will also see **diffraction**, but this time there should be a more definite pattern to it. This is really worth seeing.

The difficult bit about this experiment is finding the small pinhole in the dark. Mark it before you go out by putting a small piece of sticky paper next to it. You could go on to try the effect of making pinholes of different diameters.

3 Now make two pinholes in the foil, about a millimetre or so apart. You should be able to see through both holes together. When you look through the pair of holes at the light source you

will see not only the spreading out effect (diffraction) but also an interference pattern. This is caused by light from the two separate holes combining ('interfering') with each other.

B Radio waves

The wavelength of light is very small. This is why we don't notice the waviness of light very often. VHF radio and UHF TV have much longer waves – about 3 m long for radio and about half of that for TV. You can show interference between radio waves using a sheet of metal and a small radio with a telescopic aerial. The metal sheet could be a length of kitchen foil pinned to some cardboard. It needs to be about a metre square for the radio experiment; about half that will do for the TV.

1 Tune the radio or TV to a 'weak' VHF station, or make it just off-tune for a strong one. The aerial should be horizontal, as shown in picture 11. You can tell it is weak or mistuned by the fact that the sound gets distorted now and again, especially when the speech or music is loud.

2 Hold the sheet of metal upright about 2 m from the aerial. Walk towards or away from the aerial, moving the metal sheet closer or further from it. As you do this, you will find places where the signal is made stronger, and places where it is made weaker.

For this experiment to work, the radio or TV will have to be in line between you and the station broadcasting the signal. If you don't know where the station is you will have to find the best place by trial and error.

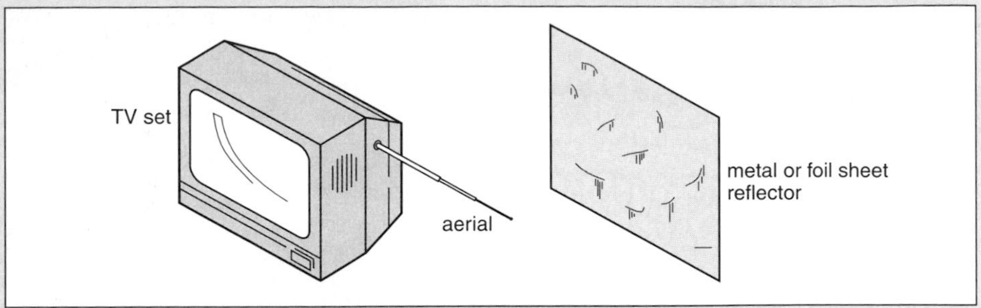

Picture 11

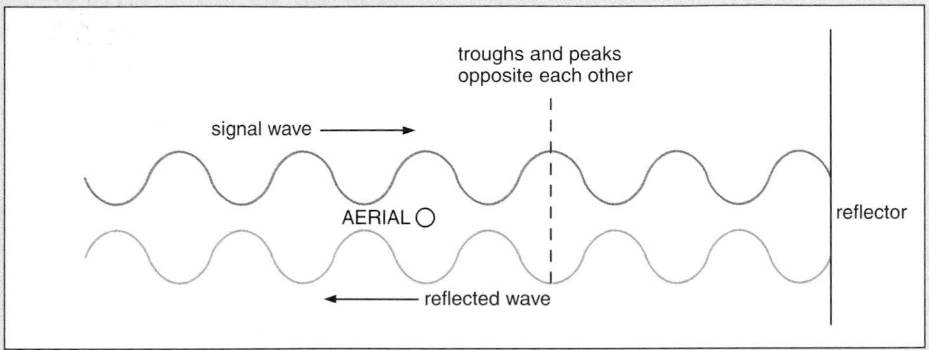

Picture 12

Picture 12 shows what is happening. The reflected wave is sometimes reinforcing the direct wave. In other positions the reflected wave cancels out the direct wave, making reception worse. The distance between successive 'cancel points' or 'reinforcement points' is half the wavelength of the radio broadcast.

C Water waves

You can experiment with water waves using a ripple tank. This is a shallow plastic tray with water in it. You can do similar experiments in a bath or washing-up bowl at home.

You can make circular pulses by touching the water surface with the end of a pencil. You can make straight waves by touching the surface of the water with a piece of round wooden rod held level.

Put objects of different shapes into the tank and see what effect they have on waves. Investigate reflection and diffraction. What happens when waves pass through gaps of different widths?

Your teacher may be able to give you extra apparatus to take these investigations further.

Questions

1 Describe an experiment you have seen or done to show that water waves spread out (diffract) when they pass through a narrow opening.

2 a Light can be 'diffracted'. Explain the difference between *diffraction* and *refraction*.

b Why don't we usually notice the diffraction of light in everyday life?

3 Design an experiment to show diffraction using sound waves.

4 Name – or describe very briefly – two scientifiic discoveries which were ignored or said to be wrong when they were first made.

5 Explain what *polarised* light is. Why do 'polaroid' sunglasses cut down glare on bright sunny days?

6 What evidence is there that light is a wave? Describe some experiments and show how they support this idea.

7 You are given a box which gives out some mysterious, unknown 'rays' when you press a switch on it. The rays make a certain kind of paint glow. How could you test if these rays were waves? (They might be particles.)

C8
Light and colour

The world is full of colour. What makes colours? How can we see them?

Picture 1 The spectrum of white light.

Splitting up light

White light is a mixture of colours. When we pass white light through a prism the colours become separated out into a **spectrum** (see topics C5 and C6). Picture 1 shows a prism splitting up white light. The same effect can be produced by tiny drops of water, and causes the **rainbow**.

Keen-eyed people say they can detect seven colours in this spectrum. In order, they are red, orange, yellow, green, blue, indigo and violet. You can remember this by the sentence 'Richard Of York Gave Battle In Vain'. Light from the Sun, or any white hot object, also includes invisible radiations, like ultra-violet and infra-red. See topic C6.

How prisms separate colours

When light goes from air into glass it slows down. This is why it changes direction – it is **refracted** (see topic C6). All electromagnetic waves travel at the same speed in a vacuum. They slow down when they enter a transparent medium, like glass. This change of speed causes refraction.

But the different colours of the spectrum travel at **different** speeds in glass. For example, violet light travels more slowly than red light. This means that it is refracted more, so that its direction is changed more than red light. The other colours fit in between, depending on their speeds in glass. Light of different colours is thus spread out into the spectrum. This spreading out is called **dispersion** (picture 2).

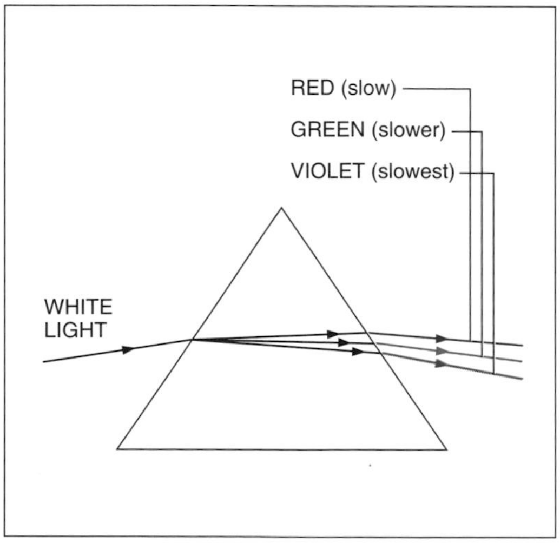

Picture 2 Light of different colours travels in different paths.

Putting white light back together again

If you collected all the seven colours of the spectrum and joined them together again you would once more see white light. You could try this, using one prism to separate the colours and another to put them back again.

Primary colours

This effect may not be a surprise to you, but what might be surprising is that you can recreate white light by using just three colours – **red, green** and **blue**. Picture 3 shows three beams of light shining onto a white screen.

Where all three beams overlap you can see that the *light is white*. The three

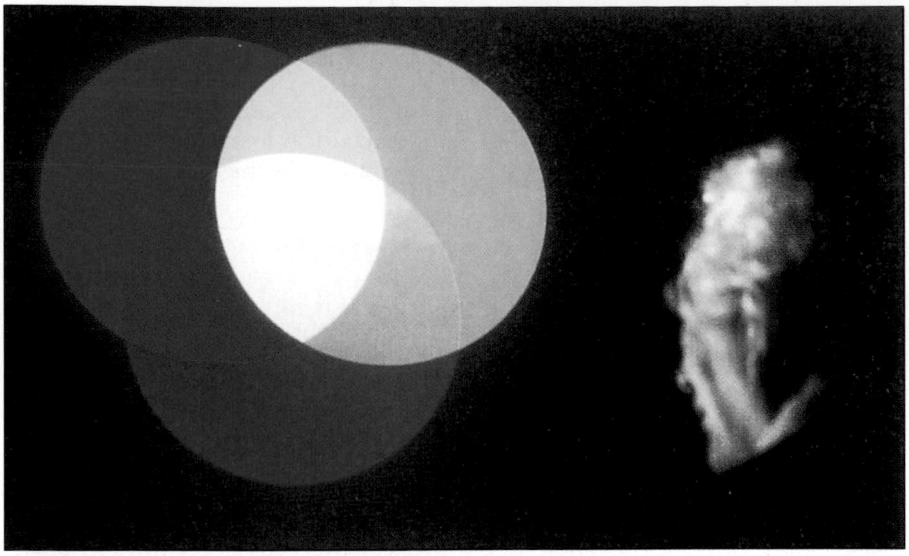

Picture 3 White light can be made from just three colours.

colours that do this are called the **primary colours** (see picture 3).

At other places, just two colours overlap. They combine to form other colours.

- Red and green combine to make **yellow**.
- Red and blue combine to make **magenta**.
- Green and blue combine to make **cyan**.

These 'double' colours are called the **secondary colours**. You get these effects when the three primary colours are balanced so that they are equally effective. By using different brightnesses you can create all the colours of the rainbow, and many other colours that go to make up the everyday world.

Colour television uses this property of primary colours. In the TV screen there are just three kinds of paints which glow when electrons hit them **(phosphors)**. The phosphors glow red, green or blue. The screen contains thousands of small 'picture elements' (pixels) each containing a set of the three phosphors. By making these glow at different brightnesses we can get the whole range of colours that we see on a TV screen. Colour films and colour printing work in much the same way, using just three basic colours.

Why is a red book red?

Paints and dyes work by **reflecting** light. When white light shines on a red surface, the dye absorbs all colours except red, which it reflects. If you shine blue light, for example, on the surface it looks dark, because there is no red light present to be reflected. The same happens when you shine green light on to the red surface.

But if you put the red surface in *yellow* light it will look red. This is because yellow light is a mixture of green and red light, as explained above. The red surface absorbs the green light but can reflect the red.

Activity B is about experimenting with different coloured light and different coloured surfaces. The fact is that the colour of an object depends not only on its own 'colour' but also on the colour of the light you view it with. The 'white' of artificial light is different from the 'pure' white of sunlight. They contain a slightly different mix of colours. This is why clothes bought in a shop under artificial lighting may look quite different when seen out of doors in sunlight.

Why is the sky blue?

The upper atmosphere contains millions of tiny particles, ranging from molecules of various gases to small dust particles, ice crystals, etc. Many of these are good at absorbing blue light. Then soon after absorbing the blue light they reradiate it. Picture 4 shows how this happens; it is called **scattering**. Thus the

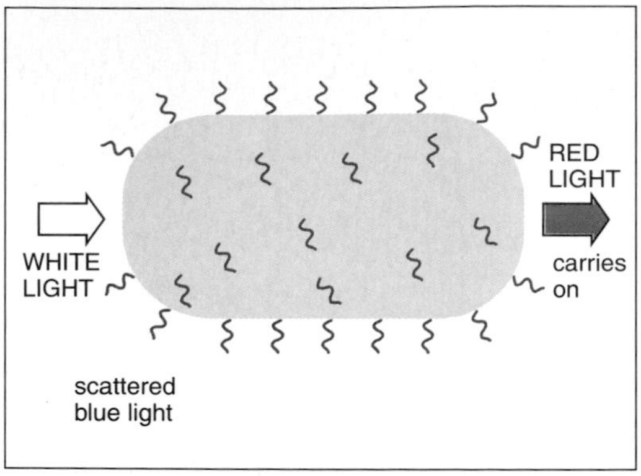

Picture 4 Atmospheric scattering.

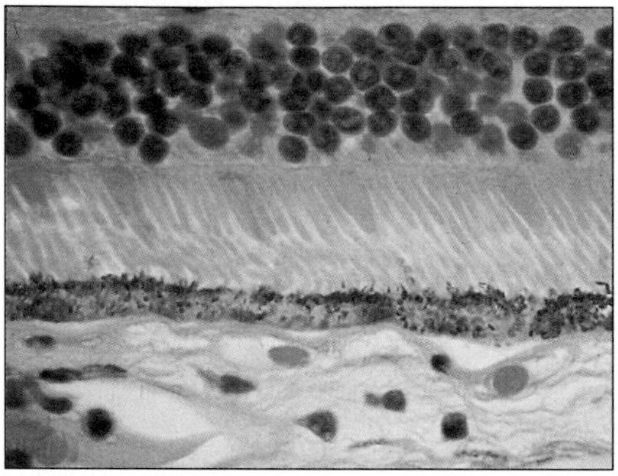

Picture 6 The retina has cells which can detect colour (cones), but most of the rod-shaped cells can't.

blue light from the sunlight passing high above us in the atmosphere is first trapped, then some of it is sent down to Earth. So the sky looks blue.

This effect also explains why sunsets are red or orange. Red light is not absorbed in this way and so carries on through the atmospheric particles. When we look at the setting Sun we see this reddish light. Most of the blue light has been absorbed and then sent out sideways (see picture 5).

Colour, energy and wavelength

Light travels as a wave. The difference between red light and, say, blue light is simply that they have different wavelengths. Red light has a longer wavelength than blue light. The diagram of the electromagnetic spectrum in picture 6 of topic C6 shows this.

The eye and brain work together when we see light. The effect of light of one wavelength makes us see 'red'; other wavelengths trigger the sensation of green or blue.

One theory of vision says that our eyes work like the TV screens described above. Some cells in the retina at the back of the eye detect the red light. Others detect only blue and a third kind detect green light.

When all three types of cell are triggered we see the light as white. Combinations of cells create different colours in the brain in much the same way as combinations of red, green and blue in the pixels of a TV screen create different colours.

Picture 6 shows some of these cells in a human retina.

The triggering effect of light on cells in the eye is caused by the energy carried by the light. The effect can only be explained by using a model of light that says it is made of particles called **photons**. The blue photons carry more energy than the green ones, and the red photons carry the least energy.

Infra-red photons don't carry enough energy to trigger any of the cells. Ultra-violet photons are invisible because they carry too much energy, and actually damage the eye cells. Our eyelids screen this dangerous radiation coming from above. But if it comes up into the eye by reflection from water or snow we can be harmed. Skiers and polar explorers guard against this 'snow blindness' by using goggles whenever the Sun shines brightly.

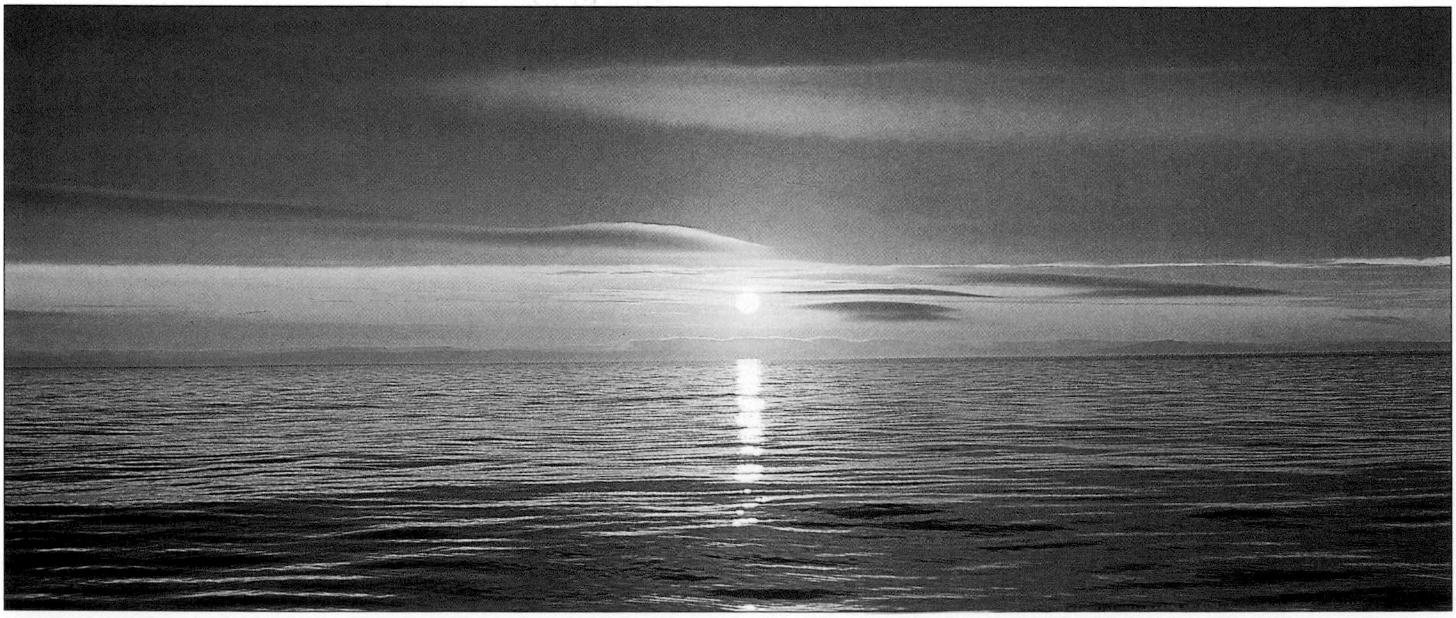

Picture 5 Sunsets are red and yellow because the blue light has been scattered.

Activities

A Producing a spectrum

1 Let nature do it for you! Keep an eye out for **rainbows**. Where must the Sun be, compared with the raindrops, for a rainbow to be made?

2 Make your own rainbow. You need a sunny day and a garden hose with a fine spray. Wear a bathing costume or raincoat, depending on the air temperature. Where do you have to stand to see the rainbow effect?

3 In the laboratory you can set up a ray box to produce a beam of white light. Pass it through a prism and view the spectrum on a white sheet of card. Picture 8 shows how to do this.

4 Repeat method 3 using a **diffraction grating** instead of a prism. A diffraction grating uses the interference effect of light. You can see similar effects in a compact disc, and the colours of butterfly wings are made using the same principle.

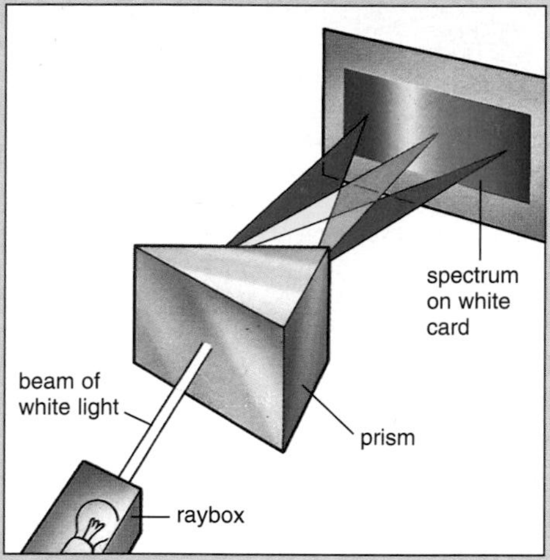

Picture 8

B Mixing light

You will need three ray boxes (or the equivalent), a white screen and some coloured filters: red, green, blue, yellow, cyan and magenta. You should have some simple way of holding the filters in the paths of the beams. The best results are obtained if the room is darkened.

Here are just a few of the investigations you can do. You should be able to think of some more.

1 Begin with the primary colours: red, blue and green. Shine them on to the same part of the white screen so that you can complete the following table:

Colours mixed	Result on screen
red + green	?
blue + ?	magenta
blue + green	?
blue + green + red	?

2 Using the secondary colours as well (yellow, cyan, magenta), what happens when you make the following mixtures?

Colours mixed	Result
yellow + blue	
red + cyan	
green + magenta	

Explain the effects you get in this experiment. (*Hint* look at the results of part 1.)

3 Investigate what different coloured objects look like in different colours of light. You could try clothing, coloured photographs, flowers, etc. Try to explain the effects you see.

Questions

1 Broxton United wear white shirts with blue shorts. Wexley Wanderers wear yellow shirts with black shorts. When they turn out for a floodlit match in the park the referee sends one team back to change their strip. Explain why the referee had to do this. (*Hint* There was nothing wrong with the ref's eyesight. They were playing under yellow sodium lamps.)

2 It is said that bees can see ultra-violet light. Design an experiment to test this statement.

3 a Suggest a reason why ordinary electric filament lamps produce a 'white' light that is different from sunlight.

b Explain why the difference between sunlight and lamp light should affect the colour of clothing.

4 Explain clearly the difference between the **refraction** and the **dispersion** of light by a prism.

5 In a prism, why is blue light refracted through a bigger angle than red light?

6 Yellow is sometimes called 'minus blue'. Explain why.

7 Why do both the human eye and a colour TV camera have just three kinds of colour-sensitive cell?

8 A red rose and a yellow rose are passed through the spectrum from a bright lamp. What colour would each appear to be in:

a the blue light,
b the green light,
c the yellow light,
d the red light?

9 'Richard Of York Gave Battle In Vain'. The capital letters give the seven colours of the visible spectrum in order: red, orange, yellow, green, blue, indigo, violet. Make up a more modern sentence to help you remember the order of the colours.

Signals from space

The only way we can learn about the Universe is from the signals it sends us. For millions of years the only signals from space that humans could detect were carried by light. The ancient astronomers of Egypt, Babylon and Greece observed the Sun, the Moon and the stars. They saw how they changed and plotted their movements through the heavens. They produced the first theories about what the Universe was like, as shown in picture 1.

Picture 1 The Egyptian universe.

The Ancient Romans weren't very interested in astronomy, and when Italy and Western Europe were overrun by 'barbarians' from the steppes of Asia in around AD 400 the old knowledge of astronomy was almost completely lost. But the study of astronomy was carried on by the Arab Muslims who conquered the Middle East and parts of Europe in the years AD 700 to 1500. If you look at a good sky map you will find that many of the star names are in Arabic.

The telescope was invented in 1610 and over the next two centuries telescopes got bigger and better. Fainter and more distant stars could be seen. Knowledge about the universe increased, but these instruments still used ordinary, visible light.

A breakthrough was to come with the marriage of two old ideas – the **spectrum** of light and the **telescope** – with a new technique: **photography**. But like many scientific discoveries, it was a long time before what had been discovered made any sense.

Newton had explained the 'colours of the rainbow' back in 1666, and had investigated the spectrum of white light. Then in 1802 an English scientist, William Wollaston, noticed that the coloured spectrum of sunlight was crossed with a number of dark lines. He did not know what caused them, and it was 40 years before the mystery was solved.

High technology 1857: the bunsen burner

Robert Bunsen invented the bunsen burner to investigate spectra. He looked at the coloured light given out by elements heated in his clear, colourless gas flame. He discovered that each element had its own spectrum, different from all the others. When heated, it gave out light energy in definite wavelengths and in its own pattern. It could be used as a 'fingerprint', to detect the very tiniest traces of any element (see picture 2).

His fellow worker Gustav Kirchhoff made the key connection. The dark lines in the spectrum of sunlight were caused by elements in the Sun that **absorbed** light energy at their own special wavelengths. Immediately, astronomers were able to work out what the Sun was made of! In fact, one *new* element was discovered, up until that time unknown on Earth. It was named helium, after the Greek sun-god Helios.

Photography was discovered in about 1800, and the solar spectrum was first photographed in 1842. Since then, millions of photographs of the spectra of stars, planets, galaxies and comets have been taken. Photographs are needed because some of these objects are very faint. A photograph can collect light for many hours, and so build up its image until it is clear enough to be developed and measured. The details of the spectrum can tell us what elements there are in the star, its temperature, and even whether it is moving or not.

Then, in 1931, a new radiation was observed coming from outer space: **radio waves**. This led to the development of **radio astronomy**, and the discovery of radio stars and galaxies, pulsars and quasars (see topic F5 and picture 3).

Since then, astronomers have been able to use nearly every part of the whole electromagnetic spectrum, from gamma rays at one end to long radio waves at the other (see topic C6). They have found that the *pattern* of the spectrum of a given element is the same all over the Universe. But they also noticed that the actual wavelengths were sometimes different. This effect was caused by the movement of the star.

The American Edwin Hubble noticed that this difference was greater, the further away the stars or galaxies were. This could only be explained by the theory that these objects were moving away from us. This led to the theory of the expanding Universe – and of the Big Bang that started it. The new 'space telescope' is named after this great astronomer.

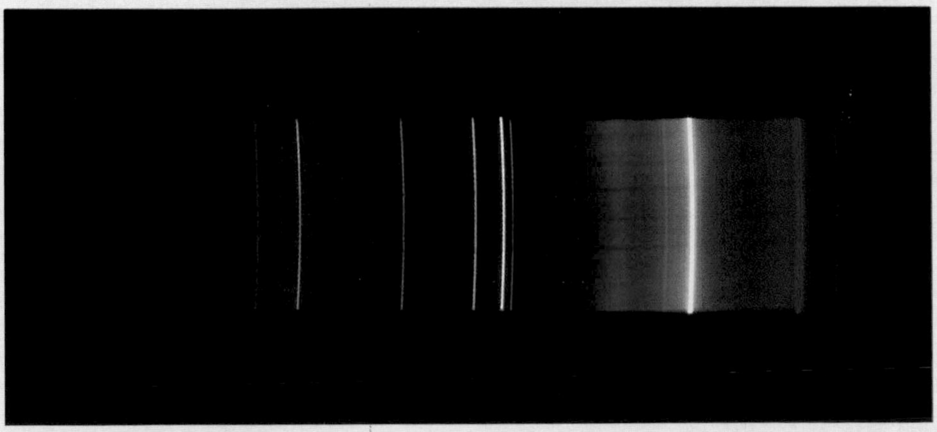

Picture 2 The helium spectrum.

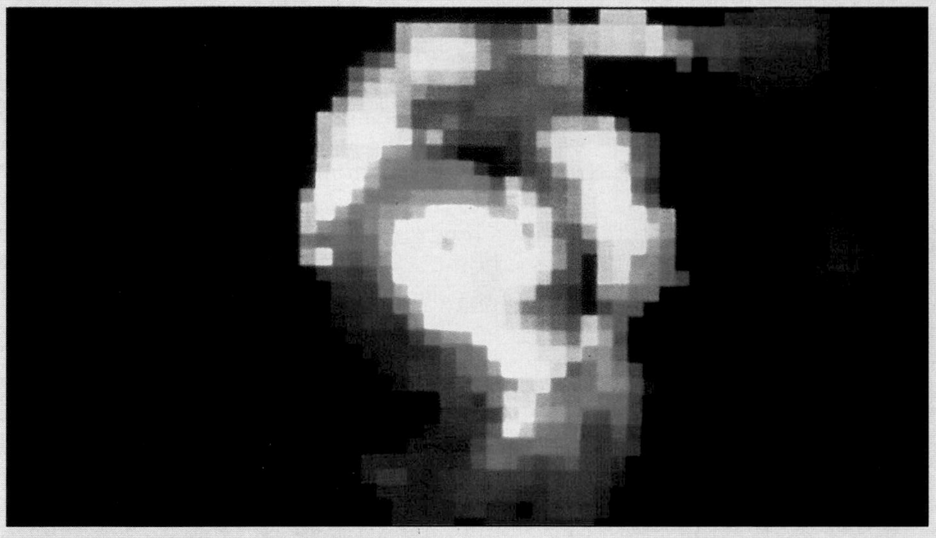

Picture 3 This image was produced using a radio telescope.

Answer the following questions:

1. Suggest why so much early astronomy was done by people living in the desert areas of the Middle East (compared, for example, with people living in Britain).
2. Why are radio telescopes so much bigger (maybe 30 m or more across) than light telescopes (up to 2 or 3 m across)?
3. Suggest a reason why it took nearly 200 years for Newton's discovery of the spectrum to be useful in astronomy.
4. Why are light, radio waves and X-rays all thought to be part of the same type of radiation? (Check with topic C6 if you are not sure.)
5. Radio waves don't affect photographic plates. How are these radiations detected and recorded?

Seeing with sound

Modern science uses all kinds of radiation to 'look' at things which are invisible, or to see through materials that light cannot penetrate. X-rays can see through flesh to spot broken bones or faulty hearts or lungs. Even the tiny magnetic fields of hydrogen atoms in our bodies can be used to give us a picture of what is going on deep inside our bodies.

One of the most useful body probes is the *ultrasound scanner*. This produces pictures like the one shown in picture 1, which shows a scan of an unborn baby.

Ordinary sound, which we can hear, has frequencies in the range of 20 Hz to 20 000 Hz. Ultrasound has frequencies well beyond the upper limit that we can hear. It uses sounds at frequencies between 1 and 15 **million** Hz/ (MHz).

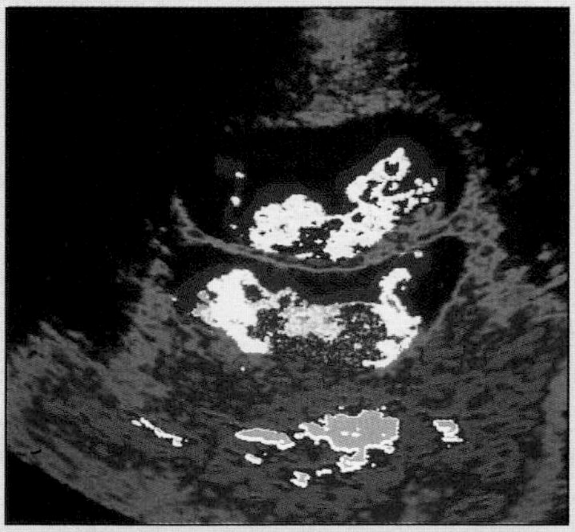

Picture 1 Ultrasound scan of twin babies in the womb.

This is higher than any animal ear can sense.

At this high frequency, the sound can travel through most materials. But some of it is always reflected back when it goes from one type of material into another. How much of it is sent back depends on the material in the way. In fact it behaves very much as light does in going through materials of slightly different transparency.

Also, the speed at which the ultrasound travels in the material depends on the material it is travelling in. This means that it can be focused. This is done in the same way as glass lenses do for light by using an ultrasound-transparent material with curved surfaces.

The advantage of using sound is that it doesn't harm the living cells, as X-rays may do. But if it is to see fine detail, the sound waves must be very small. They have to be slightly smaller than the small parts (e.g. blood vessels) of the object being looked at (picture 2).

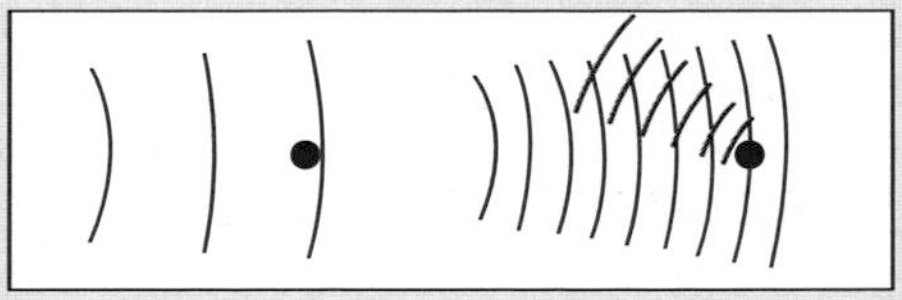

Picture 2 Long waves miss the fine detail.

This is the reason for using such very high frequencies. The higher the frequency, the smaller the wavelength. This is because of the wave formula:

$$\text{wavelength} = \frac{\text{speed}}{\text{frequency}}$$

The speed of sound in the human body is about the same as it is in salt water – about 1500 m/s. If we want to see detail to about 1 mm, the wavelength has to be no more than this length. This means a frequency of 1.5 MHz. In hospitals, ultrasound scanners use frequencies between 1 MHz and 15 MHz.

Answer the following questions.

1. Why can't we hear ultrasound?
2. Doctors prefer to use ultrasound for looking at babies in the mother's womb, even if the images produced aren't quite as clear as they could get using X-rays. Why is ultrasound preferred to X-rays?
3. Use the formula given above to calculate the size of the smallest object you could 'see' using ultrasound at 15 MHz.
4. Bats find their way around at night, and detect their insect prey, using ultrasound at about 50 kHz (50 000 Hz). Suggest why they don't need to use frequencies a lot higher than this, as in ultrasound scanners.
5. Draw a diagram showing what an ultrasound scanner might 'see' if it looked at an orange.
6. Another use for ultrasound is for cleaning things. When ultrasound is beamed at dirty fabrics the particles of dirt fall off the fibres. Suggest why: (a) the particles fall off, (b) this method is used for cleaning very old or very expensive materials.

D1
Where does energy come from?

All life on Earth needs energy; we can control it, but cannot create it. Are we using it wisely? Is the world going to run out of energy?

We use energy to make things work. We use it to cook with, and the food we eat is our personal supply of energy. Without this energy, we would die in a matter of weeks. Long before then, we would begin to feel ill and very weak.

This topic is about where the energy we use actually comes from. We usually take it for granted. Just press the switch and electrical machines start to work, or the heating comes on. We stop at a garage and fill up with petrol; someone comes and delivers oil, coal or coke to our homes. The gas supply is always there when we want it.

The pie chart (picture 1) shows how energy is used in the UK. Most of it is fairly evenly shared out between home, industry and moving things about. A smaller amount is used for what are called 'services', which means things like schools, hospitals, town halls, shops, etc.

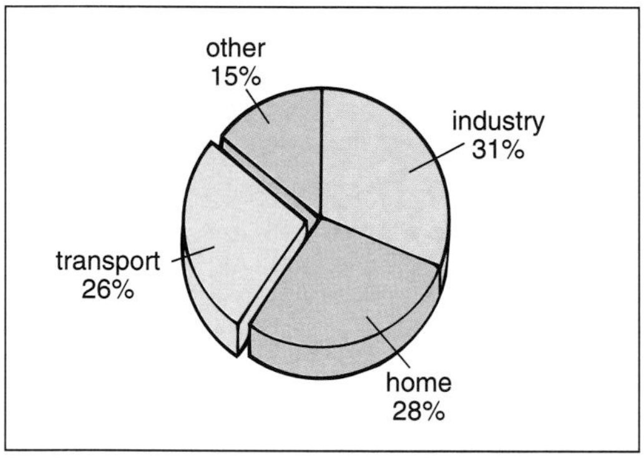

Picture 1 What do we use energy for?

How much energy do you use?

One way or another every person in this country uses, each year, the energy that could be got from burning 3.5 tonnes of oil. North Americans use more than twice as much, and the average for the world is 1.5 tonnes per person. Topic D2 is about measuring energy, and it shows you how to measure the amount of energy you use, per day.

Changing energy to suit our needs

Of course, the energy you use is not all supplied from oil. One of the great things about energy is that it can be changed into various 'forms', and can be moved about in so many different ways. What is really happening is that the energy is being transferred from one 'system' to another.

A system can be something quite simple, like a spinning wheel. It can also be something very complicated, like a human cell or a power station. Let's take a look at how the energy you get from an electric fire actually got there. It took a longer time than you might think!

Moving along the energy trail

Think of sitting in front of an electric fire. The energy has moved along quite a long trail before it reached you.

The start of the trail – the Sun

The Sun is millions of kilometres away, and the energy from the fire that warms you started just there, millions of years ago. Nuclear fusion (see topic D7) makes the Sun very hot (picture 2). This makes the Sun send out energy as various kinds of **radiation** (see topic C6). A very small fraction of this gets to the Earth and keeps it warm.

Some of the radiation energy, visible light, is used by plants to make the chemicals they need to grow through a process called **photosynthesis**. In photosynthesis, the simple molecules of carbon dioxide and water are turned into new, more complicated molecules of sugar and starches. These are **carbohydrates**.

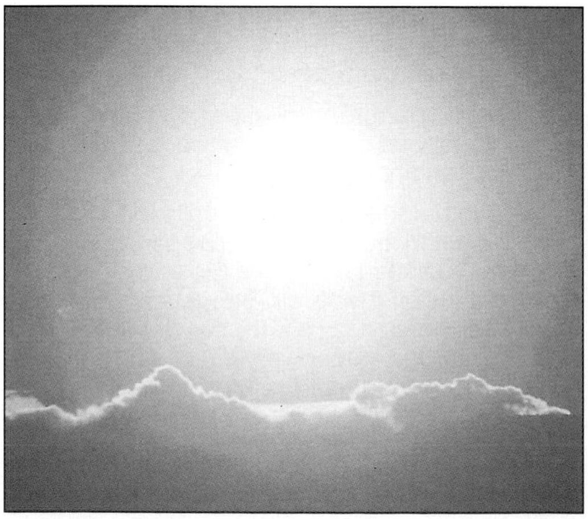

Picture 2 Nuclear fusion changes mass to energy. This is why the Sun is so hot.

Forming fossil fuels

Over millions of years, the carbohydrates in ancient plants have been converted to fossil fuels: oil, coal and natural gas.

Fossil fuels contain many different chemical compounds, but the most important ones are **hydrocarbons**.

Energy from fossil fuels

Fossil fuels are now our major source of energy. The energy is released by combustion with oxygen. The waste products are oxides, mostly of carbon (carbon dioxide) and hydrogen (hydrogen oxide – water). This is the reverse of the process which formed the hydrocarbons in plants, by which solar energy was used to convert carbon dioxide and water into sugars with the release of oxygen into the atmosphere.

The main hydrocarbon fossil fuels are: coal, crude oil and gas. Crude oil is a mixture of oils from which useful fuels such as diesel, petrol and paraffin can be extracted. Gas is mainly methane, one of the simplest hydrocarbons.

The fuel–oxygen system

The hydrocarbon chemicals in fossil fuels can only release their energy when they change into other chemicals. The most common way is by combustion (burning). They combine with oxygen and heat up their surroundings, producing the waste gases steam and carbon dioxide. The energy cycle has brought us back to where it started all those millions of years ago, as shown in picture 3.

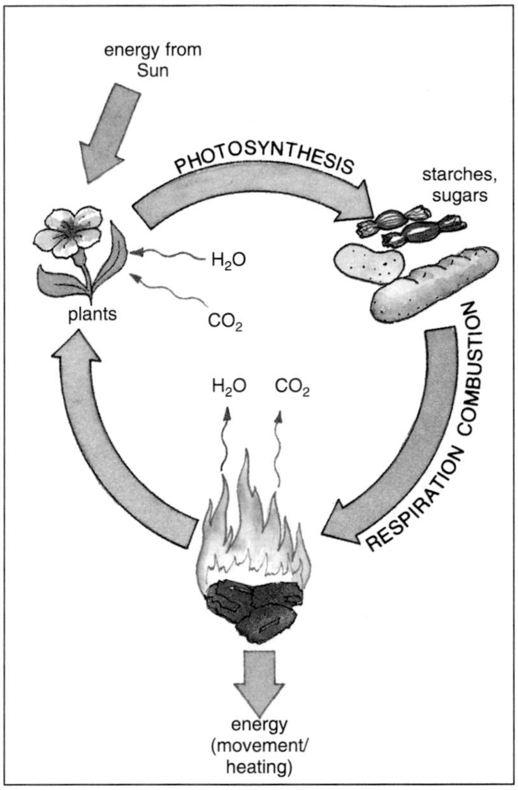

Picture 3 Water and carbon dioxide are recycled in the Earth–Sun energy system.

From coal to electric fire

Most of our electricity is generated in power stations that burn coal (see topic E11). As it flows through the resistance wire in the bars of our electric fire, it delivers energy and the wire glows red hot. It is not as hot as the Sun, but it gives out energy in the same way, as radiation. Our skins absorb this radiation, warming up as they do so. It has been a long trail from the Sun to the electric fire, and picture 4 sums up the changes.

The problem with fossil fuels

The main problem with fossil fuels is that we are using them up far more quickly than they were made. For example, by the year 2040 there will be no more oil left. Britain's North Sea oil wells will be pumped dry by the time you are settling down to raise a family, but coal will last longer because there is much more of it. Picture 5 tells you how long we expect the reserves of fossil fuels to last. They could last longer, or be used up sooner. This depends how sensibly we use them.

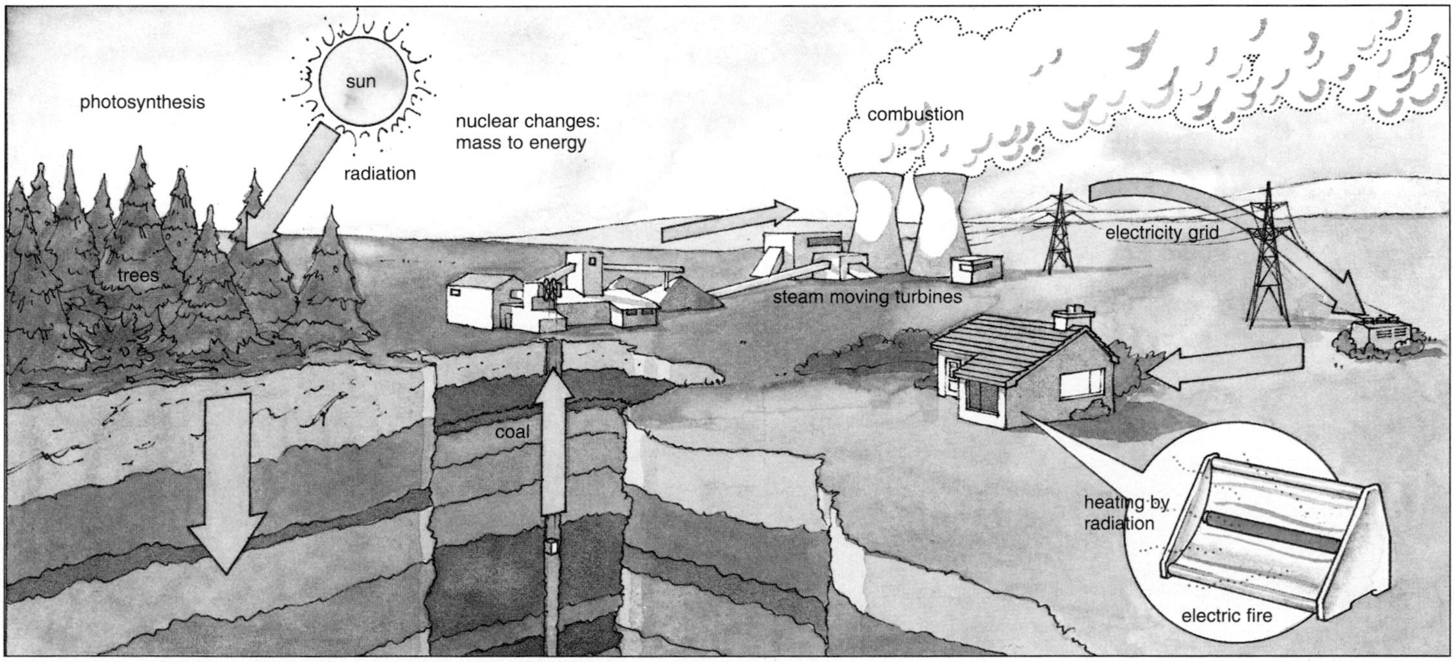

Picture 4 The Sun is our main energy source – but it might take a long time to become useful.

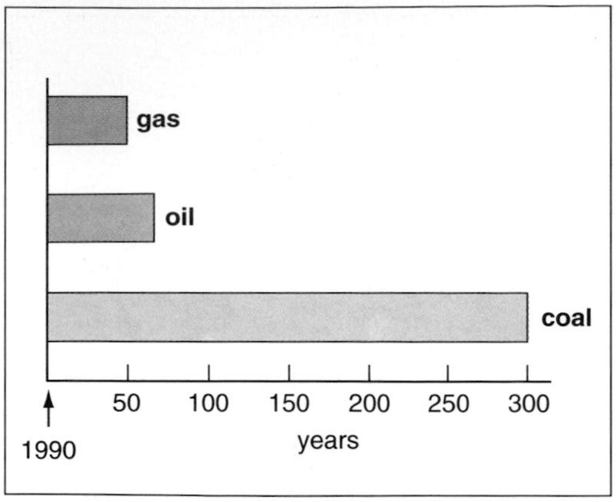

Picture 5 These are estimates of how long world supplies of fossil fuels will last – if we go on using them at the present rate.

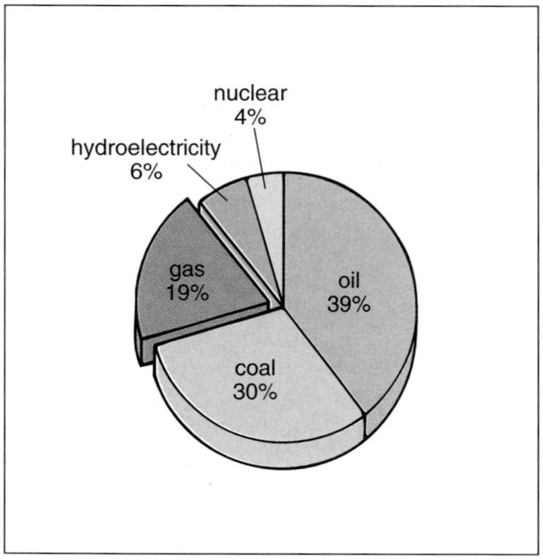

Picture 6 The world's main energy sources.

Picture 7 Most people on Earth use wood as their main fuel. However, in some countries the wood is not being replaced.

A great deal of the energy we obtain is wasted because we don't manage it sensibly – see topic D4.

We might also begin to make use of alternative sources of energy. These could be renewable sources such as wind, sun, tides and waves. We can make use of the energy of 'biomass' – from plants and from animal wastes. These sources of energy are dealt with in topic E11. We might also make more use of nuclear energy – see topic D7.

Energy supplies

Most of the energy that we use on Earth comes from fossil fuels – at present this is almost 90% of the total. The pie chart in picture 6 shows the main sources of energy that the people of the world use. But it does not show all of it. It shows only the 'artificial' energy that we buy in the form of fuels and electricity.

The chart does not show the energy that we get 'free', for example, the energy coming from the Sun.

All the crops on Earth rely on this solar energy to keep them warm enough to grow, and to give the light they need to photosynthesise. It warms up sea and land, and keeps people warm in summer, so that they don't need to buy so much fuel. We should remember that for most of human history, energy from the Sun was the only energy we were able to use.

Neither does the chart show the energy used by millions of people all over the world that they collect for themselves. It might surprise you to learn that most people on Earth rely on **wood** for their heating and cooking (picture 7). These people live in Africa, and much of Asia. The advantage of wood is that it is a **renewable** energy source – provided people keep on planting trees to replace the ones they cut down for fuel.

What is energy?

We can usually recognise energy when we come across it, but it is hard to say what it is. The simplest way to describe it is to say what it can do. The main things that it can do are:

- **work**, by means of applying forces to move things,
- **heat**, making things get hotter, melt, boil or evaporate.

Energy is not a 'stuff', like air or atoms, or even like electric charge. It is to do with the way things are arranged.

When an elastic band is stretched, the molecules are rearranged. The forces beween them can pull the rubber back to its original shape. When you stretch the band you have done some work – by applying a force and moving it. When the band goes back it can apply a force – perhaps to a stone in a catapult. It does work on the stone. Each time the force is applied to move something it does work – and energy is transferred to another system.

Potential energy

A stretched elastic band looks innocent enough. If you had never seen or used one you wouldn't guess what might happen if it was let go. But it is able to give energy – dangerously – to a stone (picture 8). We use a special term to describe the energy 'hidden' in the stretched elastic band. We call it **potential energy**.

A stone at the top of a cliff can fall and do some damage. Water in a dam high in the mountains can flow downhill and make a hydroelectric power station produce electricity. These are another two examples of potential energy. This time it is due to the way 'things are arranged' in a gravity field. We call it **gravitational potential energy**. Gravitational energy is dealt with further in topic B4.

Kinetic energy

It takes **work** to make something move. Things will only start to move if a force acts on them, like gravity, or the force of a stretched piece of rubber. Work is a way of transferring energy, and the moving object picks up the energy from whatever system provides the force. The energy it carries can be used to do more work. Because we make so much use of moving objects we have a special name for the energy they carry. It is called **kinetic energy**. (See page 43.)

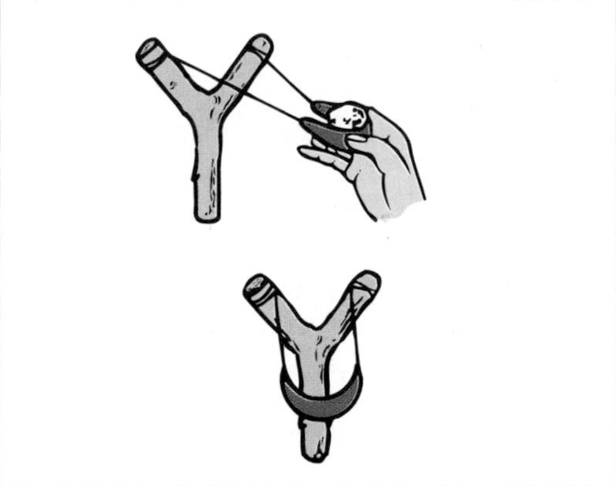

Picture 8 The stretched elastic stores potential energy, then gives it to the stone as kinetic energy.

Are we using too much energy?

Fifty years ago most people travelled long distances by bus or train. Now we tend to go by car. Then, people washed clothes by hand, instead of using a washing machine. Men shaved with razor blades fitted into a holder, instead of using an electric razor. Not many people had central heating. They just wore more clothes in winter!

We now expect to find fruit and vegetables in the shops at all times of the year, not just in their 'natural season'. This is because we can freeze them and keep them for years, if necessary.

All this makes life a lot more comfortable, but it does take a lot of energy. There was a time when people were very worried that the world was 'running out of energy'. There was an 'energy crisis'. The price of energy went up. Oil, coal and electricity cost more. This made people try to use less energy.

In the 1990s energy has become slightly cheaper. In the UK we have been able to use gas and oil from the North Sea. People have become more careless in their energy use. Now, the problem that is worrying people is the *polluting effect* of energy use. Burning fuels produce carbon dioxide, which increases the greenhouse effect. They often give off gases which make rain more acid.

Do we need to use as much energy as we do? Do North Americans need to use twice as much energy as Britons? What changes would there be in your life if you had to cut your personal energy use by half? And what will happen when everybody in the world is able to use energy at the rate that Western countries do?

Of course, fossil fuels will not last for ever. British oil and gas will run out by early next century. Would it be wise to make it last longer by using it more carefully?

Topic D4 tells you more about energy, and in particular about the laws of energy that allow us to control it. Knowing more about what energy is should help us use it more wisely.

Activities

A Where does your energy come from?

Make a list of the ways in which energy gets into your home. Find out from your parents which source of energy costs you the most per month. It is likely that the one that costs you the most is the kind that you use most. Try making a pie chart of your results.

B The geography of energy

Use a geography book or atlas to find out where the main sources of energy are in the United Kingdom. Explain why some parts of the country are (a) sources of coal, (b) good for making hydroelectricity, (c) used as the sites for nuclear power stations.

Questions

1 Where does the energy we use come from? Name three of the main energy sources used in this country.

2 Why are coal and oil called 'fossil fuels'? Name one other fossil fuel.

3 Name three devices (or things) that can store energy so that it can be used later. Describe how one of them works.

4 a What is the energy source most commonly used in transportation (moving people and goods about)?
  b Suggest two ways in which the UK could cut down on the amount of energy it uses for transportation. For each way, write a sentence or two explaining whether or not you think people would readily accept your suggestion.

5 Think about the energy involved when you ride a bicycle up a hill. Write down an 'energy trail' (as in picture 4) showing the various systems the energy goes through. Start with the energy in the food you ate before you rode the bike. Make a guess as to where all the original energy has gone by the time you are standing on the top of the hill.

6 Think through a typical day, from getting up in the morning to going to bed at night. Make a list of as many as possible of the energy-using things you have used during the day, and say what energy source it tapped. One kind is given for you to start with.

Device	Source
1 bedside lamp	electrical power station

D2 Measuring energy

Wherever energy comes from we can measure it in the same unit – the joule.

Picture 1 Using energy.

Look at the packet

Energy is measured in **joules**. Picture 2 shows the label on a packet of cereal. Amongst other things it tells you that when you eat one serving (45 g) it could supply 635 kJ (635 000 joules) of energy. This is a lot of joules – more than half a million! It is roughly the same as the amount of movement energy you would gain if you fell off a cliff 1000 m high. It is twenty times the energy carried by a high-velocity rifle bullet.

How much energy do you need to live?

The average 16-year-old girl needs to take in 9 million joules of energy a day. Boys of the same age need about 12 million joules a day.

Twelve million joules is about enough to lift a 60 kg person a height of 20 km. Mount Everest is less than 9 km high! Obviously you do more with your energy intake than just **move**.

So what do you actually do with all this energy? We need energy to keep us moving about – our muscles are doing work. But we use nearly as much when we are asleep. It seems that just keeping alive takes a lot of energy!

Working

One way that scientists measure energy is by seeing how much work it can do. This is quite simple, and is dealt with in topic B4, where we look at energy and force in a gravity field. Forces do work when they move something. First we need to measure the size of the force (in newtons). Then we measure the distance (in metres) that the object moves in the direction the force is acting.

Then we can calculate:

$$\begin{aligned}\text{Energy used} &= \text{work done}\\ &= \text{force} \times \text{distance moved in the direction of the force}\\ \boldsymbol{E}\ \text{joules} &= \boldsymbol{F}\ \text{newtons} \times \boldsymbol{d}\ \text{metres}\end{aligned}$$

Suppose it takes a force of 25 N to move a saw when you cut a piece of wood, and you move it 0.2 m each time. Then one cutting movement needs 25 N × 0.2 m = 5 J of energy. If it takes twenty sawcuts to get through the wood, you need to supply 100 J (picture 3).

James Joule – heating with energy

James Joule lived over 150 years ago. He was one of the first scientists to do experiments which actually measured how much energy was needed to *heat* something.

It seems obvious now that it takes energy to make things hot – just think of the electricity and gas bills. But in those days scientists thought that heating was done by a mysterious gas that seeped in and out of things to make them hot or cold.

James Joule did experiments to show that when you do work, by moving a paddle wheel against the friction of water in a container, the water gets hot (picture 4). More importantly, he showed that the more work he did the hotter the water got. He was *doing work* to *heat a body*.

We now know that energy can appear in all kinds of different ways, doing different jobs. We have also discovered the strange fact that we can only use the energy when *something changes*.

Energy and change

Norway gets most of its electrical energy from hydroelectric power stations. In Britain we get most of ours from power stations which run off coal and gas. In both cases, changes have to occur before we get the electricity we need.

In Norway, water stored in dams high in the mountains has to run downhill.

NUTRITION INFORMATION

Typical composition by weight

	per 100 g	per 45 g serving
Energy	1410 kJ 330 kcal	635 kJ 150 kcal
Protein	9.8 g	4.4 g
Carbohydrate	72.8 g	32.8 g
Fat	2.1 g	1.0 g
Dietary Fibre	10.5 g	4.7 g

Picture 2 Breakfast energy!

The water has to *change its position* in a gravity field (picture 5). In an ordinary power station, coal or oil has to be burned. This is a *chemical change*, in which hydrocarbon molecules combine with oxygen in the air.

In both examples there are other changes as well. The falling water loses potential energy *(mgh)* and does work to drive the turbines. In a coal-fired power station the chemical reaction heats up water, which turns to steam. The steam applies force to turbines, and they do work in turning the generators.

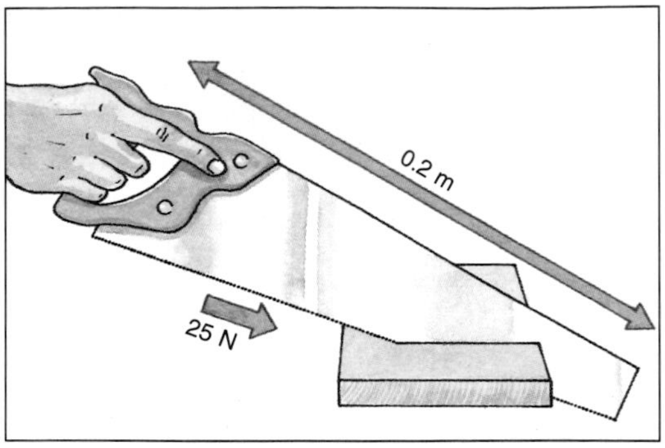

Picture 3 Work and energy.

Systems

A useful idea is to think of the energy as being in a **system**. The water in a reservoir is able to do work because of the pull of gravity on it. This pull is caused by the Earth, so it makes sense to think of the *water–Earth system* as having the energy. The water wouldn't be much use on its own.

In a coal-fired power station the fuel will only heat water if it burns. This needs oxygen. So here we have a *fuel–oxygen system*. When we use energy we are always moving it from one system to another – or to several others. But there is a very important law of physics that says that the total quantity of energy always stays the same. The trouble is that most of the time it doesn't all go from the starting system to the one we want it to go to! See topic D4 for more about the laws of energy.

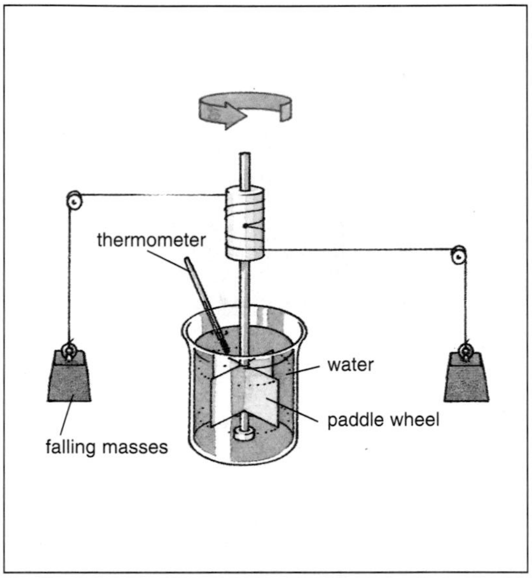

Picture 4 Joule's Paddle Wheel Apparatus showed that 'heat is a form of energy'.

A joule is a joule is a joule

We can measure energy using a lot of different techniques once we realise that moving energy from one system to another doesn't alter the fact that it is still **energy**. We can lift a can of beans up on to a shelf in all sorts of ways. But whatever source the energy comes from, it always takes the same amount of work to do the lifting. So the same quantity of energy has to be transferred, whether it is done by an electric robot, a conveyer belt or a human being.

Similarly, it takes a standard quantity of energy to warm a kilogram of water by 1°C. This is the principle behind the ways of measuring energy described below.

How to measure energy

This is a useful reference section: use it when you need to measure energy for an investigation or when dealing with energy in another topic.

1 **Doing work.** You need to measure the force (***F*** in newtons) involved and the distance (***d*** in metres) moved. Then use the formula:

$$\text{work done} = \text{energy } E \text{ transferred} = \text{force} \times \text{distance}$$

$$\text{or } E = Fd.$$

2 **Measuring potential energy.** When you do work against the force of gravity you always increase the potential energy of the object being moved. If it has a mass ***m*** it will have a gravity force on it of ***mg***. This is its **weight**. When you move it a through a height ***h*** you do work and transfer energy to

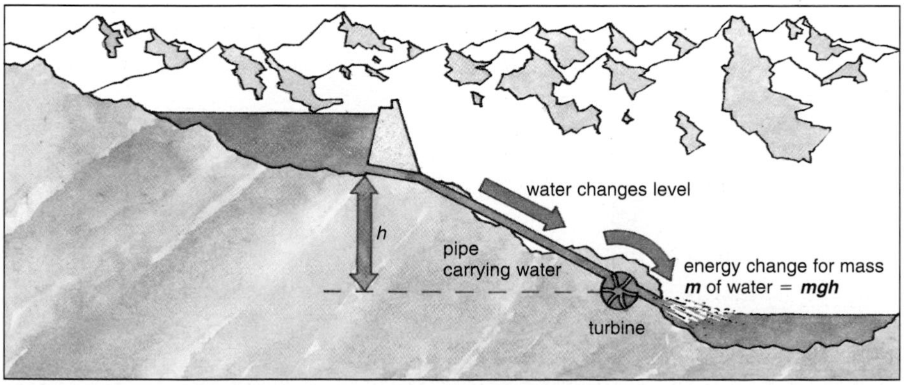

Picture 5 Energy transfers in a hydroelectric power station.

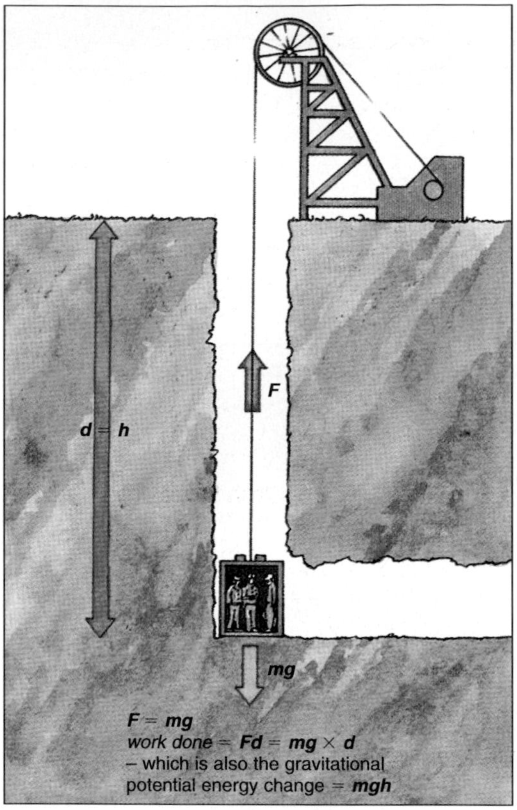

Picture 6 Doing work against gravity: $E = Fd$

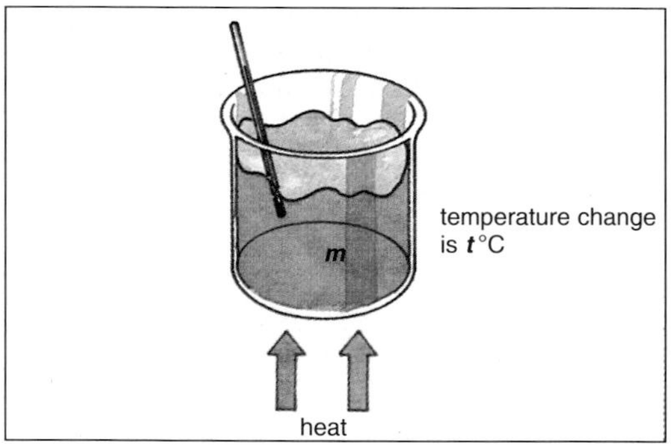

Picture 7 Heating water: $E = mst$.

the object as potential energy. As above we can calculate this as:

$$\text{work done} = \text{force} \times \text{distance}$$

$$\text{or energy transferred as potential energy, } E = mgh$$

3 **Using temperature measurements.** You need to measure the mass (m in kg) of material being heated and the temperature change (**t** in °C) produced. Then look up in tables the amount of energy (s) needed to heat 1 kg of the material through each Celsius degree. This is the **specific heat capacity**, s. In the case of water, s = 4200 J/kg °C. Finally, you can use the formula:

$$E = mst$$

to find the energy E transferred by heating.

4 **Using electrical measurements.** The work done by an electrical current to a device is measured by using the formula:

$$E = VIt$$

(V is voltage, I is current in amps, t is time in seconds; see picture 8 and topic E6).

5 **Kinetic energy.** The energy, E, possessed by a moving object is calculated using the formula $E = \frac{1}{2}mv^2$, where m is the mass of the object in kilograms and v is its speed in metres per second.

Power and energy

Power is a measure of the rate at which we can do work or transfer energy. Power is measured in **joules per second**, called **watts**.

$$\text{power} = \frac{\text{work done}}{\text{time taken}} \quad \text{or} \quad \frac{\text{energy transferred}}{\text{time taken}}$$

So power = VI (from 4 above) or Fv (from 1 above) where v is speed (distance/time).

A more powerful engine can do work more quickly than a less powerful one. Practical devices have powers of several thousand watts, so we tend to use the unit **kilowatt (1 kW = 1000 watts)**. Power also measures the rate of energy transfer: a 2 kW heater heats up water twice as quickly as a 1 kW heater.

Picture 8 Measuring electrical energy.

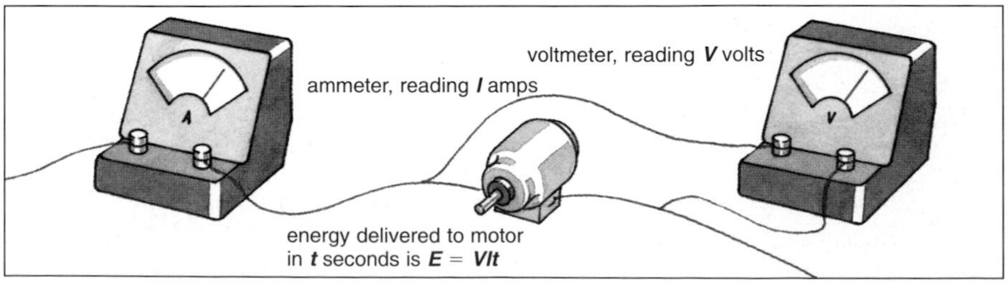

Activities

A Self-energised heating

1 Rub your hands together quickly. Describe any energy changes that you notice.

2 How does your body use muscles to keep itself warm without moving your arms and legs?

B How much work do you do ...

1 When you climb upstairs?

2 When you lift a stool and put it on a table or workbench?

3 When you open a door?

4 When you move a laboratory trolley across the room?

5 When you lift this book from the floor to the top of your workbench or desk.

To answer these questions, make measurements of force and distance. You will need a newton meter, and a set of bathroom scales to measure your own weight. Assume that a mass of 1 kg has a weight of 10 N. Use the formula for doing work, $E = Fd$.

C Investigating the heating effect of electrical energy

1 Set up the circuit shown in picture 9. Your task is to find out how much energy is delivered to the heater by the electric current in five minutes, and what effect this has on the material X. X may be a liquid or a solid block.

CARE! Do not let the heater cool in a liquid – switch off, take the heater out, and allow it to drip and cool in air.

You will need to measure:

a the temperature of X before you start and after the current is switched off,
b current (I), voltage (V) and time of flow (t seconds). Use the formula $E = VIt$ to calculate how much energy was supplied. 'X' will be given to you by your teacher. You may be given more than one material, or different groups may investigate different materials.

2 Collect together the results for different materials and put them into a table. Write a note describing how the different materials were affected by the energy supplied to them.

3 Can you suggest why materials behave differently?

D Measuring the effective energy output of a bunsen burner

1 Get a large tin or beaker and put 0.5 kg (0.5 litres) of cold water into it.

2 Put the container with water on a tripod and place it on a heating mat.

3 Measure and record the temperature of the water.

4 Light the bunsen burner and put it under the water container. Start a stopwatch as you do so.

5 Stir the water with the stirring thermometer and when the temperature reaches about 50°C turn off the bunsen burner and stop the stopwatch. Keep stirring the water until its temperature becomes steady. Note down this final temperature and the time the bunsen was used for.

6 Calculations.

a Work out the rise in temperature of the water, t.
b Calculate the energy given to the water by using the formula $E = 0.5 \times 4.2 \times t$ kJ.
c Work out how much energy was supplied to the water per second. This is the effective power output of the bunsen burner.
d Was this a fair test of the energy that a bunsen burner can provide? Give reasons for your answer.

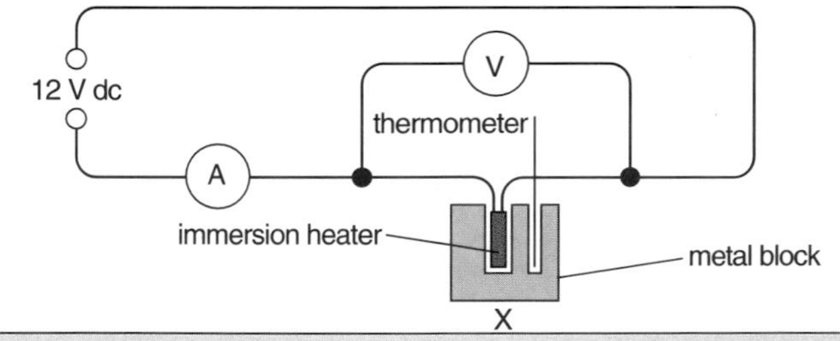

Picture 9

Questions

Use the formulae given in this chapter to answer the following.

1 It takes a force of 30 N to push a box along the floor. How much work do you do when you move it 5 m?

2 How much energy is released in a 12 V electric lamp when a current of 0.5 A flows in it for 1 minute?

3 A kilogram of copper needs 400 J to raise its temperature by 1°C. How many joules would it take to:

a warm 5 kg of copper by 1°C?
b warm 6 kg of copper by 20°C?

4 Mount Everest is 8848 m above sea level.

a Calculate how much energy it would take to lift someone weighing 600 N straight up through this height.
b In fact, a climber would use much more energy than you have calculated in (a) to climb Mount Everest. Give at least three reasons for this.

5 Design an experiment to find out one of the following.

Say what you would need to measure and give an idea of how it might be done.

a How much energy can you get by burning 1 kg of wood?
b How much energy does a gerbil need in a day?
c How much energy does the Sun deliver on a square metre of ground per minute on a sunny day?
d How much energy does it take to do the washing up?

6 How much does the temperature of a 2 kg mass of water rise when it is given 21 kJ of heating energy? Use the fact that it takes 4.2 kJ to warm 1 kg of water by 1°C.

7 A rock weighs 2 kg and is just on the edge of a cliff 12 m above the beach.

a What is the potential energy of the rock? (Assume $g = 10$ N/kg.)
b The rock falls off the cliff. How much kinetic energy will it have just before it hits the beach?
c Use a calculator to work out the speed of the rock just before it hits the beach. How much will air resistance affect the speed of the rock?

8 A loaded lift needs a force of 6000 N to move it upwards at a steady rate.

a How much work does the force do when the lift moves 25 m upwards?
b If the time it takes to do this is 12 s, show that the power needed is 12.5 kW.

D3
Using energy

We use energy – and misuse it. Studying this section and the next could save you a lot of money...

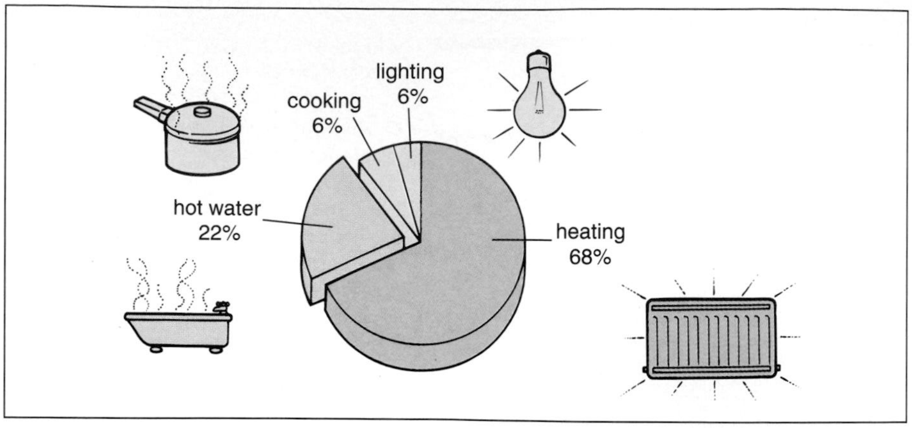

Picture 1 How we use energy in the home.

The costs of energy

Energy is expensive. You have to pay for producing it. You have to pay for moving it to where you want to use it. Getting fossil fuels out of the ground is expensive. 'Human fuel' – food – is even more expensive to produce.

But there are other costs when we use energy. We get most of our energy from fossil fuels. The unwanted by-products are carbon dioxide and some other gases which cause pollution in one way or another. We are only now waking up to the fact that the bills for the greenhouse effect and acid rain and other kinds of pollution have still to come in.

This section deals with the way we use energy in the home, and how we might save money by using less, and wasting less. Look at the pie chart in picture 1. It shows what we use energy for at home.

Home heating

Most of the energy we use at home is used to keep ourselves and our surroundings warm. Nearly all of this heating energy comes from the combustion of fossil fuels, such as coal, oil or gas. We can use the fuels directly or indirectly (see table 1).

Electricity is not a fuel: it is just a very good way of moving energy from one place to another. But the energy it carries is produced in power stations and most of these use fossil fuels.

Table 1 Direct and indirect use of fuels.

Directly
coal, oil or **gas** in fires, stoves, room heaters, central heating systems
Indirectly
electricity in fires, convector heaters, storage heaters

Heating costs

Table 2 shows how much it costs to provide heating using different sources of energy. The most expensive is 'daytime' electricity. Prices will change, of course. This may be due to inflation and changes in world production of oil, for example. But the prices tend to stay much the same in comparison with each other.

Table 2 Costs of producing energy.

Energy source	Cost of producing	
	Yearly cost for typical house (£)	1 megajoule (p)
solid fuel/coal	400	0.02
oil	300	0.015
gas	310	0.016
bottled gas (propane)	550	0.027
electricity		
– daytime	1400	2.0
– night-time	400	0.75

Energy is measured in joules. One joule is a very small quantity of energy. It is about how much you would use to lift this book from a chair to a table. It usually takes a lot of energy to heat things up. For example, to boil a kettle holding 1 kg of water needs about a third of a million joules (0.33 MJ). If this energy were used in working intead of heating, it could raise the kilogram of water higher than the top of Mount Everest! Heating things uses up a lot of energy, and it's by far the biggest part of your household energy use. A 1-bar electric fire is rated at 1 kW (see below). This fire delivers a thousand joules *every second*. In an hour it would deliver 3 600 000 joules (3.6 MJ). This amount of energy is also called a **kilowatt-hour**.

Cleaning, washing and bathing

How much does it cost to have a bath? This depends on how hot you like it,

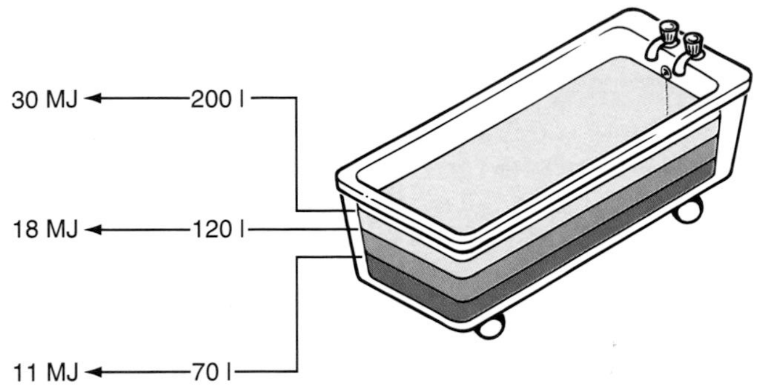

Picture 2 The energy needed to have a bath.

and how much water you use. A standard bath, just about as full as you can have without it spilling, will take 200 litres of water (picture 2). A litre of water has a mass of 1 kg, so you would use 200 kg of water. Tap water is at an average temperature of 10 °C in winter, a hot bath is about 45 °C.

We can use the formula $\boldsymbol{E} = \boldsymbol{mst}$ (see topic D2) to calculate how much heating energy this needs:

$$\text{energy needed, } \boldsymbol{E} = 200\text{ kg} \times 4200\text{ J/kg °C} \times 35\text{ °C}$$
$$= 29.4\text{ MJ}$$

You can use the data in table 2 to work out how much this would cost using different energy sources. Using the most expensive, electricity, it would cost about 50p. It should be cheaper to take a shower – activity B asks you to estimate how much taking a shower costs (picture 3).

Table 3 shows how much energy is needed for different cleaning tasks.

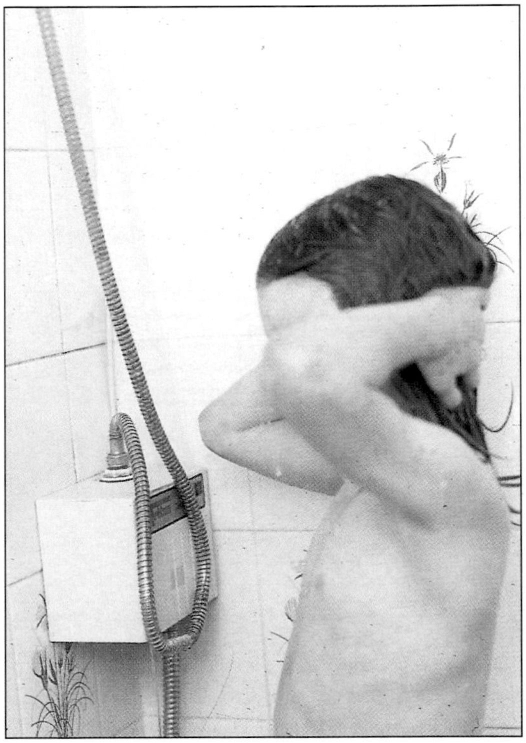

Picture 3 Taking a shower.

Table 3 Energy needed for cleaning tasks.

Washing up (using typical quantities of water)			
in a sink (8 litres)	2 MJ (very hot)		1.3 MJ (hot)
in a plastic bowl (5 litres)	1.3 MJ (very hot)		0.8 MJ (hot)
Washing machine (for clothes)			
using 17 litres of water		heating	5 MJ
		pump, motor	1 MJ
Vacuum cleaning			
for 1 hour		3.6 MJ	

Cooking

Cooking means heating food to a temperature high enough to change the tough fibres of meat and vegetables into a softer form that we can digest. It also kills any bacteria that might be in the food. Cooking takes time, to make sure that the changes, which are in fact chemical reactions, take place.

The higher the temperature the quicker the changes take place. Frying foods is quicker than boiling them. Frying and roasting temperatures are high, from 150 to 240 °C, compared with the boiling water temperature of 100 °C. Salt water boils at a higher temperature than pure water, but only by a degree or two.

Pressure cooking

Water under pressure needs an even higher temperature before it boils. This effect is used in pressure cookers (picture 4). In these cookers, water is kept

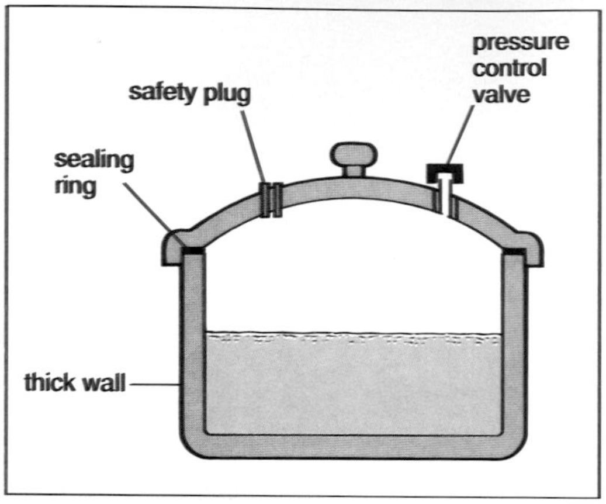

Picture 4 Pressure cookers save energy. How?

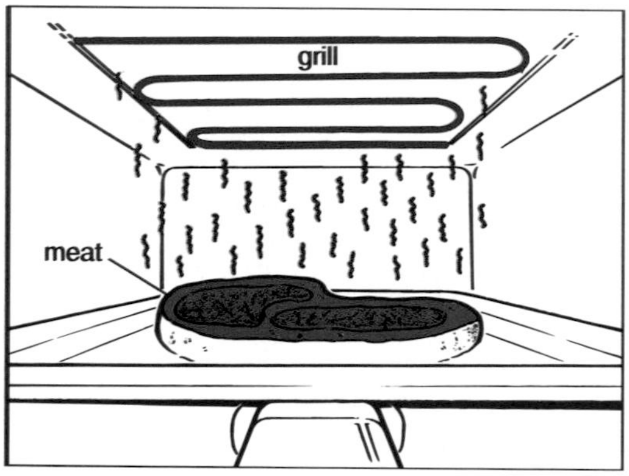

Picture 5 Radiant energy from the hot grill is absorbed in the surface of the food.

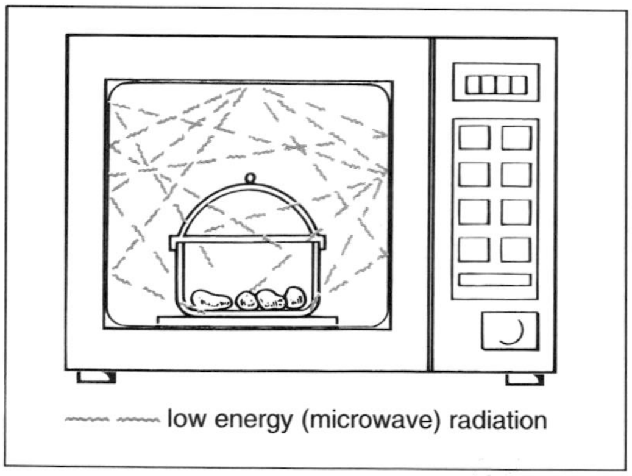

Picture 6 Low energy microwave radiation can pass through glass and plastic and carry heat energy deep into food, where it is absorbed easily by water and fat.

boiling very gently (just *simmering*) at about 120 °C. Even this small rise in temperature reduces cooking times by over a half, thus saving quite a lot of energy.

Cooking with radiation

You do this every time you grill some food. A grill is simply a piece of metal, heated by gas or electricity. Red hot metal gives out not only energy we can see (as red light) but also energy radiation that is invisible – infra-red radiation (see topic C6). In fact, most of the radiant energy in a grill is carried by the infra-red radiation (picture 5). This is absorbed by molecules in the food and the food gets hot, so getting cooked.

Microwaves are like infra-red radiation, but the energy is carried by longer waves (picture 6). The advantage of microwaves is that the waves travel deeper into the food before getting absorbed. This means that the food is cooked on the inside as well as the outside.

In a grill – and with frying and boiling – the energy has to travel in from the surface. This is slow. We can try to speed it up, by making the fat or the grill hotter. But if we do, the outside may burn while the inside is still raw. Another advantage of microwave cooking is that the microwave radiation is not trapped by glass or plastic. It just affects the food material, and particularly the water in it. This saves energy because only the food is heated, not the food container.

Lighting

Good lighting is important. We all spend a great part of our lives under 'artificial' light, and poor lighting causes eyestrain and headaches. Well designed lighting also makes places pleasant to work and live in. The physics of lighting involves:

- how light is produced,
- the colour and colour balance of light,
- how light is reflected or absorbed by objects,
- the energy costs and efficiency of lighting.

Topics C5 and C8 deal with these ideas.

Transferring energy thermally

Modern life is based on our ability to make use of a wide variety of energy sources. Most of the energy we use is for heating things – in cooking and keeping warm. Also, when we use energy to make things work we find that much of the energy we put in ends up making things hot. For example, the energy from petrol finally ends up making brake blocks hot. When we run we get hot. To control the heating and cooling we move energy **thermally**. When thermal transfers occur things are *heated* or *cooled*, or a substance *evaporates, freezes, boils* or *melts*. The words in italics name *thermal processes*, and are described fully below.

Conduction

A hot object can lose energy by transferring it through another substance which touches it. A hot flame will heat the end of a metal rod, and before long the other end of the rod gets hot too: energy has moved along the rod by **conduction**. Metals are all good thermal conductors. If you hold the end of a piece of wood in the flame it will burn, but the end you are holding will stay cool for a long time. Wood is able to conduct energy, but is not as good at this as a metal is. Wood is such a poor conductor it may be called an **insulator**.

Conduction works because when a substance is heated its particles gain energy. In a gas or a liquid they move around more quickly, thus gaining kinetic energy. In a solid the particles vibrate more, gaining a mixture of potential and kinetic energy. This is just like a mass bouncing up and down on the end of a spring. We notice the extra energy as a rise in **temperature**. When one end of

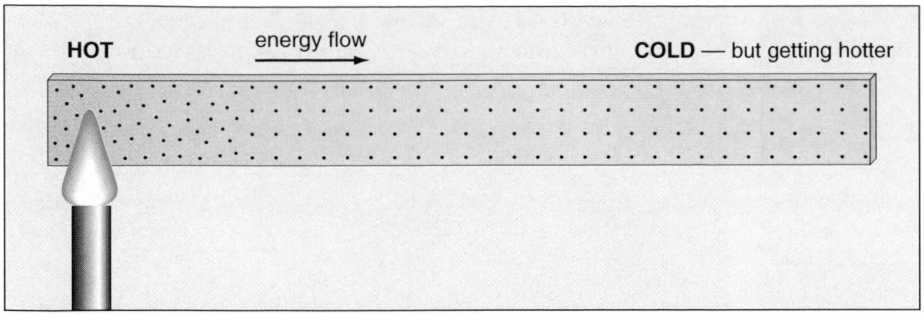

Picture 7 Conduction in a solid. The free electrons in metals are good energy carriers.

a solid is heated the extra vibrations at the hot end affect neighbouring particles, which vibrate more. In turn they affect their neighbours and before long we find that the far end of the solid is getting hot too. Conduction is a vital process in cooking, for example. This is one reason why pots and pans are usually made of metal.

Convection

When a gas or liquid is heated the extra movement of its particles makes them spread out more. This means the fluid gets less dense. As the heated fluid is usually surrounded by cooler, denser fluid it floats upwards, carrying its extra energy with it. 'Hot air rises'. The warmed fluid is replaced by cooler fluid, which is then heated and floats away. The hot object is continually losing energy and so cooling by this process called **convection**. The flow of fluid is called a **convection current**.

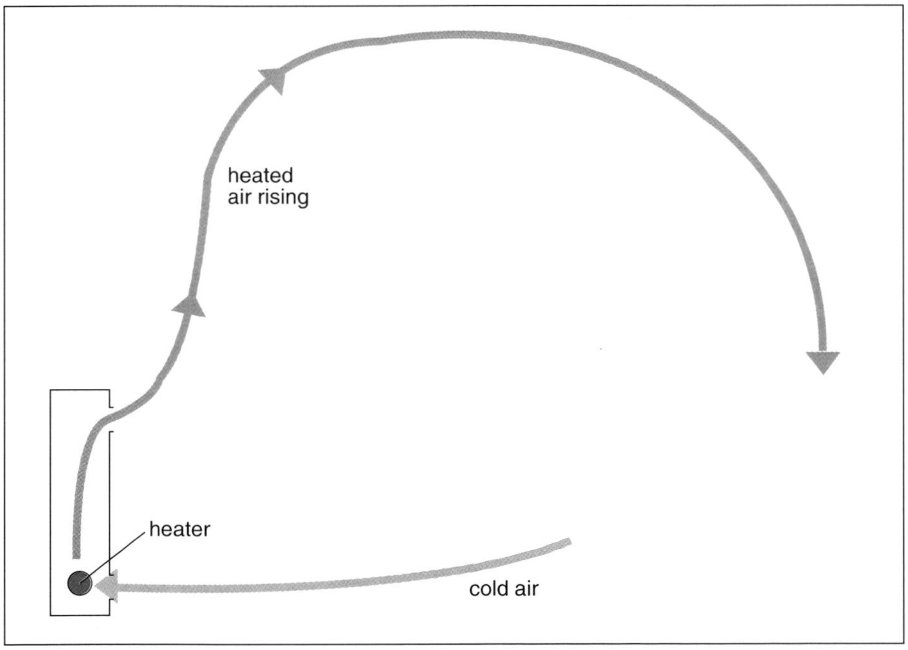

Picture 8 Convection currents in a room.

Radiation

All objects radiate electromagnetic radiation (see topic C6). A hot object radiates more energy than its cooler surroundings, so it loses energy and cools down. Most of the energy is radiated in the waveband called **infra-red**. This consists of electromagnetic waves just longer than light, just off the red end of the visible spectrum. We can feel these rays with nerve cells in the skin – particularly those in the back of the hand.

Picture 9

Picture 10

Controlling thermal loss – or why elephants have big ears

Energy loss by convection and radiation is greater when the area of the hot surface is greater. An elephant is the largest land animal and generates a great deal of waste energy from its metabolism. Biologists know that the larger the animal the smaller its surface area is compared with its mass. Elephants are in danger from overheating; mice are more likely to freeze to death. An elephant uses its ears as coolers by making its blood flow through the large ear flaps (picture 9). The large area increases radiation and allows more convection as more air can be heated by contact. Small animals often keep warm by huddling together to reduce the surface area exposed to cold air (picture 10).

Picture 11

Radiators – good and bad

Domestic radiators are designed to have large surface areas for their volume (picture 11). This allows better convection as more air can be heated as it flows over them. They are not good radiators – partly because of their shape but also because they are usually painted white. White and shiny surfaces are not good at radiating infra-red; the best kind of surface for this is a rough black one.

Objects can be heated by absorbing infra-red radiation. This is how cooking grills and toasters work. Again, black and rough surfaces are better than white or shiny surfaces at absorbing infra-red radiation. It doesn't take long for overtoasted bread to catch fire once it gets blackened.

Insulators

When we want to stop hot objects cooling down we surround them with insulators. Many plastics are good insulators, as are paper, wool, fur and fat – which have important biological uses! Air is a very good insulator, but when it is heated it tends to float away in a convection current. This can be stopped by trapping the air – in pockets between fibres (rocksil, glass fibre, wool, fur, expanded polystyrene) or in layers as in double glazed windows. The trapped air gets warm but does not conduct much energy through it. In cold weather it is better to wear several layers of thin clothes than one thick layer. Picture 12 shows some common insulating materials.

Picture 13 shows various ways in which thermal transfer of energy may be reduced in the home.

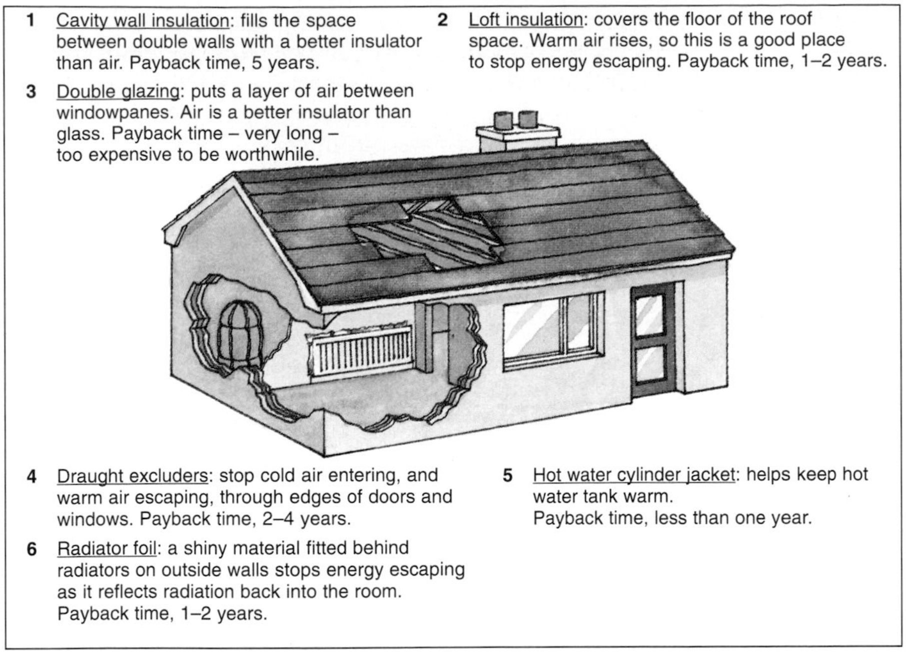

1 Cavity wall insulation: fills the space between double walls with a better insulator than air. Payback time, 5 years.
2 Loft insulation: covers the floor of the roof space. Warm air rises, so this is a good place to stop energy escaping. Payback time, 1–2 years.
3 Double glazing: puts a layer of air between windowpanes. Air is a better insulator than glass. Payback time – very long – too expensive to be worthwhile.
4 Draught excluders: stop cold air entering, and warm air escaping, through edges of doors and windows. Payback time, 2–4 years.
5 Hot water cylinder jacket: helps keep hot water tank warm. Payback time, less than one year.
6 Radiator foil: a shiny material fitted behind radiators on outside walls stops energy escaping as it reflects radiation back into the room. Payback time, 1–2 years.

Picture 13 How to save energy at home.

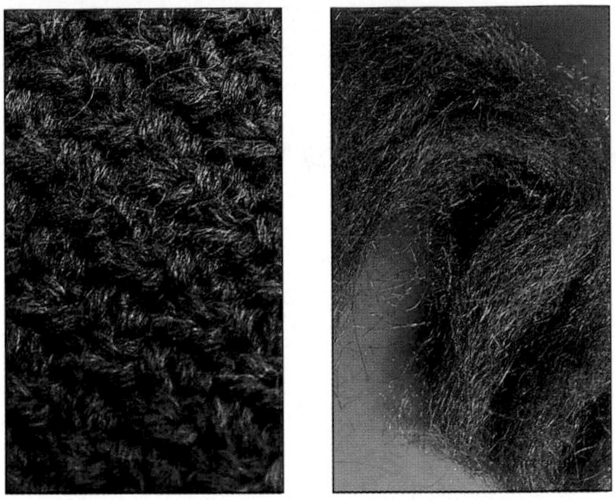

Picture 12

Making things hotter

The energy required to make a kilogram of any material hotter by 1°C is called its **specific heat capacity**. Different materials have different values of specific heat capacity: it takes less energy to heat a kilogram of copper by 1°C than it does to heat a kilogram of water by 1°C. See table 4.

Water has a very large specific heat capacity. Hot water is a useful energy store: when the sea is warmed by the summer sun it keeps warm well into the winter. Britain has a mild winter climate because it is an island. The Gulf Stream helps too: it is a flow of sea water heated in the tropics that is still quite warm after it has flowed across the Atlantic as far as Scotland and Norway.

Table 4

Substance	Specific heat capacity (J/kg °C)
copper	380
aluminium	886
iron	500
lead	127
glass	600
water	4200

Changing state

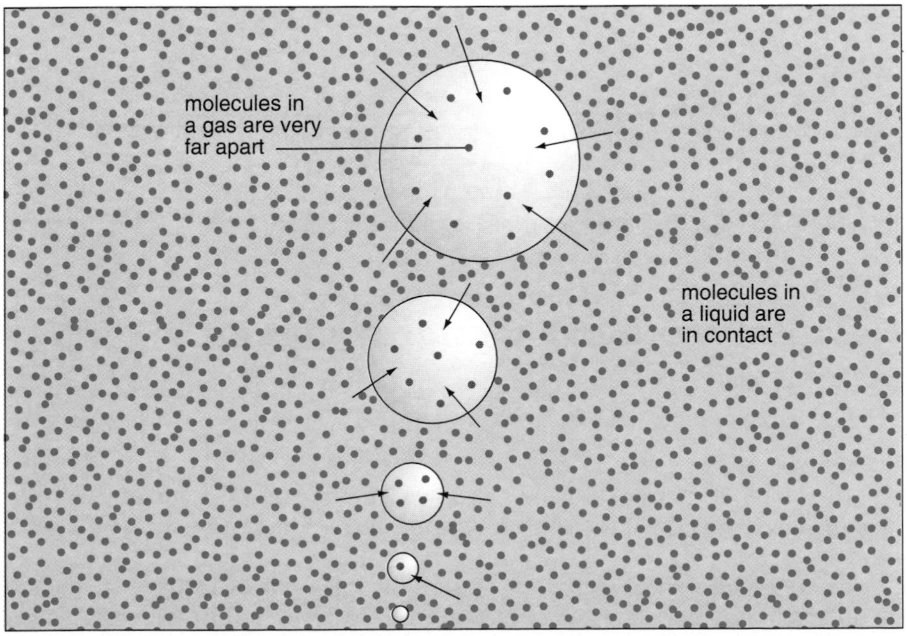

molecules in a gas are very far apart
molecules in a liquid are in contact

Picture 14 Boiling is rapid evaporation of molecules into bubbles inside the liquid.

Cooks in a hurry sometimes think that they can cook potatoes faster by turning up the gas or electricity under the boiling water. But all that happens is that the water boils away faster. It doesn't get any hotter and the potatoes take just as long to cook.

When the water is heated the energy we put in makes its molecules move faster. Its molecules are gaining kinetic energy. Some molecules will move faster than others and are able to escape from the surface – they **evaporate**. When the water is hot enough a kind of rapid internal evaporation takes place. The faster molecules gather together in bubbles, usually at certain points at the bottom of the container. More molecules get into the bubbles which swell and rise to the surface. We say that the water is **boiling** (picture 14). Molecules of water are moving from being part of a liquid to being part of a gas: the water is gradually **changing state**.

When it reaches its boiling point of 100 °C the energy going into it is being used to change its state, not raise its temperature. The energy needed to do this is called **latent heat. Specific latent heat** is the energy transferred when a kilogram of a substance changes state. It always takes more energy to change the state of a substance than to heat it by one Celsius degree. For example, it takes 4.2 kJ to heat a kilogram of water through 1°C, but 334 kJ to melt a kilogram of ice and 2.26 MJ to boil a kilogram of water. The temperature changes of ice as it is steadily heated are shown in picture 15.

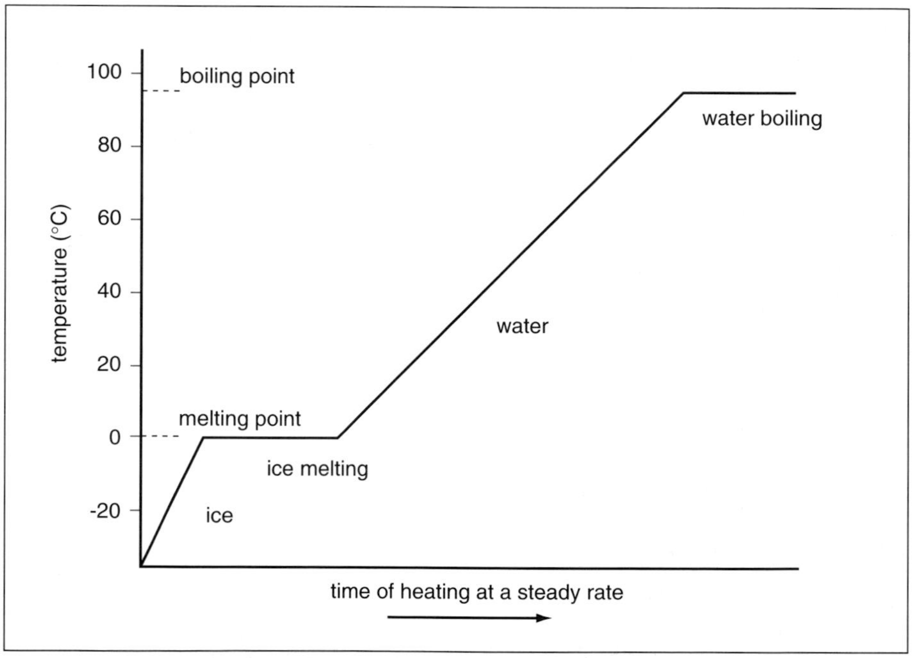

Picture 15 Temperature changes when heating water from ice to steam.

Calculating thermal energy changes

We can calculate the energy required to heat a substance that doesn't change state by using the formula:

$$E = mst$$

where E is the energy supplied in joules, m the mass in kilograms, s the specific heat capacity of the substance and t the rise in temperature. s has the units J/kg °C (or J/kg K).

The energy required to change the state of a mass m of a substance already at the melting or boiling temperature is given by $E = mL$ where L is the specific latent heat.

Refrigerators rely on the high specific latent heat of the refrigerant liquid. Liquids boil more easily under a low pressure. In a refrigerator the liquid is made to flow into a chamber at a lower pressure. The liquid boils and takes energy from its surroundings to do so. The surroundings cool. The vapour is then pumped into long tubes outside the refrigerator where it is compressed by a pump and liquefies. (See pictures 4 and 5 on page 113.) The condensing vapour releases its latent heat to the surroundings. You can see the tubes at the back of the refrigerator in picture 4 (page 113) – they get quite hot when the refrigerator is working hard.

Activities

A Energy and you

What energy do you use at home during a day? Keep a diary for one day and note down what energy-using devices you use, and how long you use them for. Don't forget to add in your share of the family energy use, for cooking, watching TV etc. Make a list like this:

Device time used (hours)
power rating (kilowatts)
energy used (time × power rating)

Hints

1 Don't worry about accuracy too much. A rough idea is all you need.

2 Electrical devices have a label on them giving the power rating. If it is in watts, divide the number by 1000 to get kilowatts.

CARE! Don't check appliances while they are switched on or while they are still hot.

3 You may have to make reasonable guesses about non-electrical devices; ask for help from your teacher if you need to.

B Take a shower!

The calculation on page 105 tells you how much it costs to take a bath. Is showering cheaper? How much energy does it use? To find out you will need to measure:

1 How much water the shower gives per minute.

2 How long you take to shower.

3 How much hotter the shower makes the cold water (the temperature rise).

(*Note:* it takes 4.2 kJ to heat 1 kg of water by just 1°C.)

C Who left that light on?

1 Count up how many electric lights you have in your home or the school science department. What (on average) is their wattage? (This is written on the bulb.) How many watts are used when they are all switched on at the same time?

2 How many watts is a typical electric heater rated at? (If you have one, look at its label to find out.) Write a comment about the energy cost of heating compared with the energy cost of lighting.

D

Plan an experiment to measure either (a) the specific latent heat of melting of ice or (b) the specific latent heat of vaporisation of water.

Questions

1 Put the following energy users into an ordered list, biggest users first: vacuum cleaner, electric kettle, torch bulb, electric cooker oven, room lamp, central heating system, microwave cooker.

If you find this difficult, the table on page 163 may help you.

2 Electrical energy costs 8p a 'unit'. An electric fire uses 2 units of electrical energy an hour. How much does it cost to use the fire for 6 hours a day, 7 days a week?

3 We spend a lot of money heating our homes in the winter. This energy comes into the home in coal, oil, gas or electricity. Where does energy go to in the end?

4 The pie chart in picture 1 on page 104 shows what the average home does with the energy that comes into it. Can you think of any other uses of energy that are not shown? Suggest why they don't appear in the chart.

5 Useful energy devices change one kind of energy into another, or move it from one place to another. What kind of energy changes or moves are involved in the following?

a An electric drill.
b A TV set.
c Using a hand saw to cut through a piece of wood.
d Using a telephone.

6 A full bath of water might need 30 MJ of energy to get the water to a nice comfortable temperature. Use table 2 to check that this would cost about 50p using electricity to heat the water. How much would it cost if the water was heated by an oil burner?

7 When you get out of an open-air swimming pool on a warm but windy day you quickly feel cold. Explain this 'wind-chill' effect.

8 On a hot day the land warms up more quickly than the sea.

a Suggest why this happens.
b As a result of this, we get sea breezes – cool winds that blow in off the sea. Suggest why these breezes occur.

9 Calculate how much energy is needed to heat a bath of water from 20 °C to 50 °C. The bath needs 300 kg of water, which has a specific heat capacity of 4.2 kJ/kg °C.

10 a How much energy would be needed to boil away the bathful of water of question 9 (starting at 20 °C)?

b How much energy would the water release to the surroundings if it cooled from 20 °C and then froze?

D4
Saving and wasting – the laws of energy

Energy cannot be created, and it cannot be destroyed. But it can be wasted.

Picture 1 Working against gravity.

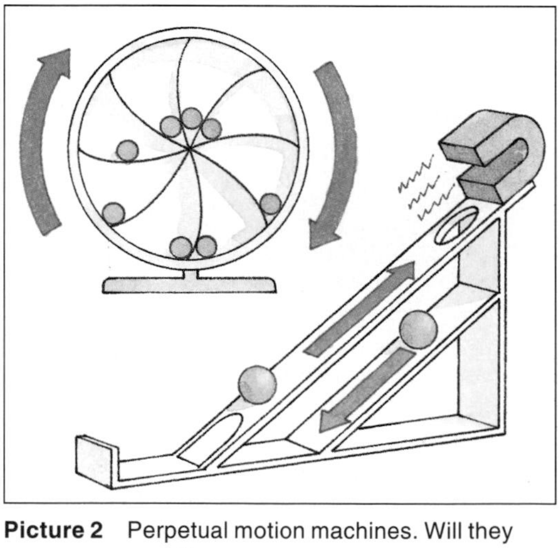

Picture 2 Perpetual motion machines. Will they work?

Whenever we use energy we are moving it from one system to another. The first three topics in this section give many examples of this **transfer** of energy. We are using the energy to **do work**. When you lift a weight you are transferring energy from your body system (sugar and oxygen in the blood) to do work against the force of gravity. If the weight is large you know that you are doing work! (See picture 1.) After you have lifted it the weight is higher above the ground and so has more **gravitational potential energy**. (See topics B4 and D1.)

There are very many other examples of energy transfers like this. The fact that energy can move from one system to another is the basis of life on earth. It is the basis of all movement, and of all the industries that we rely on in the modern world.

In studying energy changes scientists have discovered the laws which describe how energy behaves. They are called the **Laws of Thermodynamics**, and this topic is about the two most important of these.

The First Law – you can't win

This law is very simple. It says that whenever any changes take place there is just as much energy at the end as there was in the beginning. Like many of the most important ideas in science, it is impossible to prove this! But the law has been tested, time and time again.

Very careful measurements in all kinds of experiments have shown that in every single case **energy has been neither lost nor created**. Of course, one day someone might do a test in which energy is lost or created, and this would disprove the law.

This first law is the law of the **conservation** of energy. Many people have tried to disprove this law, and all of them have failed. It would be so nice to be able to create energy from 'nothing'. Life on Earth would be very convenient if someone could design an engine or a machine which gave out more energy than you put into it.

Picture 2 shows two designs for such a machine. Look at them. Can you see how they are supposed to work? Can you see why they won't work?

What the law means in practice is that with any machine or engine the best we can do is get out as much energy as we put into it. But even this is optimistic. For real machines we always get less energy out than we put in. This is because of the *Second Law*.

The Second Law – you always lose!

Whenever we use energy to do a job of work some of the energy we put in seems to escape. It just doesn't go where we want it to.

When you lift a weight you give it some potential energy. But this is less than the energy produced in your muscles by the chemical reaction (respiration) between sugar and oxygen. Some of that energy goes to make your muscles warmer (see picture 3).

When you do a lot of work you have to sweat a lot to get rid of this 'waste energy'. It ends up warming your surroundings. The molecules in the air move a little faster as a result. They gain some kinetic energy.

The Second Law simply says that when work is done there is always some energy that will somehow escape and spread itself out. It usually ends up as 'heat', which in basic energy terms means that millions upon millions of molecules move a little faster.

Can we get this 'waste' energy back?

Yes – we *can* get this energy back. There is no law of physics that stops us. All we have to do is slow down all those molecules and do some useful work with the energy they lose. Or we could concentrate the energy in one place to warm something up. For example, we could put this energy into water in a central heating system.

The problem is, how can we concentrate this spread-out energy in one place? It is not easy to do, particularly if the energy has spread out a long way over millions of different particles.

Making spread-out energy concentrated

If you have a refrigerator at home this is exactly what it is doing. It is taking movement energy from the molecules of the foods inside it. They cool down as a result, so that the food stays fresh longer. The energy they lose is given to the air. You can check this effect for yourself. At the back of the refrigerator you will find a set of tubes which feel warm because of the energy that the food has lost (picture 4).

But this energy is still wasted. After all, we don't normally buy refrigerators to use as house-warmers. But what if we used the same idea, say, to take energy *out of the surroundings* and feed it into our homes? This is simply using a 'refrigerator' in reverse! Such heaters do exist, and they are called **heat pumps**. They take energy out of the air or the ground instead of out of food, and 'pump' it *into* the house to warm it.

Picture 5 shows a commercial heat pump. It is used in large buildings. These need ventilating, which means that warmed, smelly air has to be taken out of the building. This has to be replaced by fresh air – which is cold in winter. One end of the heat pump is placed in the warm 'exhaust air' and takes the heat energy out of it. This energy is pumped to the cold air coming into the building, so that it is 'prewarmed'. This cuts down the heating bills.

Something for nothing?

But this effect doesn't happen all by itself. Refrigerators and heat pumps contain a liquid which has to be pumped around the system. The pumps are usually driven by an electric motor and this needs energy to run it. When all the energy sums are done we find that we still get less energy out than goes in, and that *overall* the energy still gets more spread out!

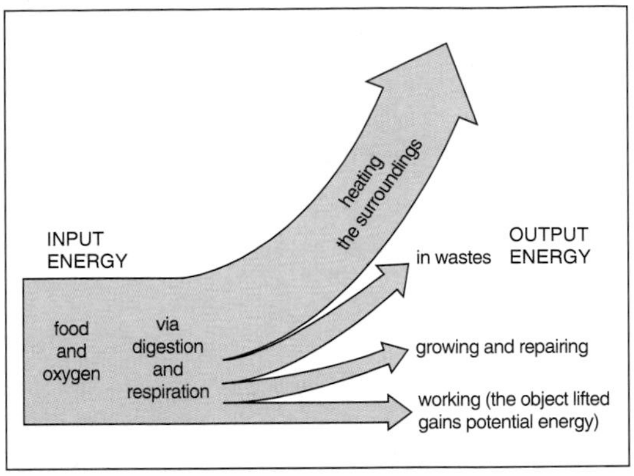

Picture 3 What the body does with the energy it gets – only a small amount can be used to do work.

Picture 4 In a fridge the energy taken out of the cooling food warms the air.

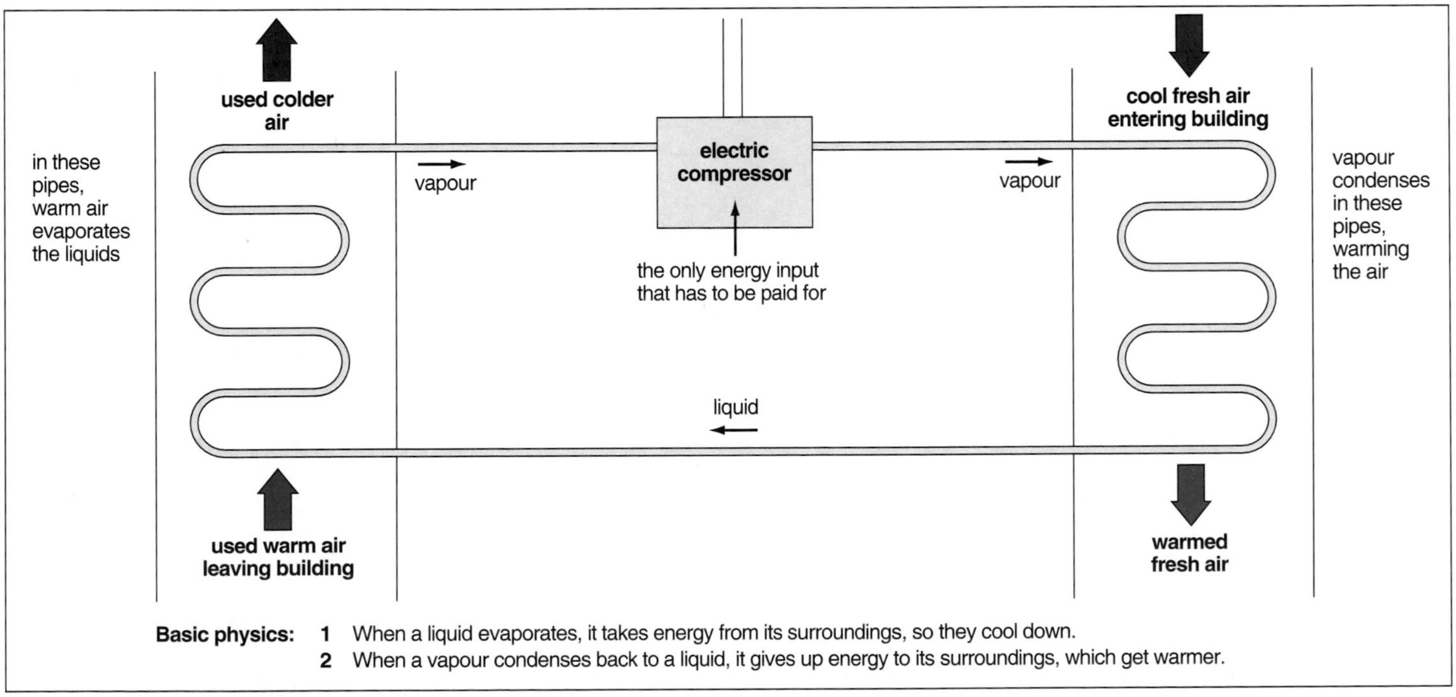

Picture 5 How a heat pump works.

Efficiency

Being *efficient* means being effective at doing a job. The **efficiency** of a machine or engine measures how good it is, in terms of how much of the energy put into it is used where you want it. Efficiency is measured by how much useful energy you get out compared with what is put in. It is usually converted to a percentage:

$$\text{efficiency} = \frac{\text{useful energy output}}{\text{energy input}} \times 100\%$$

Table 1 shows the typical efficiency of some energy devices. Some of them, like engines and some machines, use energy from a fuel system to do work. Cars, bicycles, electric drills and trains do this. Other devices are used to make energy more 'usable'. They might do this by taking energy from a fuel–oxygen system and putting it into an electrical system. This is what power stations do. Electricity is very useful because it makes it so easy to move energy from one place to another.

Table 1 Typical efficiency of energy devices.

	Engines and machines producing movement or doing work (%)	**Energy 'movers'** (%)
train: diesel engine	36	–
car: petrol engine	15	–
train: steam engine	15	–
train: electric motor	90	–
car gears	–	93
bicycle	–	90
car jack	–	15
electric power station	35	–
transformer (electrical)	–	97
human muscle	40	–

Gears and *transmission systems* in cars, trains and bicycles are the mechanical versions of electric transmission. They carry energy from one part of a **mechanical** system to another. They also allow the force that eventually does the work to be made small or large, according to what is needed.

Useful laws

The laws of energy were discovered in the 19th century. They were also very useful in helping to design engines. It was scientists' understanding of these laws that helped improve steam engines and led to the development of car engines (internal combustion engines).

Some puzzling questions – and a surprising answer!

But there were very important questions about energy that these laws couldn't explain. Two of these questions were to do with the Sun and the Earth. We know that the Sun is sending out huge quantities of energy. It has been doing this for thousands of millions of years. What is not so well-known is the fact that the Earth is also giving out energy. This energy is seeping up from the centre of the Earth, causing volcanoes and earthquakes, warming the atmosphere and, eventually, being lost to space. *Where does this energy actually come from? Why does the Sun keep on shining? If the Earth is losing so much heat, why doesn't it cool down?*

The answer to these questions was given by the physicist Albert Einstein. He was able to prove that **matter** – the stuff that makes ordinary atoms and molecules – can be converted to energy such as in electromagnetic radiations. The Sun keeps on shining by actually losing mass – at the rate of four million tonnes a second.

Most people have heard of Einstein's famous equation that calculates the amount of energy E that can be obtained by destroying a quantity of matter, m:

$$E = mc^2$$

where c is the speed of light.

This discovery meant that scientists had to think again about the First Law, the Law of Conservation of Energy. *It would only work if mass was thought of as a kind of energy!* This was a very strange idea. This story continues in topic D5.

Activities

A Talking about biology and energy

Read about – or remind yourself about – the energy flow through an 'ecosystem'. Discuss, and come to an agreement about the following questions:

- What is the source of the energy that all the organisms make use of?
- Where does it all go in the end?
- Which organisms are best (most efficient) at using energy?
- In an ecosystem, materials are often recycled. Is energy recycled?

Write down, briefly, your agreed answers to these questions.

B Moving forever

Design a 'perpetual motion' machine – a machine that goes on moving by itself, forever, without needing any fuel supply or energy input. Draw a picture of your design, with a few words of explanation.

C The efficiency of a machine

Design an experiment to measure the efficiency of a machine. This could be a pulley system, a car jack, a wheel-and-axle, etc. When you have designed your experiment, get it checked by your teacher before you do it.

Hints and tips
You will need to measure the forces involved – the **effort** and the **load**. You will also need to measure the **distances** that these forces move.

The input energy is the work done by the effort. The output energy is measured by what happens to the load.

In both cases the same formula applies:
work = force × distance moved
(measured in the direction the force acts). If you have forgotten about machines look up topic A4.

D The efficiency of an electric motor

Use a low voltage electric motor. Make it lift a load and measure how much work it does in doing this. The formula is given in activity C.

You can measure the electrical energy supplied to the motor in one of two ways. The easy way is to use a joulemeter which is a special electrical energy meter.

Or you can use an ammeter, a voltmeter and a stopwatch. The energy supplied electrically is then given by the formula:

energy = voltage × current × time in seconds.

Questions

1 A car stands in front of the owner's house. It has a full tank of petrol. After a long drive the car comes back and stops in front of the house. The tank is now empty. What has happened to the energy that was stored in the petrol? (There is a very short answer to this question!)

2 The Moon is the main cause of the tides in the sea. Careful measurements show that the Moon is actually slowing down as it goes around the Earth. Use the Law of Conservation of Energy to explain this.

3 A small hoist (pulley system) lifts a load and gives it 3000 J of potential energy. The person who used the hoist supplied it with 5000 J of work. What is the efficiency of the hoist?

4 The efficiency of a type of car jack is 25%. It takes 1000 J of energy to lift a car high enough to replace a wheel. How much work must be done by the worker who uses the jack?

5 Why do you think engines (petrol, steam) are so much less efficient than gears or bicycles?

6 Picture 6 shows the energy system of a light bulb. It is called a 'Sankey Diagram'. It shows that energy is delivered electrically, and that most of this energy is wasted. Only a small percentage is delivered as useful light.

Draw a similar diagram for one of the following:

a Boiling a kettle of water on a gas ring.
b Sawing through a log of wood.
c Just sitting on a chair.
d Winding up an old-fashioned (spring) clock.

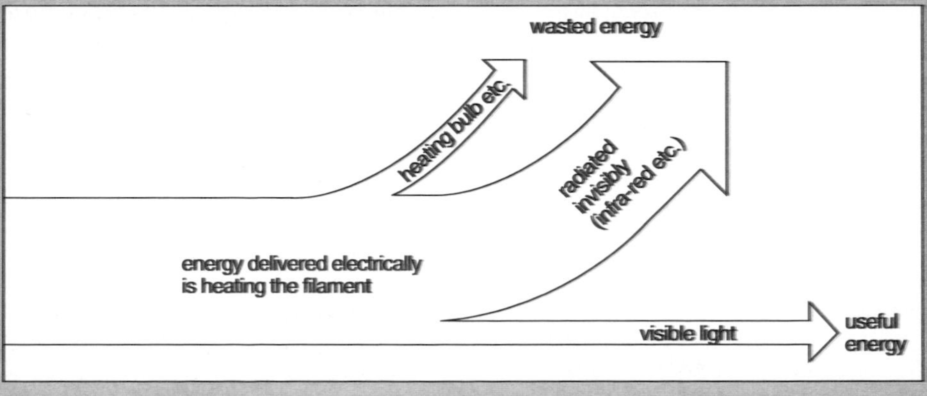

Picture 6

D5 Radioactivity

One of the great discoveries of the 20th century was a new energy source. Matter itself could be transformed into energy.

Picture 1 shows people protesting against a new nuclear power station that was being built at Sizewell in Suffolk.

We live in a world which is using up its fossil fuels many times more quickly than they can possibly be replaced. When they are burnt they release carbon dioxide which will very likely change the Earth's climate, by the greenhouse effect.

Nuclear energy seems an ideal alternative to fossil fuels. The materials are quite cheap. When they are used they do not make any polluting gases. For coal-fired power stations there are transport problems in getting hundreds of tonnes of coal to the site every day. Nuclear power stations do not have this problem.

These are the kinds of reasons which have led many countries to build nuclear power stations. In France, for example, more than half of their electricity is generated by nuclear power. In the UK we generate just under 20% of our electricity in this way.

But there are also many objections to using nuclear power. Many countries have decided not to build any more nuclear power stations. This topic and the next deal with the physics of nuclear energy, its benefits and dangers.

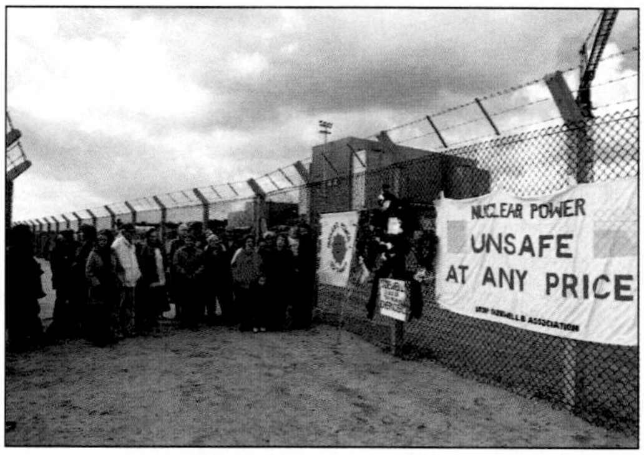

Picture 1 Not everyone wants to use nuclear energy.

Radioactivity

Radioactivity was discovered in 1895 by a French scientist called Henri Becquerel. A **radioactive** substance is one that sends out very energetic rays. There are three types of ray. All of them can damage living things, but they are also very useful. When they were first discovered nobody knew exactly what they were. So they simply named them **alpha, beta** and **gamma** rays, after the first three letters of the Greek alphabet.

Alpha, beta, gamma

Table 1 summarises the properties of these rays. It took scientists twenty years after they were first discovered to work out what the radiations actually were, and that they were coming from the **nucleus** of the atom. The structure of the atom is summarised in picture 2.

One property that these radiations possess is their ability to **ionise** atoms and molecules. The radiations knock electrons out of the atoms to turn them into **ions** (picture 3). The atoms and molecules become positively charged. Thus the radiations are called **ionising radiations**.

The reason they are dangerous to life is that they ionise atoms in living cells, which can kill the cells (see topic D8).

The radiations travel at high speeds, as if they are shot out of the nucleus like a bullet from a gun. What was puzzling to the scientists who first worked with these radiations was where they got the energy from to do this. We now

Table 1 Nuclear radiations.

Radiation type	What they are	Range in air	Stopped by	Comments
alpha	Positively charged. **nuclei** of helium (^4_2He)	A few centimetres	A sheet of paper	Because they are so massive and carry a double positive charge they easily affect atoms. They make lots of ions and don't travel far. Alpha emitters are quite safe unless they get into the body.
beta	Negatively charged. Fast-moving **electrons**	A few tens of centimetres	A few millimetres of aluminium	Electrons are small and so can travel further than alpha particles as they don't collide as often. Dangerous but easily stopped.
gamma	Uncharged. Very short wavelength **electromagnetic waves** (high-energy photons)	They go on indefinitely	A metre or two of concrete	These are genuine 'rays'. They don't ionise atoms very easily and so travel a long way. They travel at the speed of light. Dangerous because they are hard to shield against.

know that it comes from the conversion of matter into energy, and this is explained more fully in topic D7.

Detecting the radiations

We detect the rays from atoms using the fact that the rays ionise other atoms. Picture 4 shows the tracks of alpha particles travelling through damp air. The water vapour in the air condenses as droplets on the **ions** made from the air by the alpha particles. This leaves a 'vapour trail' like the ones made by high flying aircraft. This picture was taken as the alpha particles travelled through a special 'cloud chamber'. This contains cool damp air, which is good at making clouds and vapour trails.

Picture 5 shows another detector which makes use of ionisation. It is a GM tube, or **Geiger–Muller tube**. It contains a gas at a low pressure. The inner wire is at a high voltage. When some ionising radiation goes into the tube it makes ions in the gas. The wire attracts them and so there is a short pulse of current when the ions hit the wire. This is amplified and can be counted by an electronic **pulse counter**. Thus each time a 'ray' gets into the tube it produces a pulse which can be counted.

Geiger counters like this are the most common way of finding out how much radioactivity is present. Radiation also affects photographic film, which can be used in film badges to monitor background radiation levels.

Alpha particles

Alpha particles are very good at ionising other atoms. This suggests that they carry a lot of energy. This is movement energy (kinetic energy).

But they don't travel very far in air. They barge through the air like a bull in a china shop, hitting lots of air molecules and knocking electrons off them (picture 4). As they do this they lose energy quite rapidly, so they soon slow down.

If we put a piece of paper in the way the alpha particles can't get through it! This is because they hit a lot of atoms in the paper.

Alpha particles are electrically charged, carrying two units of positive charge. This is twice as much as the (negative) charge carried by an electron.

Because alpha particles are positively charged they are affected by both electric and magnetic fields. Scientists have worked out exactly what alpha particles are by measuring how strongly they are affected by these fields.

These measurements show that alpha particles are in fact **helium nuclei,** which are four times as heavy as hydrogen nuclei. They have, therefore, an atomic mass of four. They are made up of two protons (positive particles) and two neutrons, joined very firmly together (picture 6).

Beta particles

Beta particles do not cause as much ionisation as alpha particles. Also, they travel much further in air before running out of energy. This suggests that they are lighter and smaller than alpha particles. They carry a single unit of negative charge. Measurements using electric and magnetic fields show that they are in fact **high-speed electrons**. An alpha particle is 7333 times as massive as a beta particle.

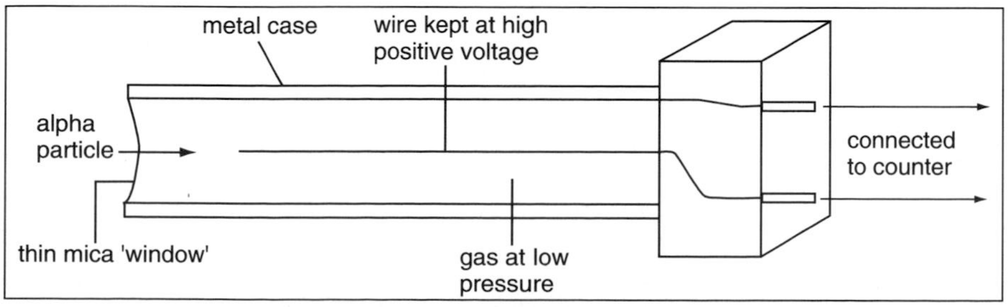

Picture 5 A GM tube. When an alpha particle, for example, enters the tube, it ionises the gas inside. This triggers off a sudden flow of freed electrons to the wire. This registers as a 'count' or a 'click'.

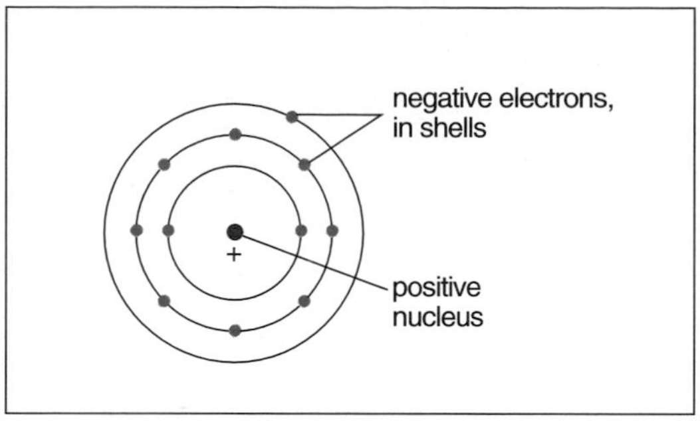

Picture 2 Rutherford's model: a nuclear atom.

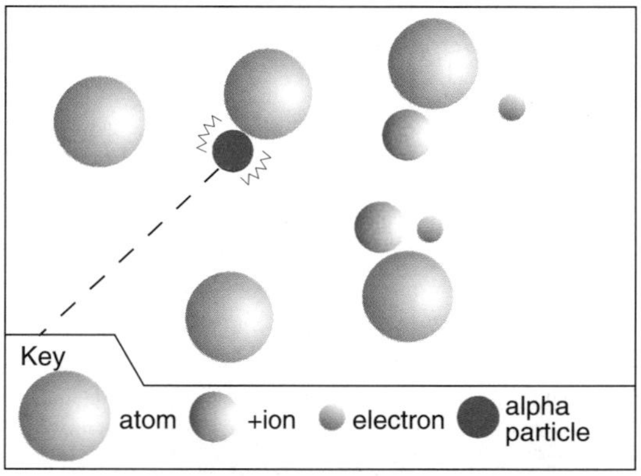

Picture 3 How alpha particles ionise atoms.

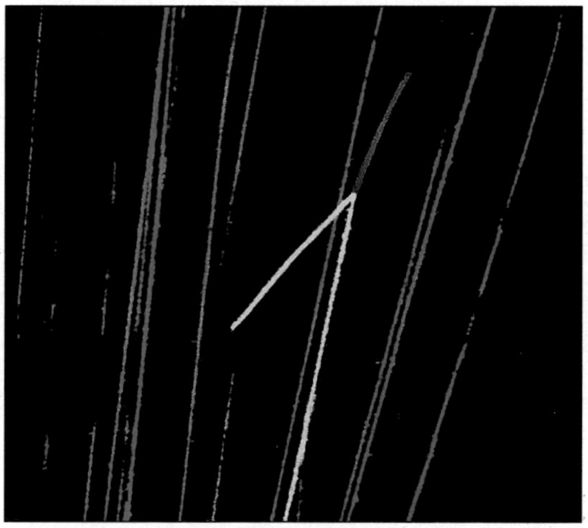

Picture 4 The tracks of alpha particles in a 'cloud chamber'.

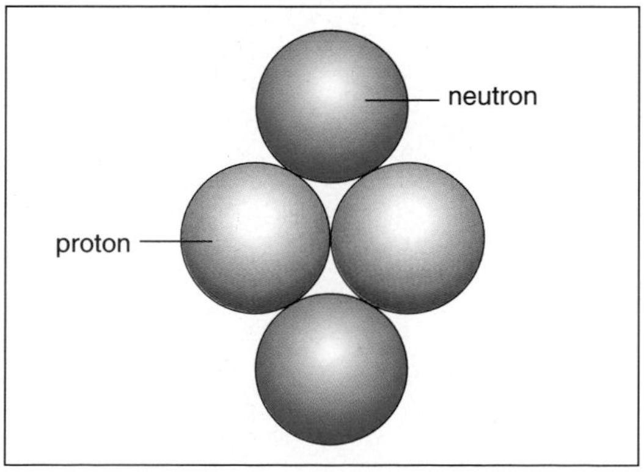

Picture 6 A helium nucleus.

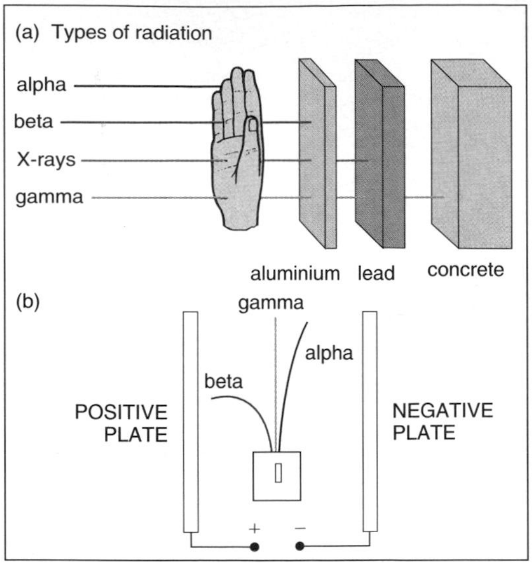

Picture 7 (a) What stops the radiations – or doesn't! (X-rays are shown for a comparison.) (b) What happens to the radiations in an electric field.

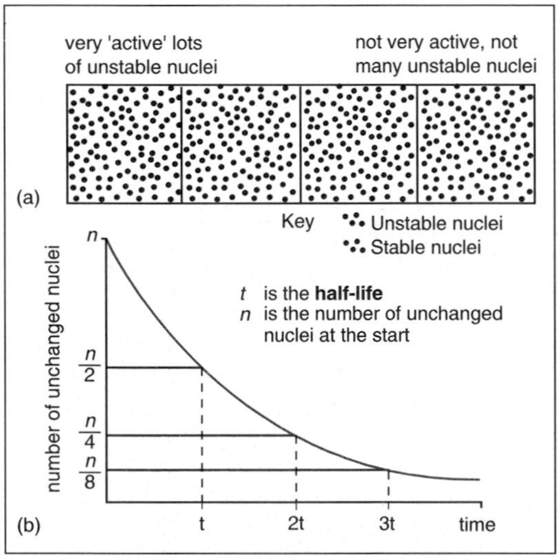

Picture 8 (a) Radioactive decay. The activity of a radioactive substance gets less all the time. This is because the number of unstable, active nuclei gets less. But there is a catch – the new nuclei may also be unstable! (b) A half-life graph.

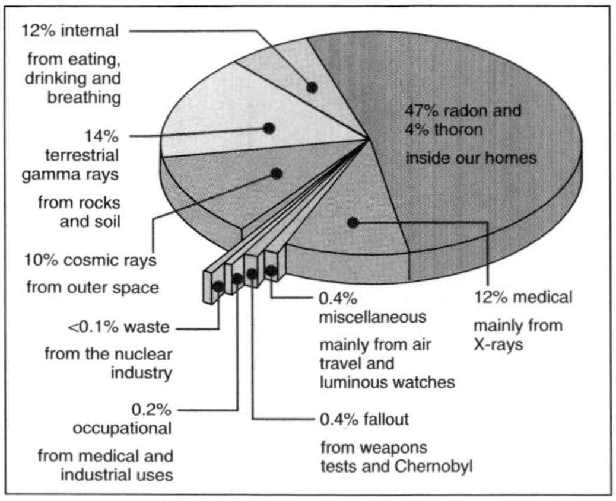

Picture 9 Where background radiation comes from.

Because they are so small, beta particles can travel through matter more easily than alpha particles can. But a few millimetres of aluminium will stop them.

Gamma rays

Gamma rays do not cause much ionisation and they travel quite freely, through air. They carry no charge and so are not at all affected by electric or magnetic fields. This means that they are very **penetrating**. They can travel through thick blocks of concrete, and it takes up to a centimetre or so thickness of a heavy metal like lead to cut down the radiation by a half.

Gamma rays are different from the alpha and beta particles because they have no mass. They travel at the speed of light, and are a type of **electromagnetic radiation**, like light and X-rays. But they carry more energy than X-rays do.

Picture 7 shows how the three kinds of radiation compare in their ability to pass through matter, and what happens to them in an electric field.

Half-life

Radiations are given out by decaying atoms. As the atom decays to something else, it 'spits out' the radiation. In a sample of uranium the nuclei don't decay all at once. In fact, only a very tiny fraction of the nuclei in the sample decay each day. It will take four and a half thousand million years for just half of the nuclei in a lump of uranium (U) to decay.

On the other hand, it will take only 52 seconds for half of the nuclei in a sample of radon gas (Rn-220) to decay. These times are called **half-lives**, and we can measure them very accurately.

Picture 8(a) shows how the number of undecayed nuclei left in a sample of a radioactive element changes with time. Picture 8(b) shows this in the form of a graph.

The **count rate** is a measure of the number of rays given out per second. As time goes on this count rate will go down, as more and more of the nuclei have decayed. What happens to the nucleus when it decays is dealt with in the next topic.

Your teacher should be able to show you an experiment about how the rate of radioactive decay gets less as time goes on. You should be able to get results to allow you to measure the half-life of a radioactive material. Some sample results are given in question 3 on page 119.

In activity A you can simulate radioactive decay.

Background radiation

Nuclear radiation is all around us. It comes from the rocks and the soil; it comes from plants and even animals. This is because they all contain tiny amounts of radioactive materials that are naturally present on Earth. Some comes from elements made radioactive by radiation from outer space, some from atomic weapons testing 30 or 40 years ago. A small amount comes from the operation of nuclear power stations. Also, the nuclear accident in Russia (at Chernobyl) in 1986 produced radioactive 'fall out'.

Picture 9 summarises where this background radiation comes from. It is too low to have a serious effect on health, but it does have some effect. Doctors estimate that background radiation causes 1200 deaths from cancer per year in Britain. It is also likely that this radiation affects the genes in sex cells, so causing slight changes from one generation to the next. This may be one of the main causes of biological **variation**, which is necessary for evolution to occur.

Radioactive dating

Radioactive elements decay into lighter elements. They decay at a known rate. So, using a special machine called a mass spectrometer, scientists can measure how much of the original radioactive element is left and how much of the new, lighter elements are present. The ratio of the two gives a fairly accurate estimate of the age of the rock.

For example, potassium-40 (K) has a half-life of 1.3 billion years (1.3×10^9 years). It decays, eventually, to a stable isotope of argon (Ar). A sample of rock is found to have three times as many argon atoms as potassium atoms. We can work out how old the rock is as follows.

Suppose there were 1000 potassium atoms to start with, when the rock was newly made.

Time in half-lives	Number of K atoms	Number of Ar atoms
start	1000	0
1	500	500
2	250	750

So it takes two half-lives to produce three times as many argon atoms as there are potassium atoms left. This means that the rock is 2.6 billion years old.

Radioactive dating has been used to measure the age of meteorites and moonrocks. These measurements suggest that the whole Solar System, Earth, meteorites and the Moon were formed at the same time – 4.6 billion years ago. For the first four billion of those years, there was no life as we know it, and people have only been on the Earth for the last 0.003 billion years. We shall learn more about how the Earth was made in topic F4.

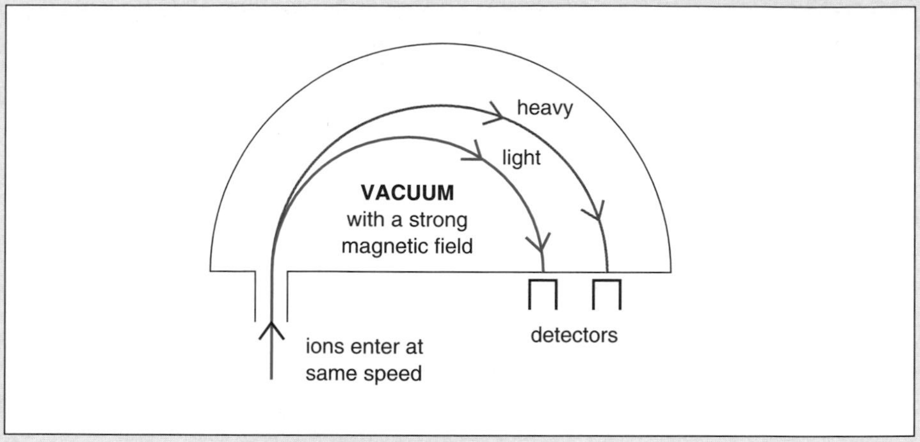

Picture 1 The principle of the mass spectrometer.
The atoms being investigated are ionised and accelerated by an electrical field into a vacuum chamber containing a strong magnetic field. The magnetic field makes the ions move in circular paths. The more massive atoms (red path) don't curve as much as lighter atoms (green path). The machine can therefore separate atoms of different mass – and uses electronics to count how many of each there are.

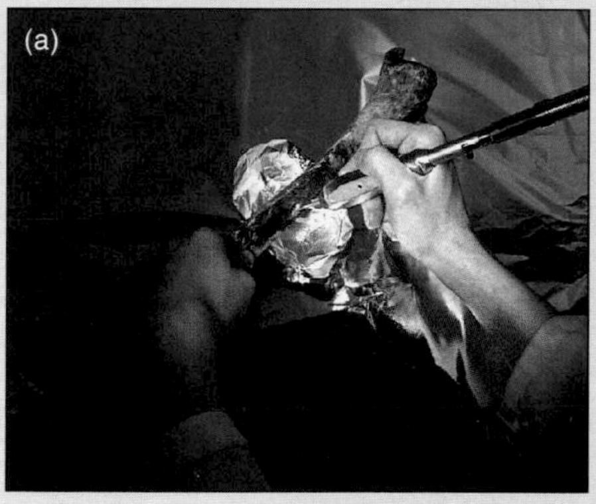

Picture 2 Radiocarbon dating using carbon-14.
(a) Scientists use very small samples – here being taken from a reindeer bone.
(b) The bone samples are dissolved in a solvent to release the amino acids containing carbon.

Activity

Half-life

The idea of *half-life* is very important in nuclear physics. It is an example of how *random* events can produce a predictable result. A random event is one that we cannot predict – like the number you get when you throw a die. Many calculators and computers will also be able to generate 'random numbers'. Radioactive decay is an example of a random event because we cannot predict when any given atom will in fact decay and give off radiation. Here are two ways of investigating such random numbers to help understand the idea of half-life.

1 Using dice
Six-sided wooden cubes can be used instead of real dice, which are too expensive. You will need 500 of them! Each cube has a spot painted on one face. When you throw one cube, there is a one-in-six chance of the spot side facing upwards. The cubes represent atoms, and if they fall spot side up they have 'decayed'.

This activity is best done by a team, otherwise it takes quite a long time. Choose a clean floor, preferably free of furniture.

a **Guess!** How many cubes will have the spot side up when you throw all the dice?

b **Now try this.** Put all the cubes in a large box and shake them a lot. Pour them out on to the floor – taking care not to lose any. Pick out all the cubes that have fallen spot-side up and put them aside. Count them. Was your prediction reasonably accurate?

c Collect all the dice that didn't 'decay' on this first throw. Now repeat stage (b) again, using these undecayed cubes. Again, collect and count the number that fell spot side up, and take them out of use. Repeat the throwing of the undecayed cubes another four times, so that you have six 'counts' altogether.

d Plot a graph of the number of cubes that decayed (the 'count') at each throw against the throw number (1 to 6). Does this look like the half-life graph of radioactive decay in picture 8(b)? Explain why they are similar, and why they are different. Hint: a millionth of a millionth of a gram of radon gas contains over 2 thousand million atoms.

e Use the graph to calculate the 'half-life' of the cubes – the number of throws needed for half of the cubes to 'decay'.

2 Using a computer
This simulation uses the ability of a computer to generate random numbers. It is written in BASIC and should run on all computers. You don't need to type in the REM statements.

```
10 CLS: REM … a simulation of radioactive decay

20 N = 2000: T = 0: remainder = N: REM … N is number of nuclei at start, when time T = 0, remainder are the nuclei left unchanged

30 DIM nuclei(N): REM … sets up an array to store results

40 FOR T = 1 TO 10

50 D = 0: REM … D is the number of nuclei that will decay in each loop

60 FOR P = 0 TO remainder

70 LET nuclei(P) = RND(6): REM this generates random numbers between 1 and 6

80 IF nuclei(P) = 1 THEN N = N—1:D = D + 1: REM … if the random number is 1 then a nucleus decays

90 remainder = N

100 NEXT P

110 PRINT T, D: REM … D is the number of nuclei that decay in each loop of the program printed next to the 'time' T

120 NEXT T

130 END
```

(*Note:* for some BASIC programs you need to change line 70 to

70 LET nuclei(P) = INT(RND*5)

a Type in the program and RUN it. Copy down (or print out) the list of numbers and plot them against T.

b Does this graph look like the half-life graph of radioactive decay in picture 8(b)? Explain why they are similar, and why they are different. (*Hint* a millionth of a millionth of a gram of radon gas contains over two thousand million atoms.)

c Use your graph to work out the half-life of the nuclei in this simulation.

d If you have time, investigate the effect of changing N and of changing the random numbers allowed (e.g. from 1 in 6 to 1 in 4).

Questions

1 Consider alpha, beta and gamma radiations. Which:

a travels at the speed of light?
b causes the most ionisation?
c has the same mass as an electron?
d is stopped by a few millimetres of aluminium?
e is the most massive?

2 Why aren't gamma rays affected by an electric field?

3 Use the figures in the table to work out the half-life of the radioactive isotope (polonium-218). There's a quick way and a long way – use the quick way!

4 A sample of a radioactive substance was sending out 4000 alpha particles a second at the start of an experiment. Ten minutes later it was sending out 2000 particles per second.

a What is the half-life of the substance?
b How long after the start would you expect to measure a count of 500 particles a second?
c How much activity (in counts per second) would you expect after ten half-lives?
d The natural 'background' count of radiation comes from radioactive materials in the ground or in the air. It is about two counts per second in most places. How long would it take for the radiation from the radioactive waste to be just less than this background count?

Time (minutes)	0	1	2	3	4	5	6	7
Count rate (counts/second)	260	205	160	129	104	82	64	51

1 a Explain what you understand by *radioactive half-life.*

b Uranium-238 has a half-life of 4.5 billion years (4.5×10^9 years). By a remarkable coincidence, the Earth is believed to be about 4.5 billion years old. How much of the original uranium-238 is still on Earth, unchanged?

2 A rock specimen is guessed to be about 100 million years old. Which of the following radioactive elements found in it would be most useful in measuring its age by radioactive dating? Give a reason for your answer.

Element	**Half-life**
uranium-238	4.5 billion years
radium-226	1620 years
lead-205	50 million years
thorium-230	80 000 years

3 A radioactive isotope of carbon, carbon-14, is used to date pieces of wood or bone dug up on archeological sites. It has a half-life of 5730 years.

a How does carbon get into (i) wood (ii) bone? (*Hint* think about photosynthesis.)

b An old wooden bow was found in a desert cave. A specimen of carbon from the wood was found to have an activity of 300 counts per minute. The same mass of carbon from modern wood has an activity of 400 counts per minute.

(i) Which specimen has more radioactive carbon in it?

(ii) Show that a reasonable estimate would be that the bow is between 2800 and 2900 years old.

D6 What happens when atoms decay?

They make new atoms!

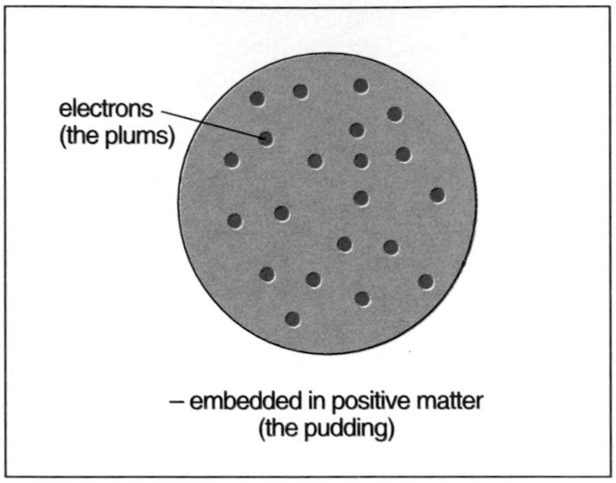

Picture 1 J.J. Thomson's atom – the plum pudding model.

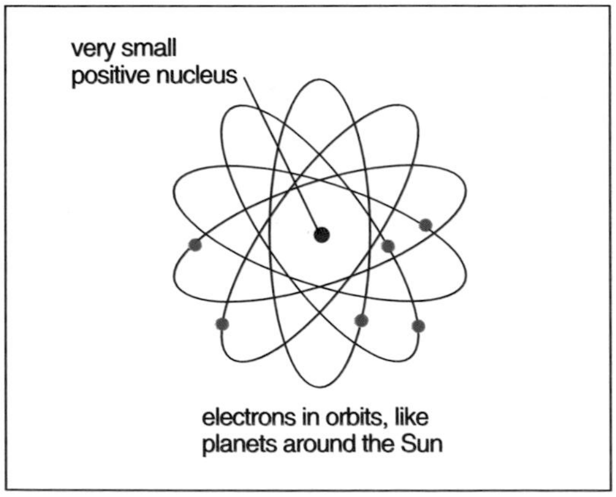

Picture 2 Rutherford's atom. It had to be the same size as Thomson's atom. But it was mostly empty space.

The nuclear atom

We now know that atoms are made up of a small, massive **nucleus**, which is electrically charged (positive). This is surrounded by a cloud of very tiny negative particles – **electrons**.

Electrons had already been discovered in 1895 before Henri Becquerel discovered radioactivity. At that time, physicists thought that the electrons were negative particles somehow embedded in a kind of positive blob, like bits of chocolate in a chocolate chip cookie (picture 1).

A team of physicists led by the New Zealander Ernest Rutherford showed that the atom was not like a cookie at all. They thought it was more like a tiny solar system, with electrons orbiting a tiny, massive positive nucleus like planets orbit the Sun. Picture 2 shows Rutherford's model of the atom.

The nucleus is itself made up of simpler particles – **protons** and **neutrons**. These particles are very nearly equal in size and mass, but protons are positively charged and neutrons are uncharged (neutral).

Picture 3 represents the structure of the atom. The nucleus at the centre is made of protons and neutrons. It is tiny, but very dense. The electrons move around outside the nucleus. They move in a random and chaotic way, but to make the picture simpler we've shown them as if they travel in 'orbits' around the nucleus.

Protons and electrons are electrically charged. Yet atoms themselves do not have an overall electrical charge. This is because *the numbers of protons and electrons are equal*, so their charges cancel out. If we add an electron, the atom gets an overall negative charge: it becomes a negative **ion**, like Cl^-. If we take away an electron, the atom becomes a positive ion, like Na^+.

Numbering atoms

The numbers of protons, neutrons and electrons in an atom decide its properties. As far as chemists are concerned, the most important thing is the number of *electrons*. Because they are on the outside, the electrons decide how a particular atom behaves in a chemical reaction. In the next two topics we will look more closely at the way the electrons are arranged.

The number of electrons in an atom is equal to its number of protons, and this is called the **atomic number**, symbol $\boldsymbol{Z}$. Each element has its own unique atomic number. For example, the simplest atom, hydrogen, has just one proton and one electron, so $Z = 1$. The largest naturally occurring atom, uranium, has $Z = 92$: in other words, it has 92 protons and 92 electrons.

If you split an atom in two, you get two new atoms. They have different atomic numbers from the original atom, *so they are new elements.* For example, when a uranium atom splits, you get one fragment with 56 protons and another with 36. These are barium ($Z = 56$) and krypton ($Z = 36$).

If you look at a copy of the Periodic Table, you will see that the elements are arranged in order of increasing atomic number.

But what about the neutrons?

Isotopes

Neutrons don't have any electrical charge, so they don't have to be balanced out by a particle with an opposite charge. This means you can add neutrons to an atom without altering its number of protons or electrons. So an element can have different 'versions' of its atoms. Each version has the same numbers of protons and electrons as all the other versions, but a different number of neutrons. These different versions, or **isotopes**, vary in mass, but they are all atoms of the same element.

Isotopes are atoms of a particular element with the same number of protons and electrons but different numbers of neutrons.

Let's look at an example – the simplest example of all, in fact. Picture 4 shows two isotopes of hydrogen. Both of them have one proton and one electron, so they both have the same chemical properties. But the second isotope has one neutron as well as the one proton in its nucleus. This makes the atom almost twice as heavy. In fact this isotope is sometimes called 'heavy hydrogen'. It is also known as deuterium.

Although it's heavier, deuterium has the same chemical properties as hydrogen. It reacts the same way, and it forms the same kind of compound. For example, 'heavy water' contains deuterium in place of hydrogen. It has the same chemical properties as ordinary water, and you wouldn't notice any difference if you drank it. It's just a little denser.

Isotopes of an element have the same chemical properties. They differ in a few physical properties such as density.

Some isotopes of ordinary elements are radioactive. These are called **radioisotopes**, and are widely used in industry and medicine.

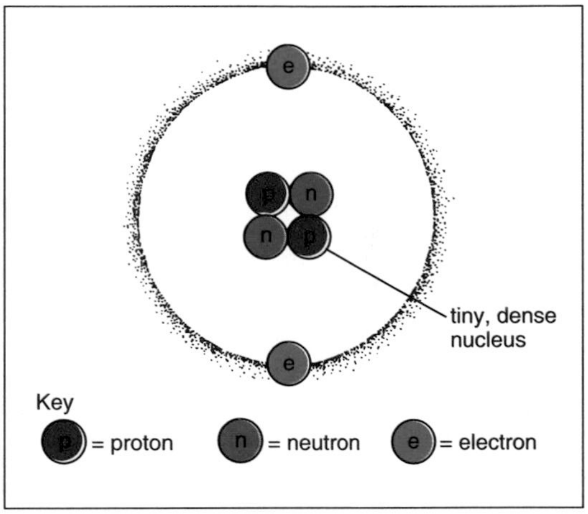

Picture 3 The particles in an atom (simplified). The atom shown here is helium.

Mass number

To make it easy to tell isotopes apart, each atom is given a mass number as well as its atomic number.

The mass number (symbol *A*) is the number of neutrons plus the number of protons.

The protons and neutrons give the atom most of its mass, because electrons have very little mass. So the mass number tells you the relative mass of the atom.

The mass number of ordinary hydrogen atoms is 1, and the mass number of 'heavy hydrogen' is 2. Picture 5 illustrates this idea for another element. It also shows how the symbol of an element can be written with the atomic number and mass number included.

Table 1 sums up the difference between atomic number and mass number.

Table 1 Atomic number and mass number.

Atomic number, Z	Mass number, A
• Z = number of protons = number of electrons	• A = number of protons + number of neutrons
• Fixed for a particular element	• Varies depending on which isotope of the element it is

If we know the atomic number and mass number of an atom, we can work out the number of protons, neutrons and electrons it must contain. For example, uranium has several isotopes. The isotope that is used in nuclear reactors is uranium-235, or ${}^{235}_{92}U$. Like all uranium atoms, it has an atomic number of 92, so it must have 92 protons and 92 electrons. It has a mass number of 235, which means its number of protons and neutrons together is 235. So its number of neutrons must be $(235-92) = 143$.

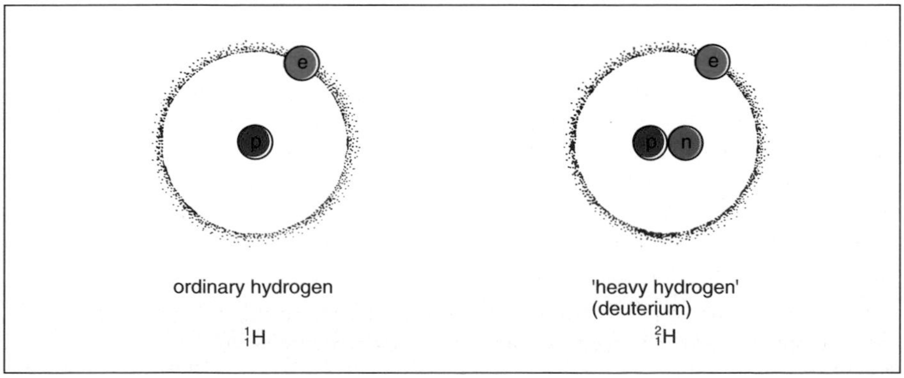

Picture 4 Two isotopes of hydrogen.

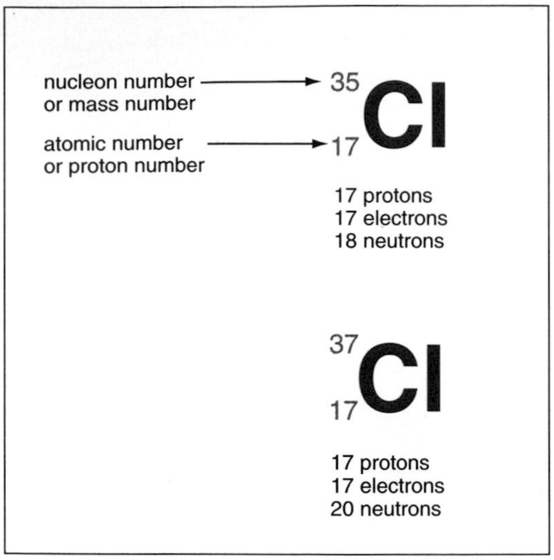

Picture 5 The atomic number and the mass number of chlorine isotopes.

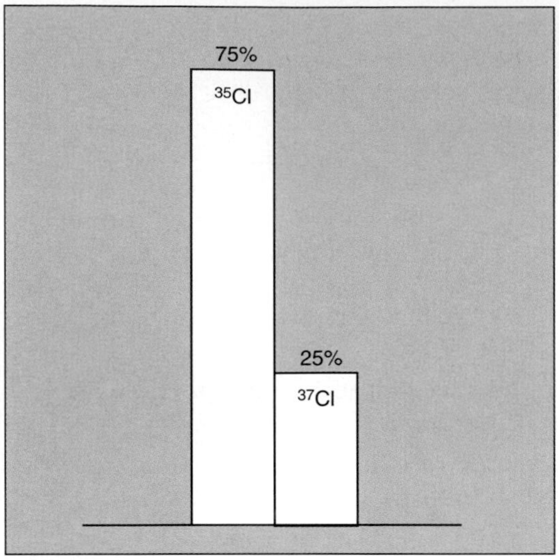

Picture 6 The abundance of two isotopes of chlorine.

Isotopes everywhere

How do we know the mass of atoms? They are much too small to weigh directly. Fortunately, a clever invention called the mass spectrometer makes it possible to find the mass of atoms indirectly. (See page 119).

The mass spectrometer shows that most elements have more than one isotope, and some have as many as twenty. Not all of these isotopes are stable. Some are radioactive, and decay into other isotopes by giving out ionising radiations.

Relative atomic mass

The relative atomic mass of an element is the mass of its atoms relative to atoms of other elements.

But which atoms are we talking about? Most elements have more than one isotope, and different isotopes have different masses. Relative atomic mass is actually an *average* mass for all the different isotopes. It is adjusted (weighted) to take account of the proportions of the different isotopes. If a particular isotope is present in larger amounts, it makes a bigger contribution to the average.

For example, chlorine has two stable isotopes. In natural chlorine, 75% of the atoms have mass number 35, and 25% have mass number 37 (picture 6). In other words, for every 100 atoms, 75 have mass 35 and 25 have mass 37. The weighted average of these mass numbers is:

$$\frac{75 \times 35 + 25 \times 37}{100} = 35.5$$

This is the relative atomic mass of chlorine.

What causes radioactivity?

The nuclei of some elements are so large that they are unstable. The uranium nucleus is like this. As time goes on, sooner or later, the nucleus will break apart. This is called **nuclear decay**. As the nucleus breaks apart it gets rid of some energy. The energy is carried away by the radiation, the alpha, beta or gamma rays. For example, a nucleus of uranium-238 decays by sending out an alpha particle at a very high speed. But the nucleus is still unstable, and will decay once more. This time it sends out a beta particle.

Even after this, the nucleus is still unstable. In fact, these changes will keep happening for quite a long time. For most of the changes the nucleus sends out a gamma ray as well as some mass in the form of a particle. The original uranium nucleus goes through fourteen changes before it becomes stable, and so non-radioactive. Uranium-238 has become a lead nucleus, Pb-206 (picture 7).

What happens to the nucleus when it changes?

The nucleus of uranium-238 is the largest nucleus of any natural element. The '238' refers to the fact that it has 238 particles in it. It contains 92 protons and 146 neutrons.

When uranium-238 decays it sends out an **alpha particle**. An alpha particle has two protons and two neutrons. The nucleus is now lighter (by four particles) and has less charge (by two units). *This means that it has become the nucleus of a different element.* In fact it has become a nucleus of thorium – thorium-234. But the thorium nucleus is also unstable. One of the neutrons inside the nucleus sends out an electron, as a beta particle, and turns into a proton.

The *mass* of the thorium nucleus stays much the same. After all, it has only lost an electron, which doesn't weigh very much at all. But it has now one more proton. This means that it behaves chemically like a different element. It has become an element called protactinium.

The decay chain doesn't stop there, however. Protactinium is also radioactive. It too decays by sending out a beta particle. This means that it too becomes a different element. Yet more changes have to take place before, finally, a stable nucleus is formed. This will be the element *lead*.

Some of these changes are shown in picture 7.

In many of these changes the nucleus also gets rid of some energy by emitting gamma radiation. This has no mass or charge, so the nucleus does not change into a different one.

Isotopes

As the nuclei change, they may become isotopes. A nucleus can lose two positive charges by emitting an alpha particle, then two negative charges by emitting beta particles. The charge on the nucleus is back to what it was originally. But the nucleus has lost mass. Nuclei with the same charge but with different masses are called isotopes. Picture 7 shows some examples of this.

Picture 7 Radioactive decay – how one nucleus changes into another.

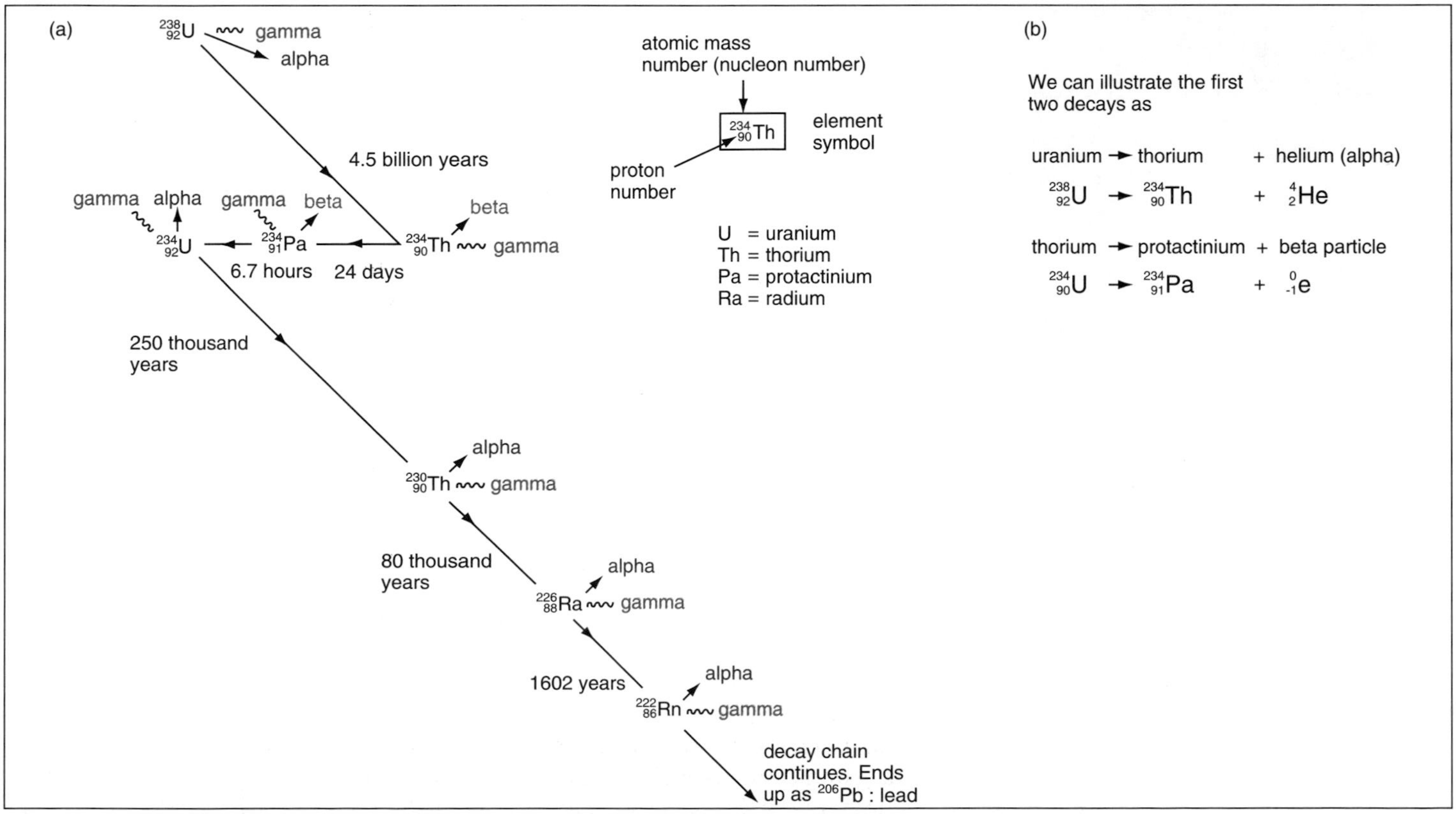

Why don't nuclei decay all at once?

No one knows the answer to this question. All we know is that some nuclei tend to decay very quickly and others very slowly. Also, no one can predict when any given nucleus will decay. It all seems to be a matter of chance, or 'luck'.

It may seem strange that what happens in such a precise subject as physics depends on 'luck'. But the laws of 'luck' are quite well known. They deal with the **probability** of some event actually occurring. Scientists have known for a long time that many everyday things are decided by the laws of probability as much as by the precise rules of Newton, for example. Many things seem to happen, or to move, in quite a **random** way. Just think of the weather, or the way molecules move in a gas.

But we can still make predictions about gases and about the weather. They might not always be accurate predictions, especially when it comes to weather forecasting. But the 'gas laws' are quite accurate, even though we can't predict how any single molecule in the gas is going to move. The laws are accurate because there are *so many* molecules in any reasonable quantity of gas. The different speeds and energies of the molecules average out to something quite predictable.

In much the same way we can predict quite accurately the 'activity' of a collection of radioactive nuclei. Again, this is because there are so many of them. In just one-hundredth of a gram of uranium, for example, there are 25 billion billion nuclei! We cannot predict what any one nucleus is going to do, but on average we can say quite accurately how many of them will decay in the next hour.

Activities

A Nuclear pioneers

Use a library to find out about the scientists who investigated radioactivity and the atom in the early years of this century. Find out about Ernest Rutherford, Marie Curie and her husband Pierre. What did they discover? How did they do it? What use have we made of their discoveries? Would it be better if they hadn't made these discoveries?

B Convincing John Dalton

Explaining an idea to another person is an excellent way of improving your own understanding, as well as theirs.

John Dalton, who produced the Atomic Theory, said 'Thou knowest no man can split the atom'. Imagine he were brought by time travel to the present. Could he be convinced he was wrong?

Work in pairs for this activity. One person will play John Dalton, the other will play themselves trying to persuade him. He would need some convincing, and would be likely to want some proof.

You will need to prepare your cases before you start.

After the activity, discuss how it went. Was 'John Dalton' convinced?

Questions

1 a Why does an atom normally have just as many protons as electrons?
b What happens to an atom when it loses an electron?
c Give an example of what might make an atom lose an electron.

2 What is the difference between a proton and a neutron?

3 In the simple model of an atom, we imagine that electrons go around the nucleus in 'orbits'.

a Explain what an orbit is.
b What might happen if the electrons stopped moving?

4 'The radioactive decay of an atom is a random event.' Make up two other sentences in which the word 'random' is correctly used.

5 a The probability of getting a 'six' in a game of dice is 1 in 6. Why?
b What is the probability of choosing a Queen of Hearts in a card game with a well shuffled pack (52 cards)?
c The probability of a certain type of nucleus decaying in the next 10 seconds is 1 in 5 million. How many would you expect to decay in the next ten seconds in a sample of 100 million nuclei?

6 Give the words that fit in the blanks in the following. The missing words are:

negative, positive, nucleus, isotopes, equal, mass number, atomic number, electrons.

Atoms are made of three kinds of subatomic particles. Protons and neutrons are found in the small central part of the atom, called the ___(a)___. Moving around outside are the ___(b)___. Protons have one unit of ___(c)___ charge, and electrons have an equal ___(d)___ charge. In a neutral atom, the number of protons and electrons is ___(e)___. This number is called the ___(f)___. The number of protons added to the number of neutrons in an atom is called the ___(g)___. Atoms with the same atomic number but different mass numbers are called ___(h)___.

7 An atom of a particular element, contains 13 protons, 14 neutrons and 13 electrons.

a What is its atomic number?
b What is its mass number?

8 Make a copy of table 2. Fill in all the blank spaces.

9 Which of the atoms in table 2 are isotopes of the same element?

10 a All atoms of a particular element have the same atomic number. Explain why.
b Atoms of the same element can have different mass numbers. Explain why.

11 a Bromine, Br, has two isotopes, with mass numbers 79 and 81. Naturally occurring bromine contains the two isotopes in equal amounts. What is the relative atomic mass of bromine?
b Boron, B, has two stable isotopes, with mass numbers 10 and 11. Naturally occurring boron contains 20% boron-10 and 80% boron-11. What is the relative atomic mass of boron?

12 Picture 4 shows two isotopes of hydrogen. There is a third isotope, called tritium, which is unstable and radioactive. Tritium atoms contain two neutrons.

a How many: (i) protons, and (ii) electrons do tritium atoms contain?
b What is: (i) the atomic number, and (ii) the mass number of tritium?

13 Write balanced nuclear equations for the following decays (see picture 7a).

a thorium → radium by alpha emission.
b protactinium → uranium by beta emission.

Table 2

Symbol	Number of protons	Number of neutrons	Number of electrons	Atomic number	Mass number
$^{1}_{1}H$	1	0		1	
$^{2}_{1}H$		1		1	
$^{4}_{2}H$					
C	6	6			12
$^{63}_{29}Cu$	29				
Cu	29	36			
$^{56}_{26}Fe$					
Mg		12	12		

D7
Nuclear energy

Nuclear energy powers the movement of continents. We can also use nuclear energy directly – but can we do this safely?

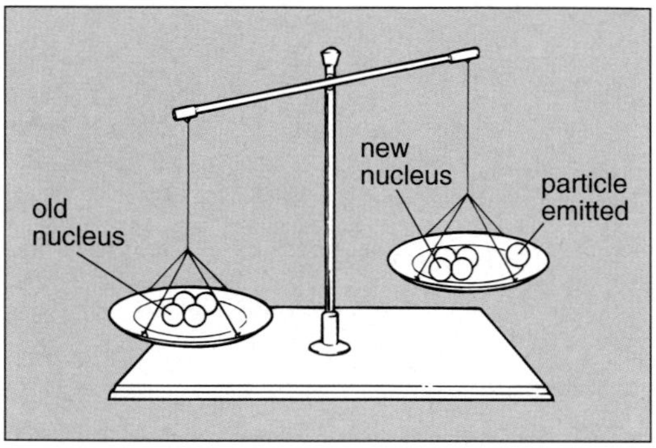

Picture 1 In a radioactive change, the new products weigh less than the original nucleus.

'Moonshine!' says top nuclear scientist

Ernest Rutherford was the physicist who found out what alpha particles were, and who discovered the nucleus of the atom. *There is enough energy in a gram of uranium to send a liner across the Atlantic!* he said in a newpaper interview, 60 years ago. *But the idea that you can actually use it is moonshine. It will take over 4 billion years to get just a half of it out!*

He was thinking of radioactivity, not nuclear power stations. When a natural radioactive substance decays, it gives out energy – but only slowly.

Nowadays we have artificial isotopes that do give out their energy in a shorter time. They are used to power instruments in Earth satellites. They are also used in heart pacemakers.

Even so, the power they can generate is very small and it is very expensive. Nuclear power stations do not rely on 'ordinary radioactivity' to produce energy. But where does the energy come from?

$E = mc^2$

When atoms decay, the energy they release appears as movement energy (kinetic energy) of the high-speed particles they send out. It was Albert Einstein (see topic B7) who came up with the surprising theory that this energy was produced by changing some of the mass of the nucleus into energy. This theory was proved when careful measurements were made. The mass of the emitted particle plus the mass of the nucleus left behind *was less than the mass of the original nucleus* (picture 1).

Energy had appeared. Mass had disappeared. These two facts contradicted the laws of physics as understood in 1905. These laws said that:

- energy could not be lost or created (Law of Conservation of Energy),
- mass could not be made or destroyed (Law of Conservation of Matter).

Einstein would say: *If we say that matter is really a kind of stored energy, then both laws can be correct. In fact, my Theory of Relativity predicts that this should happen. The 'energy value' of any piece of matter is given by my formula* $\mathbf{E = mc^2}$. *No problem.*

The missing mass, $\boldsymbol{m}$, was converted to kinetic energy, $\boldsymbol{E}$. The quantity $\boldsymbol{c}$ is the speed of light. This is a very large number – 300 000 000 m/s. It is the *square* of this number which multiplies with the mass to give the value of the energy. This means that it doesn't take much mass to produce a lot of energy.

But the main problem still remained. There was no way to speed up the rate at which ordinary, naturally radioactive materials decayed and produced their energy. The energy was there, but dammed up so well that it could only trickle out at a uselessly small rate.

Nuclear fission

The breakthrough into 'atomic energy' came in 1938. Physicists working in Berlin proved that some of the unstable uranium nuclei don't just decay by giving out a small particle or some gamma radiation, as described in topic D5. Instead, they split up into two nearly equal parts.

But just as with radioactive changes, mass was lost and converted to energy. What was the more important, *the splitting could be controlled*. Then, in 1939, the Second World War began. It was clear to some physicists that the immense store of energy in a lump of uranium could be released very quickly. The result would be a huge explosion – **a nuclear bomb**.

The bomb was built – it took five years to do this – and two 'atomic bombs' were dropped on Japan by the USA in the summer of 1945. The nuclear age had begun.

The process of splitting nuclei to give energy is called nuclear **fission**. The same process is used in a **nuclear reactor**, but of course it is controlled so that it happens much more slowly than in a bomb. To explain how it works we need to remember what the nucleus of an atom is like.

Atomic nuclei

Atoms contain negative electrons moving around a positive core – the nucleus. But a nucleus is not just a blob of positively charged matter. The main parts of a nucleus are the protons and the neutrons (see picture 2). Protons are positively charged and neutrons do not carry an electric charge.

Some nuclei have too many protons and neutrons and tend to be unstable. This causes radioactivity. (See topics D5 and D6.) But some very large nuclei may split into two parts, instead of undergoing ordinary radioactive decay.

The chain reaction

This splitting is what goes on in a nuclear bomb or reactor. When the nucleus splits in two main parts it also shoots out one or more spare neutrons. These can fly into another nearby nucleus quite easily – and make that nucleus split. In turn, the new neutrons may shoot off into other nuclei and cause them to split.

This builds up into a **chain reaction**, with nucleus after nucleus splitting and triggering off others. Each time a nucleus splits it gives out energy. This process is shown in picture 3. You can compare it to an avalanche on a mountain slope. When someone throws just one stone it can cause them all to cascade down the slope.

The result of an uncontrolled chain reaction is an explosion. This is what happens in a nuclear bomb. In a nuclear reactor the reaction is controlled. The uranium is spread out, as thin rods (**fuel rods**). In between the rods are other rods, made of a material that absorbs neutrons. If all the neutrons are absorbed no further reactions are possible and the reactor stops giving out energy.

In a typical reactor, the absorbing rods (**control rods**) are moved in and out of the fuel rods. This controls the rate of the fission reactions and the amount of energy released. Picture 4 shows the main parts of a nuclear reactor. Other rods (**moderators**) slow down the neutrons so that they are better at causing fission.

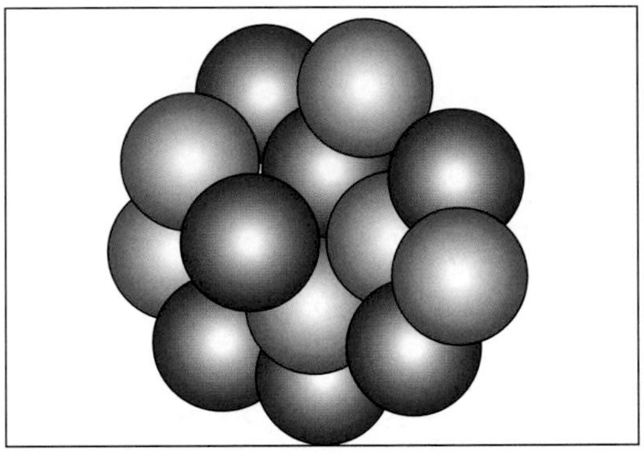

Picture 2 An oxygen nucleus. It has eight protons and eight neutrons.

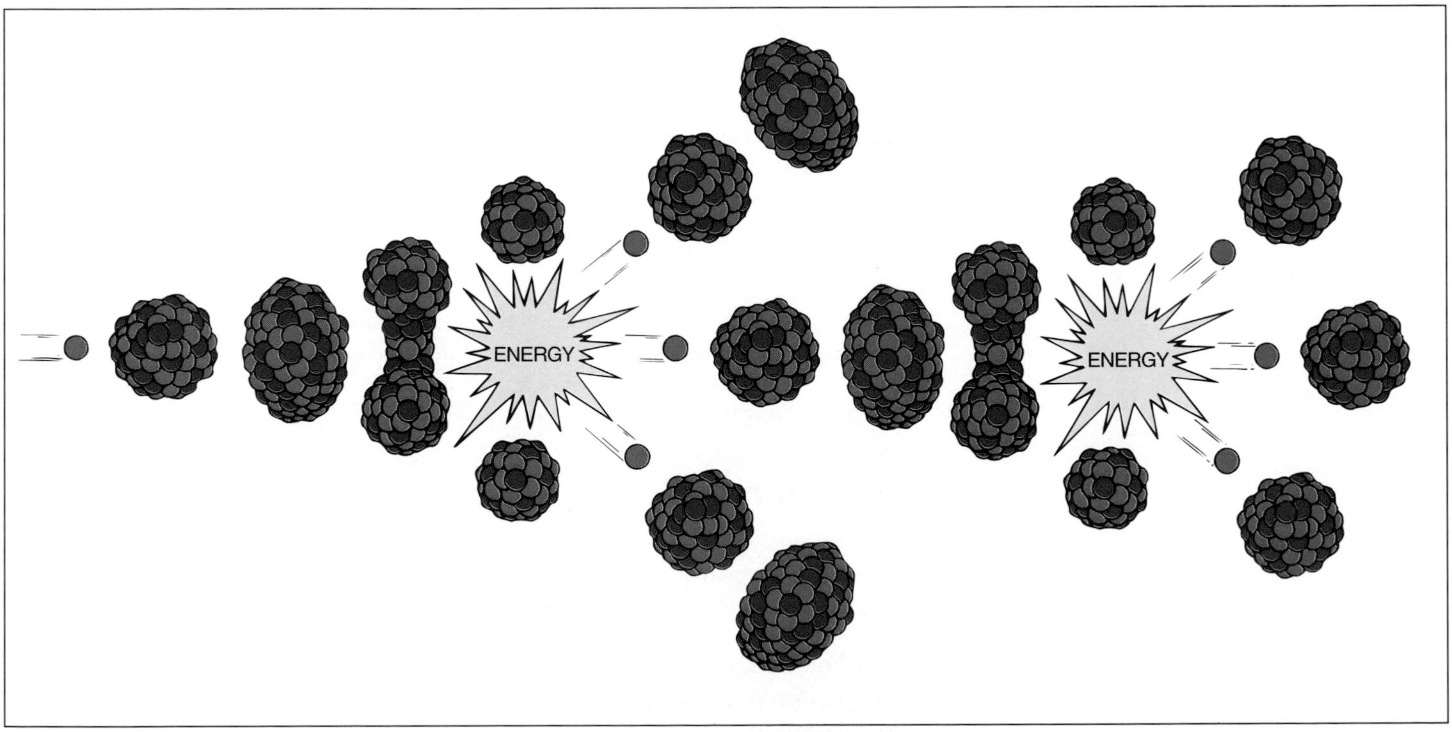

Picture 3 A chain reaction.

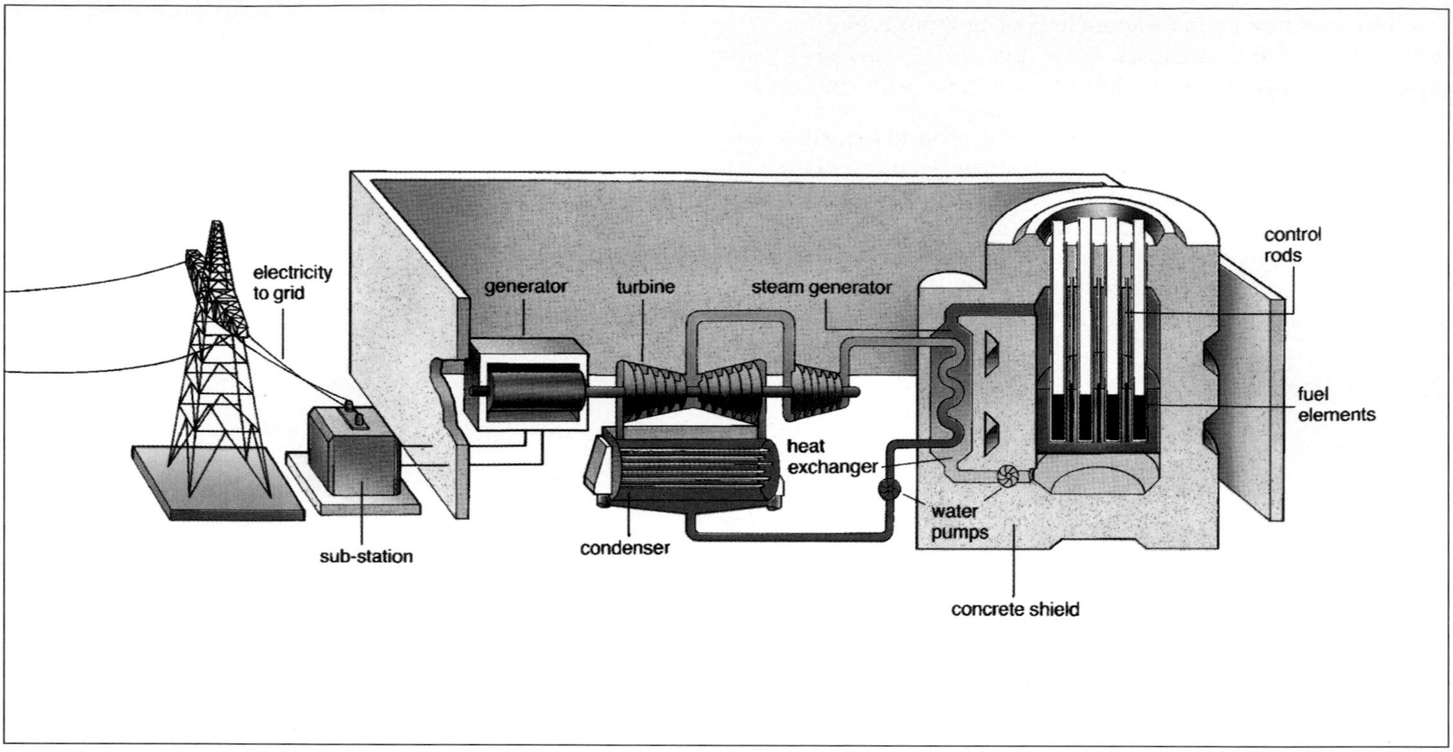

Picture 4 The workings of a nuclear reactor.

The energy released when the nuclei split up heats the fuel rods. The hot 'core' of the reactor then heats water or some other fluid. This hot fluid may become radioactive and has to be kept inside the reactor. The fluid moves to carry its energy to the heat exchanger where it is transferred to boil water. The steam produced drives an ordinary steam turbine.

The turbines turn generators, as in an ordinary coal-fired or gas-fired power station.

Nuclear waste

When the uranium nuclei in the fuel rods split they form two smaller nuclei. These nuclei are radioactive. Eventually the fuel rods are used up and have to be replaced. The old rods are now very radioactive.

Also, the neutrons that are not used in the fission process are absorbed by control rods and other parts of the reactor. This makes them become radioactive as well.

After anything from 20 to 50 years, the working parts of the reactor are worn out, and have also become highly radioactive. When the reactor is dismantled these materials have somehow to be disposed of. This process is called **decommissioning**. It now seems that this could be very expensive. This means that the total costs of nuclear power are much higher than was thought when the first nuclear power stations were built.

Nuclear fusion

But there is yet another way to get energy from nuclei. The Sun and the stars get their energy from the opposite process to nuclear fission. They use the fact that when light nuclei join together to make heavier ones, energy can be released. Once again, the energy comes from lost mass.

In the Sun, the process involves the nuclei of hydrogen isotopes (protons and deuterons) joining together to form helium nuclei. This process is called nuclear **fusion**.

Could we use fusion to produce energy on Earth? This energy would come from a very cheap material – hydrogen. The process would produce less radioactive waste. Research has been going on for nearly 50 years to produce **controlled fusion**. So far this research has been unsuccessful; the only 'practical' device to have been developed is the hydrogen bomb (picture 5). Although the latest experiments have shown some success, this source of energy is not likely to be available until well into the 21st century.

Picture 5 A hydrogen bomb. So far, we can't control nuclear fusion to give a steady supply of energy.

Activities

A Find out about nuclear power stations

Read all you can about nuclear power stations.

People disagree about whether nuclear power is a good idea or not. Make a list of the points that could be made *for* and *against* using nuclear power to generate electricity. You should consider: *safety*, *cost per unit of electricity*, *pollution*, *convenience of use*, *storing nuclear waste*, *the greenhouse effect*, etc.

Some of the points will be 'scientific', but some may be important but not based on scientific evidence. Mark the ones you think are scientific with a capital S.

B The case for and against nuclear energy

Use a library to find out about the following. Make short notes on each one, then combine your thoughts and knowledge into a poster which could be entitled either:

1 Ban the bomb! or

2 Nuclear weapons have kept the free world free!

Topics:

1 The effects of nuclear radiation

2 The hydrogen bomb

3 Hiroshima

4 The end of the 'Cold War'

5 ICBMs

6 The nuclear winter

Try to get a good balance of fact and opinion.

Questions

1 Explain briefly why a nuclear chain reaction is like an avalanche of snow or rocks on a steep mountainside.

2 Nuclear 'fuel' – uranium – is quite cheap. Give two reasons why it is still expensive to produce electricity from nuclear power stations.

3 Explain what the *control rods* do in a nuclear reactor.

4 a Describe an atomic nucleus.
b 'Carbon-14 is an *isotope* of carbon-12.' Explain what an isotope is, in terms of the difference between these two types of carbon.

5 People argue a great deal about whether nuclear power stations should be built. Give three reasons in each case:

a in favour of nuclear power,
b against nuclear power.

6 a Use the formula $E = mc^2$ to calculate how much energy in joules could be obtained from 1 kg of matter if all of it could be turned into energy. The speed of light, ***c***, is 300 000 000 m/s.
b The total energy we can actually get from 1 kg of uranium is very much less than the answer you should have got for part (a). Why is this?

D8 Radiation and life

Ionising radiations are all around us. Only a small amount is due to human activities.

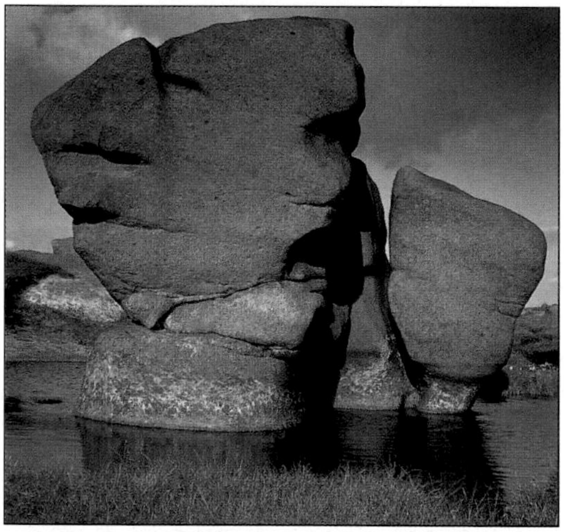

Picture 1 Granite outcrop in Derbyshire – granite often contains radioactive elements.

Why is radioactivity dangerous?

The alpha, beta and gamma radiations from a radioactive material travel at high speeds. Also, alpha and beta particles are electrically charged. When they go into living cells they can kill or damage them. They can do this because they ionise molecules that are vital to life. A large 'dose' of radiation kills so many cells that the effect is like being burned by fire.

Alpha particles are easily stopped. Even a sheet of paper is enough. But beta and gamma radiations can get deep into the body so that cells in internal organs are damaged (see topic D5).

For low levels of radiation you lose just a few cells. This in itself is not dangerous. After all, our bodies contain lots of cells. The danger comes from the fact that the radiation can *change* some of the chemicals we have in cells. These are the complex molecules of DNA and RNA that control how the cell works.

As a result, the cell may go out of control. It grows and divides just as if it was an independent organism that feeds on our bodies. It becomes a group of **cancer cells**.

Also, if sperm or ova cells in the reproductive system are changed, the result could be children with birth defects. For example, they could be born with badly formed or missing limbs, or brain damage.

Table 1 Exposure to radiation in everyday situations.

	Type of exposure	Radiation received (microsievert)
1	radiation due to nuclear power stations for a year	10
2	watching television for a year	10
3	wearing a radioactive luminous watch for a year (now not very common)	30
4	having a chest X-ray	200
5	exposure to fall-out in Britain from nuclear bomb testing in 1959	350
6	radiation from a brick house, per year	750
7	working for a month in a uranium mine	1 000
8	typical dose received by a member of the general public in a year	1 500
9	maximum dose allowed to general public per year	5 000
10	maximum dose allowed to workers exposed to radiation per year	50 000

Picture 2 Nuclear waste transporter.

Table 1 shows the radiation doses you might get in different situations, together with the 'allowed doses' for ordinary people and workers in the nuclear industries. They are measured in microsieverts, which is a measure of how much energy the radiation delivers to the body.

We cannot escape from ionising radiation. Some comes from outer space, as fast-moving particles. Most rocks contain a tiny amount of some radioactive elements. In many parts of the country radioactive decay produces the radioactive gas **radon**. This seeps into buildings and can be breathed in. The effect of all these sources is to produce the natural **background radiation**.

Granite rocks, which have come from deep inside the Earth, contain more than the average amount of radioactive elements (picture 1). People living in granite areas should make sure that their houses are well ventilated. They should get their homes checked now and again for radon, and if too much is found they should seal their floors.

Biologists believe that background radiation is one of the causes of changes to genes in the reproductive cells of all living things. These changes help to produce **variation** in living things, allowing evolution to take place.

Radioactivity can be useful

Radioactive isotopes are used in industry and in medical treatment or diagnosis. For example:

1 Radioactive isotopes that emit gamma radiation can be used instead of an X-ray machine to check if an oil pipe has a fault. X-ray machines are large and need a power supply – a gamma source can be small and so is more portable for use in remote areas.
2 Radiation can kill cancer cells. For example, a radioisotope of iodine can be injected into the body where it collects in the thyroid gland to help treat cancer of the thyroid.

Half-life and nuclear waste

As explained in topic D7, nuclear reactors produce **nuclear wastes**. Picture 2 shows waste being transported. Radioactive materials are also used in industry, and produce waste. Some of these waste materials have very short half-lives (see topic D5). This means that they give out their radiation very quickly. They are very dangerous – for a short while. But most of the radiation is gone after a few months.

For any radioactive material, after ten half-lives the material is only a thousandth as active as it was at the start. It has been divided in half ten times. But some radioactive waste materials have half-lives running into hundreds of years. These materials are called low-level waste. Storing these safely is a major problem. There is no way we can speed up the rate at which they decay. Half-lives are fixed and do not change.

Storing radioactive waste

Because it is dangerous to humans, low-level radioactive waste has to be stored safely, so that the radiations don't get out. It is stored inside containers made of metal, glass or concrete which absorb the radiations. If low-level waste is to be stored underground, great care will have to be taken to make sure that the containers stay unbroken, perhaps for thousands of years.

These problems of waste disposal have caused many countries, including the UK, to draw back from building a lot of new nuclear power stations. The cost of dismantling the power stations safely and storing the waste seems to make nuclear energy less economic than people once thought.

Activities

A Radioactivity all around us

Use a library to find out about one of the following uses of radiation. Make notes or a poster so that you can report back to the rest of the class.

1 Smoke detectors.
2 Radioactive tracers in hospitals.
3 Using radioactive materials to check for faults in metal objects.
4 Finding the age of old objects using carbon-14.
5 Using radiation to treat cancer.

B Are you at risk?

Radon gas is radioactive. It can be dangerous if it is allowed to build up in houses or other buildings. Find out what kind of radiation it emits.

Trace a map of the British Isles. Use an atlas to find out which areas are over granite or other igneous rocks. Mark these areas on your map. Find out whether your local council has any plans for checking or dealing with radon gas.

Questions

1 You can't escape from ionising radiation on Earth. Name two natural sources of this radiation.

2 Describe briefly two effects of ionising radiation on living things.

3 a What are the three kinds of ionising radiations that are emitted by a radioactive substance?
b Describe how the human body can be protected from each type.
c From which of the sources of radiation given in table 1 are you personally most likely to be at risk?

4 Why are radioactive substances with a short half-life more active than those with a long half-life?

5 Describe two ways in which radioactive waste (e.g. from hospitals) could be stored safely.

6 Ultra-violet light is also an 'ionising radiation'. What dangers does this present to human beings on Earth? How can these dangers be reduced?

Good tidings?

New Energy Source Planned for South Wales!

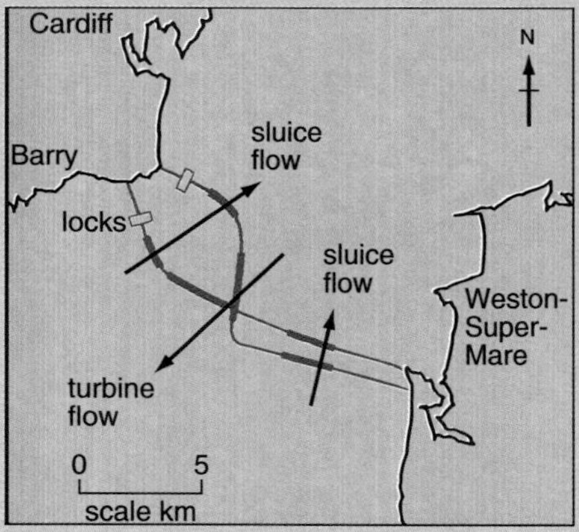

Picture 1 Map of the proposed barrage.

Picture 2 Artist's impression of the Severn Barrage.

Plans have been published for a major project that might revolutionise Britain's energy resources. This will use the fashionable idea of *renewable energy*. The idea is to build a huge dam (called a **barrage**) across the estuary of the River Severn, between Cardiff and Weston-super-Mare (see map, picture 1).

The estuary acts as a funnel for the tides as they flow in. At the site of the proposed dam the sea rises and falls a remarkable 11 m twice a day. This is more than the height of a three-storey house. The barrage will be 16 km long. Millions of tonnes of sea water will be channelled to flow through turbines as the tide comes in and out.

The result will be a supply of 8000 MW of electricity. This would make it the largest tidal power station in the world. Its power output would be equivalent to four nuclear power stations, or a 'wind farm' of 2500 wind generators, each 90 m tall!

Picture 2 shows what it would be like if it was built. The turbine blades would be huge, as our artist's impression shows (picture 3). This is the most exciting project for pollution-free energy ever!

Picture 3 A turbine blade.

Letters to the Editor

Threatened wildlife

I was horrified to read the article about the dam across the Severn Estuary. Don't these people know that this is the one of the best wildlife sites in Britain? Every year millions of wading birds and wildfowl feed and nest in the estuary. The mudbanks are one of the few remaining wetland areas that these birds can use. If this barrage is built these mudbanks will be lost for ever. Is Man's greed for ever more energy to waste on unnecessary luxuries like colour TV and central heating yet again going to kill millions of other living things on this planet?

Think again, planners. Save, don't waste!

Yours sincerely,

Amanda Williams, President
Severn Society for the Protection of Birds

Cheap at the price!

This proposal for a Severn Barrage is to be greatly welcomed. We have already wasted billions of pounds of taxpayers' money on dangerous and unsightly nuclear power stations. It wouldn't be so bad if they could produce cheaper electricity!

Over the years thousands of Welsh coalminers have lost their lives producing coal which is burned and lost for ever. Think of how much harm this is doing to the Earth through the Greenhouse Effect! This barrage will cost just 8 billion pounds! Worth every penny, I'd say.

Yours sincerely,

D. Evans (Ex-miner, Monmouth)

Power for the future

Don't these moaners and whingers realise that if this country of ours is going to play its rightful part in the new Europe we need plentiful supplies of energy. Otherwise we are going to be left behind even places like Spain and Italy!

And don't they realise that coal has had its day? Haven't they heard of the Greenhouse Effect? Would they rather have four nuclear power stations on the estuary? Which is more important, human beings or birds?

Come on! Let us move boldly into the future!

Yours very sincerely,

Jane Smithers
Managing Director, New Age Electronics Ltd

Nuclear benefits

So what is wrong with having four nuclear power stations on the Severn Estuary? The one already there at Hinckley Point has done no harm whatsoever. Billions of pounds have been spent already in developing this highly efficient and safe (yes safe!) source of energy. How many people have been killed in or around any nuclear power station in the UK? None! Think of how many miners have been killed in the mines – thousands!

The very tides that will be tamed in this ridiculous, anti-wildlife and unsightly project are carrying away the waste heat from the nuclear power station. The warmth encourages fish and will improve fishing in the area. The dam will in fact stop any of the young salmon swimming up the estuary to the head of this world-famous fishing river.

A well-regulated nuclear power station is pollution-free, takes up little space and will produce electricity at a third of the fuel cost of coal.

This is the real future for Britain's energy. After all, there is only one Severn Estuary – we can build as many nuclear power stations as we like.

Yours sincerely,

L. Marshall
Department of Engineering, Avon University

Barry Beach

What about the beach at Barry Island? All the sand will be under water. It's not fair.

J. Lewis (age 7)

Role play – the public inquiry

By law, a Public Inquiry has to be held before the Barrage can be built. Anyone with an interest can ask to give evidence or make a case in this inquiry. It will be chaired by an eminent lawyer, who should not take sides and is willing to help inexperienced people.

You will be given (or may be allowed to choose) the role of one of the letter writers above, or a representative of the Department of Energy (Mr Nigel Smythe or Ms Louisa Davenport).

You may need a small team of researchers to help you prepare your case. You may be able to think of other groups of people with an interest in the development, such as local anglers, councillors and hotel keepers from one of the many holiday resorts in the area.

At the end of the activity, the class can vote for or against the proposal.

A sun-warmed house

Picture 1 shows some houses in Chorley, Lancashire. They have been designed to make best use of the Sun's heat. The houses face south, and they have a special energy-trap, called a **sunspace**, at the front.

Picture 1 Using the Sun's heat to keep warm.

This is made mostly of glass. In winter the energy that enters the room makes it comfortably warm as long as the Sun shines. The floor is made of special tiles that can 'hold the heat'. Picture 2 shows the principle of two kinds of sunspace.

The rest of the house still has to be heated in winter, but even so the sunspace is useful when the Sun isn't shining. Energy that would normally escape through an outside wall is kept inside, because the sunspace acts as a good insulator.

In these specially designed houses there are only small windows on the north side of the house. This is to help keep down energy loss. Also, the walls are built to be good insulators. Once the house is warm, its walls and funishings act as a large 'heat store'. This means it stays warm for a long time. Heating costs are cut to about a half of what they are in a normal house. Try answering the questions.

1 Most energy leaves a house by means of *thermal conduction*.

a Name (i) three materials which are often used in buildings and are good insulators, (ii) three materials which are bad insulators.

b Explain briefly how 'thermal conduction' actually happens.

2 a How does 'solar energy' actually get from the Sun into the house?

b What problem might the people who live in these 'sunspace' houses have in the summer? How could they solve this problem?

3 What physical property decides whether or not a material is 'good at holding heat'?

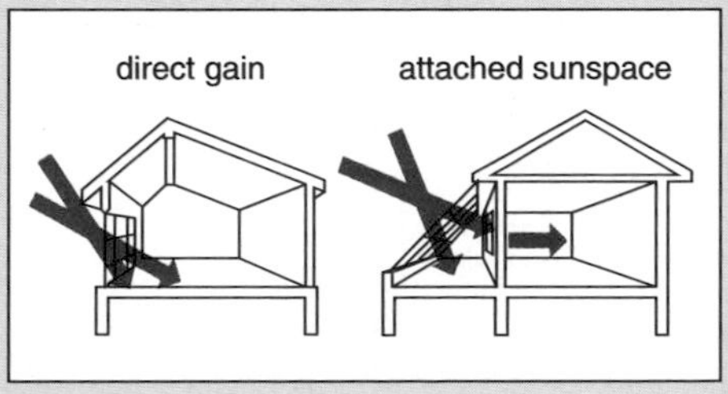

Picture 2 Two kinds of sunspace.

4 The walls of an energy-efficient house might be 'cavity walls', which means that they are double walls with an air space in between.

a Describe how such walls help to reduce energy losses.

b What other part of the sunspace (other than its brick walls) is likely to use the same principle as a cavity wall?

5 A normal house might cost its owners £400 in heating costs during the winter. An energy-efficient house will reduce this by at least 50%. But it might cost £6000 more to build.

a How long will it take this extra building cost to be paid back in energy saving? Do you think it is worth building such houses?

b One of the main causes of the greenhouse effect is burning fossil fuels. How could building energy-efficient houses help counteract this effect? What could a responsible government do to help people make their houses more efficient?

E1 Electric signals

The brain, computers, traffic lights, telephones – all these deal with messages. They all use electricity to make them work.

Picture 1 Electric currents can carry messages.

Picture 2 Electricity is used for controlling light, as well as producing it.

Messages and moving charges

When you pick up a telephone an electric current starts to flow. When you speak into it the microphone in the handset changes the strength of the current to match the sounds you make.

When a car comes up to some traffic lights it affects a magnetic sensor in the road. This sends an electric message to a control box to let it know that the car is there. The control box has to decide how and when the lights need to change (picture 2).

When you tread on a drawing pin in bare feet your pain sensors send a message to both brain and muscles so that you react pretty quickly. The message is carried by a moving electric pulse through very long nerve cells.

What is needed for electricity to be a messenger?

These devices use electricity to carry a message, and for this to work three things are needed:

- electric charge which is free to move,
- energy to move the charge,
- a material that charges can move through – a conductor.

Circuits

The examples above are quite complicated devices, using many conductors connected together in complicated ways. But however complicated it may look the basic plan of any electrical device is quite simple: it is a collection of **circuits**. A simple circuit (picture 3) has the energy source (a battery), a switch, some wires and, say, an electric buzzer. The wires are made of a metal which is a good conductor – usually copper.

Luckily, the electric charges are already in the conductor! A metal contains many millions of charged particles that are free to move. These particles are called **electrons**, and all atoms contain them.

For a signal to get to the buzzer, the buzzer has to be connected to the battery by conductors. All the battery does is to provide a *force* to make the electrons move. How it does this is explained later (page 174).

The switch is there to make a gap in the circuit. Air is a very poor conductor – we say it is an *insulator* – so electrons cannot move across the gap. It doesn't matter where the gap is. It is like a blockage on a single road system (picture 4). If cars pile up at the gap, they cause a traffic jam that will tail back to stop cars getting any further. For traffic to flow it has to be able to get into and *out* of the system.

Exactly the same principle applies to electric charges. They need a complete path which runs from one side of the battery to the other. A gap anywhere in the circuit will stop the charge moving. When you close the gap by pressing the switch, the charge starts moving and carries its message to the buzzer, which makes a sound.

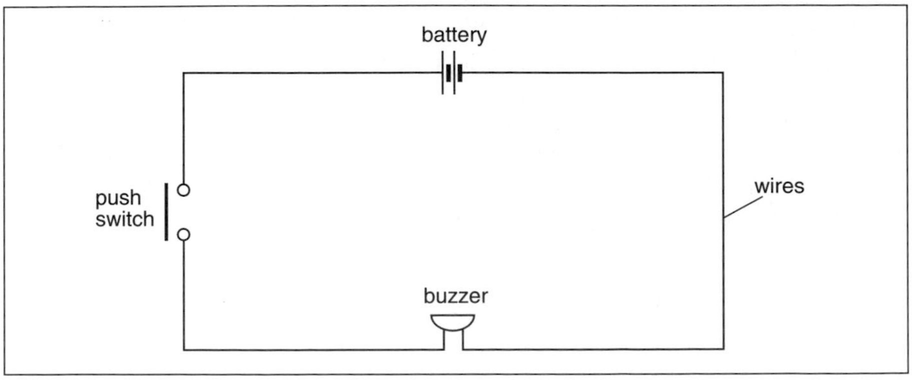

Picture 3 A simple circuit.

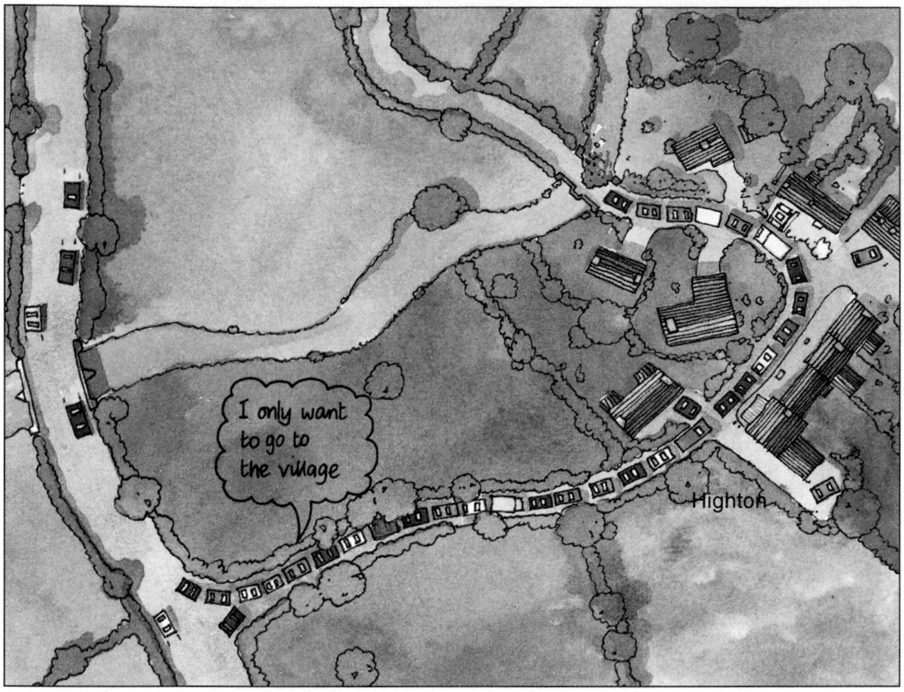

Picture 4 Electricity is like traffic; a gap in a circuit is like a blocked road.

What can electricity do?

We recognise electricity by its effects. The moving charges in a circuit can:

1 make conductors hot (in lamps, heaters),
2 produce magnetic forces (in electromagnets, motors, loudspeakers),
3 make special chemicals give out light (in LEDs, fluorescent lamps, TV screens),
4 cause chemical changes to take place (in electroplating, charging batteries, etc.).

The first three effects are especially useful in everyday life. Most electrical devices in the home use one or more of these effects (see picture 5). The rest of the topics in this section describe and explain the uses of these effects more fully.

Electric charge and electric current

An electric current is a flow of charged particles (see also topic E5). Current is measured in amperes, by an instrument called an ammeter. A small torch bulb may carry a current of 0.2 amperes (0.2 A), a car headlamp bulb may carry twenty times as much (4 A).

The current in a lamp is a flow of electrons. The charge on a single electron is very very small. It takes many millions of moving electrons to carry the charge that flows through an ordinary torch bulb in just one second. This large number is hard to think about and work with, so we need a more sensible unit of charge. Instead, we use **the quantity that moves when a current of one ampere flows for one second. This amount of charge is called a *coulomb* (or C for short)**.

Obviously, if 1 ampere flows for 2 seconds then 2 coulombs of charge will have moved; if 2 amperes flow for 2 seconds then 4 coulombs will move (picture 6 overleaf).

Charge, current and time are linked as follows:

$$\text{charge moved} = \text{current} \times \text{time}$$

$$(\text{coulombs}) = (\text{amperes} \times \text{seconds})$$

(a) Lighting

(b) Keeping cool

(c) Listening to music

(d) Ironing

(e) Watching television

Picture 5 Electricity can be used for many different jobs.

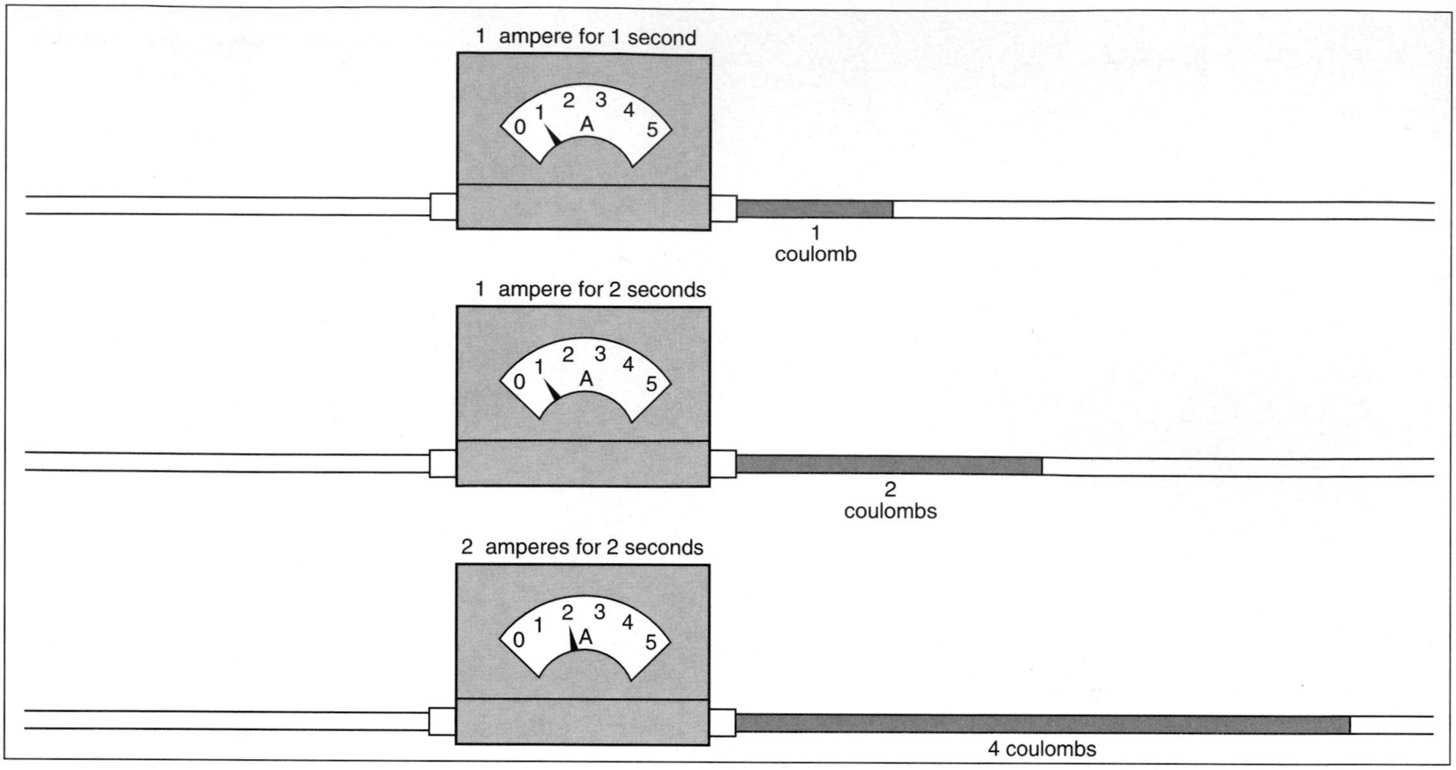

Picture 6 Charge = current × time.

Symbols, circuits and formulae

The best way to learn about electricity is by doing experiments and investigations, solving problems, making things work – and talking about them. The activities at the end of the topics will help you to do this. You will meet a lot of new ideas and have to work things out for yourself – with help from your teacher.

Electricity is so useful that it has a language of its own, mostly using circuit diagrams and special symbols to stand for the devices that it uses.

Formulae are used to work out what is happening, or going to happen, in a circuit. All the information that you will need in this section is summarised in tables 1 and 2. Use them when you need to look things up.

Table 1 Symbols in electricity.
The rest of the topics in this section explain what these words and formulae mean, and how to use them. They are all collected here for you to use when you need to.

Circuit symbols					
cell	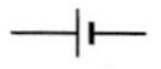	capacitor		battery	
microphone		variable power supply	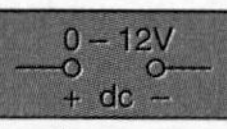	motor	
lamps	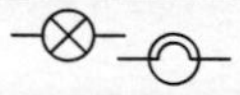	loudspeaker	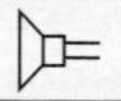	resistor	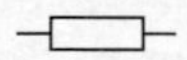
transformer		switches	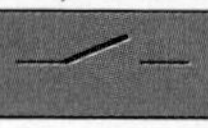	bell	
LED		buzzer		variable resistor	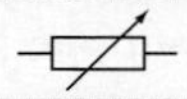
ammeter		voltage divider	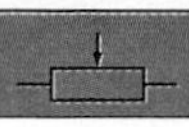	voltmeter	
fuse	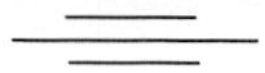				

Symbols for quantities

current	I	potential difference (voltage)	V	power	P
resistance	R	energy	E		
charge	Q	time in seconds	t	capacitance	C

Symbols for units (measurements)

amperes (current) **A**	volts **V**	(ohms) resistance **Ω**

Useful formulae in electricity

Charge, current, time	$Q = It$
Voltage, current, resistance	$V = IR$
Power	$P = VI \quad P = I^2R \quad P = \frac{V^2}{R}$
Resistors in series	$R_t = R_1 + R_2 + R_3 +$ etc.
Resistors in parallel	$\frac{1}{R_t} = \frac{1}{R_1} + \frac{1}{R_2} + \frac{1}{R_3}$ etc.

Table 2 Formulae in electricity

Activities

A What uses electricity?

Make a list of as many things as you can see in the room that use electricity.

B What do people think about electricity?

1 (Home activity) Find ten people and get them to tell you in one sentence what they think electricity is. Write down what they say and tick the statements that you agree with.

2 (Group activity.) Get together with three or four other pupils in your class and look at the 30 or 40 statements you have obtained between you.

Choose the ten most important – or interesting – and write them out on a poster-sized piece of paper for the rest of the class to see.

3 (Class activity.) Decide, as a class, the final ten most important, accurate or interesting statements about electricity that have been produced.

The result could seriously worry your teacher!

Questions

1 Make lists of:

a five materials that don't conduct electricity (insulators),
b materials that do conduct electricity (conductors).

2 What units and instruments are used to measure:

a current,
b voltage,
c resistance?

3 What carries the electric charge through a lamp filament?

4 Electric current in wires is a flow of electrons. Why then don't scientists and electricians measure electric current in 'electrons per second'?

5 Why don't electric charges flow through a conductor unless it is part of a 'complete circuit'?

6 Why are metals usually good conductors of electricity?

7 Use table 1 to help you decide what will happen when the switch is pressed in each of the following circuits (picture 7).

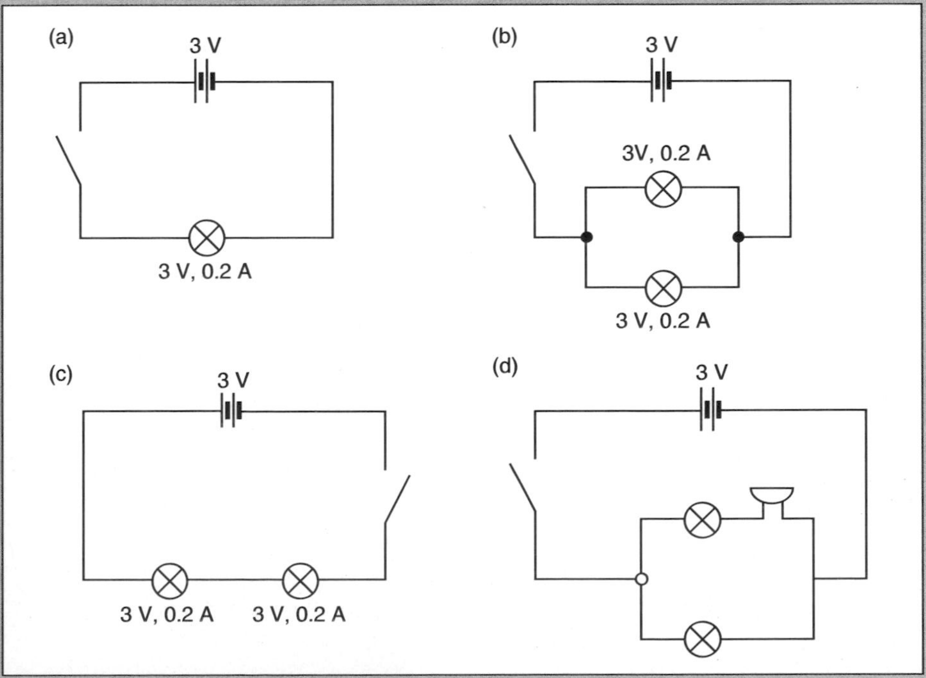

Picture 7

E2 Magnets

Magnetism is a mysterious kind of force. It comes from two sorts of magnets, permanent magnets and electromagnets.

Magnets and magnetic forces

Most people play with magnets when they are children. They are useful for finding lost pins and holding notes on fridge doors. These magnets are the kind that keep their 'magnetic power' for a long time, and so are called **permanent magnets**.

Permanent magnets are usually made from special kinds of iron, steel and other alloys. Sometimes the metal particles are baked with clay to make ceramic magnets or mixed with plastic to make flexible magnets. They can attract other things made out of iron or steel. But when you have two magnets together another strange effect can be seen. They can repel each other.

The magnetic compass

A magnet tied to a piece of thread so that is free to swing will line itself up in a roughly north–south direction. This effect was discovered by the Chinese over a thousand years ago; they soon used it to help them find their way at sea and in unknown territory. This effect is used in the magnetic compass. (See picture 1.)

The mysteries of magnetism began to be solved about 400 years ago, in the time of the first Queen Elizabeth of England. It was a time of great sea voyages, when Western Europeans sailed the world in search of trade, plunder and conquest.

Queen Elizabeth had a doctor called William Gilbert. He experimented with magnets and compasses and produced a theory to explain how compasses worked. He claimed that it must be because the whole Earth is a magnet. The huge Earth-magnet attracts and repels the small compass magnets so that they always line up in the same way (picture 2). On the whole, he had the right idea.

Magnetic fields

Magnets can be made in any shape. The simplest shape is a bar magnet. Cover a bar magnet with a sheet of white paper, carefully sprinkle iron filings over the paper and tap it gently with a pencil. You will see the filings forming into a pattern. What has happened is that the small bits of iron have been turned into little magnets and lined up by the forces produced by the big bar magnet.

The pattern shows us the direction of these forces, and gives an idea of how strong they are. It shows what is called the **field** of the magnet. Activity B asks you to set up some fields, plot them and draw them.

The iron filings just give a rough idea of the field. You need to use your imagination to draw the field lines sensibly, so that you go from the 'real' iron filings to the imaginary field, as shown in picture 3.

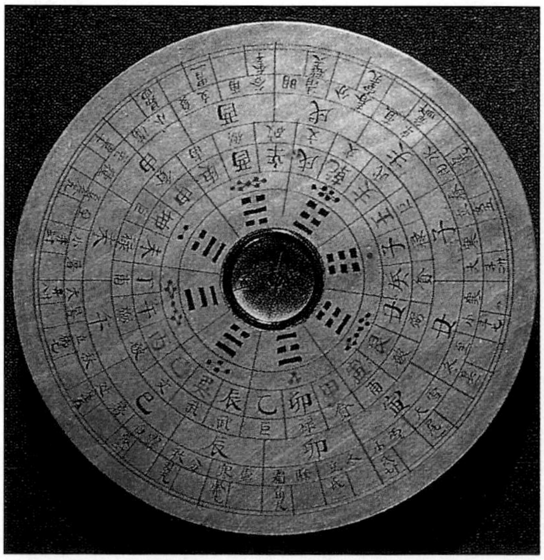

Picture 1 Compasses were invented by the Chinese.

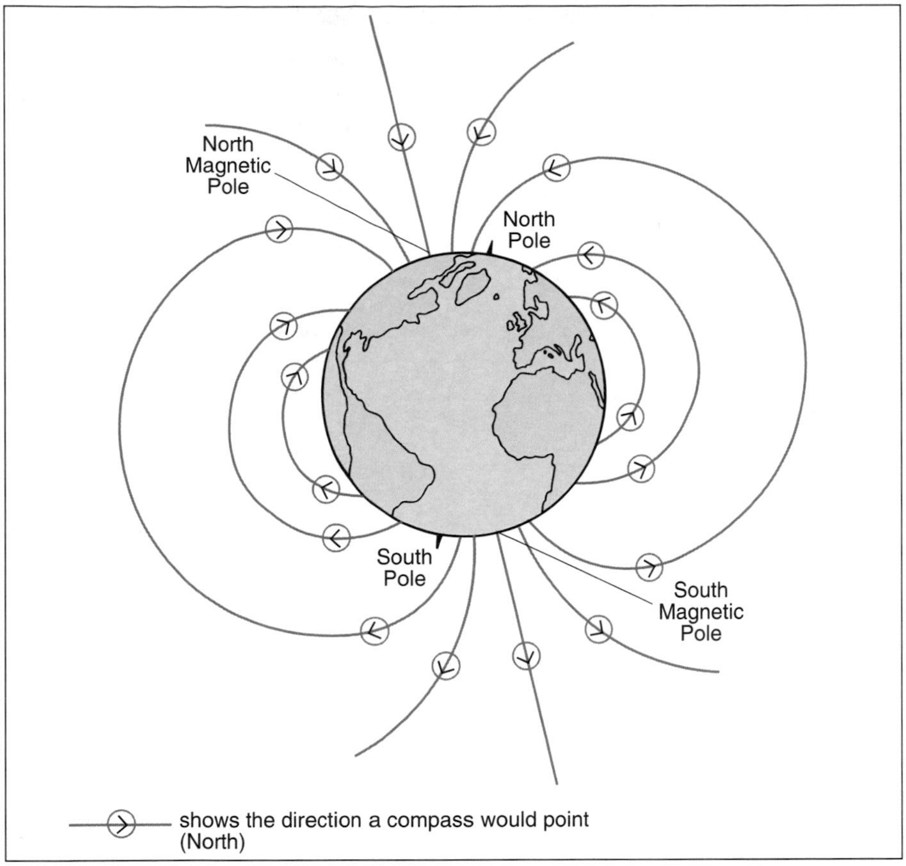

Picture 2 The magnetic field of the Earth.

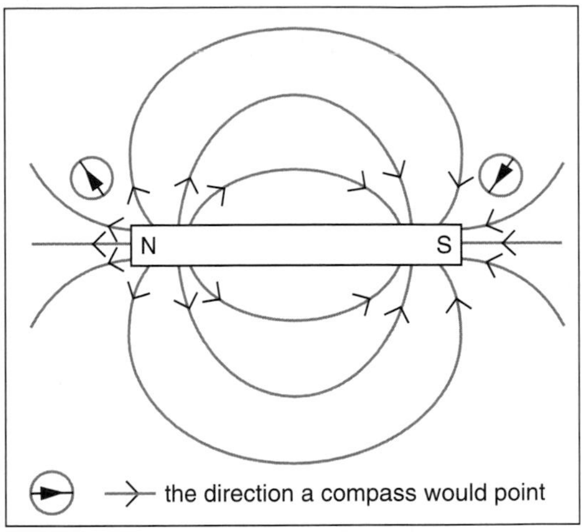

Picture 3 The magnetic field of a bar magnet.

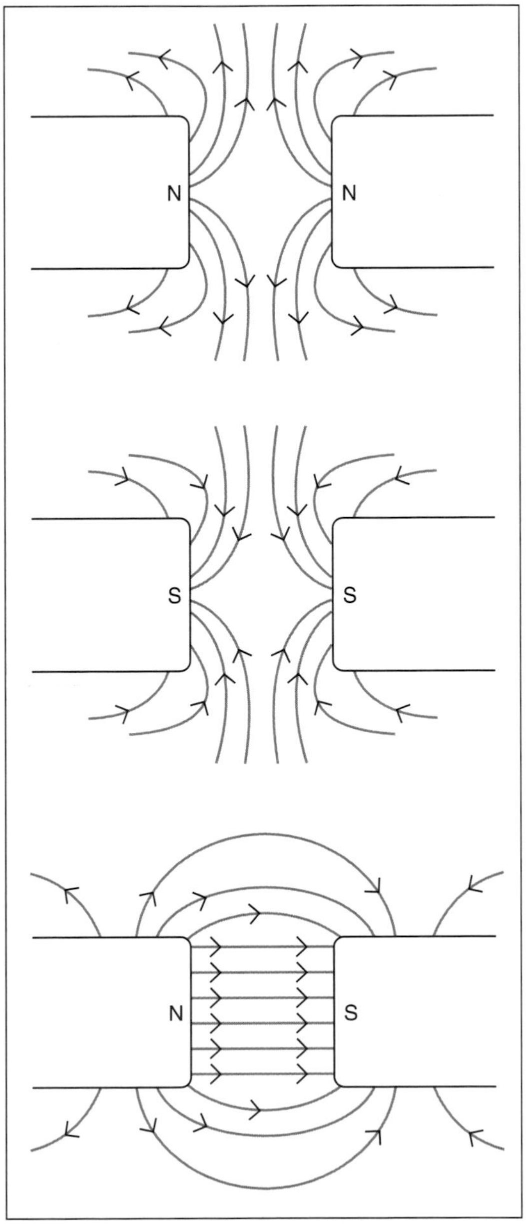

Picture 4 The fields between magnetic poles.

The Earth's magnetic field

The Earth has a magnetic field of its own, but it is quite weak. It is too weak to line iron filings up. But if you set up a thousand compasses all around your school, they would line up to show what the Earth's field is like in your area. It wouldn't look very interesting.

The direction of the field lines is the same as the way a compass would point (to the north). The arrows in picture 3 are in the direction that a small compass needle would point if you put it in the field.

A suspended bar magnet, or a compass needle, lines up so that one end points north, the other south. The end (or 'pole') that points north is called the north-seeking pole, or N-pole. The other end is the south-seeking or S-pole. They show the direction of the field lines (or lines of force) of the Earth's magnetic field.

Attraction and repulsion

The rule about magnets is quite simple:

like poles repel; unlike poles attract

This means that N-poles attract S-poles, and vice versa. N-poles repel N-poles and S-poles repel S-poles. This seems to be a basic law of nature; much the same applies to electric charges (see topic E5). The field-patterns of like or unlike poles near each other seem to show this (picture 4). The lines go as directly as they can from N-pole to S-pole, but veer away from each other when like poles are placed close to each other.

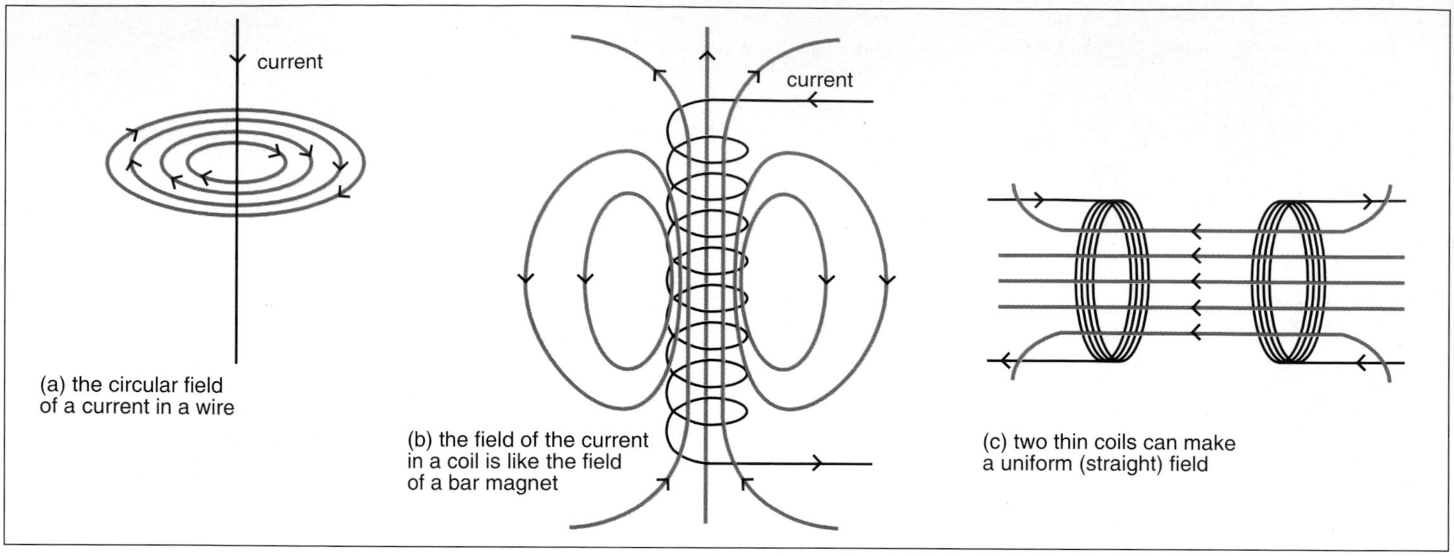
current
(a) the circular field
of a current in a wire
current
(b) the field of the current
in a coil is like the field
of a bar magnet
(c) two thin coils can make
a uniform (straight) field

Picture 5 How different magnetic fields can be made.

Electromagnets

Electromagnets are easy to make, and can be very strong. There is a magnetic field around every conductor carrying a current. Picture 5 shows how different kinds of effect can be made by winding the wire in different ways.

An electromagnet can be made to have a field just like the field of a bar magnet. All you have to do is wrap the wire around a pencil to make a coil – see picture 5(b).

The field can be made a lot stronger if the coil is wrapped around a piece of iron. This is because the iron is turned into a magnet, and adds its strength to the field of the coil itself (picture 6).

You can use a small compass or iron filings to investigate the direction of the field near electromagnets.

Why electromagnets are useful

Electromagnets can be switched on and off, so that you can have a magnet only when you want it. Also, by making the current larger or smaller you can make the force field stronger or weaker. Electromagnets are more controllable than permanent magnets. Permanent magnets and electromagnets are used in many everyday devices, and you will meet them again (topics E6, E7, E9 and E11).

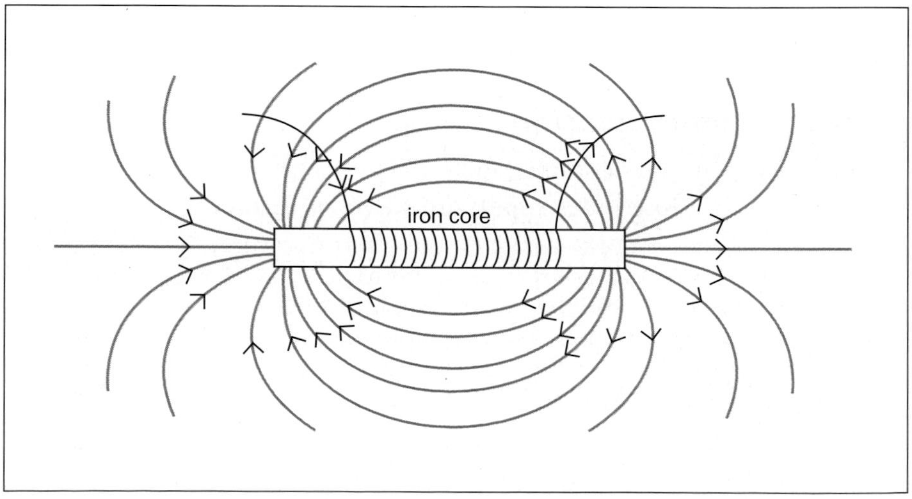
iron core

Picture 6 The field of an electromagnet.

Activities

A Where do we use magnets?

Look for many places or things in your home where magnets are being used. List all the ones you find. Are they permanent or electromagnets? Draw or describe one use in as much detail as you can.

B Looking at magnetic fields

To show magnetic fields with iron filings you have to work carefully. The following rules might help.

CARE! Wear goggles in case iron filings get blown into your eye and try to keep them off your skin. Wash your hands after you've used them.

1 Use fairly stiff paper and make sure that it is level and well supported above, but close to, the magnet(s). Use books or pieces of wood.

2 Sprinkle the filings gently, from at least 20 cm above the paper. Don't use too many – a few iron filings go a long way, and make a clearer pattern. Tap the paper gently with a pencil to make the pattern as clear as you can.

3 Keep the filings away from direct contact with the magnets – they are hard to get off again!

4 Use your imagination to draw the field pattern as a set of lines – don't try to draw every filing!

5 When you've finished, pour the filings on to another sheet of paper and fold it gently to pour the filings back into the sprinkler.

Fields to look at and draw:

a) a bar magnet,
b) a horseshoe magnet,
c) the magnets in a door catch or refrigerator seal,
d) two N-poles near each other,
e) two S-poles near each other,
f) an N-pole and an S-pole near each other,
g) the field of an electromagnet or coil (your teacher will probably have a special mount for these, to make it easier to set up).

C Maps and compasses

One of the snags about using a compass to find your way is that it doesn't point exactly north–south.

1 Find out why this is.

2 Use a good compass and a local Ordnance Survey map (1 to 25 000 or 1 to 50 000). Line up the map so that north on the map is aligned with true north on the ground.

3 Identify some local landmarks from the map.

D What decides how strong an electromagnet is?

You will need: some insulated single strand wire, iron or alloy to use as a core, an electricity supply that can produce a large current at a low voltage, a way of controlling and measuring the current, plus other equipment that you will have to work out for yourself.

1 Think of two or three things that might decide how strong an electromagnet is. Then think of how you might measure how strong it is.

2 Plan out an investigation for testing your ideas, then check with your teacher to see if what you want to do is practicable.

3 Carry out your experiments and write a report about them and what you find out.

Questions

1 Which of the following objects or materials would be attracted by a magnet?

a paper,
b glass,
c copper wire,
d wood,
e iron,
f carbon,
g a knife blade.

2 Copy the following arrangements (picture 7) and sketch the field patterns you would expect to find. Mark in the field directions (the way the N-pole of a compass would point) of:

a a bar magnet,
b a long coil of wire carrying a current,
c two N-poles near each other,
d a large N-pole opposite a similar S-pole (e.g. a pair of Magnadur magnets).

3 Explain the following as clearly as you can, using words or diagrams or both.

a What is the 'law of poles' for magnets?
b What is a magnetic field?
c Why does a compass needle line up north–south?

4 a Give two differences between permanent magnets and electromagnets.
b Why aren't electromagnets used in compasses?

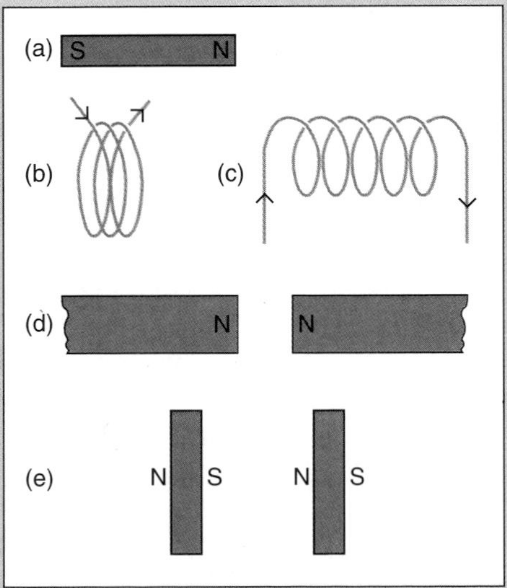

Picture 7

Picture 8

E3 Controlling electricity: current and resistance

To make the best use of electricity, we need to be able to control it. We can also use electricity to control other things.

Picture 1 The sliders move over resistors to control electric signals in a recording studio.

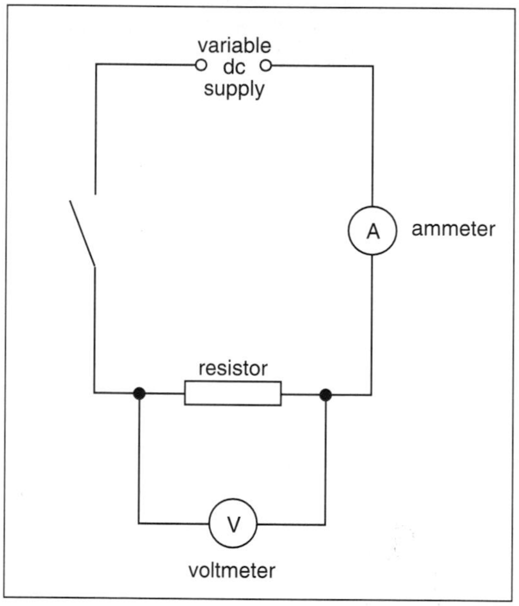

Picture 2 A circuit for measuring resistance.

Resistance

With a given energy source, such as a battery or a generator, the size of current that flows is decided by the **resistance** of the circuit. All conductors resist the flow of electric charge to some extent, but some are better at it than others. The bigger the resistance of a conductor the harder it is for electric charge to flow through it. For a given voltage applied to it, the current would be less.

It is like water flowing downhill in a river. If the bed of the river is smooth the water can flow easily, and more can get through in a given time. But if the bed of the river is rocky the water can't flow so easily. It will move downhill more slowly, and a lot of energy is wasted – you can hear the noise and see the water being thrown up in the air. We find the same kind of effect in a conductor with a high resistance. It cuts down the flow of charge – and energy is released. The conductor gets hot.

Resistors

A **resistor** is a special type of conductor made from a high resistance metal or alloy, or perhaps carbon.

A resistor is designed to have a fixed resistance, so that for a fixed voltage exactly the right size of current goes through the circuit.

Measuring resistance

Resistance is measured in units called **ohms** (Ω). A 10 Ω resistor would have twice the resistance of a 5 Ω resistor. For a given applied voltage the current in the 10 Ω resistor would be half of that in the 5 Ω resistor.

The size of current is worked out using the formula:

$$\text{current} = \frac{\text{voltage}}{\text{resistance}} \quad \text{or} \quad \boldsymbol{I} = \frac{\boldsymbol{V}}{\boldsymbol{R}}$$

We can switch this formula around to calculate resistance, knowing the current for a given voltage: $\boldsymbol{R = V/I}$

A simple test circuit (picture 2) allows you to measure current and voltage and so calculate the resistance of a resistor.

Variable resistors
Picture 3 shows examples of a very useful type of resistor. By moving a sliding contact, more or less resistance material is put in the way of the current, so making the current smaller or larger. Picture 4 shows how it does this.

These devices can be used in simple circuits to change the size of a current, but they are most often used to control the size of the applied **voltage**.

Picture 3 Resistors can be 'variable': you can control both current and voltage by varying the resistance.

Voltage

Voltage is not an easy thing to imagine. It measures what the battery or supply actually does, which is to give energy to make charges flow through conductors. We measure the voltage of a supply in terms of how much energy it gives to a **coulomb of charge**. In a lamp circuit the energy would be mostly given to the lamp, heating up its filament.

If a coulomb of charge delivers **6 joules of energy** as it goes around a circuit then the supply voltage is 6 joules per coulomb. We call this **6 volts**. The voltage across a conductor is also called **potential difference** (pd).

Another way to look at it is in terms of current and power. This is more practical because the instruments we use measure amps, not coulombs.

The voltage of an energy source such as a battery decides how much **power** a given current can deliver. Power is the rate at which energy is provided, in joules per second or **watts** (W). See topic D3 for more about power and energy.

A current of 1 A from a 6 V battery can deliver 6 W (6 J of energy per second) but, a current of 1 A from a mains supply at 230 V will deliver 230 W.

So the voltage of a source tells us how many watts it could provide per ampere of current, according to the formula

$$V = \frac{P}{I} \quad \text{or} \quad \text{volts} = \frac{\text{watts}}{\text{amperes}}$$

You choose the energy source to suit the power you want to use. The mains supply to a house in the UK is 230 V. This means that small currents can be used to run most of the devices we have in our homes. We can see this from the formula, if we rearrange it as $P = VI$. The bigger V is, the smaller I can be to get the same result.

In the USA the mains voltage is 110 V. Their devices need a bigger current if they want the same power. This means they have to be made with lower resistances.

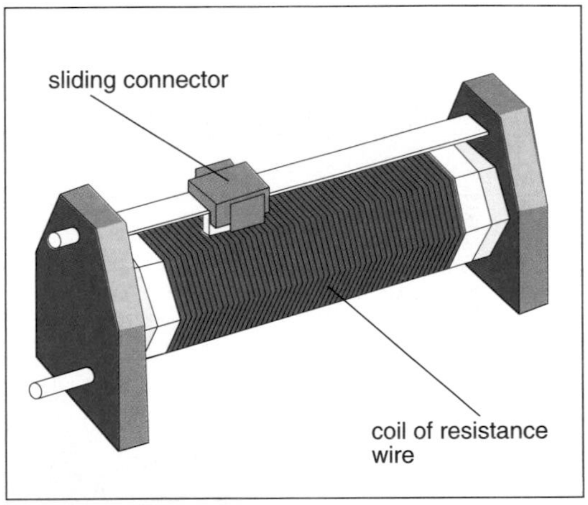

Picture 4 A rheostat – 'flow controller'.

Controlling voltage

When you turn the volume control of a radio or cassette player you are using a variable resistor to control the voltage somewhere in the amplifier circuit. This decides how loud the sound that comes from the loudspeakers will be.

The volume control is a variable resistor. The voltage of the signal being amplified is first of all fed across the whole resistor as shown for a battery in picture 5. By moving the sliding contact you can get all, or just a part, of the input voltage fed to the amplifier. The bigger the voltage that gets to the amplifier, the louder the sound will be in the loudspeaker. When used like this the variable resistor is called a **voltage divider** or *potential divider*. It divides up the total voltage into smaller amounts.

The potential divider
Picture 5 shows a circuit which uses a potential divider. AB is a resistor, such as a uniform length of resistance wire, with a sliding contact S. The wire is usually wrapped into a coil. When AB is connected to a voltage supply, such as a battery, current flows through it. The voltage drop across the resistor, from A to B, is the voltage of the battery, say 6 V. S is shown as a quarter of the way between A and B. The voltage between S and B is thus three-quarters of the whole 6 V, which is 4.5 V. Half way down it is 3 V. Thus by sliding S up and down the resistor AB we can get any voltage we like between 0 V and 6 V.

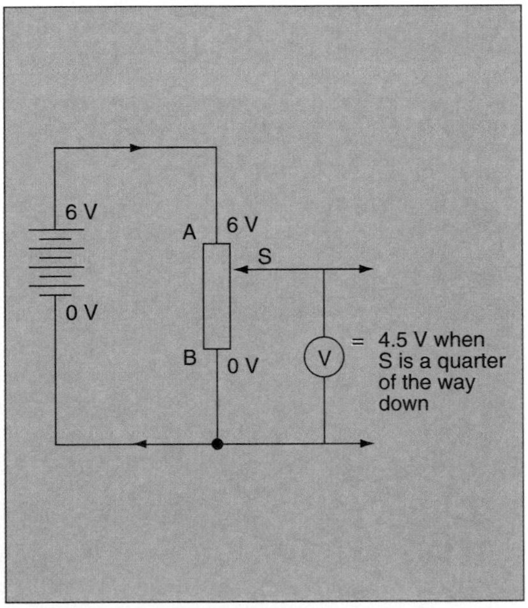

Picture 5 The potential divider.

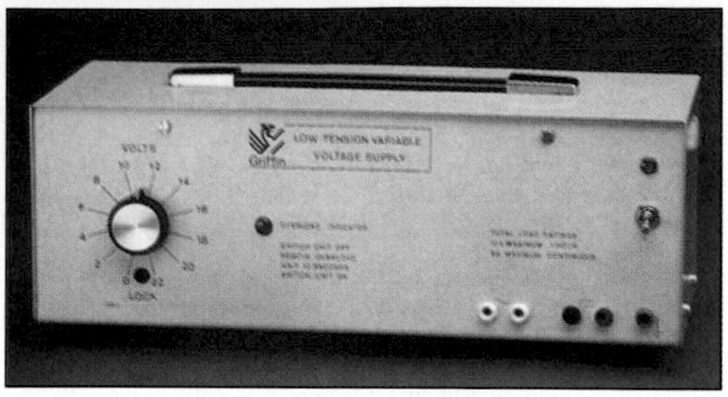

Picture 6 A variable power supply.

Whenever you turn the knob on a volume control you are likely to be moving a slider along a potential divider, so changing the size of the voltage input to an amplifier.

Variable power supplies

Picture 6 shows a typical low-voltage power supply. Its output can be changed, using a control knob, from 0 to 22 V. The main part of the power supply gives a fixed voltage. The control knob is connected to a variable resistor which changes the output to anything between zero and the maximum, using a voltage divider.

Measuring current and voltage

Current is measured with an **ammeter**, and voltage with a **voltmeter**. Both of these instruments look much the same, and may in fact work on exactly the same principles. This can be confusing, because what they measure is very different. Also, they are placed differently in circuits.

Ammeters tell us how much electric charge is passing though a circuit per second. Remember that 1 ampere is a flow of 1 coulomb of charge per second. Ammeters have to be put directly in the path of the current, so that they can check everything that goes through the circuit (see picture 7).

Voltmeters are trickier. They take a sample of the current in a device or circuit and then *calculate* the voltage that must be across it. They have to keep the 'sampling current' small if they are not to change the circuit too much. This means that they have high resistances and are connected *across* the device being tested (see picture 8).

Many of the meters used today use an electronic circuit to measure current or voltage. They give the result as numbers in a liquid crystal display (picture 9). They are digital meters.

Picture 7 An ammeter will read the current going through it.

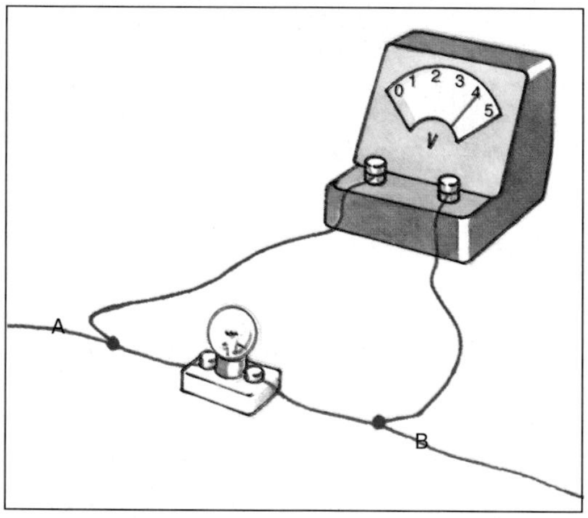

Picture 8 A voltmeter samples some of the flow and 'works out' the voltage between two points (A and B).

Ohm's Law

For many useful conductors there is a simple rule which connects current, voltage and resistance. If we double the applied voltage, the current is doubled. If we halve the voltage, the current is halved. This effect doesn't work with all conductors, but is true for metals and for carbon, if they don't get too hot.

For most circuits we can use the rule to calculate in advance what will happen when things change.

The rule is: **for a given conductor at a constant temperature the current in it is proportional to the applied voltage**. This is known as **Ohm's Law**.

We can write this as a formula $\boldsymbol{I = V/R}$ where $\boldsymbol{R}$ is a constant. We can use this formula to make calculations with all values of $\boldsymbol{V}$ for a given conductor. But we have to be careful, because the resistance might change if the conductor gets hot.

Activity C is about this useful 'law' of electricity.

Does a filament lamp obey Ohm's Law?

Picture 10 shows how current varies with voltage for a 12 V, 24 W lamp, of the kind used in car headlamps. Its resistance at 12 V is 6 Ω. (You should check that this value is correct.) But at 6 V its resistance is smaller than 6 Ω. This is not because the tungsten filament in the lamp is breaking Ohm's Law, but because the temperature is changing – at 12 V the metal is white hot at over 2000 °C. If the temperature was kept constant at, say, room temperature, the filament would have the same resistance at all currents and voltages.

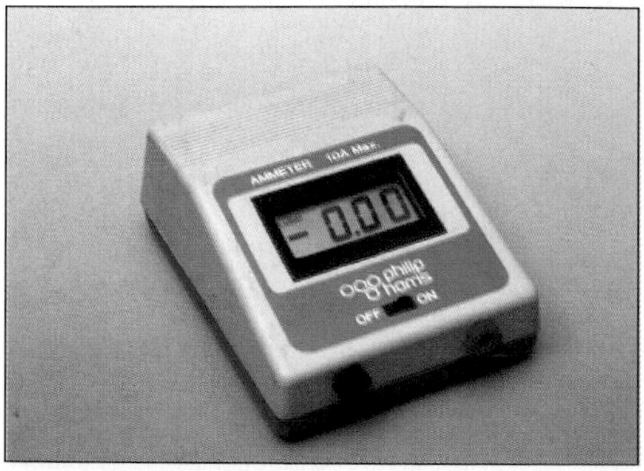

Picture 9 A digital meter.

What is a law?

Some laws in physics are unbreakable. Gravity always behaves in the same way (see topic B4). Mass–energy cannot be created or destroyed. In every energy change, some always gets less usable. Of course, the universe is large and can come up with some surprises. But physicists are pretty sure that if any of these laws were broken it would only be because there was a better or stronger law to take its place.

Ohm's Law is not like these. It doesn't say what *must* happen. It just describes how some materials behave. It applies only to metals, ionic solutions and perhaps carbon. There are lots of conductors that don't 'obey' Ohm's Law. This doesn't worry anybody! If the Law of Conservation of Mass–Energy were broken, the Universe would be a different place!

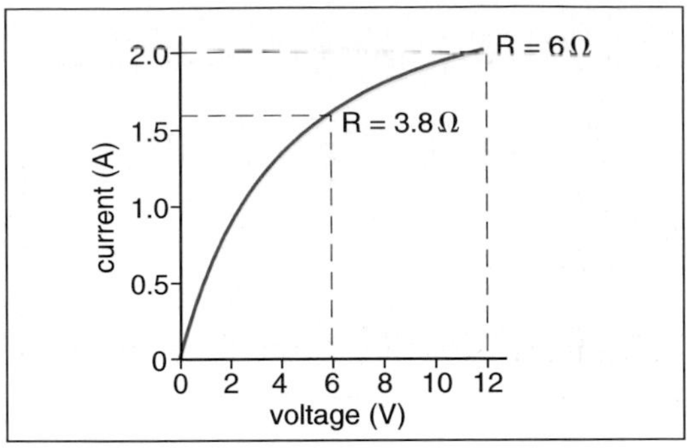

Picture 10 Current and voltage for a filament lamp.

Activities

A Measuring resistance

Use the circuit shown in picture 2 (or a similar one given to you by your teacher) to measure the resistance of as many of the following as you can. Make sure that you check the rated voltage of the device so that you do not exceed it and possibly damage the device you are testing.

1 a 12 V lamp,

2 a standard ('electronic') resistor,

3 a small electric motor,

4 a voltmeter (think!),

5 a small electric heater.

B Looking at the label

All electrical devices used in the home must by law have certain information printed on them. Look at some devices and find this information.

1 Copy out what electrical information is given on any one device (e.g. a food mixer, battery radio, electric razor).

2 Use the information to make the following calculations for any three devices:

a) the current it takes in normal use,
b) its resistance.
You may need to use the formulae given in this topic:

$$R = \frac{V}{I} \quad P = VI \text{ or } V = \frac{P}{I}$$

$$\text{or } I = \frac{P}{V}$$

C Investigating Ohm's Law

Ohm's Law says that for a given conductor at a constant temperature the current in it is proportional to the applied voltage.

1 What does 'proportional' mean? How could you test two sets of measurements to see if they are proportional to each other?

2 You will need the equipment as used for activity A (see picture 2) and a metal (e.g. wire) resistor. Set up a circuit to measure the current in the wire for six different voltage values. Does the wire obey Ohm's Law?

3 Replace the wire with a 12 V lamp and repeat the experiment. Does the lamp obey Ohm's Law?

Questions

1 a Name the instruments used to measure current and voltage and draw their circuit symbols.

b Copy the circuit in picture 9 and label the empty circles with A or V to show which would be ammeters and which voltmeters.

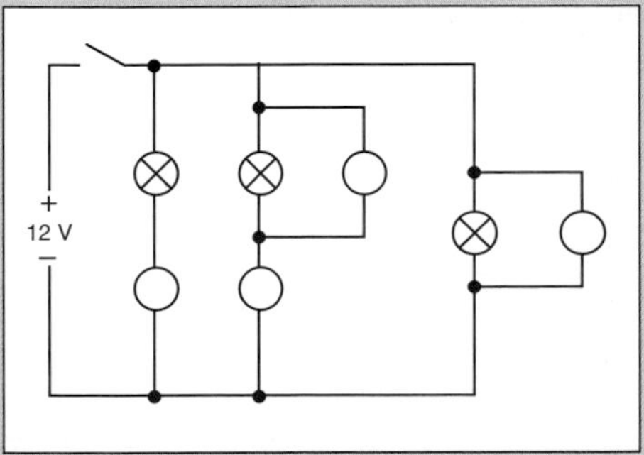

Picture 11

2 You find two wires made of the same metal. One wire is long and thin, the other wire is short and thick. Which do you think would have the bigger resistance?

Give a reason for your answer.

3 People often try to understand about electricity by comparing it with water flowing in a river.

a In what ways is water in a river like electricity in a wire?
b In what ways is it different?
c Can you think of anything else that is like electricity flowing in a wire?

4 Batteries with the same voltage marked on them are sometimes very different in size. Suggest a reason for this.

5 Use the formula $R = V/I$ to work out the resistance of the following devices:

a a lamp that takes a current of 2 A from a 12 V supply,
b a lamp that takes a current of 0.5 A from a 12 V supply,
c an electric toaster that takes a current of 3 A from a 230 V supply,
d a cake mixer that takes a current of 2.2 A from a 230 V supply.

6 Car headlamps are powered by a 12 V battery or alternator and have a typical resistance of 2.5 Ω. How much current must each lamp take from the supply?

7 Why must ammeters be connected in line (in series) with a device, but voltmeters be connected across it (in parallel)?

8 Draw the circuit you would use to measure the resistance of a torch bulb to be used in a 3 V torch.

9 A resistor used in an electronic circuit must obey Ohm's Law.

a One such resistor is labelled '20 ohms'. What current would be in it when the following voltages are applied across it: (i) 20 V, (ii) 10 V, (iii) 2 V?
b Another resistor is labelled '2 kΩ'. What voltage would need to be applied to produce a current of 10 mA in it?

E4 Using circuits

The key to using electricity is the circuit.

Picture 1 A Christmas tree. How are the lights controlled?

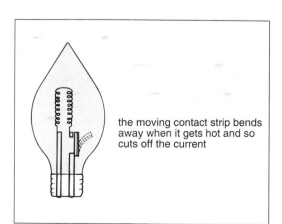

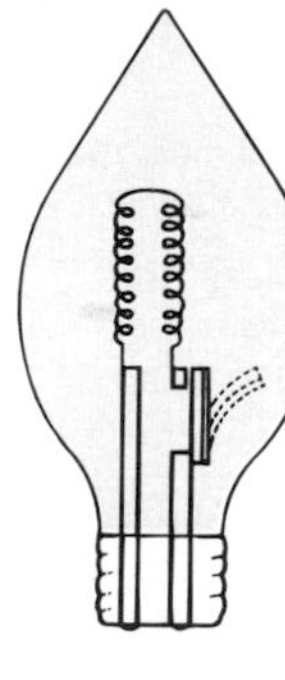
the moving contact strip bends away when it gets hot and so cuts off the current

Picture 2 How a flashing lamp works.

How do flashing lights work?

Picture 1 shows a Christmas tree, decorated with coloured lights that can flash on and off. The flashing is controlled by just one bulb that is different from the others. When the filament in it gets hot enough it switches itself off. Then it cools down and switches itself on again (see picture 2). When this control lamp is out all the other lamps go out as well. They only work when the control lamp is on.

Sometimes a lamp in your home stops working and goes out. But this doesn't make all the other lamps go out. Why is this?

Series and parallel connections

The Christmas tree lights are connected in a line, one after the other, as shown in picture 3. When a connection is broken in one lamp the charge cannot flow, so all the lamps go out. This way of connecting things in a circuit is called **series** connection.

In a house the lamps in a room are connected in a different way. It would be very annoying if all the lights went out just because one lamp wasn't working. In the home, each lamp is connected separately to the mains supply, as shown in picture 4. Each lamp can have its own switch, and we can have any of the three lamps on, or none of them. This is called **parallel** connection.

Why do we use parallel circuits in the home?

Electrical devices in the home are connected in parallel because we want to control them independently of each other. Each device is connected directly to the mains, so that it gets its proper voltage. Also, we can easily connect other devices into the circuit, without having to 'break it'.

Of course, the more appliances we connect, the more energy we will use, and the more it will cost. This is because when we connect more devices in the circuit in parallel we must take more current from the supply in order to make these extra devices work. This means that the total resistance must get less!

Resistance in parallel: more means less!

We can understand this idea by seeing what happens to the current drawn from the supply when we add more things to a parallel circuit. Take a simple circuit that you could try for yourself in the lab (activity A, picture 12). If we start with just one 12 V lamp, say, we can calculate the current through it by using the formula $\boldsymbol{I = V/R}$.

For one lamp this might be just 1 A. If we add another lamp it too will need 1 A to make it work – and the supply will have to deliver 2 A.

In the first case the circuit resistance is 12 Ω:

$$\boldsymbol{R} = \frac{\boldsymbol{V}}{\boldsymbol{I}} = \frac{12\ \text{V}}{1\ \text{A}} = 12\ \Omega$$

In the second case, with two lamps, the supply delivers 2 A, so the circuit resistance is now 6 Ω:

$$\boldsymbol{R} = \frac{\boldsymbol{V}}{\boldsymbol{I}} = \frac{12\ \text{V}}{2\ \text{A}} = 6\ \Omega$$

What would be the circuit resistance if another similar lamp were to be added?

You can work out the answer (4 Ω) in this simple circuit by common sense, but in more complicated circuits you will need to use the formula for resistors in parallel: $\boldsymbol{1/R = 1/R_1 + 1/R_2 + 1/R_3}$ etc. This formula is needed when the devices added in parallel have different values of resistance.

Resistors in series

Picture 5 shows resistors connected in series. If you try this (activity B) you will find that the more lamps you add the dimmer they get! This is another reason why lamps are usually connected in parallel. The ammeter shows that the current gets less as more lamps are added. This means that the resistance of the circuit has **increased**. When we add resistors in series the total resistance goes up:

$$R = R_1 + R_2 + R_3 \text{ etc.}$$

Picture 6 shows how complicated circuits can get! But all the components you can see in this computer are connected in series and/or in parallel, and the engineers who designed and made it know what current each component has to carry.

The resistance of a metal wire depends on four things:

- Its **length** – the longer it is the more resistance it has.
- Its **area of cross-section** – the larger its area of cross-section the less its resistance is.
- The **material** it is made of – gold, silver and copper are better at conducting electricity than iron, for example. Also, we can make metal alloys that are more resistive than pure metals. Electric heaters use high-resistance alloys like nichrome and constantan.
- **Temperature** – the resistance of a metal wire increases with temperature.

The above factors are important in designing circuit components. For example, a filament lamp has to have exactly the right resistance, so designers have to choose the right length and thickness of wire once they have chosen the metal out of which the filament is to be made. They also have to allow for the fact that the resistance they measure at room temperature is much less than the resistance when the filament is white hot.

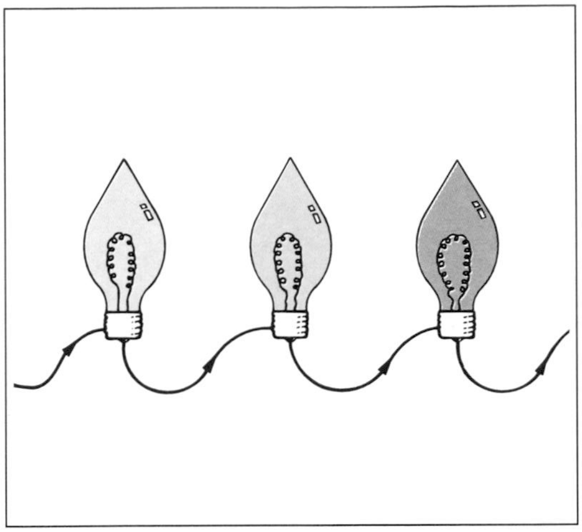

Picture 3 Christmas tree lamps are connected in series. The same current goes through each in turn.

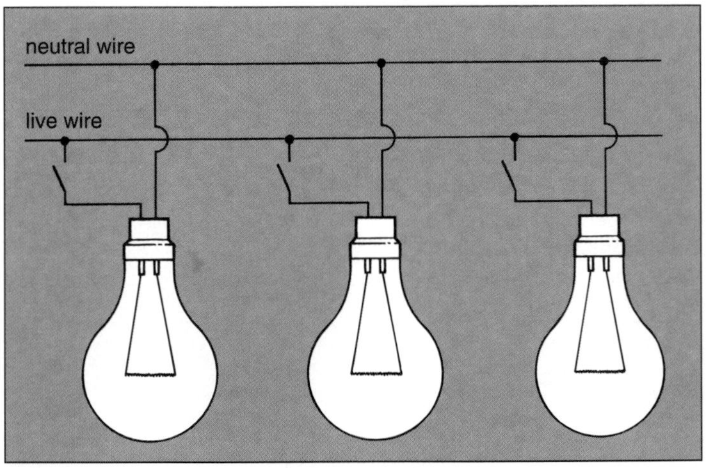

Picture 4 House lights have the lamps connected separately to the mains (i.e. in parallel).

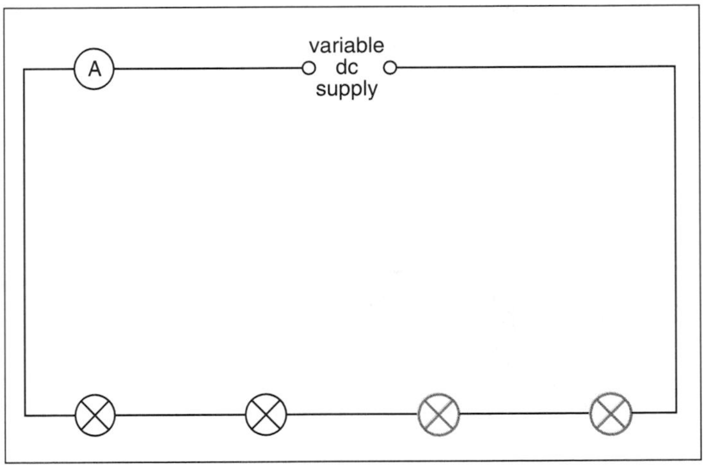

Picture 5 Adding lamps in series.

Picture 6 Inside a computer – some circuits are quite complicated!

Controlling electricity with semiconductors

Semiconductors are materials which conduct electricity less well than ordinary metallic conductors like copper. They are often made from combinations of materials such as germanium and silicon. They are poorer conductors than metals because they have fewer charged particles (electrons) that are free to move and so carry a current.

A **thermistor** (picture 7) is a resistor made of semiconductor material. When it is heated electrons are freed and its resistance gets less. Its resistance will depend in a known way on its temperature. This means that a thermistor can be used as an electric **thermometer** to measure temperature and in **thermostats**, where a current needs to be switched on or off at a particular temperature.

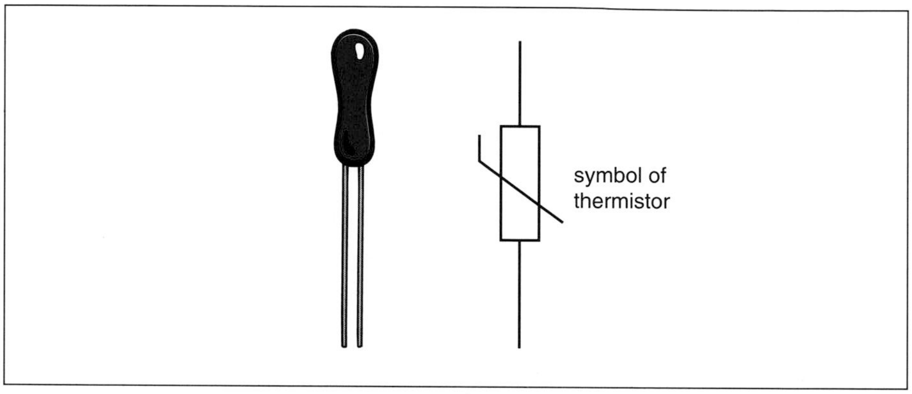

Picture 7 A thermistor – a temperature-dependent resistor.

Light can also provide the energy to release electrons in some semiconductors. This effect is used to make light dependent resistors or **LDRs**. Picture 8 shows a typical LDR. In the dark its resistance might be 100 000 Ω (100 kΩ). In bright sunlight so many electrons are freed that its resistance falls to about 100 Ω.

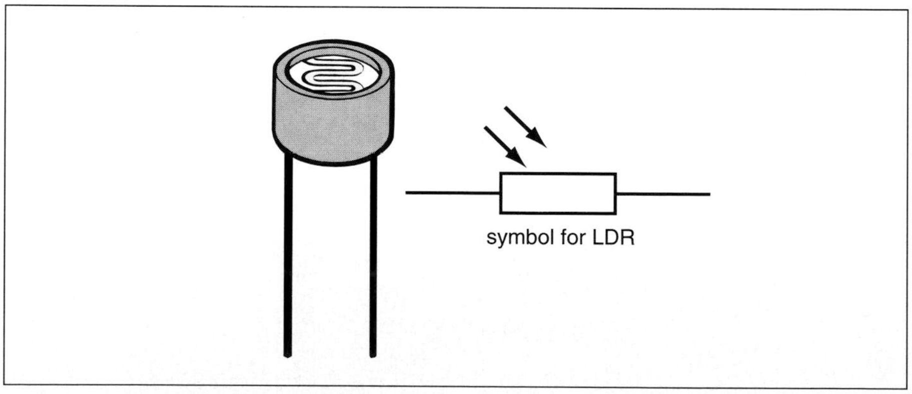

Picture 8 A light-dependent resistor.

So, by connecting them in the right circuits, we can use LDRs to convert changes in light intensity into electrical signals.

Diodes

A **diode** (picture 9) is a device that allows electricity to flow through it in one direction only. In other words it is a conductor in one direction and an insulator in the other. Diodes are made using semiconductors. They are used in many applications in electronics and microelectronics. A simple application is to protect a device that might be damaged if it is connected the wrong way to a power supply (picture 10).

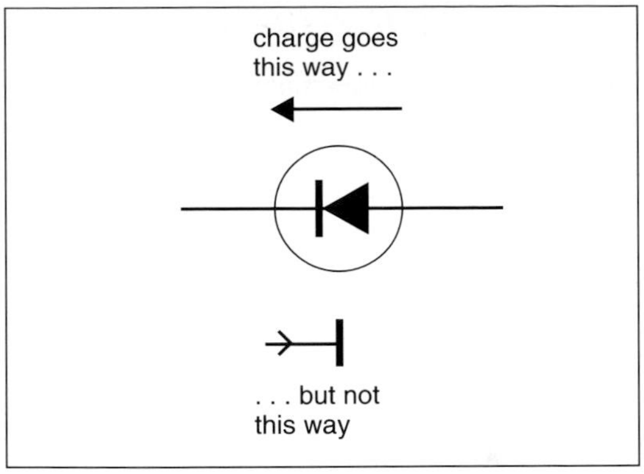

Picture 9 Action of a semiconductor diode.

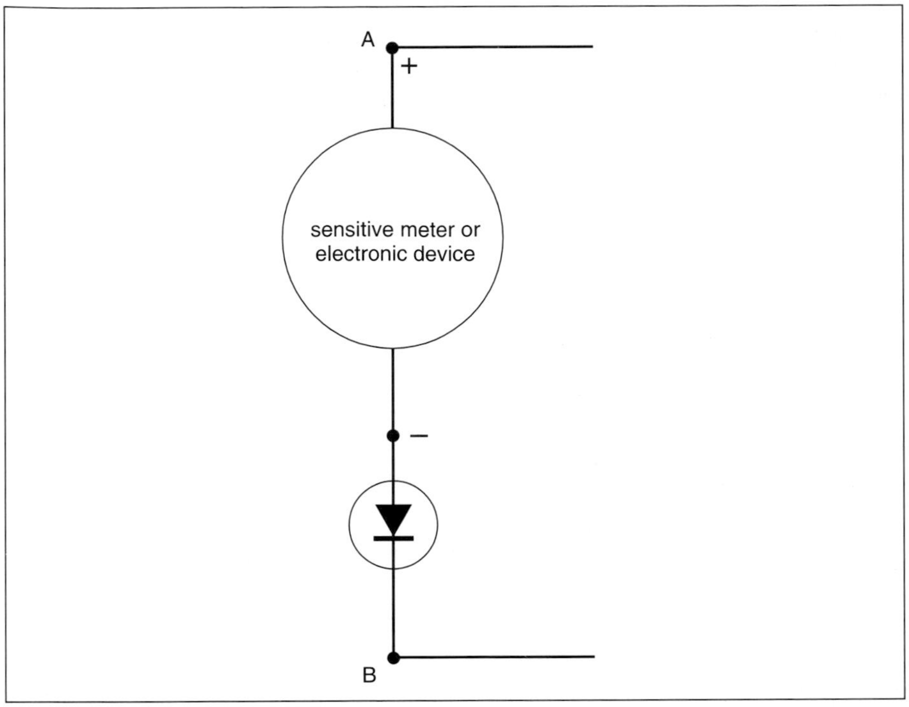

Picture 10 A diode used to protect a device against incorrect connection. When A is positive current flows normally. What will happen if B is connected to positive?

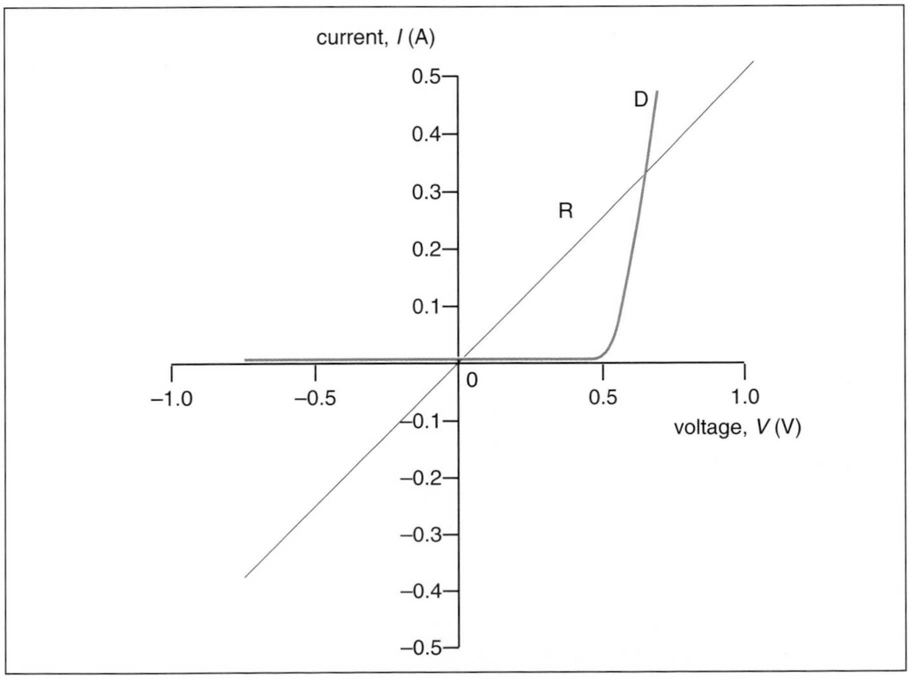

Picture 11 Current versus voltage for a metal resistor (R) and a diode (D). No current flows in the diode when the voltage is reversed.

Activities

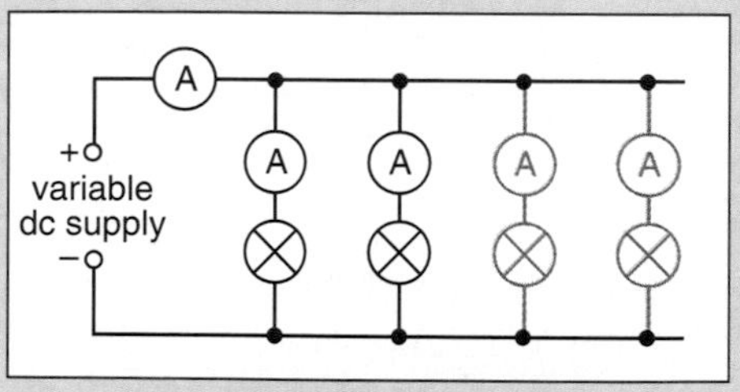

Picture 12 Adding lamps in parallel.

A Lamps in parallel

Picture 12 shows a simple circuit for testing what happens when lamps are connected in parallel. Unless your lab is very well equipped you may have to make do with just one ammeter and move it around the circuit to wherever you need it.

1 Set up the circuit with just one lamp, set the supply to 12 V and **check it with a voltmeter**.
2 Measure the current that goes through both the lamp and the power supply and note it in a copy of table A below.
3 Add another, similar lamp in parallel with the first. Check that the voltage of the supply is still 12 V – it may need adjusting – and record the current in each lamp and the current delivered by the power supply.
4 Repeat with as many lamps as you and your teacher consider is safe.

Analysis of results

a What is the connection between the current delivered by the supply and the sum of the currents in the lamps?
b Calculate the resistance of one lamp.
c Calculate the circuit resistance for each arrangement.
d Check that the circuit resistance $\boldsymbol{R}$ can be calculated by the formula $\boldsymbol{1/R = 1/L + 1/L + 1/L}$ etc., where $\boldsymbol{L}$ is the resistance of one lamp.

Table A

Number of lamps	Current in each lamp				Current delivered by supply
	1st	2nd	3rd	4th	
one		-	-	-	
two			-	-	
three				-	
four					

Number of resistors	Current in circuit	Voltage across each component
one only		
two		
three		
four		

Table B

B Investigating a series circuit

Picture 5 shows how conductors can be connected in series.

1 Use up to four similar resistors and investigate what happens as you connect them to a power supply in series. Each time you add a new one, measure:
a) the current in the circuit,
b) the voltage drop across each component.
Set out your results in a table like table B:
2 Describe clearly what happens to the current and the voltage.
3 Calculate the resistance of each component and the total circuit resistance in each arrangement.
4 Check that the total circuit resistance $\boldsymbol{R}$ is given by the formula $\boldsymbol{R = R_1 + R_2 + R_3 + R_4}$ etc.

C Thermistors

Picture 13 shows a simple circuit for investigating thermistors.

1 Measure the current in the thermistor and the voltage across it.
2 Use the formula $\boldsymbol{R = V/I}$ to calculate the resistance of the thermistor at various temperatures between about 20 °C and 70 °C. Set your results out in a table.
3 Plot a graph of resistance against temperature.
4 Suppose you wanted to use the thermistor to measure temperatures. How would you use this graph to help you?

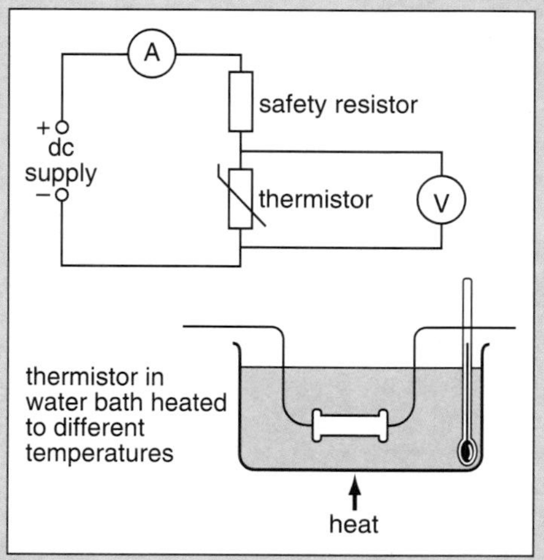

Picture 13

5 Would you be able to use the results from this experiment to measure temperatures below 0 °C or over 100 °C? Explain your answer.

D Sensing light

Light meters are useful for, say, taking photographs or for checking on how light intensity affects the growth of plants.

Design an investigation to find out how a light-dependent resistor might be used as a 'light meter'.

Check your plan with your teacher. (*Hint* One problem you will have to solve is how to make this a fair test, i.e. produce 'equal units' of light.)

Questions

1 Draw circuit diagrams showing:

a a battery driving two lamps in series with a switch,

b a battery driving two lamps in parallel, with a switch for each one.

2 Give *two* reasons why the lamps at home are connected in parallel rather than in series.

3 Draw circuits showing how you could connect:

a a lamp in parallel with a small electric motor, run off a 12 V battery, with a switch that controls both lamp and motor.

b a lamp and motor as above, but with each having its own separate switch.

4 Some cars have heated rear windows, with the heater switched on and off by the driver. The makers of the car guard against the driver leaving the window heater on whilst the car is parked overnight.

a Why would this be a stupid thing to do? (Try to think of two reasons.)

b The simplest way for the car manufacturers to stop this is by making sure that the window heater can't be on unless the ignition switch is also on (the ignition switch has to be on for the engine to work). Draw a simple circuit showing how the two switches are connected.

5 For this question you may need to use the formulae given in the topic for calculating resistances in series and in parallel.

a A 6 Ω and a 2 Ω motor are both run from a 6 V battery. They are connected in parallel. How much current is drawn from the battery?

b Ten Christmas tree lights are connected in series to the 230 V mains supply. A current of 0.5 A is drawn from the mains. What is the resistance of each lamp?

c A 12 V car battery has to supply a heater and a starter motor. They are connected in parallel and have resistances of 12 Ω and 0.5 Ω respectively. What is the effective resistance when both are switched on? What current does the battery have to supply?

6 Picture 14 shows a circuit that includes an LDR. When light shines on the LDR its resistance becomes a lot less than what it was in the dark.

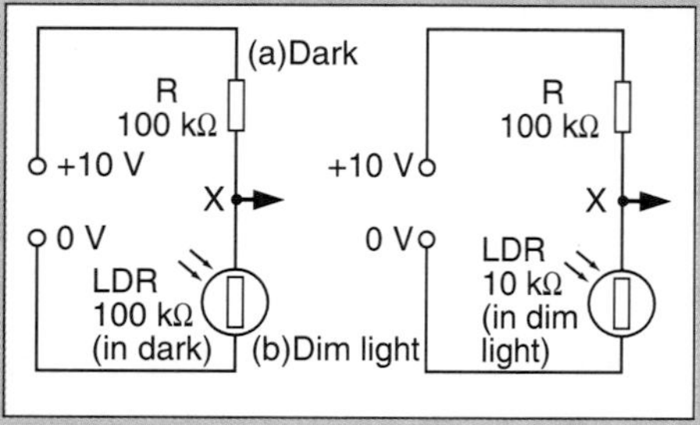

Picture 14

a The resistor R and the LDR are connected in series. Jamal says, 'Whatever the resistances of R and the LDR, the same current will flow in both.' Do you agree with this? Give a reason for your answer.

b In the dark the LDR has the same resistance as the resistor R. What is the voltage at point X?

c In dim light the resistance of R stays unchanged but the LDR's resistance decreases to 10 000 Ω. What is the voltage at point X now?

d In bright light the resistance of the LDR becomes less than a hundredth of its dark value. Which of the following is a reasonable (nearest) guess at the voltage at point X in bright light?
(i) 10 V (ii) 5 V (iii) 1 V (iv) 0 V
(*Hint* you need to know that the voltage across a conductor is proportional to the current in it.)

7 Two students did an experiment in which they measured the resistance of a thermistor at different temperatures. The results they got are shown in the table.

a Plot a graph of resistance against temperature for this thermistor.

b The students wanted to use the thermistor as a 'remote thermometer', to measure the temperature in a bird's nest from a distance. Draw a simple circuit they could use to do this.

c They found that the resistance readings they obtained varied between 85 Ω and 110 Ω. What range of temperatures did this give for the nest?

d Suggest what made the temperature in the nest change like this.

Temperature, *T* (°C)	0	10	20	30	40	50	60	70	80
Resistance, *R* (ohms)	300	200	140	100	70	50	35	25	18

E5 What is electricity?

We use 'electricity' every day, but it is more than just a good way of making things work ...

Picture 1 Amber is fossilised tree-sap.

Picture 2 Static electricity is easy to produce.

The amber mystery

People have known about electricity for thousands of years. The word electricity comes from the Greek word for amber – *elektron*. Amber is the fossilised sap of pine trees, and is used to make beads and jewellery. It is a shiny, clear, golden material, which may contain the fossils of insects trapped in it (picture 1).

One snag with amber jewellery is that it seems to get dusty very easily. The ancient Greeks noticed this, and worked out that amber had the mysterious ability to attract small objects to it. This happens when a piece of amber is rubbed by cloth. If you don't happen to own any amber, you can get the same effect by rubbing a plastic pen or comb (picture 2).

The rubbed amber produces a force of attraction which came to be called 'amber force' – or **electricity**. The force was very small, and the effect was completely useless, unlike the forces, say, of magnetism. At least magnets could tell you which way north was. So electricity was forgotten about.

Picture 3 Being charged with electricity is like falling – it doesn't hurt until you touch the Earth!

The rediscovery of electricity

When electricity did become important it wasn't for good scientific reasons. This renewed interest began just over 200 years ago. At that time 'science' as we know it didn't exist. 'Scientists' called themselves 'natural philosophers'. Some of them were people who were rich and had money and spare time to spend on their hobby, like Robert Boyle who discovered 'Boyle's Law' for gases.

Many earned a living as doctors, like William Gilbert who did experiments on magnets. Galileo (page 46) started off as a doctor of medicine.

Some were clergymen, like Copernicus, who put forward the strange new theory that the Earth went round the Sun, and not vice versa. Some were astronomers or mathematicians, like Isaac Newton.

Some discoveries were made by 'artisans', people who were good with their hands and earned a living making clocks and other instruments. Michael Faraday (see page 168) began life as a bookbinder.

Most of the early scientists we know about lived in Europe or the British colonies in North America. There were very important discoveries made in China and India, but few of these were heard about in the West.

Picture 4 A Wimshurst Machine.

The shocking history of electricity

In the early days the best fun was to be had from 'electrifying' people. Small boys were easily persuaded to be hung up by silken ropes and 'charged' up (picture 3). They were stroked with dry cloths until their hair stood on end. In the dark, you could see sparks leaping from them to anybody standing close by.

Later, machines were invented that used amber-like materials to produce electricity just by turning a handle (picture 4). It was quicker than stroking people with a dry cloth.

The whole thing became so popular that you could earn a living by electrifying people in fairgrounds. People thought that getting charged up was

Picture 5 Shocking people has always been fun!

good for the health, and paid money to be strung up and electrified.

In Holland in 1746, Peter van Musschenbroek tried to electrify water in a bottle, and by accident found a new effect. The 'charge' could be stored in a jar. This was the first **capacitor**, and was called a Leiden Jar. This was because he did the experiment in his home town of Leiden.

Now things got more serious – enough charge could be stored to give people a severe shock. The shock could kill small animals and birds, and melt thin wire.

In Paris, 180 of the King's guards were lined up, holding hands, and connected to a charged jar. They all leaped high in the air, at the same instant. The experiment was repeated with 300 Carthusian monks, formed into a line 100 m long. The results were equally spectacular and even more crowd-pleasing (picture 5). History does not record what the monks thought of it.

Shocks became popular as a cure for gout and rheumatism, and electricity was suddenly all the rage.

A theory of electricity

What was going on? What *was* electricity? Where did it come from? Many interested people tried to answer these questions, and it wasn't until the early years of this century that they could be fully answered. But a very good start was made by an American called Benjamin Franklin, who lived from 1706 to 1790 (picture 6).

He started life as a printer's apprentice and then became a successful printer. It was only at the age of 40 that he saw some experiments in electricity, and was so fascinated by them that he sold his printing press and spent his whole time experimenting. He was the first man to realise that lightning was a huge electric spark. He flew a kite into thunderclouds, at great risk to his life, to collect charge from them. He learned enough to invent the first lightning conductor, for which he became famous.

Later on he became even more famous as a revolutionary politician when the American colonies rebelled from Britain and became the United States of America.

Picture 6 Benjamin Franklin – rebel, scientist, ambassador and inventor of the lightning conductor.

Positive and negative

Franklin's theory of electricity was simple. He said that every object, even animals and small children, contains electricity. If it has more than its normal share of charge he called it 'plus', if less it was called 'minus'. Since then we have learned that in fact there are two kinds of electric charge, but we still call them 'plus' and 'minus' or **positive** and **negative**.

Electric forces are caused by the attraction or repulsion between these two kinds of charge (picture 7):

like charges repel, unlike charges attract.

Just as with magnetism and gravity, we imagine there to be an **electric field**

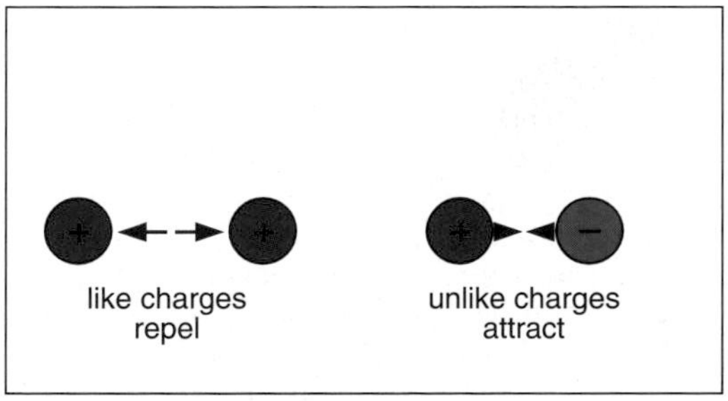
+
+
like charges repel
+
−
unlike charges attract

Picture 7 Like charges repel!

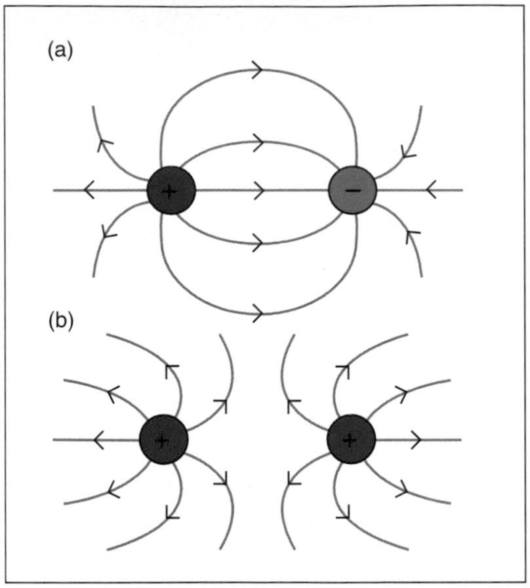

Picture 8 Electric field lines.

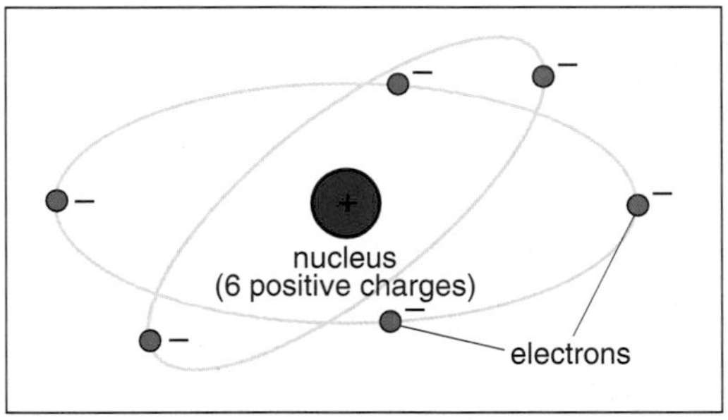

Picture 9 Atoms contain equal numbers of positive and negative charges.

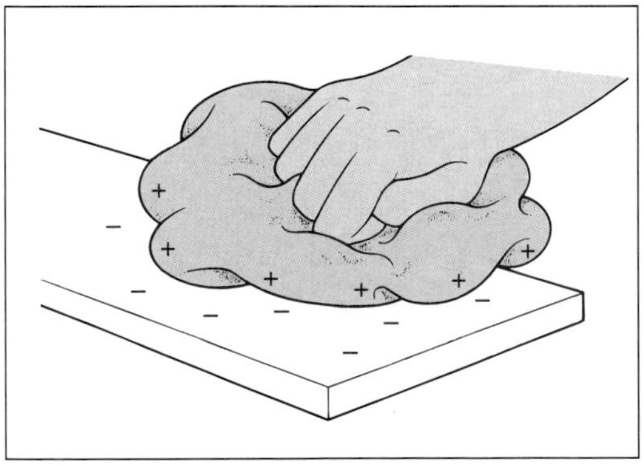
Picture 10 Charging by rubbing. The cloth leaves electrons on the plastic strip. The strip becomes negatively charged and the cloth becomes positive.

near charged objects. We draw field lines (lines of force) with the direction positive to negative (picture 8). This is the direction a positive charge would move under the forces of attraction or repulsion.

In magnetism, we never seem to get N-poles or S-poles on their own. They come together, in opposite pairs. But we can get free electric charges, both positive and negative ones. This is because all matter is made of charged particles which can be separated.

Electricity and the atom

All matter is made up of atoms. In turn, atoms are made of a central massive nucleus surrounded by a cloud of very light particles called electrons. The nucleus is positively charged and attracts the cloud of moving electrons because they are negatively charged. The charge on the nucleus is exactly balanced by the charge on the electron cloud. This means that the atoms, and the material they are made of, are normally uncharged. They are **neutral** (picture 9).

How objects get charged

Electrons are very small and are easy to move. When a piece of almost any material is rubbed with a cloth electrons are pulled off. Sometimes they go from the cloth onto the material, sometimes they go the other way, depending on the materials (picture 10).

This movement of electrons makes both materials electrically unbalanced. One will gain electrons and it becomes negatively charged, the other loses electrons and becomes positively charged.

Moving air can produce the same effect as moving cloth. Cars travelling at speed can have electrons rubbed off them as they pass through the air, and become charged up. Hot air rising on sunny days can become charged, and the charge can be given to water drops in clouds. Sooner or later the clouds have enough charge to cause lightning and thunder (picture 11).

Conductors and insulators

Any substance can be electrically charged, but if the material is a conductor the charge might flow away. The most likely place for charge to flow to is the Earth, simply because the Earth is so big that it can hold a huge amount of unbalanced charge without becoming noticeably charged up.

Human beings are quite good conductors, and for a body to be 'electrified' it has to be kept off the ground by good insulators. Otherwise the charge would flow away to the ground. This is why the children who were charged up in fairgrounds were strung up on silk ropes. Silk was then one of the best insulators known.

Picture 12 shows a girl who has been charged up to about 100 000 V. The force of repulsion between the like charges on her head and on her hair causes it to flare out. Luckily the electric current is not big enough to give her a dangerous shock. (See page 165.)

Picture 11 Lightning.

Static electricity

When electric charges do not move the effects they produce are called **electrostatic**, and the objects are said to be charged with **static electricity**. Static electricity can be a danger. Small sparks can cause explosions in flammable vapour, such as in the empty holds of oil tankers. Workers and machines have to be properly earthed so that charge doesn't build up.

Picture 12 A hair-raising experience.

Chemistry

Chemistry only happens because atoms and molecules combine together or break apart. This involves making or breaking chemical bonds. The bonds that hold atoms to each other are electric forces. If these forces didn't exist there would be no molecules, no chemical changes, no chemistry and no life on Earth.

A metal contains a large number of **free electrons** that are not attached to any particular atom. They are free to move and it is their flow that makes an electric current in a metal. There are so many of them that all metals are good conductors – although some (like gold, silver and copper) are better than others.

Semiconductor materials also contain free electrons, but very much fewer than in metals. Semiconductors are useful because we can control the number of free electrons, and we make use of this in such things as transistors, thermistors and microelectronic devices.

A current of electricity is simply a flow of charged particles. Many chemical compounds split up when they dissolve in water to make charged particles called **ions**. For example, copper sulphate splits up into a *positive* copper ion and a *negative* sulphate ion. Solutions containing ions are called **electrolytes**. Electrolytes are used in metal plating (an example of **electrolysis**) and in batteries (see topic E10).

Static – friend and foe

(The uses and dangers of static electricity)

Static electricity is easily produced by **friction**, as described on page 154. This process works very well when the air and the materials rubbing together are dry. Very high voltages can be produced – up to 100 000 V or so – on insulators or insulated conductors. In very dry weather moving cars become charged by friction as they move through the air – and so do the driver and passengers. The rubber tyres are good insulators. The occupants may feel an electric shock as they leave the car and touch the ground – and so will anyone outside the car who, say, touches the car to open the door. To avoid these effects some cars are fitted with **conductor strips** hanging from the car, just touching the ground.

In dry conditions walking on a carpet, stroking a cat or taking off a sweater may separate enough charge for small shocks and even small sparks to be produced. This charge is too small to be harmful in ordinary conditions, although cats do object to having sparks extracted from their noses. But sparks from static electricity can cause catastrophic effect in certain circumstances.

- Empty oil tankers contain flammable vapours which can be ignited by sparks, and special anti-static clothing must be worn by people working in or near the tanks.
- Flour milling produces a very fine flour dust which fills the atmosphere; the dust is easily ignited and if so will explode – again special anti-static precautions have to be taken.
- The delicate microchips in a computer are easily damaged by quite small electrostatic effects; people inserting or replacing them need to wear earthed 'bracelets' to ensure that their hands are not at voltages different from the components.

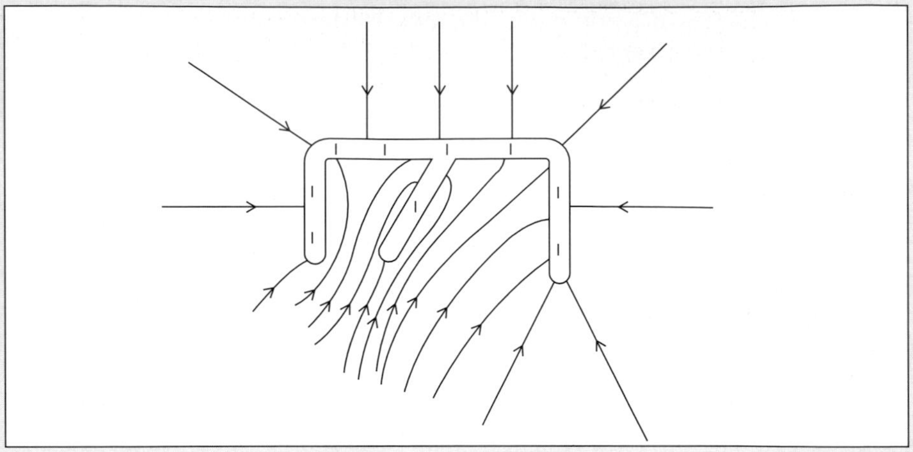

Picture 1 Electrostatic paint-spraying. The small drops of paint follow the field lines and can cover all surfaces of an akwardly shaped object.

But static electricity is also made use of in several modern applications. Often they use the effect of one charged object producing an electric field to attract and guide the movement of smaller charged objects. Here are some examples.

- When paint is sprayed through a nozzle the droplets become charged by friction. An object being painted is kept at a fairly high voltage with an opposite charge and the droplets are attracted to it. This is very useful when the object has a complicated shape – the paint follows the field lines and covers parts of the object which would otherwise be hidden from the spray (see pictures 1 and 2).
- A similar use is in spraying crops, where the crops, naturally earthed, attract the charged drops of chemicals to the underside as well as to the top side of the leaves.
- Photocopiers work by using bright light to produce an image of what is to be copied on a special electrically charged plate. Light discharges the plate where it hits it, leaving an 'electrical image' of what is being copied. Black powder is attracted to this charged image and then transferred by contact to a sheet of paper to make the copy. The powder is then fixed to the paper by heating it.
- Ink-jet printers use a small electric field to control the movement of very small charged ink drops on to the paper.
- Industrial chimneys (e.g. in power stations) have charged plates which attract and hold small polluting particles to stop them getting into the atmosphere.

Picture 2 Painting a new car.

Activities

A Getting things charged

It is easy to charge things up with electricity. The main thing to remember is that the following experiments will only work well if the materials are *dry*. The best way to dry them is to use a hair dryer. Good plastics to use are polythene, nylon or acetate.

1 Take a strip of any plastic material and rub it with a dry cloth. Test that it has become charged by trying to pick up small pieces of paper.

2 Now try some of the following:

a Hold the charged end close to your ear. Do you feel or hear anything?

b Recharge the strip and hold it close to a thin stream of water falling from a tap. Describe or draw what happens.

B The laws of charge

To investigate these you can use some light metallised balls and strips of two different kinds of plastic (e.g. polythene and acetate). The balls are held hanging from a ruler by thin nylon thread (picture 13).

Try the following experiments and draw or describe what happens. Do they agree with the rule that like charges repel, unlike charges attract?

1 Charge up one of the strips by rubbing it with a dry cloth and touch both of the metallised balls with it. They should become charged with the same sign of charge, and you will see the effects of the electrostatic force.

2 Charge up the other strip and bring it gently up to the balls. What happens?

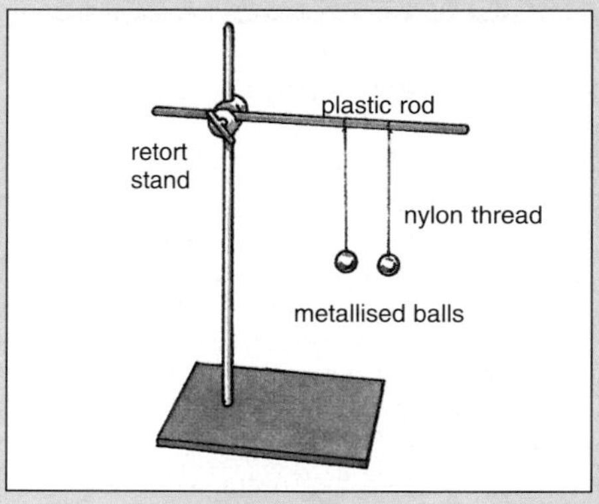

Picture 13 Investigating the laws of charge.

Questions

1 What are the two kinds of electric charge?

2 a What do people mean when they talk about 'static'?

b What happens when an object becomes electrically charged by 'friction'?

c Give two examples of things that become 'accidentally' charged in this way in everyday life.

d Sparks from charged objects can give a shock, or possibly start a fire. For *one* of the examples you gave in part (b), state

i) how you could stop the charges building up,

ii) how you could let the charge get away safely.

3 Explain what the following mean:

a conductor,

b insulator,

c static electricity,

d earthing.

4 Why do you think 'static electricity' wasn't much use in the 17th century? Describe any practical use you know for it nowadays.

5 Why is electricity so important in chemistry? Write a short essay explaining how chemical changes in atoms and molecules involve electric charges.

E6 Using electricity: heating and lighting

Electricity is useful because it can carry energy from one place to another and we use it to do many different jobs.

Electric heating

When electrons flow through a conductor they collide with the atoms in the conductor. As they do this they give energy to the atoms. The energy is simply movement energy, transferred from the moving electrons to the atoms. The atoms are fixed, and just vibrate a little more (picture 1). We feel this extra vibration as a rise in temperature – the conductor warms up.

The electrons soon speed up again after the collisions, pushed on by electric forces. These forces are provided by a battery, or a cycle dynamo or the generators in a large power station. Most of the work done by electrical devices in homes and factories uses the energy from fuels burnt in power stations – see topic E11.

Resistance wires

Electric heaters need special kinds of wire as conductors. The wire in an electric fire element is usually an alloy of different metals. The alloy needs to have the right properties:

- a high resistance,
- a high melting point (to stand the high temperatures produced),
- chemical stability (so that it doesn't burn or corrode at high temperatures in air).

Types of heater

Picture 2 shows four types of electric heating device. Only one of them gets to be red hot, with a temperature of 600 to 700 °C. This is the ordinary electric fire, which radiates energy as electromagnetic waves from the hot coil of wire.

An electric kettle has an element which doesn't need to get hotter than about 100 °C, the boiling point of water. If it does, perhaps when the kettle boils dry, an automatic switch cuts off the current.

The night storage heater is very heavy because it is full of special bricks which can store a lot of energy when they get hot. They take a long time to heat up, but take an equally long time to cool down. This is why they are so useful. They release their energy to heat up the room slowly, so that the room is heated over a long period of time. Inside the bricks there is an electric heater,

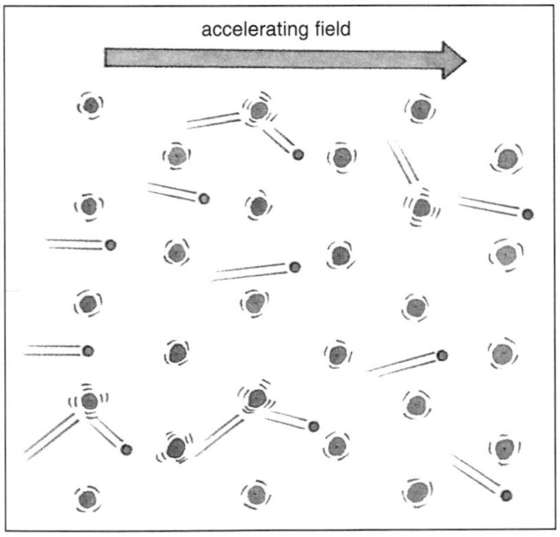

Picture 1 Electrons give energy to atoms in a conductor by colliding with them.

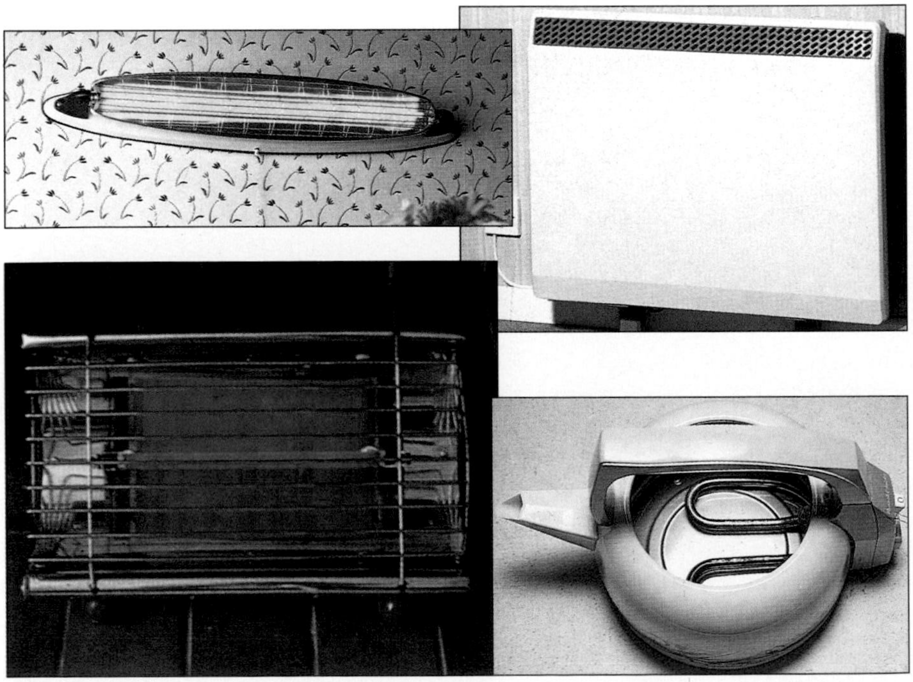

Picture 2 Different ways of using electrical heating.

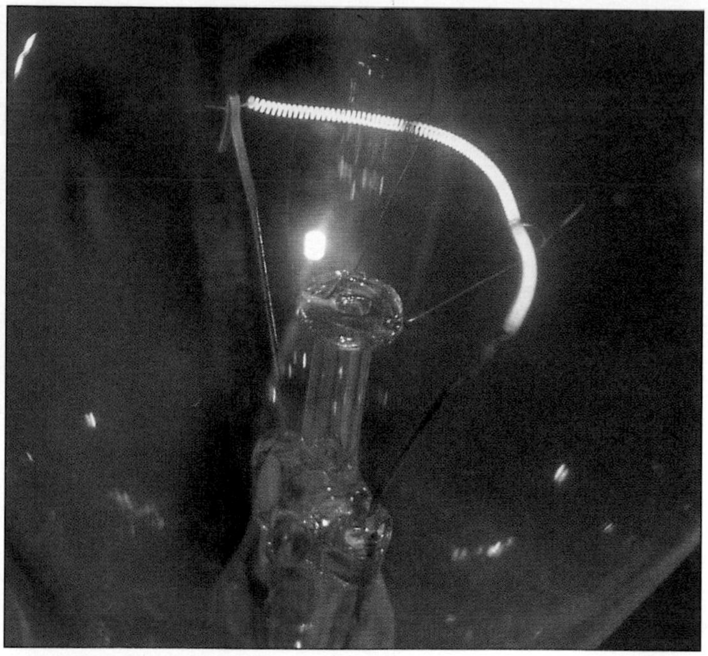

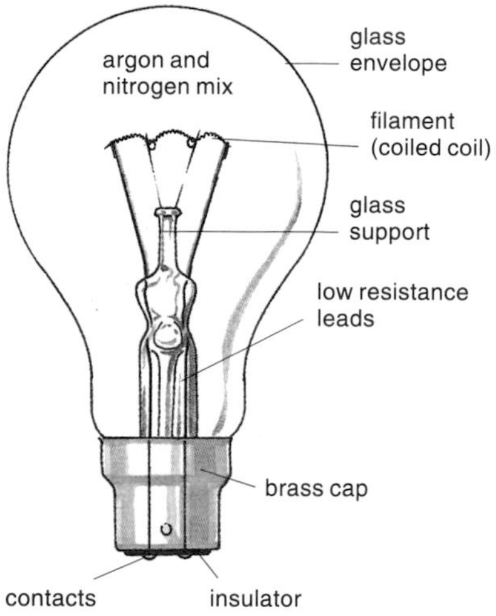

Picture 3 The parts of an ordinary filament lamp.

which heats up the bricks at night. Electricity is cheaper at night – see page 187.

Infra-red heaters are another kind of low temperature heater. Unlike ordinary electric fires the hot wire is embedded in a special glass. This means that it can't be touched, and so these heaters are safer for use in bathrooms where the danger of electric shock is greatest.

The glass gets hot, but the heater relies on the fact that radiation energy can get through the glass. It is this **infra-red** radiation that warms up the room and the people in it.

Electric lighting

There are two main kinds of lighting used in the home. The oldest is the filament lamp (picture 3). This contains a very thin and long piece of wire (the 'filament'). It is made of a metal, tungsten, that can be heated to such a high temperature that it becomes white hot but doesn't melt. At this temperature it would burn in air, so it is kept inside a glass bulb filled with gases that don't react with it, such as argon and nitrogen.

Although it is glowing white hot, and sending out a lot of energy as radiation, most of the energy comes out as invisible (infra-red) radiation. You can feel this if you put your hand near the bulb. In fact, only 2 or 3% of the energy supplied to the lamp is turned into visible radiation (light).

Fluorescent lamps

Fluorescent lamps are more efficient. A 40 W fluorescent lamp produces as much light as a 150 W filament lamp – and far less heat (picture 4). They work on a completely different principle.

The lamps are filled with a gas (mercury vapour) at low pressure. Electrons flow through the gas and collide with the gas atoms. When collisions take place the mercury gives out invisible (and dangerous) ultra-violet radiation. But don't worry, this radiation doesn't escape from the lamp. It hits a special **phosphor** paint on the inside of the lamp and makes it glow white (picture 5). It is much the same as what happens in a TV tube (see page 188), where high-speed electrons are used to make the phosphors glow different colours.

Picture 4 Fluorescent tubes being checked.

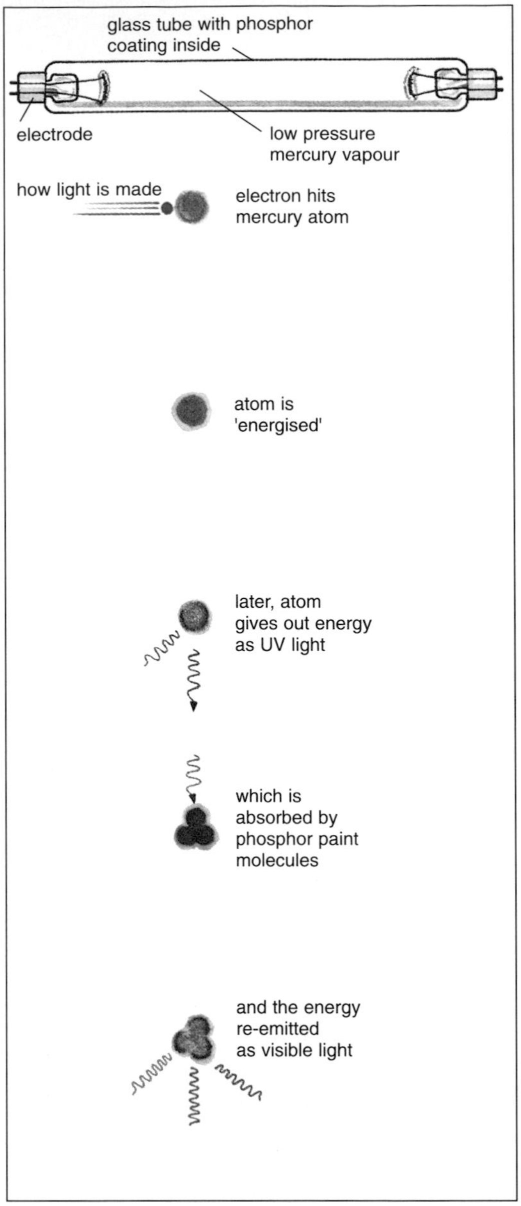

Picture 5 How a fluorescent tube works.

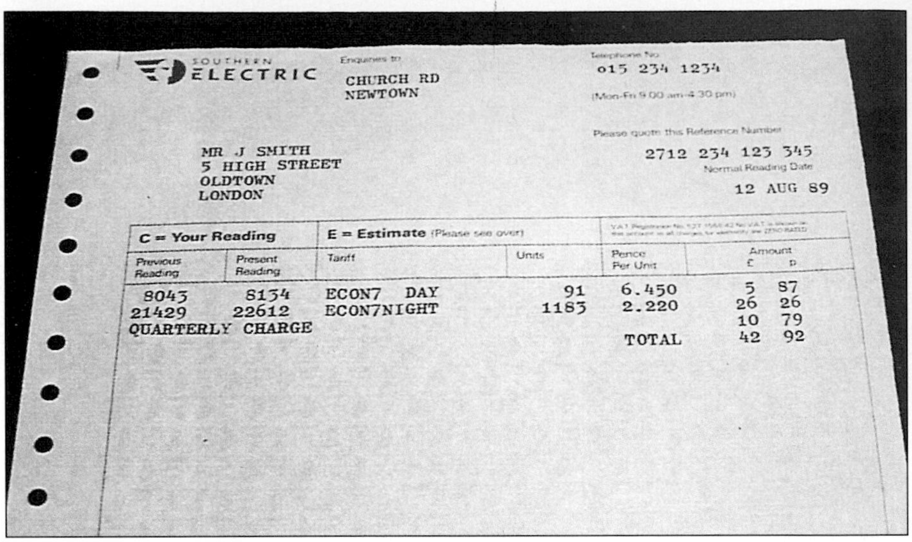

Picture 6 Your electricity bill.

How much does electricity cost?

The electricity boards don't make us pay for 'electricity'! We get that free. What we pay for is the **energy** that is transferred when the electricity runs machines and heaters in our homes.

In science we measure energy in joules, but this is too small a unit to be easily used in everyday life. Of course we could use kilojoules or megajoules, but the electricity boards use a unit of energy called a **kilowatt-hour**. An electricity bill is shown in picture 6.

The 'units' in the bill are in fact kilowatt-hours, and as you can see some cost more than others. The cheap units are the ones used overnight, for putting energy into storage or water heaters. The kilowatt-hour is quite a sensible unit, in practice. It is equivalent to 3.6 megajoules (3 600 000 joules). It is the energy transferred when, for example, you use a 1 kilowatt electric fire for an hour.

Power ratings

The power rating of a device is given in watts or kilowatts. It tells us how much energy the device uses each second. Thus 1 watt is 1 joule of energy per second, a kilowatt is a thousand joules per second. A piece of electrical equipment, like a TV set or a lamp, will usually have its power rating printed on it (picture 7). The power of a device is decided by how much current it takes at its correct operating voltage.

In the home the voltage is kept at 230 V, and the current is then decided by the resistance of the equipment. We can use the formula $\boldsymbol{I = V/R}$ to calculate the current, if we know the value of the resistance.

We can use the formula:

$$\text{power} = \text{voltage} \times \text{current} \ (\boldsymbol{P = VI})$$

to calculate the power rating if we know current and voltage. We can also use it to calculate the current needed to provide a desired power. Then we can use the first formula to find out what resistance the device needs to have. This is what the manufacturers have to do when they produce the electrical equipment we buy.

Table 1 gives some typical power and current ratings for mains-operated equipment in the home.

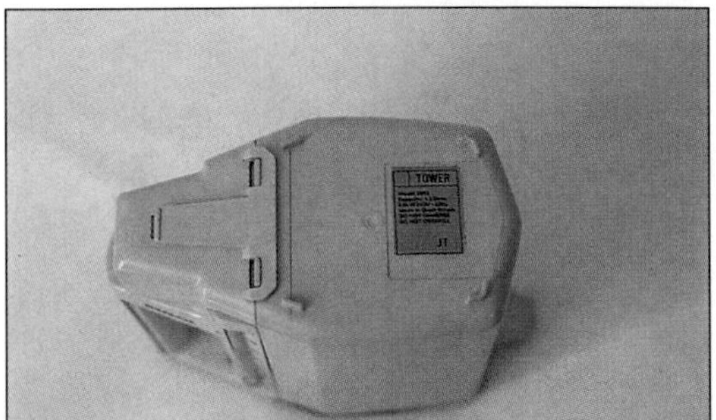

Picture 7 Look for the power rating on your kettle or hair dryer.

Table 1 How much power do appliances use?

Appliance	Power rating (kW)	Voltage (V)	Current (A)	Resistance (Ω)
High power				
storage heater	2.0	230	8.7	26.0
cooker (total)	14.0	230	61.0	0.04
microwave oven	0.65	230	2.8	82.0
3-bar electric fire	3.0	230	13.0	18.0
Medium power				
1-bar electric fire	1.0	230	4.3	53.0
electric kettle	2.0	230	8.7	26.0
hair dryer	1.0	230	4.3	53.0
vacuum cleaner	0.8	230	3.5	66.0
toaster	0.9	230	3.9	59.0
iron	1.0	230	4.3	53.0
drill	0.3	230	1.3	177.0
Low power				
refrigerator	0.12	230	0.5	460.0
lamp	0.06	230	0.3	767.0
hairstyling brush	0.020	230	0.09	2560.0
radio cassette player	0.012	230	0.05	4600.0
calculator	0.005	6	0.08	75.0

Activities

A How much power do you use?

1 Do this activity at home at 7 pm one evening. Find the power of each of the electrical devices that you are using at that time. **CARE!** Be careful to look at labels on kettles, cookers etc., when they are cool and not while they are working. Alternatively, use table 1. Work out how much total power you are using.

2 Find out how much you have to pay for 1 'unit' (kilowatt-hour) of energy. (If you can't, assume it to be 8p.) Now calculate how much it would cost to run all these devies for 2 hours.

B Measuring the power rating of a device

Use the following circuit (picture 8) to measure the power required to run some or all of the devices listed below.

Power	Device
	6 V lamp 12 V lamp low-voltage heater electric motor

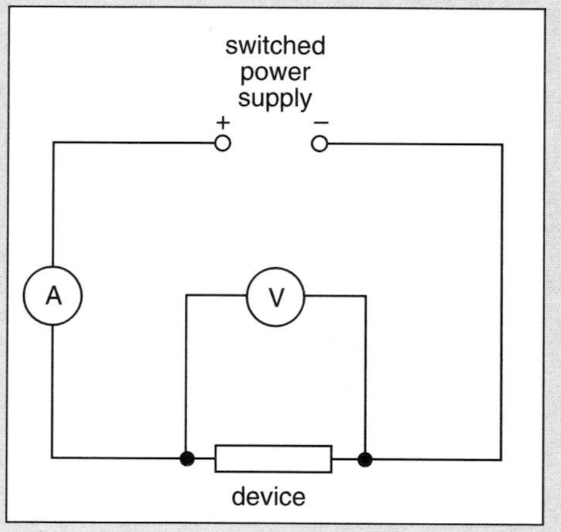

Picture 8

Questions

1 Suggest a reason why electrical energy is cheaper at night.

2 Use the formula:

power = voltage × current

to work out the power needed to run the following devices:

a a 12 V car headlamp that takes 4 A,
b a vacuum cleaner motor that takes 3 A from the mains supply at 230 V,
c a washing machine heater that takes a current of 11 A from the mains supply at 230 V.

3 Use the formula:

resistance = voltage/current

to work out the effective resistance of each of the devices in Question 2.

4 Use the data given in table 1 to work out the cost of using some electrical appliances as described below.

Assume the cost per unit (kilowatt-hour) of electrical energy to be 8p.

a Using a 3-bar electric fire for 4 hours.
b Using a hair dryer for half an hour.
c Using a calculator for 10 hours.
d Leaving two 100 W electric lights on for 10 hours a day for a week.
e Using a microwave oven to cook something for 10 minutes at full power.

5 Copy out the following passage, filling in and underlining the missing words. Choose the words you need from the following list:

current, voltage, thousand, power, energy, resistance, second, hour, cost.

Your electricity bill asks you to pay for the ___________ you have used, not the voltage or the ___________ supplied. The ___________ rating of an electrical appliance tells you how much ___________ it uses per ___________. The bigger the power rating, the more it will ___________ to use. A label on the device that says '1 kW' means that it will use ___________ at the rate of ___________ joules per second.

E7 Using electricity safely

Electricity can be very dangerous; in fact it is probably the most dangerous thing you let into your home.

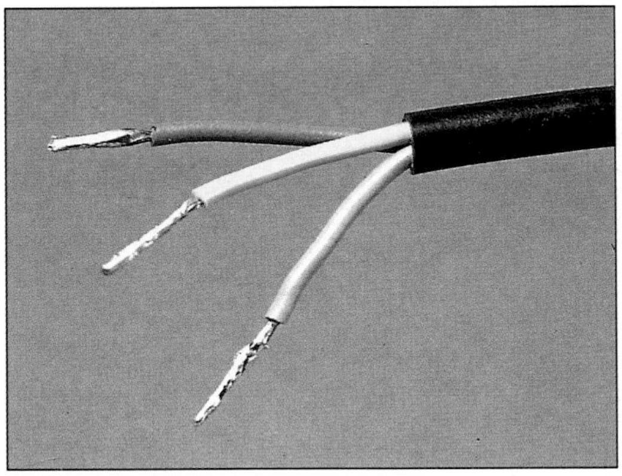

Picture 1 A three-wire cable.

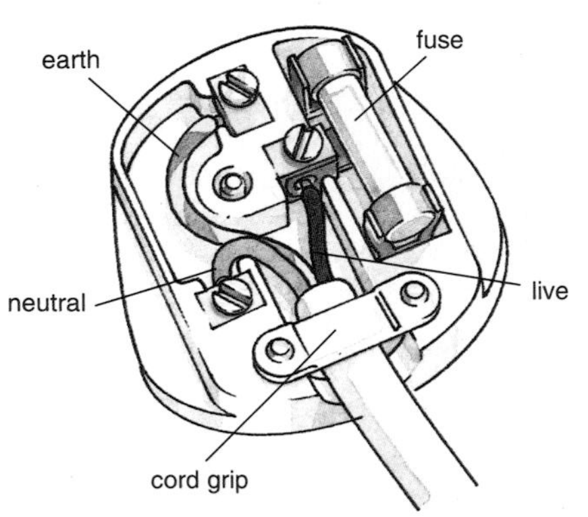

Picture 2 A correctly wired three-pin plug.

Stick to the rules!

There are very strict rules about how houses should be wired and how electric appliances should be made. This is because electricity can give a strong electric shock which may kill. It can also cause fires. Most of the fires started in homes and buildings are caused by electrical faults. How can we guard against these dangers?

The three-wire system

The mains supply uses three wires (picture 1). One pair carries the current 'out and back'. These are the **live** and **neutral** wires. The household supply is **alternating**. The '230 volts' of the mains supply is actually a kind of average of the alternating voltage. Actually, mains voltage swings from +325 V to −325 V 50 times a second.

All household devices would work perfectly well with just these two wires, but there is a third wire, the **earth** wire. This is for safety. The three wires are colour-coded, as shown in picture 1.

If an electric appliance is properly made and connected using a three-pin plug (picture 2) it should be impossible for you to get a shock, or for a fire to start, even if something goes wrong.

The earth lead connects the metal case of an appliance to the ground inside or just outside the house. If a fault occurs which would make the case live, electric charge will flow harmlessly into the earth. This stops the charge going through you to earth, or through another part of the appliance which might get too hot (picture 3).

Fuses and circuit breakers

The path to earth has a very low resistance, so that as soon as a fault occurs the current that flows is very large. This could be dangerous, because it could make the conductor too hot and start a fire. To guard against this a **fuse** or **circuit breaker** is built into the circuit. Modern wiring systems have both.

There is a fuse in each three-pin plug, and many devices have fuses built into them as well. A fuse is simply a short length of wire inside a protective case (picture 4). The wire is made of an alloy with a low melting point. A current

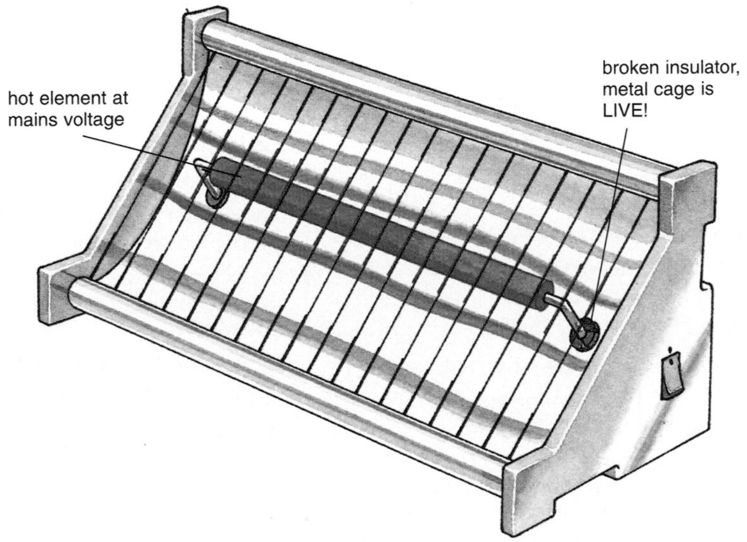

Picture 3 What happens if the case of this electric fire is not earthed? (What would have happened if it was earthed?)

larger than its 'rated' value will make the wire hot, and it melts. This breaks the circuit and current stops flowing.

A circuit breaker is usually built into the central distribution board where the mains supply enters the house. It is usually near the fuse box. There are quite small ones that fit into mains sockets so that you can use them to protect you whenever you use especially dangerous equipment. You should use them for electrical devices used out of doors, such as lawn mowers (picture 5).

Circuit breakers use an electromagnetic or electronic device to cut off the current if it gets too large because of a fault, or if current is leaking to earth. They are very sensitive and can detect quite small faults. They work much more quickly than a fuse. They give extra protection because even a small current going through the wrong part of a device can cause overheating, with the risk of fire. An ordinary fuse might not 'blow' under these conditions.

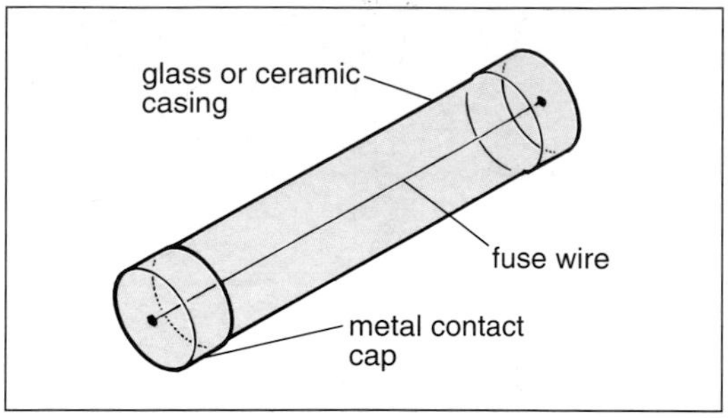

Picture 4 A fuse.

Double insulation

Some equipment is 'doubly insulated', so that the live wire cannot reach any outside metal part at all. This means that the equipment does not have to be earthed. Even so, it still needs to be protected by a fuse or circuit breaker in case the lead (cord) is damaged.

Picture 5 A circuit breaker adds extra protection for devices used outside.

Electricity and the human body

The human body is quite a good conductor of electricity – once the electricity gets inside it. This is because the human body is largely water, with all kinds of salts dissolved in it.

Luckily, when the skin is dry it is quite resistant to electricity. Also, if you are wearing rubber or plastic soled shoes the charges can't get out easily. So people may touch bare wires at mains voltage and still survive, although they will certainly feel the shock and it's not a lot of fun.

The most dangerous condition to be in is to have a wet skin and bare feet (picture 6). This makes bathrooms very dangerous, electrically, and special care is needed. To start with, all switches in bathrooms have to be operated by 'remote control', using lengths of insulating cord. Heaters with bare wiring are banned. Bathrooms are not the places to watch TV or listen to mains radios! The makers of electric showers have to make sure that the water is kept totally insulated from the mains electricity.

What happens when you get an electric shock?

The nervous system of the body works by means of electricity. Muscles are controlled by electrical messages from the brain or from nerve sensor cells. When a current enters the body it can override the nerve signals. You lose control of muscles. This means that you might be unable to let go of a live wire, your body might quiver uncontrollably, and you might be unable to speak. This can happen with a current as small as fifteen *thousandths* of an ampere.

If the current is larger it could cause burning, due to its heating effect. But the real danger is that the heart stops beating. The heart, like any other muscle, is controlled by electrical nerve pulses. If these are overridden by an electric shock the heart might stop beating, and you will also stop breathing. Death follows in a very short time.

Thus the first aid treatment for electric shock is similar to that for drowning – heart massage and mouth-to-mouth resuscitation. But first-aiders must be careful to switch off the electricity first, otherwise there would be two patients to deal with.

Picture 6 Water conducts electricity well: wet bodies are at risk. Why are bathroom light switches safer than an ordinary switch?

Good advice

The local electricity company produces pamphlets which give very good advice on the safe use of electricity. They can be got free from any showroom. The most common dangers are due to old, frayed wiring, or cuts in new wiring.

Picture 7 Danger! This is a serious fire risk.

Everyone should know how to fit a mains plug correctly, and to use the right fuse in it. Appliances should now come with the plug already wired and with the correct fuse fitted.

It is dangerous to 'overload' a circuit. This might be done by connecting high-current appliances (like heaters or even TV sets) to low-current lighting circuits. Instead, they should be connected to the correct 'ring-main' circuit. This is the circuit that has three-pin sockets and the wiring is thick enough to carry the current without overheating. But even this circuit can be overloaded if you use adaptors which allow you to connect too many appliances. Picture 7 shows a selection of dangerous fittings.

Activities

A Danger warning

Make a poster warning either:

1 cooks or

2 children

about one electrical danger they have to guard against.

B Make a safety check

Make a survey of the electrical appliances, wires or fittings in your home that might be a source of danger and need attention. List them and say what needs doing to each.

C Learn to get it right

Practise wiring a three-pin plug. Do this under supervision at school, so that your work can be checked.

D Are you prepared for shocks?

You go into your kitchen. To your horror a member of your family is lying on the floor, still holding an electric iron. You see that the iron has a frayed cable. It is clearly a case of severe electric shock.

What would you do?

If you don't know, find out!

Questions

1 Why are the three wires in a household electrical cable colour-coded? What are the colours for:

a live,
b neutral,
c earth?

2 Cartridge fuses (as in picture 4) are normally available as 3 A, 5 A or 13 A.

a What would probably happen if you used a 3 A fuse in the plug for a 3 kW electric heater?
b Why is it bad practice to use a 13 A fuse in the plug for a 60 W desk lamp?
c What happens when a fuse 'blows'?
d You buy a second-hand hair dryer, in good condition, but without a plug fitted. The dryer is labelled '230 V, 800 W'. What fuse would you choose to put into the plug? Explain how you worked out your answer.

3 You can get a deadly shock from the 230 V mains, but can be charged up to over 100 000 V by a Van de Graaf machine without danger. Explain these facts.

4 Give four precautions used to cut down the risk of electrical accidents in the home. Write a sentence about each of them, so that a younger person could understand why they are used.

5 a What is a 'short circuit'?
b What does 'earthing' mean?
c Why are many electrical appliances 'earthed'?
d Why is a short circuit especially dangerous when it happens in a device which isn't earthed?

6 Circuit breakers (page 165) are often used nowadays instead of fuses – especially with appliances that take a large current to make them work.

Why are circuit breakers better than fuses in these cases?

7 Design and sketch a way you could use electromagnetism to switch a current off if it got too big.

8 Most fires in homes and offices are caused by electrical faults. Explain how an electrical fault can start a fire.

A steam iron

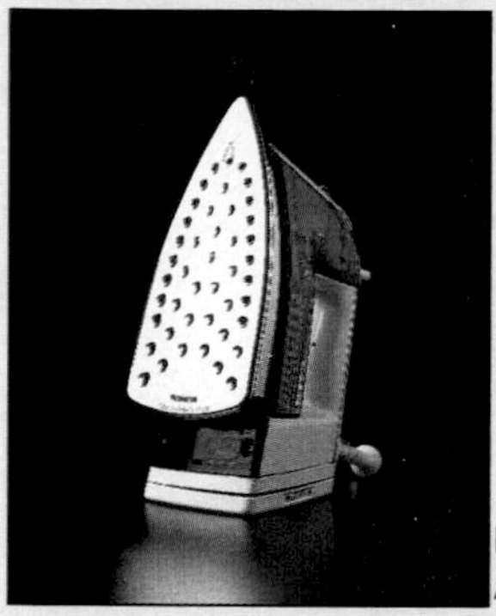

Picture 1 A modern iron.

Picture 1 shows a modern steam iron. It is made in three separate parts, or *sub-assemblies.* Each sub-assembly is made of lots of smaller parts, totalling more than a hundred altogether. The sub-assemblies are:

- the handle,
- the soleplate (metal base),
- the thermostat.

The handle sub-assembly

This is made mostly of plastic. It has to be light and be a good insulator for both heat and for electricity. It also houses the terminal block for the electrical connections. It has to be well-designed, both to look good and to make it comfortable to use.

The soleplate sub-assembly

This is made mostly of metal. It has a smooth outer case, particularly underneath, where the metal is in contact with the clothes being ironed. The soleplate has to heat up quite quickly and also allow the energy to transfer from the heating element to where it is useful.

The soleplate contains the heating element, which is a coil of resistance wire that gets hot when an electric current flows through it. It has to be insulated from the main soleplate to avoid electric shocks to the user. This is done by packing the coil in a compressed powder of magnesium oxide (picture 2).

The coil also heats the steam chamber, in which water is boiled to provide steam for making clothes easier to iron. Water is a good conductor of electricity, which is another reason for having the heating coil so well insulated.

The thermostat sub-assembly

This controls the temperature of the ironing surface of the soleplate. It does this by switching the current on and off as needed. This means that it has to be made out of very reliable components. In the ordinary life-span of the iron the current will be switched on and off many thousands of times.

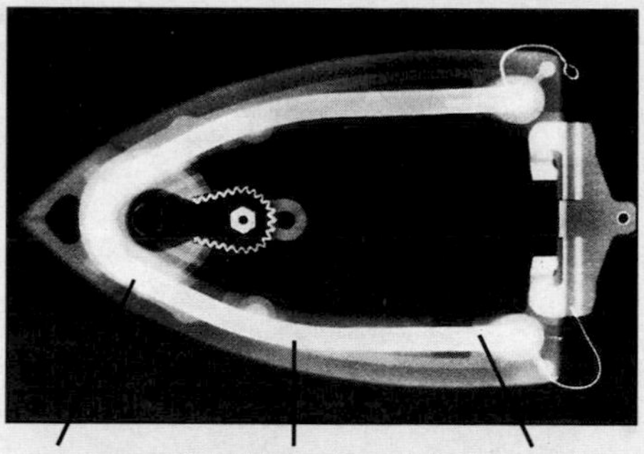

Picture 2 Inside a steam iron.

Picture 3 shows how the thermostat switch works. It uses a bimetallic strip. This consists of two different metals welded together. One metal expands more than the other when it is heated. Because of this the strip bends when it is heated. Thus when the iron gets hotter than it should be, the contact is broken and the heating coil is switched off. The thermostat control works by moving the contacts nearer together or further apart, so that the contact is broken at the required temperature. Answer the following questions.

1 a Give three reasons why plastic is used in the handle, rather than metal.

b Suggest another material that could be used instead of plastic, and suggest a reason why it *isn't* used.

2 a Why is the heating coil surrounded by an insulator?

b Plastic could be used instead of magnesium oxide as an insulator around the heating coil. Suggest two reasons why the magnesium oxide might be a better choice.

3 Use the diagram (picture 3) to decide which of the metals used in the bimetallic strip expands the most when heated.

4 a In use the bottom of the iron is surrounded by steam, and it is used over a wide range of temperatures. Suggest what properties the material used to make the base of the plate must have if the steam iron is to be usable for a number of years.

b The material used for the outside of the soleplate is a *mild steel* plate covered with a smooth coating of *zinc*. The inside of the soleplate is made of cast *aluminium*. Give one reason in each case for the use of these materials (printed in *italics*).

c Which part of the steam iron is most likely to break down after many years of use? Give a reason for your answer.

5 How did 'irons' get their name?

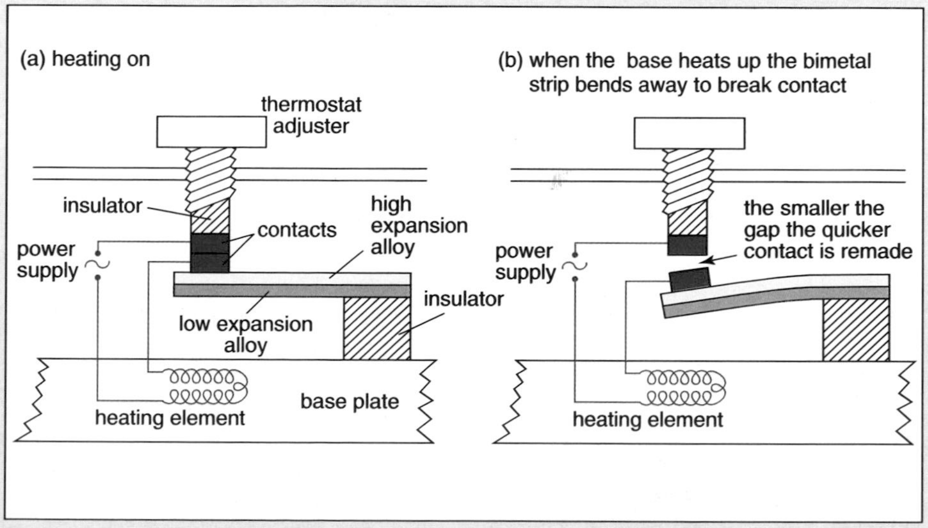

Picture 3 How the thermostat switch works.

E8 Using electricity: motors and dynamos

Electric currents and magnetism can work together to make things move.

Picture 1 Michael Faraday lecturing to his students.

Poor boy makes good!

Two hundred years ago it wasn't easy for a poor boy to get an education, even if he was a genius. Michael Faraday (born in 1791) was the son of a blacksmith. He learned to read and write and do arithmetic but left school at thirteen to work as an errand boy for a bookbinder.

At fourteen he was promoted to apprentice bookbinder. Keen to learn, he started to read the books that he bound. He was fascinated by the science books, especially the ones about physics and chemistry. He spent some of his small pay on materials and started experimenting at home. He made lots of smells – and an electrical machine.

Later on, he went to lectures put on for the public at a great research laboratory in London called the Royal Institution. He was very interested by four lectures given by a famous scientist called Sir Humphrey Davy, who was the director of the Institution. He made careful notes of what he heard and wrote them out neatly. He used his skills to bind these notes and sent them off to the great man, with a letter asking for a job as a lab assistant.

He was given the job, and at the age of 21 he was able to give up bookbinding for ever. Twelve years later Michael was made Director of the Institution, and had become one of the most famous scientists in the world. Nearly everything you will learn about in this chapter was first discovered by him. The equipment he used can still be seen at the Royal Institution.

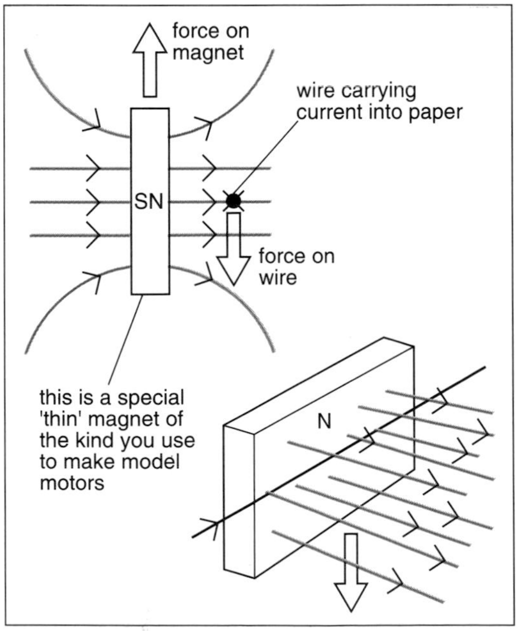

Picture 2 Interaction between a magnet and a wire carrying a current.

Electricity and magnetism working together

An electric current produces a magnetic field (see page 142). Put a wire in the field of a magnet and pass a current through it. Both wire and magnet will try to move. There is a force between them caused by the interaction of their magnetic fields (picture 2). This is the **motor effect** which is used in all electric motors, from toy cars to large electric locomotives.

Strangely, the force is exerted at right angles to both the current direction and the magnetic field lines. When you change the direction of the current in the wire, the force on it changes to the opposite direction too. Changing the poles around so that the field is now in the opposite direction also changes the direction of the force on the wire.

You can work out which way the wire will move using Fleming's Left Hand Motor Rule:

Use your left hand: align your **F**irst finger in the direction of the magnetic **F**ield, and your se**C**ond finger in the direction of the electric **C**urrent. Put your

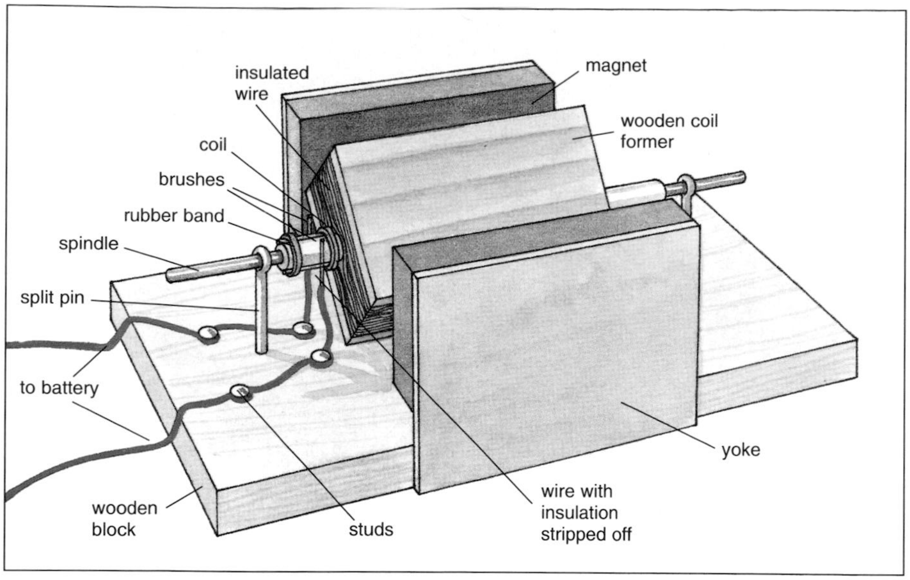

Picture 3 A model electric motor you could make.

thu**M**b at right angles to both fingers – it points in the direction of the **M**otion of the wire. Check that this works for Picture 2.

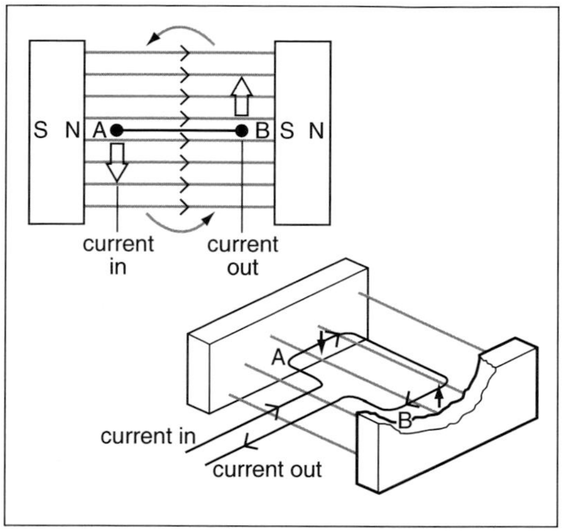

Picture 4 The forces on a coil in a magnetic field make it spin.

Electric motors

Simple electric motors are scaled up versions of ones you can build yourself from a length of wire and two magnets (picture 3, and activity B). A model motor uses a special pair of slab magnets that give a straight field between them. The force makes a turning effect that is greatest when the spinning coil is at points A and B (picture 4). The design lets current into the coil only when it is at this position.

Small working motors

Picture 5 shows the inside of a small electric motor. A motor like this is used in electric drills or vacuum cleaners. It has a much longer coil than your 'home made' one, and its magnetic field is made larger by wrapping the coil around some soft iron. This turns the coil into an electromagnet (topic E2). It is called an **armature** when it is used like this.

The problem with a spinning electromagnet is to get the electric current into it and out again. This is done by using sliding contacts called **brushes** which just touch the ends of the spinning coil. A real motor has more than one coil with more than one pair of brush contacts. As the motor spins round, one coil after another is brought into action so that the force is almost continuous and in the same direction.

The field is not straight as in the motor that you might make in the school laboratory. It is radial, like the spokes of a wheel. This means that the coils are always at right angles to the field lines and so they always have a strong force on them. In a real motor the magnets producing the field are electromagnets, not permanent ones.

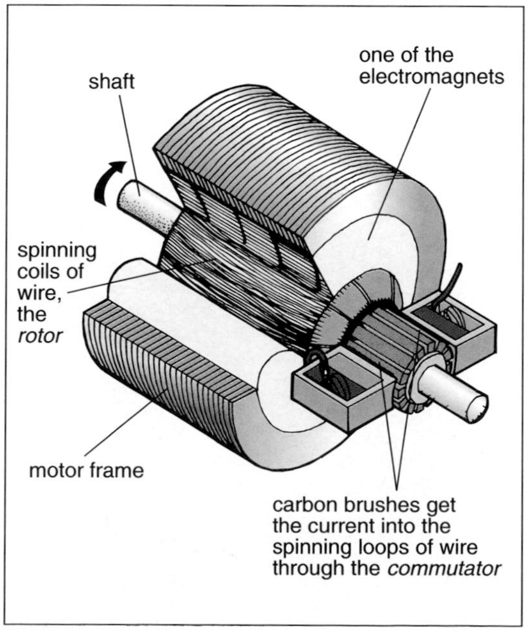

Picture 5 A large electric motor that has been cut open.

Electricity from magnetism?

Michael Faraday didn't stop at making magnetism and electricity work together to produce movement. He thought that there ought to be a way of using movement and magnetism to produce electricity. It took him seven years to think of a way of doing it, but what he discovered is the scientific basis of the electricity industry – **electromagnetic induction**.

Picture 6 overleaf shows a modern version of his experiment. When the current in the first coil is switched on the meter shows a pulse of current in the second coil. Nothing happens when the current in coil 1 is flowing steadily, but another pulse occurs when it is switched off.

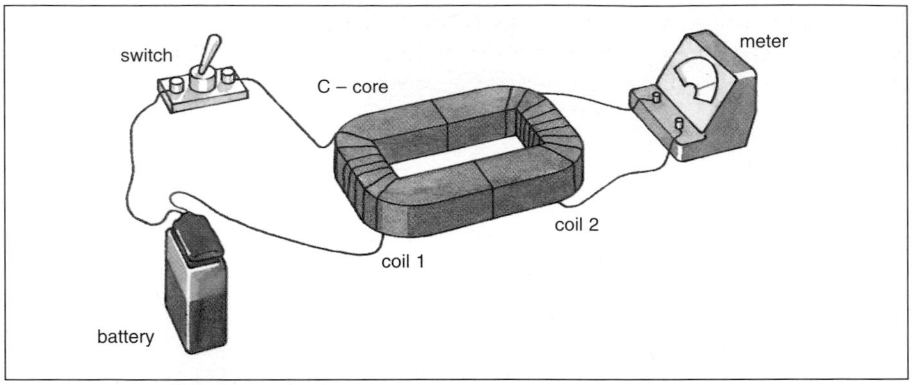

Picture 6 A modern version of Faraday's discovery of induced electricity (the transformer effect).

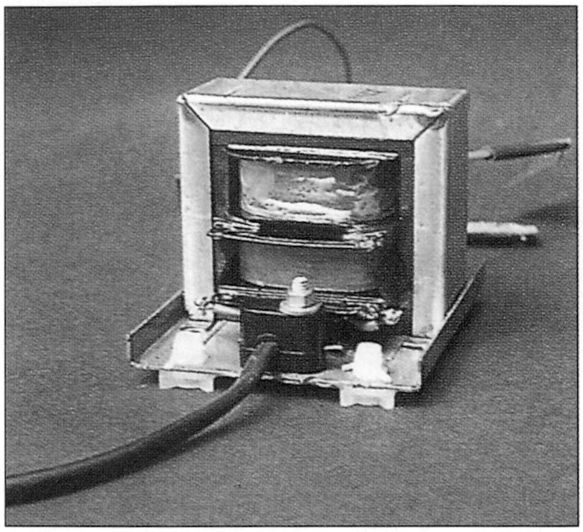

Picture 7 A transformer.

If you alter the current in coil 1 steadily, by using a rheostat in the circuit, you get a steady current in coil 2.

All this happens because a voltage is **induced** in coil 2 whenever a current is changed in coil 1. The modern application of this is the **transformer** (picture 7). There is more about transformers in topic E11.

Faraday tried to imagine what must be happening. He had already thought up the idea that magnetic fields could be explained in terms of lines of force. He explained this new effect by imagining that as the current was being switched on and off so were the lines of force of its magnetic field. The voltage in the second coil was made only when the lines grew and died away.

A generator

So what would happen if he made the lines of force come and go by a different method, by moving a magnet into and out of a coil? He tried this (picture 8) and it worked. Once more a current was produced. The same thing happened when he kept the magnet still and moved the coil instead.

He had invented the first **electric generator**, or **dynamo**. A simple dynamo (picture 9) has the same parts as an electric motor. Both have spinning coils surrounded by magnets. In the motor, putting a current through the coil makes it spin. In a dynamo, making the coil spin produces an electric current. Large dynamos, called generators, are used in power stations to produce the mains supply that we use to run so many things in the home and in industry.

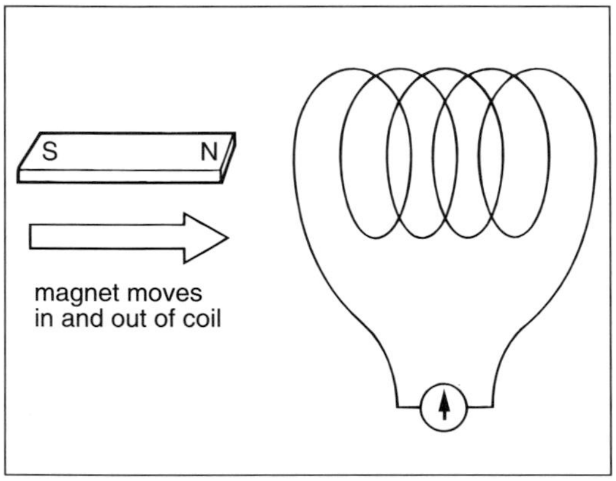

Picture 8 Current is shown on the meter only when the magnet moves in or out of the coil (the dynamo effect).

The laws of electromagnetic induction

When a wire or a coil moves through the magnetic field the size of the induced voltage depends on a number of factors. The voltage increases when:

1. the speed of the wire or coil is increased,
2. the strength of the magnetic field is increased,
3. the number of turns on the coil (or the length of the wire cutting the field) is increased,
4. the area of the coil cutting the field is increased.

Remember also that the voltage is induced only when the wires cut across the field lines. No voltage is produced if a conductor moves parallel to the field lines (picture 10).

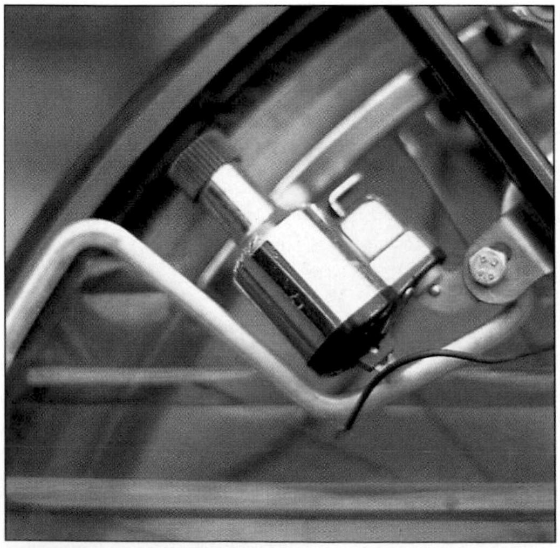

Picture 9 A bicycle dynamo.

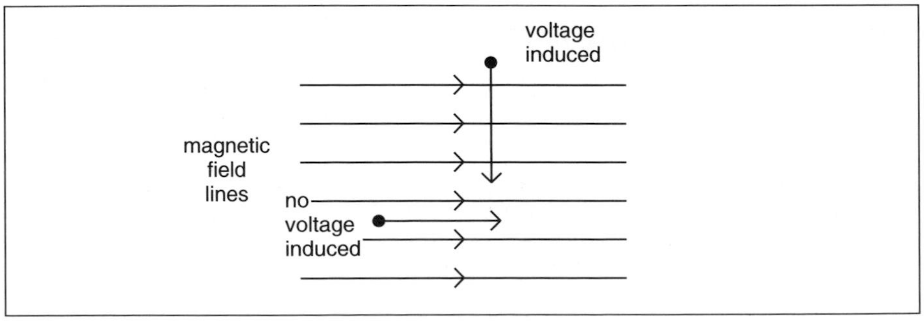

Picture 10

Using electricity to carry energy long distances

Most railways now use locomotives driven by electric motors.These are powered by generators which can be many hundreds of kilometres away .

The main advantage of electricity is that it is so easy to move it from one place to another. A disadvantage is that it is hard to store. Topic E11, *The electricity industry*, deals with the production and supply of electricity.

Activities

A Investigating the motor effect

You will need a pair of slab magnets fitted to a U-shaped piece of soft iron, a low voltage, high current power supply, some wire and some wire cutters.

1 Cut out three pieces of wire as in picture 11 (a), and fix the two longer ones to the red (+) and black (–) terminals of the power supply.

2 Hang the small piece of wire over the other two, as in picture 11 (b).

3 Slide the soft iron with the magnets over this cross-wire so that it is in the field of the magnets. Switch on the current and see what happens.

4 How can you change the direction in which the cross-wire moves?

B Making an electric motor

To do this you will need a special kit. It may look like the model motor shown in picture 3. Follow the instructions given in the kit carefully. When you have got the motor to work answer the following questions.

1 Find two ways to make the motor spin in the opposite direction.

2 How can you make the motor spin faster?

3 Give two differences between this model motor and the ones used to power an electric drill.

C Making a dynamo

Relax. You have already made one. Disconnect the power supply from the motor you made in activity B and hand it back to your teacher. Collect a sensitive meter and connect it to where the power supply was connected. When you spin the motor the meter should show a small current.

D Investigating transformers

Try to repeat Michael Faraday's experiments with a pair of coils wound around an iron bar or ring. You may be given special apparatus for this.

Things to explore

What happens if you have many more turns in the secondary (output) coil than in the primary? Can you make the lamp connected to the secondary coil light up? How do you know that magnetism is involved? What happens if you use low-voltage alternating current (ac) instead of direct current (dc) in the input?

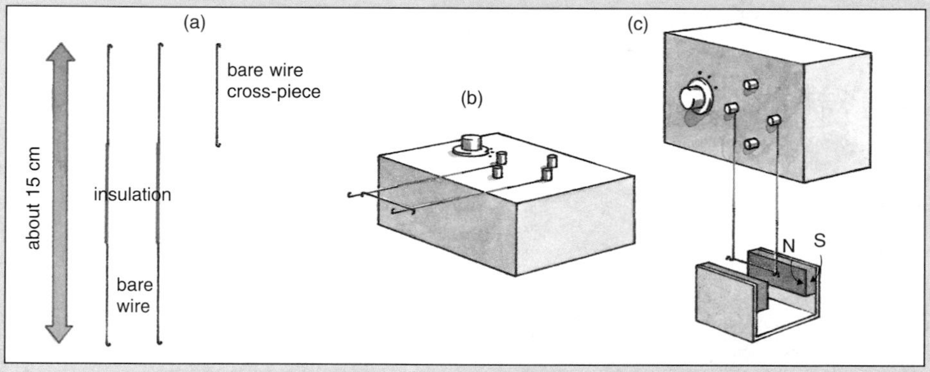

Picture 11 Investigating the motor effect.

Questions

1 Picture 11 (c) shows how you might investigate the force on a wire carrying a current in a magnetic field. What would happen if:

a the magnets were swapped around, so that the S-pole was to the left and the N-pole was to the right?
b the battery connections were then changed so that the current flows in the opposite direction?
c the current was made bigger?

2 Name (a) two devices that use an electric motor to move something from one place to another and (b) two devices that use electric motors to do something else.

3 a Give one place where you would expect to find a transformer being used.
b What is it being used for?

4 Look at picture 8, which shows a coil connected to a meter, and a magnet. When the magnet is moved slowly towards the coil the meter shows a current.

a What would happen to the current if the magnet was moved more quickly?
b What would happen to the current if the magnet was kept still and the coil was moved towards the magnet?
c What would happen to the current if the magnet was moved, but this time away from the coil?

5 You have made a model electric motor and it works! What could you do to:

a make it turn faster,
b make it spin in the opposite direction,
c make it work as a dynamo?

6 An electric motor is used in a small hoist for lifting goods a height of 5 m to the second floor of a factory. The motor is rated at 800 W. When it was tested it was found to lift a load weighing 600 N to the second floor in 4 seconds.

a How much work did the motor do on the load?
b Show that this hoist is about 94% efficient.
c Suggest two reasons why the hoist is unlikely ever to be 100% efficient.

E9
Electricity from frogs?

To the ancient scientists all electricity was 'static'. Then by accident, an electric current was discovered...

The first electric current

When electricity was 'rediscovered' 300 years ago (topic E5) it was 'static' electricity. Apart from entertaining people in a shocking way it wasn't much use. But in 1780 an Italian doctor, Luigi Galvani, discovered a way to produce a continuous flow of charge – in fact the first electric **current**. Like many discoveries in science it was a kind of accident.

Galvani was interested in electricity and had all kinds of equipment in his home. The story goes that Galvani was preparing some food for his sick wife, who happened to like to eat frog's legs. When they were laid out ready for cooking his wife noticed that whenever a spark was produced by a nearby 'electric machine' the frog's legs twitched.

A missed meal

She never got to eat the frog's legs. Galvani started experimenting with them to find out why they twitched. He found that it happened when the leg nerves were stimulated by electric sparks. Then, to his great surprise he found that the legs twitched even when the machine was not working. But this only happened if the ends of the nerves were touched by metals.

He then drew the wrong conclusion. He thought that the electricty came from the frog's legs. It just needed the metals for it to be conducted away. After all, if you can get electric eels (picture 2) why not electric frogs?

Picture 1 'You cannot be serious!'

The first battery

Galvani did his experiment in 1780, and it aroused great interest amongst the electrical hobbyists of the day. But it took another fourteen years for the true cause of 'frog electricity' to be explained. This was done by another Italian, Alessandro Volta. He showed that the source of the electric current was not the frog's leg at all. It was caused by the fact that Dr Galvani had used *two different metals, in the presence of salt water*. The frog's legs had been preserved in salty water. And Dr Galvani had indeed used a zinc dish and steel scalpels, and he had also touched the legs with copper wires.

Volta used this idea to make the first battery. He made it from alternating pairs of zinc and copper discs separated by cloth soaked in salt water (picture 4). This produced a continuous flow of what he called 'artificial electricity'.

Modern batteries work on the same principle (picture 5). There are many different kinds. But each must use a pair of metals with a solution in between.

Picture 2 An electric eel.

Picture 3 Dr Galvani experimented with frog's legs.

The most common batteries use carbon and zinc separated by a solution (**electrolyte**) of ammonium chloride. Carbon often acts like a metal, electrically. Ordinary torch batteries are of this type.

Other batteries use such metals as nickel, iron, cadmium or mercury.

Galvanometers and **volts** are named after these two Italian scientists who did the early work in making 'artificial' electricity.

Cells

A pair of electrodes separated by an ionic solution is called an **electric cell**. The solution has to contain ions so that charge can flow between the metal electrodes. A battery is really a collection of more than one cell, although we often use the word for any kind of cell (see topic E11).

Electricity and chemistry

The news of Volta's battery soon spread across Europe and it was realised that electricity had a lot to do with chemistry. Michael Faraday's boss Sir Humphrey Davy became famous by using the new 'current' of electricity to break down compounds by what is called **electrolysis**. He discovered new elements like sodium, potassium, calcium and magnesium.

The use of various metals in electric cells led to the idea that metals can be arranged in an **electrochemical series** as shown in table 1. The voltage of a cell is decided by how far apart its metal electrodes are in this series.

Picture 6 shows a variety of batteries in use today.

Table 1 Part of the electrochemical series.

Element	Voltage compared with hydrogen
calcium	–2.76
sodium	–2.71
magnesium	–2.37
zinc	–0.78
cadmium	–0.40
hydrogen	0.00
copper	+0.34
mercury	+0.79

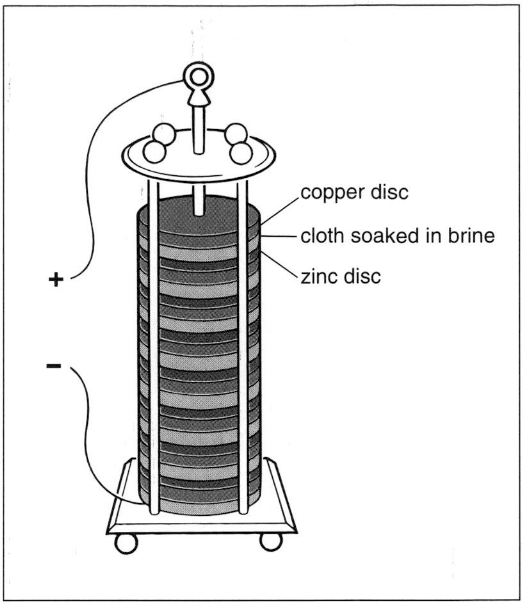

Picture 4 The first battery used zinc, copper and salt water.

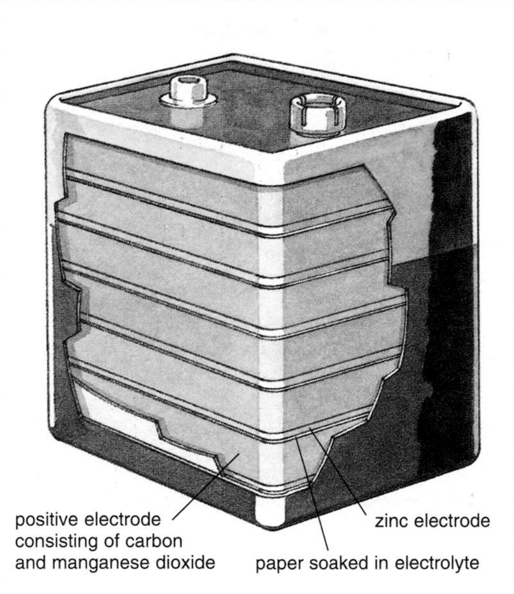

Picture 5 A modern carbon–zinc battery.

Picture 6 All these batteries rely on the electrochemical series.

Activities

A Fruit electricity

It is possible to get electricity out of a lemon. All you have to do is to stick in two electrodes made of different metals. Design an investigation to see how effective this source of electricity is. Check your plan with your teacher before you carry it out.

Will it work with other fruits? What metals work best? Is this a practical, economic source of electricity?

B Using batteries 1

1 Make a list of everyday devices that use batteries to make them work.

2 For each one, say why batteries are used instead of mains electricity.

3 Find out the cost of a battery and how long it will run one of the devices you have listed.

4 Look at the labelling on the device. Try to find out its power in watts or kilowatts. Calculate the cost of using batteries to run it, per kilowatt-hour. Is it cheaper or dearer than using mains electricity?

(Mains electrical energy costs about 8p per kilowatt-hour.)

C Using batteries 2

Find out the answers to the following questions. You can ask people, read pamphlets, use a library.

1 List as many different types of battery as you can (i.e. based on different combinations of chemicals).

2 In what way are car batteries different from ordinary 'torch type' batteries?

3 Many pocket calculators use solar cells. How do solar cells work?

4 What is 'animal electricity'?

D The electrochemical series

Design an experiment to check the order in which elements appear in the electrochemical series. You can use a voltmeter (preferably a digital one) and a solution of dilute acid. Suitable elements include: copper, zinc, nickel, magnesium, aluminium, iron and tin.

Do not carry out your experiment until you have checked it for safety with your teacher.

(*Hint* To get reliable results make sure that the samples are clean. Use some emery cloth to scrape off any dirt, grease or layers of oxide.)

Questions

1 Name four metals that are used in making batteries.

2 How could you use four 1.5 V cells to make a 6 V battery? Draw a simple diagram of the arrangement.

3 What do you think happens when a battery 'runs down'?

4 A one-cell battery is labelled 1.5 V. It is used in a device that takes a current of 0.2 A from it. It runs out after 10 hours of continuous use.
a What power does the battery supply?
b How much energy does it deliver?
c How many coulombs of charge does it supply?
(You will need to use some of the formulae given in table 1, topic E1.)

5 a What are ions?
b Why does the solution in a battery have to contain ions?

How does it work? An electric bell

The diagram below shows the main parts of an electric bell. Your task is to describe how it works. You can use some clues, which are given here.

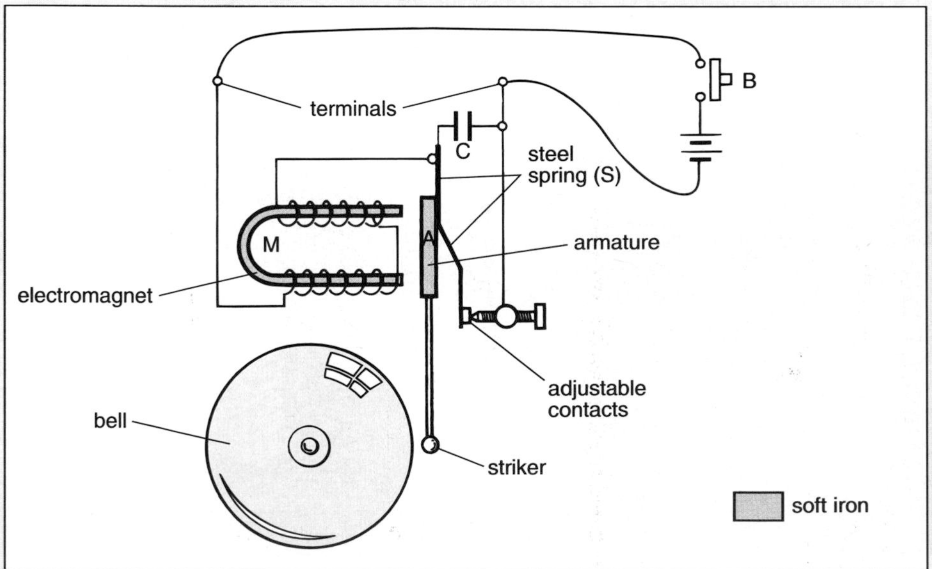

Facts

1 When you press the bell-push (a switch, **B**), current flows through the circuit that includes the electromagnet.

2 The core of the electromagnet (**M**) is made of an alloy (e.g. 'soft iron') which is easily magnetised in a magnetic field, but loses its magnetism very quickly when the field disappears.

3 The bell hammer is connected to a piece of springy steel (**S**), which has another piece of soft iron attached to it (**A**).

Clues

What happens to the circuit when the electromagnet pulls **A** towards it?

Then what happens to the electromagnet?

Tasks

1 Now describe as clearly and logically as you can how the bell keeps on ringing as long as you keep your finger on the bell-push.

2 The circuit also contains a capacitor (**C**). This helps to stop damage that might be caused by high-voltage sparking. Where does this voltage come from?

Seeing further and more clearly

The Hubble Space Telescope was launched in April 1990. It had been designed over a period of twenty years, and will cost $8 billion. It will be effective in space for just fifteen years. Picture 1 shows what it looks like in space. The main tube is a Newtonian telescope, with a very large main mirror.

The telescope is designed to see further and more clearly into the depths of space than ever before. The telescope can be used to send its images to one of several detecting instruments in turn. The most spectacular results will probably come from the 'wide-field' camera. This can take large, clear pictures of large objects like nearby galaxies and planets.

Picture 1 The Hubble Space telescope.

It will get its advantages by being outside the Earth's atmosphere. Earthbound telescopes have to look through many kilometres of air. This air makes stars 'twinkle' – which means that their images dance about and aren't clear. Using bigger telescopes just means getting a bigger blur. Also, some radiations are absorbed by the atmosphere, and so never reach the Earth's surface.

Astronomers rarely look through telescopes. The images of stars and galaxies are usually recorded on film. But this method is no good for the Hubble Telescope! Instead, it uses silicon chips.

These chips are very thin layers of semiconductor material. They contain thousands of tiny photon detectors, the pixels. There are a quarter of a million of these to every square centimetre of chip. The photons of light trigger off each pixel when they hit it. They are over a hundred times more sensitive than the best film, so they can detect much fainter images. They are also small enough to make accurate pictures.

They are called *charge-coupled devices* (CCDs), and picture 2 shows a part of one of them. Four of them are used together in the wide-field camera in the Space Telescope. When photons of light hit a pixel, it releases an electron. This charged particle then moves to form a current. The currents from all the pixels are very carefully aligned to form a signal which can be sent back to Earth. The number of electrons from each pixel tells us how much light hit it. A computer is used to convert the signal current into a picture.

This is just like the way TV works. Indeed, modern TV cameras use CCDs, which means that they are sensitive enough to take pictures in the dark – you can see this in nearly every TV news bulletin.

The image is made on the array of CCDs by the main telescope. They can detect all kinds of radiation – light, UV and even X-rays. The telescope can't focus X-rays – they go straight through it! But light and UV can be focused very accurately. The mirror is curved, and 2 m in diameter. Its aluminium surface is smoothed to a tenth of a wavelength of light. If it was scaled up to be the size of the USA the biggest bump on it would be just 2 cm high. This means it can make best use of the accuracy given by the CCDs.

Now try the following questions.

1. What are the advantages of having a telescope in space, compared with one on Earth?
2. Give a reason why cameras with photographic film would not be much use in the Hubble Telescope.
3. Explain what you understand by the word *photon.*
4. Why does the mirror surface have to be so smooth?
5. What is the advantage of having the main mirror as large as possible?
6. Give two advantages of using CCDs in this telescope.

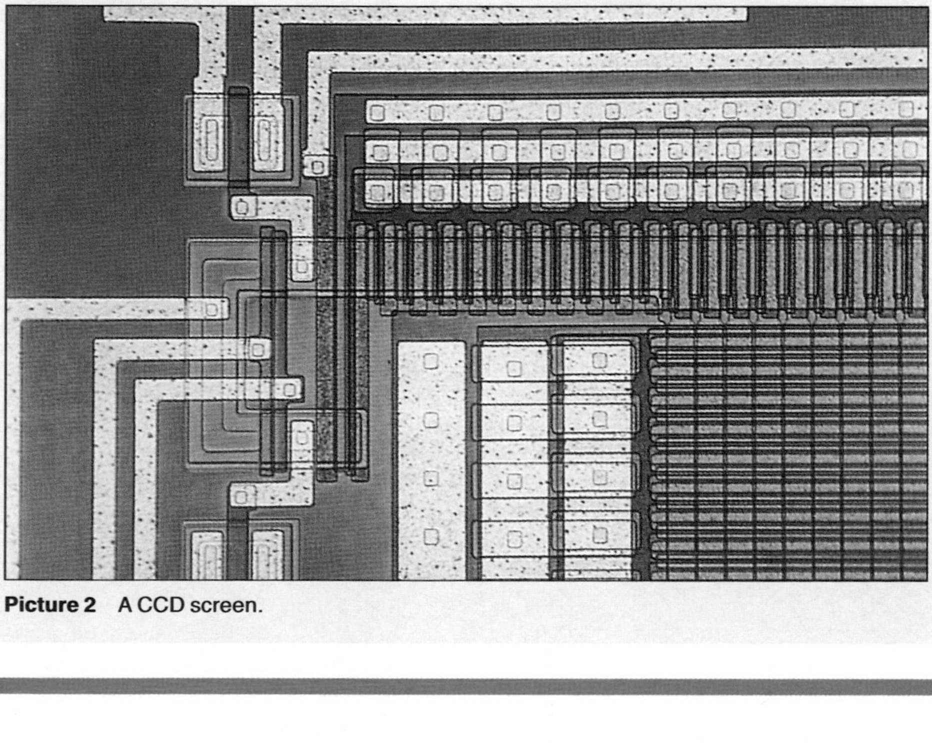

Picture 2 A CCD screen.

E10
Ions and electrolysis

Atoms and groups of atoms can gain or lose electrons, so becoming charged particles called ions.

The solid objects you meet in everyday life are in fact held together by electric forces – by positive charges attracting negative charges. These electric charges exist because matter is made up of atoms, which consist of negative **electrons** attracted to and held together by the positive **nucleus** of the atom. The details of how atoms join together are often very complicated: this is what the whole subject of **chemistry** is about. But the basis of chemistry is the fact that atoms can gain or lose electrons. When they do so they become charged particles called **ions** (picture 1).

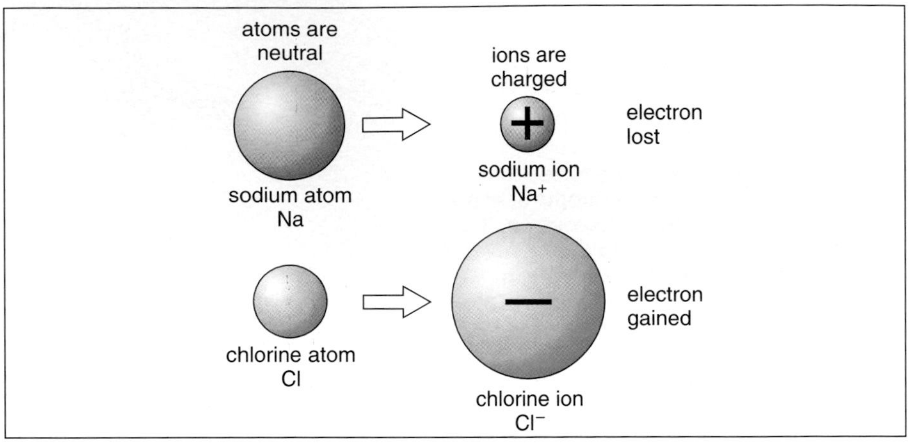

Picture 1

For example, a sodium atom is normally neutral, but can lose an electron to become a **positive sodium ion**:

$$Na \rightarrow Na^+ + e^-$$

A copper atom can easily lose two electrons to become a **positive copper ion**:

$$Cu \rightarrow Cu^{2+} + 2e^-$$

Why metals are good conductors

Because their atoms can lose electrons easily, metals are good conductors (picture 2). The 'free' electrons can move about very easily and so carry a current – a flow of electrons – when a metal is made part of an electric circuit.

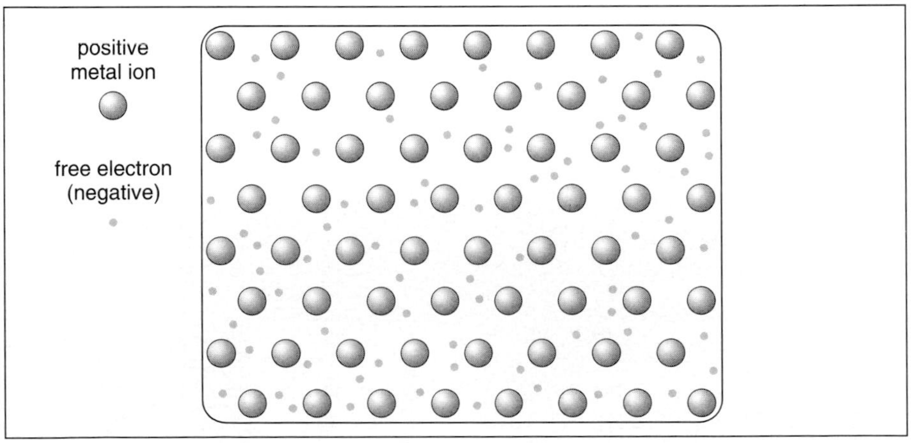

Picture 2 Metals are made of a regular lattice of positive ions with a cloud of loose electrons that can move about freely.

Ionic solids

Non-metals tend to find it easy to gain electrons. For example, a chlorine atom may pick up a spare electron from a metal and become a **negative ion**:

$$Cl + e^- \rightarrow Cl^-$$

Oxygen tends to gain two electrons:

$$O + 2e^- \rightarrow O^{2-}$$

Many everyday substances are compounds of a positive metal ion joined with a negative non-metal ion. It is the electrical attraction between the oppositely charged ions that holds them all together to make a solid. Such compounds are called **ionic** compounds. For example:

copper oxide CuO: $Cu^{2+}\ O^{2-}$
sodium chloride $NaCl$: $Na^+\ Cl^-$

So far we have met only simple ions, where a single atom has lost or gained electrons. But groups of atoms can gain one or more electrons and join with metal ions:

copper sulphate $CuSO_4$: $Cu^{2+}(SO_4)^{2-}$

$(SO_4)^{2-}$ is the **negative sulphate ion**. Other common ions like this are: the nitrate ion $(NO_3)^-$, the carbonate ion $(CO_3)^{2-}$, and the positive ammonium ion $(NH_4)^+$.

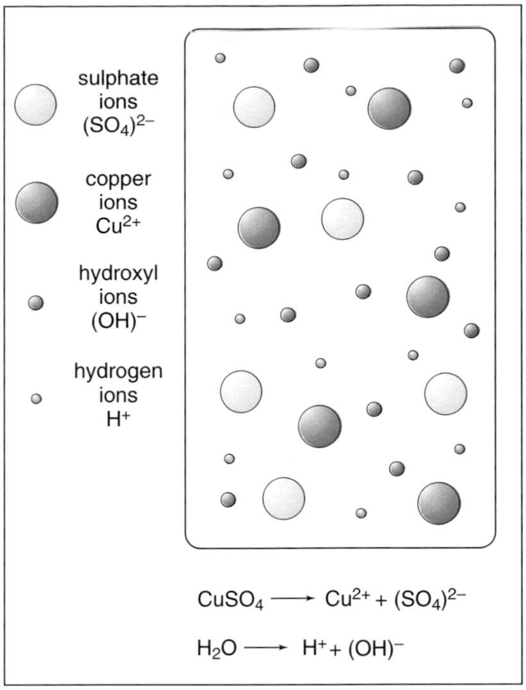

Picture 3 Ions in a solution of copper sulphate. Some water molecules also break up into positive hydrogen ions and negative hydroxyl ions.

Electrolytes

One of the most useful things about ionic compounds is that many of them dissolve very easily in water to make a solution that conducts electricity. This happens because the water weakens the forces between the ions and they separate. For example (see picture 3):

$$CuSO_4 \rightarrow Cu^{2+} + (SO_4)^{2-}$$

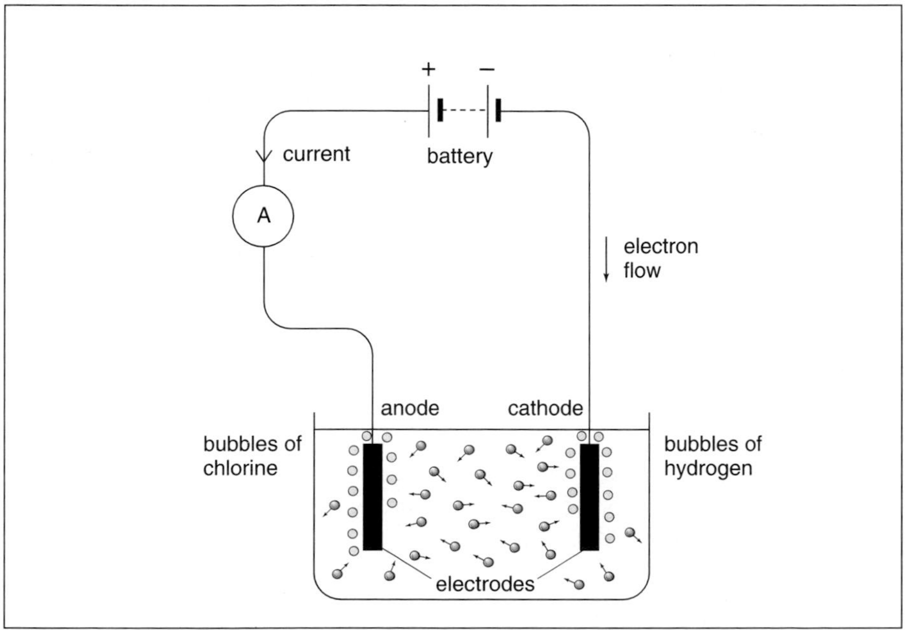

Picture 4 The electrolysis of salt water (sodium chloride solution). Negative chloride ions go to the anode. There they lose electrons, become chlorine atoms and bubble off. Positive sodium ions go to the negative electrode (cathode). At the cathode there will be both sodium and hydrogen ions, but only hydrogen ions collect electrons to become atoms. Sodium ions stay in solution. The hydrogen bubbles off as a gas.

The solution is called an **electrolyte**. When an electrolyte is made part of an electric current can flow, carried by the ions. Positive ions move towards the negative terminal; negative ions move towards the positive terminal. The terminals, called **electrodes**, are usually metal plates or carbon rods. When ions reach the electrodes they gain or lose electrons. They stop being ions and become ordinary neutral atoms once again. The atoms may react chemically, but usually the electrodes are chosen so that the atoms are simply collected. Metal atoms will form a thin plate on the electrode; atoms of a gas will bubble off and can be collected (picture 4).

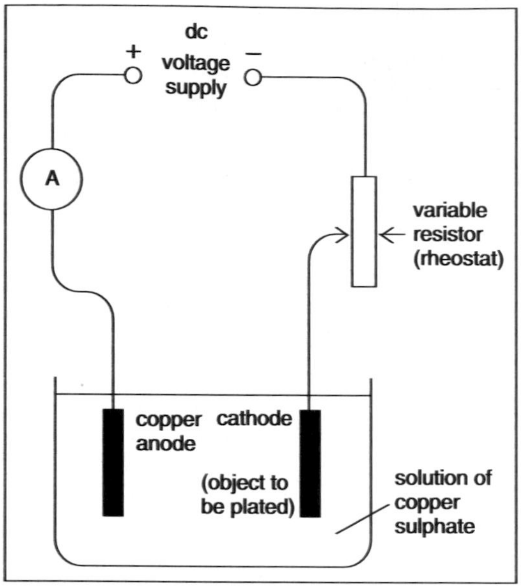

Picture 5 Electroplating with copper. Copper ions move to the cathode which becomes plated with copper. Copper ions leave the anode and go into the solution.

Electroplating

Electroplating is widely used in industry. It is used to put thin layers of a metal that is more attractive, or protective, but usually more expensive, onto a cheaper, or stronger, metal. For example, steel handlebars are plated with chrome, which is shiny and doesn't get rusty. Nickel spoons are made to look better by being plated with silver.

Picture 5 shows a simple circuit you could use for putting a layer of copper on a steel or carbon electrode (**CARE!** copper sulphate is poisonous). Note that the positive copper ions plate the negative electrode (called a **cathode**). The quantity of metal deposited on the cathode depends on the current. Remember that the current is a flow of copper ions. It also depends on the time for which charge is allowed to flow:

- mass deposited increases when the current increases,
- mass deposited increases when the time for which current flows increases.

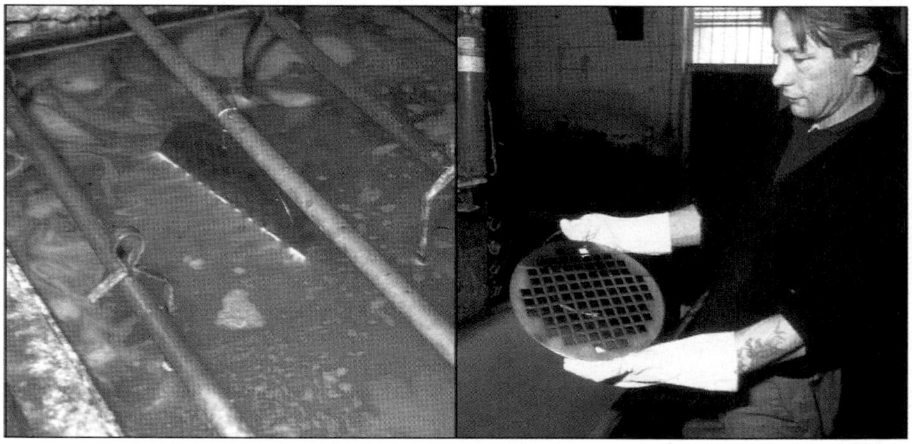

Picture 6 A sieve being electroplated with zinc. The part above the surface of the bath (left) remains unplated, as can be seen in the picture on the right.

Molten electrolytes

Ionic substances can be melted, although they do so at very high temperatures. When they melt the ions are free to move and the liquid is able to conduct electricity. This effect is used, for example, to get pure aluminium out of molten bauxite (an impure ore containing aluminium oxide). The aluminium oxide has to be heated to over 2000 °C.

Activities

A

Look at the metal objects in your kitchen or tool box. Are any of them electroplated? How can you tell?

B

Dip an iron nail into a solution of copper sulphate. **CARE!** Copper sulphate is a poison. Describe what happens to the nail and suggest what might have caused it.

C

Design an experiment to check that the mass of a metal deposited during electrolysis is proportional to both the *current* and the *time* for which it flows.

Think about the following:

- there are two independent variables – so ensure that the experiment is 'fair',
- the mass of metal deposited will probably be quite small,
- the metal will not plate well if the current is too large,
- the fresh metal may be easily corroded.

Discuss your plan with your teacher to make sure that it is sensible and safe before trying it out.

Questions

1 What are the main differences between atoms, molecules and ions? Give two examples of each.

2 Look at the chemical formulae in the following list of ionic substances. What ions would you expect to find in each substance?

a sodium chloride ($NaCl$)
b potassium chloride (KCl)
c ammonium chloride (NH_4Cl)
d barium chloride ($BaCl_2$)
e hydrochloric acid (HCl)

3 Look at picture 5, showing how to electroplate with copper. State and explain what would happen if

a the size of the current is decreased,
b the voltage of the supply is increased,
c the circuit is switched on for a longer time,
d the supply voltage is kept constant but the area of the electrode plates is increased.

4 What changes would you make to the electroplating system shown in picture 5 if you wanted to plate the cathode with silver?

5 In an electroplating tank in a factory they find that when using a current of 2 A it takes 2 hours to plate a set of bicycle frames with the required thickness of chromium. How long would it take if the current was changed to 1.5 A?

E11 The electricity industry

This topic deals with how electrical energy is generated and then transported to where it is needed.

Picture 1 Fiddler's Ferry coal-fired power station. The towers are used to cool the low-pressure steam after it has passed through the turbines.

The power station

Picture 1 shows a large power station. You can see the huge stock of coal that will be taken in at one end. At the other end are the pylons holding the wires through which the electricity will be carried away. The diagram (picture 2) shows the main parts of the power station where the energy conversions take place.

The energy changes in a power station

Energy is released when coal burns with the oxygen of the air. This energy is used to boil water and then heat the steam to a high temperature. Burning coal also produces large amounts of carbon dioxide which goes into the atmosphere, together with other waste gases such as sulphur dioxide.

The steam is made very hot so that it is at a very high pressure. This means that it can provide very large forces to turn the huge steam turbines. This takes energy from the steam, which cools down, but doesn't become so cool that it condenses back into water.

The spinning turbines (picture 3) are connected to the coils of large generators. These coils carry current and act as large electromagnets. As they spin they induce a high voltage in the fixed coils surrounding them (see page 169 and picture 4). This causes a current which is fed into the **National Grid** system that carries the electricity to wherever it is needed (picture 5).

Picture 3 The turbine hall at Didcot Power Station. On the left, a stripped turbine is open to view.

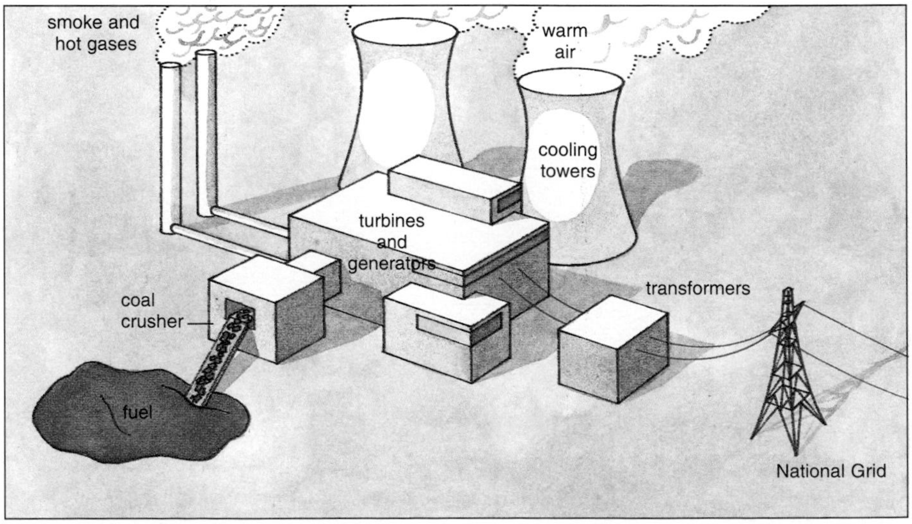

Picture 2 The main parts of a power station.

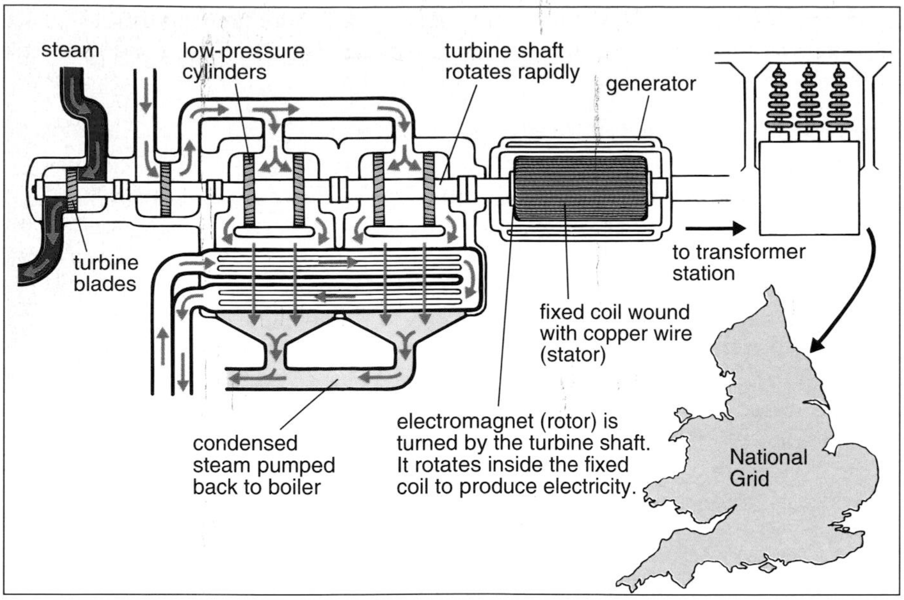

Picture 4 The structure of a large generator.

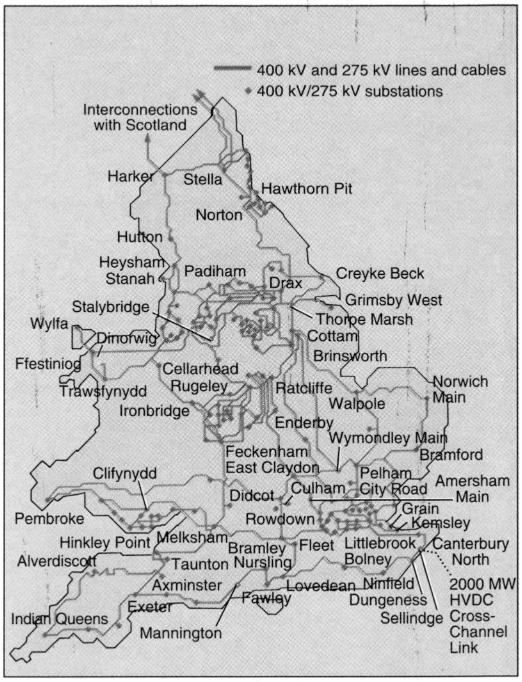

Picture 5 The main power lines of the National Grid.

Energy flow in a power station

Picture 6 shows the energy flow through a typical power station. A large power station might be rated at 1000 megawatts. This means that every second it delivers 1000 million joules of energy. This is about the same as the total power output that could be produced by every human being in the United Kingdom working flat out. No modern industrial country could survive on slave labour!

But to produce this energy, fuel equivalent to an energy of 3000 million joules per second has to be supplied. *Two-thirds of the energy input is wasted.*

This means that most power stations powered by fossil fuels can only be 30 to 40% **efficient**.

How is the energy wasted?

Some of the waste is 'accidental', because energy leaks out to warm up the air. For example, it moves as hot air from the boiler chimneys, and wiring gets hot.

But most of the waste is *necessary* waste. This is because the turbines can't take all of the energy out of the steam. This leaves lots of steam which is still warm, but cooler than it was when it went in, and too cool to make any turbines work.

This is the reason for the cooling towers. They are used to take energy from the 'used' steam, so condensing it back to water. This energy usually ends up warming a river or the sea.

This waste seems a great pity, but it is a consequence of one of the most ruthless laws of physics. This is the Second Law of Thermodynamics, which says that whenever you try to do something useful with thermal energy some of it always ends up in the wrong place (see topic D4).

In this example, the wasted energy goes into the cooling system and eventually into the surroundings.

Can we make better use of this waste energy?

The waste energy can be put to good use. It is stored in warm water. The water is not hot enough to be useful to make electricity – it could not make the steam turbines work. But is quite warm enough to heat homes and other buildings.

In Germany most towns have their own small power stations, and they often pipe the 'waste' hot water to people's homes to keep them centrally heated. These are called **combined heat and power schemes**. They reduce waste and make electricity cheaper.

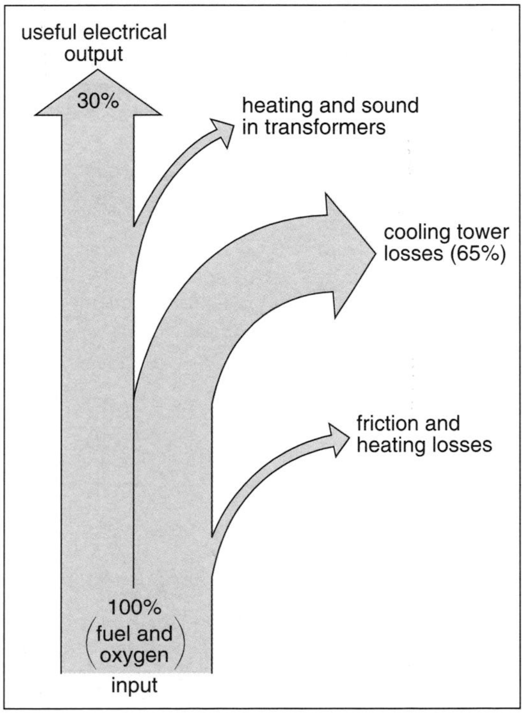

Picture 6 Energy flow in a power station that is 30% efficient.

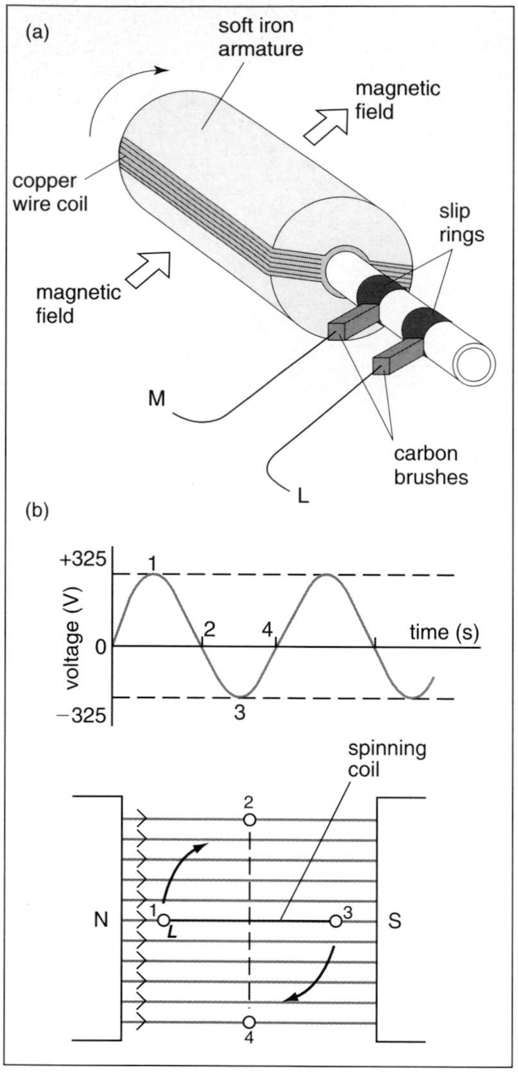

Picture 7 (a) Current is taken from the spinning coil via carbon contacts (brushes) which rub against copper slip rings. The slip rings are connected to the two ends of the coil.
(b) The voltage of the mains supply swings between +325 V and −325 V, 50 times a second
Numbers 1, 2, 3, 4 show where one side (L) of the spinning coil is when it produces the outputs marked 1, 2, 3, and 4 on the graph.

In the UK most power stations are larger and have been built a long way from towns and cities. This means that using them to produce 'combined heat and power' is not economic.

Alternating current

The turbines spin the field coils of the generators at high speeds. The wiring is arranged to give **alternating current**. This is done by making the voltage produced by each coil change direction every half-turn. This means that the current changes direction as well. It flows one way for half the time, then in the opposite direction for the next half. This change-over occurs every 1/100 of a second. How this is done is shown in picture 7. Only one coil is drawn, to make the idea clearer.

The rate of spinning and the number of coils is designed to make each coil change (**alternate**) its voltage and current completely 50 times a second.

The speed of movement, the large magnetic field and the large number of turns used mean that the voltage produced is quite high: 25 000 V.

There is a good reason for producing alternating current (ac) rather than direct current (dc), like a battery produces. It is because it makes it easy to change the voltage of the supply, using transformers. This is explained next.

How do we get our electricity?

The generator produces a large current at an output voltage of 25 000 V, which is extremely dangerous. It could be arranged for this to be 230 V, as used in the home, but this would be very uneconomic. In fact the voltage is made even higher as it leaves the power station. It is raised to 275 000 V or even 400 000 V (picture 8). The reason for this is the resistance in the cables which take the electricity from the power station to a home or factory.

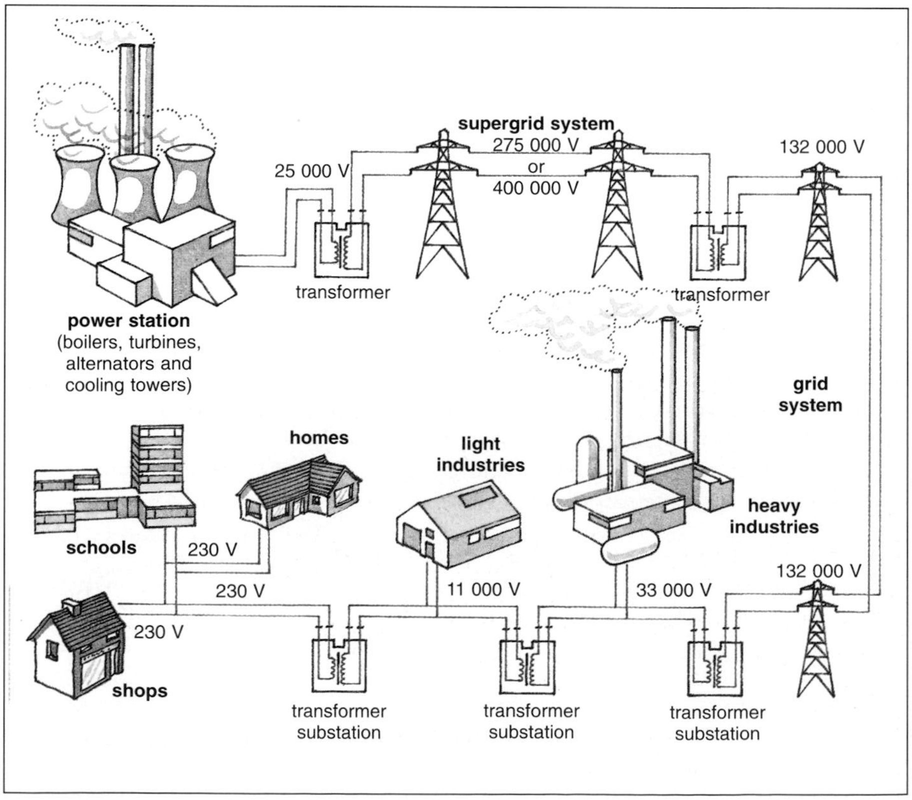

Picture 8 Voltages in the National Grid system.

Why is electricity transmitted at very high voltages?

Most people live and work many hundreds of miles from the power stations that produce our electricity. This is because the stations are built near good supplies of fuel and cooling water.

Whenever a current flows in a conductor some power is lost in heating the conductor. Engineers can cut down this energy loss by supplying the current at very high voltages.

The power loss in a conductor is given by $P = VI$, where V is the voltage drop across the conductor. We can change this to give power loss in terms of the current I and the resistance R of the cable. This gives $P = I^2R$ (because $V = IR$). The engineers want the loss in the cable to be as little as possible. They do this by making the resistance (R) of the cable as small as possible. The resistance can be cut down by using very thick cables (see picture 9).

Even so, there will always be some cable resistance, and there comes a point when the cost of making the cable is greater than the value of the energy we are trying to save. The only other thing they can change is the current in the cable. This is done by using very high voltages.

Picture 9 A power cable.

High voltage, low current

The delivered power is also given by $P = VI$. This time V is the voltage drop at the end where the customer wants to use it. The power is the same for a low current at a high voltage as for a high current at a low voltage. Suppose the customer wants 100 000 W of power to be delivered. This could be done, for example, either by sending 200 A at 500 V or by sending 1 A at 100 000 V.

Now suppose the cable resistance is 2 Ω. The cable loss in the first case (voltage 500 V, current 200 A) is:

$$\text{power loss} = I^2R = 200 \times 200 \times 2 = 80\,000 \text{ W}$$

This would leave only 20 000 W for the customer!

In the second case (voltage 100 000 V, current 1 A) we get

$$\text{power loss} = I^2R = 1 \times 1 \times 2 = 2 \text{ W!}$$

It makes very sound economic sense to send the electric power down the cable at high voltages. But you would not be too happy at having a mains supply at 100 000 V. This is a very dangerous voltage. This is where transformers come in.

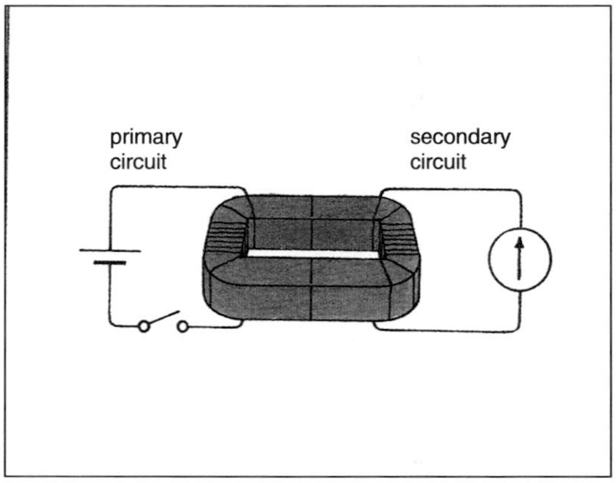

Picture 10 Electromagnetic induction happens when a magnetic field is changing or a conductor cuts through the field.

What transformers do

Faraday's experiment with two coils (page 169) gives the basic idea of how transformers work. We can switch a current on and off in the primary coil. This produces and then takes away a magnetic field in the iron core (picture 10). The changing field induces a voltage in the secondary coil.

Now, when an alternating current is supplied to the primary coil it also produces a changing field in the iron core. This field changes as the current changes. Just as with the switching experiment this changing field also induces a changing voltage in the secondary coil.

But, if you have investigated transformers (activity D, topic E8), you will know that the voltage in the secondary coil depends also on *how many turns* there are in the coils. If there are more turns in the secondary than in the primary coil, the output voltage is bigger than the input voltage. If there are less turns in the secondary than in the primary, the voltage is reduced. Thus we can have **step-up transformers**, which increase the voltage, and **step-down transformers**, which do the opposite (picture 11).

This leads to the transformer rule:

$$\frac{\text{Output voltage}}{\text{Input voltage}} = \frac{\text{secondary turns}}{\text{primary turns}} \quad \text{or} \quad \frac{V_{out}}{V_{in}} = \frac{N_{sec}}{N_{pri}}$$

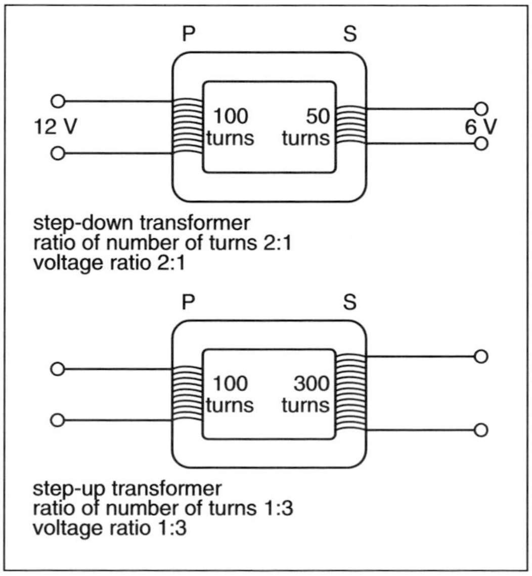

Picture 11 Transformer ratios.

Transformers and the Grid System

Step-up transformers are used at power stations (pictures 1 and 2) to raise the 25 000 V produced by the generators to the higher voltages which are so efficient for transmitting electricity over long distances. The network of cables carrying current at these very high voltages is called the **National Grid**.

The cables are carried on tall pylons which are easy to spot when you travel about the country. Very many people live in Southern England, and they need a lot of electricity. Some of it comes from as far away as Scotland or France (by undersea cables). The normal Grid supply voltage is 275 000 V, but for moving electricity very long distances the **Supergrid** is used, using a voltage of 400 000 V.

At the customer end, step-down transformers are used. They lower the Grid voltage to the 550 V used in some factories and the 230 V used in the home, in shops, etc.

Clean and efficient energy?

Devices that are run from electricity are the most efficient of all the ones we use in the home or in industry. Electric motors are about 90% efficient, compared with a petrol engine which may be only 20% efficient. Similarly, electric trains are three times as efficient as diesel engines. An electric fire uses 100% of the energy it receives to heat the room. Coal fires and oil central heating systems lose some energy in hot air and fumes going out of the chimney.

These figures are impressive, but a little misleading. Back at the power station the laws of thermal energy take their inevitable toll (see above). Producing the electricity in the first place is only 30% efficient, which is about the same efficiency as a diesel engine. This loss is there even if we use nuclear energy to power the turbines. The loss is due to the nature of all **thermal engines**, like turbines, that rely on heating to make them work.

Thermal power stations also produce much of the polluting gases, such as sulphur oxides and nitrogen oxides, that cause acid rain. This is because coal and oil contain impurities. But what is more, all fuels produce carbon dioxide when they are burnt. It has only recently been realised that this 'harmless' gas may be seriously affecting the environment on a global scale. It is the major gas involved in the 'greenhouse effect'.

Another problem is that sooner or later, the fossil fuels that we use to run power stations will be used up.

Nuclear power stations

Nuclear power stations are just about as efficient (or inefficient) as oil or coal-fired power stations. They normally produce little pollution – unless there is an accident, as happened at Chernobyl in 1986. But they do generate radioactive waste, which needs to be stored for perhaps many thousands of years (see topic D7).

Are there other ways of getting electrical energy?

Electricity is not a *source* of energy. It is a very useful means of *transferring* energy. Power stations and batteries are systems that use sources of energy like the combustion of fuel, nuclear fission and reactions between chemicals to make electric charge move along wires. The moving charges can make things hot (in water heaters etc.) or move things (using electric motors). Most sources of energy are non-renewable. Sooner or later we shall use up all the natural fossil fuels, and possibly even the radioactive elements used in fission reactors. Both sources of energy have environmental effects in that their waste products can cause more or less dangerous pollution. These facts have led to a great interest in non-polluting or renewable energy sources.

Renewable energy sources

Taking the very long view there are no such things as renewable energy sources. But what we mean are sources that rely on sunlight, winds, waves,

Picture 12 A hydroelectric power station.

tides, flowing water or biological materials. All these rely on energy from the Sun – and the Sun will eventually die, as even stars do (see Topic F4). But our Sun is likely to keep providing this energy for the next 5 billion years or so, which is forever on a human time scale.

The interior of the Earth is hot (see page 194) and can be used as an energy source. Iceland makes use of this **geothermal** energy to provide hot water for space heating in its main towns. This energy is largely due to radioactive decay in rocks which will eventually cease, but the half-life of the elements involved is many millions of years.

Picture 13 A wind farm.

Picture 14 Solar panels

Hydroelectric power stations provide most of the energy transferred electrically in Norway and they are important also in France. The systems rely on gravitational potential energy as an energy source in mountain areas with enough rainfall or snow melt to provide water that can turn turbines as it flows downhill. The water is recycled by the natural global water cycle, powered by energy from the Sun, that returns lowland and sea water to the mountains.

The kinetic energy of wind is one of the oldest sources of renewable energy. Sails have powered ships for thousands of years. Windmills have been in use since about 600 AD and their use as generators of electricity is becoming more and more popular. They are set up in *wind farms* (picture 13) containing arrays of large windmills: the wind farm in Delabole (Cornwall) contains ten wind generators each able to produce 400 kW of power when the wind blows at a speed of at least 5 m/s. Wind is an unreliable energy source; it doesn't blow at a steady speed at all times. However, such systems can be used to top up a steady supply available from conventional power stations.

Sea waves also carry a great deal of kinetic energy. As with wind, they are an unreliable source and it is not as easy to collect the energy for useful applications. **Tides** are caused by gravitational forces exerted by the Sun and Moon. This rise and fall of sea water can be tapped as an energy source. The best known tidal power station is at the Rance Estuary in Brittany, France.

Sunlight and the **infra-red** radiation from the Sun can be used directly to generate electricity or heat water and buildings. Well designed buildings can make best use of the available solar energy and so reduce the need for other energy sources. **Photovoltaic** cells made from semiconductor materials can generate electricity, but at present they are expensive. They are useful in warm sunny climates where heating is not a large drain on energy sources, and particularly in isolated places which would be expensive to connect to a national grid system.

Biomass or biological fuels like wood may be renewable if properly managed. Wood is the main domestic fuel in many tropical countries. Agricultural wastes, like straw and sugar cane stalks, have been considered as an energy supply. Such materials may be fermented to produce an alcohol which can be used to run internal combustion engines. Again, these materials provide energy at too high a cost to compete with fossil fuels at present prices.

Concentrated and dispersed energy sources

The problem with most 'alternative' energy sources as described above is that the energy is spread over a wide area or volume of space. The materials involved have a low *energy density*. Think of the energy in wind compared with the same amount of energy stored in a material like oil – or in uranium. This means that wind farms need more ground area than fossil fuel power stations of the same output.

Cheap electricity?

Coal-fired power stations can't be switched off easily. The furnaces have to be kept going all the time, because if they cool down they get badly damaged. Thus many power stations are running all the time, both day and night.

At night most people are asleep. Factories are closed down, few trains are running. The demand for electricity is much less than in the daytime.

But the power stations are still burning fuel, even if the turbines are not working at full capacity. It is more economical for the electricity supply industry to sell electrical energy cheaply at night than not to sell it at all. Thus many homes and factories have heaters which are time-switched so that they use only night-time electricity (see page 161).

Activities

A

Somewhere near your house or school there will be a transformer which reduces the voltage of the electricity supply to 230 V. Find the transformer, sketch it and describe it. Write down any official notices that might be on it and explain what they say.

B

Ask questions, read pamphlets, look up books in the library to help you answer one or more of the following questions.

1 Where is your nearest power station? What fuel(s) does it use?

2 Why is electricity cheaper at night?

3 In the mountains of North Wales, at Ffestiniog and Dinorwic, there are special kinds of power station called 'pumped-storage' stations. What are these and how do they work?

4 Where in the British Isles would you expect to find:

a hydroelectric power stations,
b nuclear power stations,
c wind farms?

What factors decide where such stations are built?

5 How does the electricity industry cope with the problem that much less electricity is used in summer than in winter?

Questions

1 Explain what jobs the following do in a coal-fired power station:

a generators,
b cooling towers,
c step-up transformers.

2 a What is the National Grid?
b Why are the cables that carry electricity held so far above the ground?
c Electricity is sent along the National Grid at very high voltages. Why must they be so high?

3 The graph (picture 15) shows the cost per metre of cable of different thickness. It also shows the cost per metre of the power loss in the cable due to resistance heating. Both of these quantities are plotted against cables of different thickness.

a Why does the cost of lost power go down when the cable gets thicker?
b Why does the cost per metre of cable rise when the cable gets thicker?
c What is the combined cost of cable-plus-power-loss for cables of thickness: (i) 10 cm, (ii) 15 cm?
d From the graph, what is the most economical cable thickness to choose?
e The graph for the cost of the cable rises much more quickly than the power saving cost falls. Suggest a reason for this.

4 a Calculate the current that needs to be taken from a 25 MW power station at a generating voltage of 2500 V.
b What would this current be reduced to if the voltage was stepped up to 400 000 V for the National Supergrid?
c What would be the effect of this reduction in current on power loss in the cables?

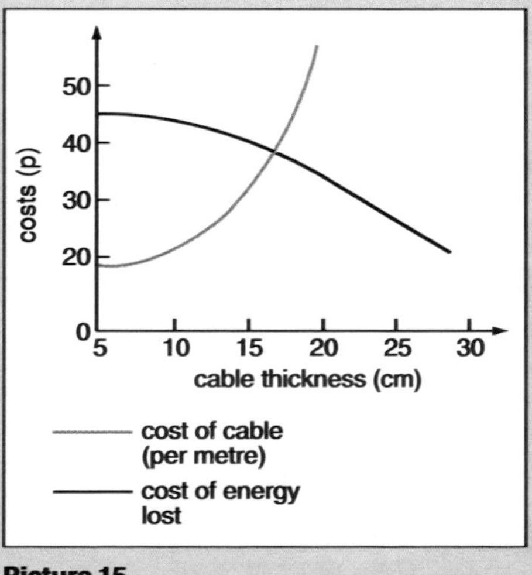

Picture 15

E12 Electrons in space

So far we have looked at electric charges flowing in wires, liquids or gases. Interesting things happen when we get the charges out on their own, in empty space...

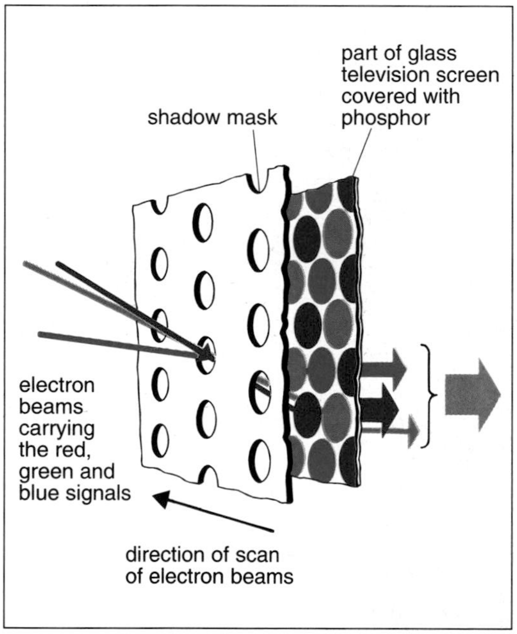

Picture 1 The screen of the picture tube has more than 300 000 coloured phosphor dots arranged in groups of three on its surface. A metal mask behind the screen has holes which keep each of the three electron beams in line with its own colour dots and away from dots of other colours.

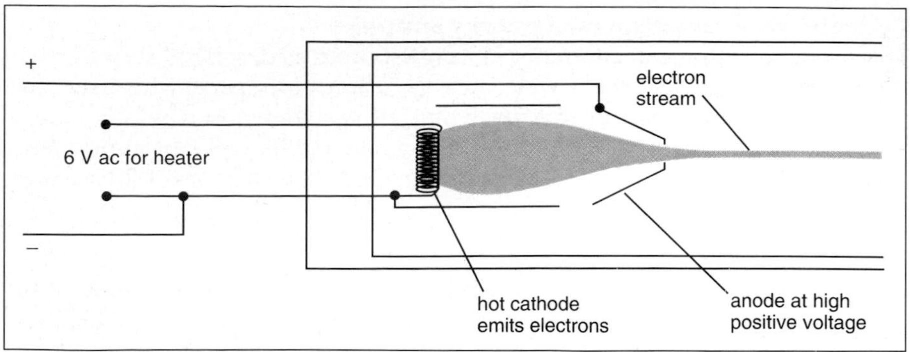

Picture 2 The electron gun in a TV tube.

A TV tube is mostly empty space. The picture screen is covered on the inside by a **phosphor**. This is a chemical which glows when it is hit by electrons (picture 1). The electrons have to be travelling fast. In a colour tube they need to hit the phosphor at a speed of over 15 million metres a second.

The electron gun

The electrons are fired from the narrow end of the tube by a device called an **electron gun** (picture 2). The electrons are produced by heating a metal oxide so that it just glows red hot. This is called **thermionic emission**.

This part of the gun is kept negative and is called the **cathode**. The electrons that 'boil off' the cathode are attracted by a metal cylinder which is kept at a very high positive voltage – the **anode**. This produces a force which accelerates them to a very high speed.

The space inside the tube must be completely empty of any gas (a vacuum), otherwise the electrons would collide with the gas molecules. The stream of electrons is focused into a narrow beam which has to be very accurately aimed so that the phosphor screen glows in exactly the right places at exactly the right times to make a picture.

Making the picture

The picture is made by **scanning** the electron beam across the screen in a series of lines which are then moved from top to bottom of the screen. There are 625 lines in a screenful, and the screen is completely scanned by the beam 25 times a second (picture 3). If you wave your fingers to and fro in front of your eyes whilst watching TV you can see odd 'gaps'. You don't normally see these gaps because it takes about a twentieth of a second for your eye – brain system to wipe away a picture. The pictures come quicker than that, so one

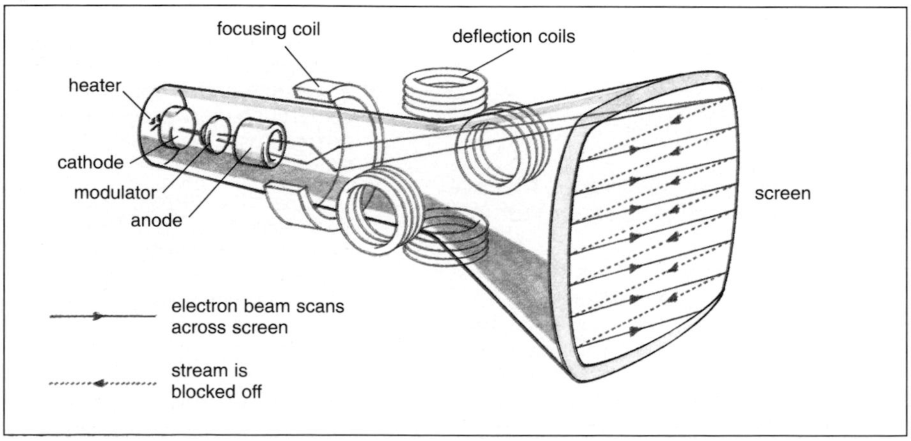

Picture 3 Scanning action. Only a few scans are shown – there are actually 625 in each 'screenful'.

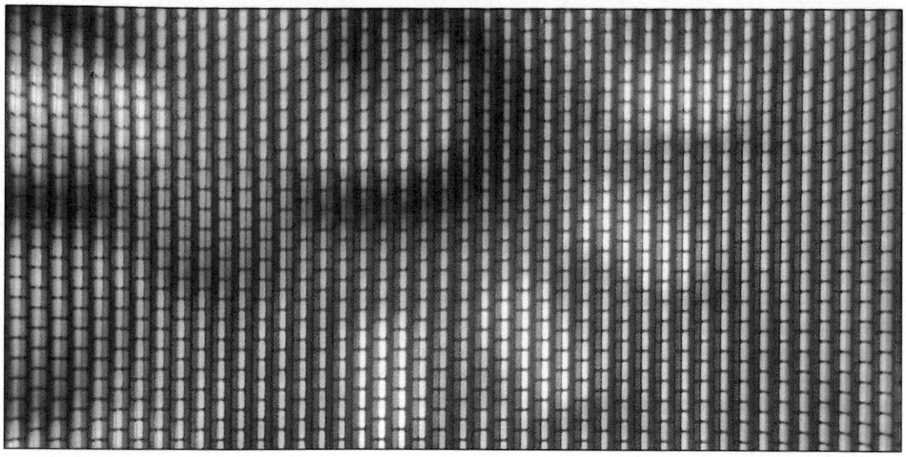

Picture 4 The 'pixels' in a TV screen. A TV picture is made of thousands of these.

picture merges neatly with the next. Better pictures can be made with more lines in a screen, and the new 'high definition' TV sets use many more lines.

Controlling the electrons

The electron beam has to move across the screen very quickly and very accurately. In a colour tube the beam is split into three, so that it can hit three separate picture cells (pixels). The pixels glow red, blue or green (picture 4). These are the primary colours (see page 90). These can be combined to give the illusion of all the colours of the rainbow.

The electrons are directed to the right place by a strong magnetic field. In picture 3 you can see the coils of wire that produce this field. Its strength is controlled by the signal sent out by the TV station and picked up by the TV aerial.

The electron stream is of course just a flow of charge – an electric current. Just like the current in the coils of an electric motor the electron stream can be moved by a magnetic field. The field can direct them to where they have to go to make the picture.

Electrons are the lightest charged objects in the Universe, so they change direction very quickly. The magnetic fields have to change very quickly to produce a new picture 25 times a second, but the electrons are light enough to follow the changes.

Picture 5 shows how a stream of electrons is affected by a magnetic field. Just as in a motor, the field has to be at right angles to the electron stream, and the direction of movement is at right angles to both field and current direction.

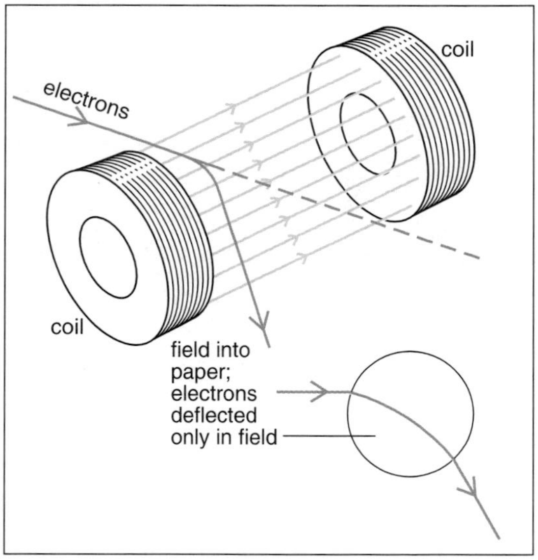

Picture 5 In the magnetic field of the coils, electrons are deflected as shown.

The cathode ray oscilloscope

Another way of changing the direction of a stream of electrons is to make use of electric forces. This is the method used in the measuring and display instrument called a **cathode ray oscilloscope** or CRO (picture 6).

The electron gun in a CRO fires its beam between two pairs of metal plates (picture 7 overleaf). A positively charged plate attracts the negatively charged electrons. The plates are arranged at right angles so that when voltages are applied the electron stream is deflected either up or down or from side to side.

The plates that move the stream vertically are called the **Y-plates**. The **X-plates** move the electrons horizontally. In a CRO the X-plates are used to move the beam steadily across the screen from left to right. This done by a steadily increasing positive voltage applied to the right-hand plate. The steady movement of the beam across the screen is called a **time-base**. It is like the 'time axis' you might draw on a graph. It allows us to see the pattern produced by an effect that is changing with time.

The signal to be studied is applied to the Y-plates. For example, if we apply

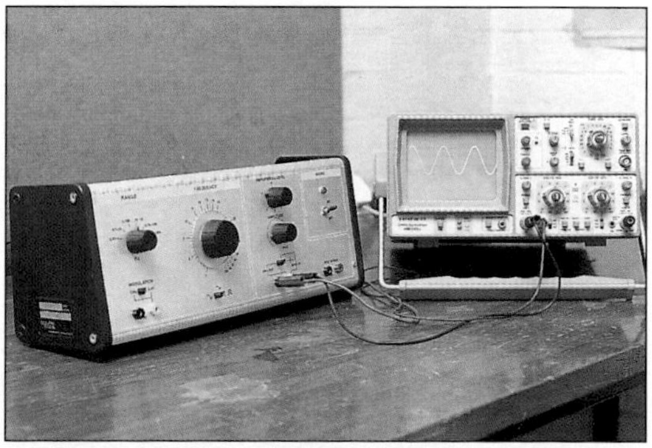

Picture 6 A cathode ray oscilloscope is a very useful instrument.

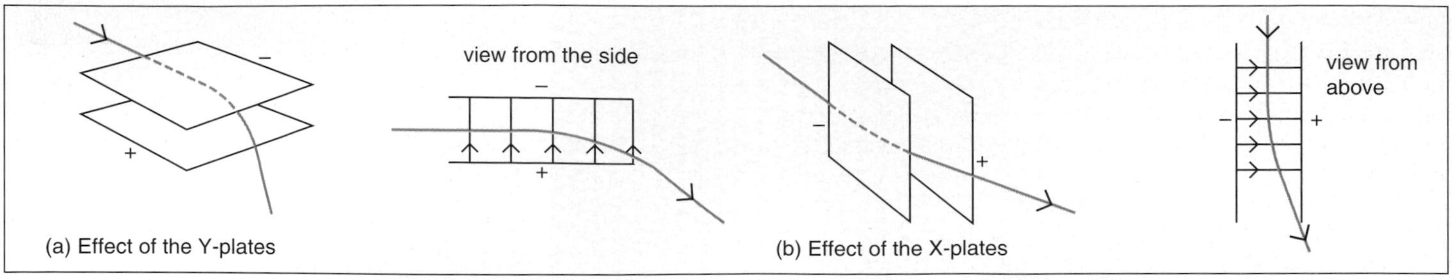

Picture 7 Using electric fields to control beam direction.

an alternating voltage it makes the beam move up and down. This is because the top plate becomes alternately positive and negative. When this plate is positive the electrons are pulled up. When it is negative they are pushed down.

This up and down movement is very fast, because the mains supply changes direction 50 times a second. If the time-base is switched off we see a straight vertical line. This is because the line is being traced, over and over again, 50 times a second.

But if we use the time-base, set to the correct speed, we see a wavy line which shows us how the voltage is changing with time. This is made visible because the beam is being moved sideways at a steady rate (see picture 8).

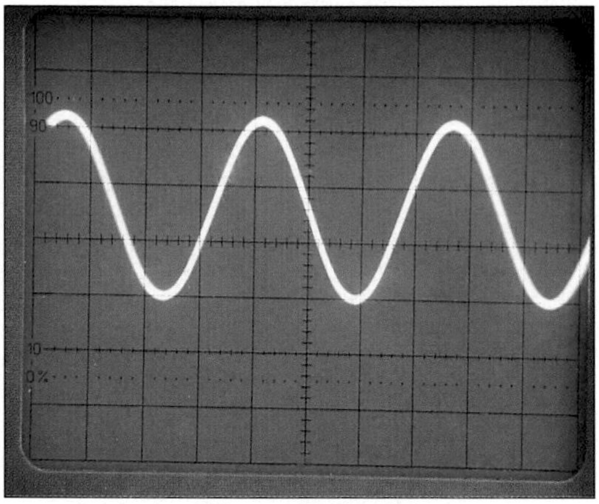

Picture 8 A combination of up and down and sideways movement can draw out a graph.

X-rays

X-rays are yet another example of a scientific discovery made by accident. A German physicist, Wilhelm Konrad Röntgen, was investigating electron streams when he noticed that an unused phosphor screen was glowing. The strange thing was that it was on the other side of the lab. It was much too far away for any 'leakage' of electrons to get to it through the air.

Röntgen brought the screen closer and found that it glowed even brighter. After testing further he proved that the glow wasn't being caused by electrons but by an unknown kind of radiation. Because he didn't know what it was he called them 'X' rays.

Röntgen worked out that the X-rays are produced when a fast stream of electrons hits glass or metal (picture 9).

Then he discovered the most interesting property of X-rays. When he put his hand in the path of the rays he saw that they cast a shadow on the screen. The shadow of his hand was a very strange one. *It showed the bones as well as the flesh* (picture 10).

Within a few weeks of this discovery in 1895, X-rays were being used in hospitals to look for broken bones, swallowed pins, blocked intestines and

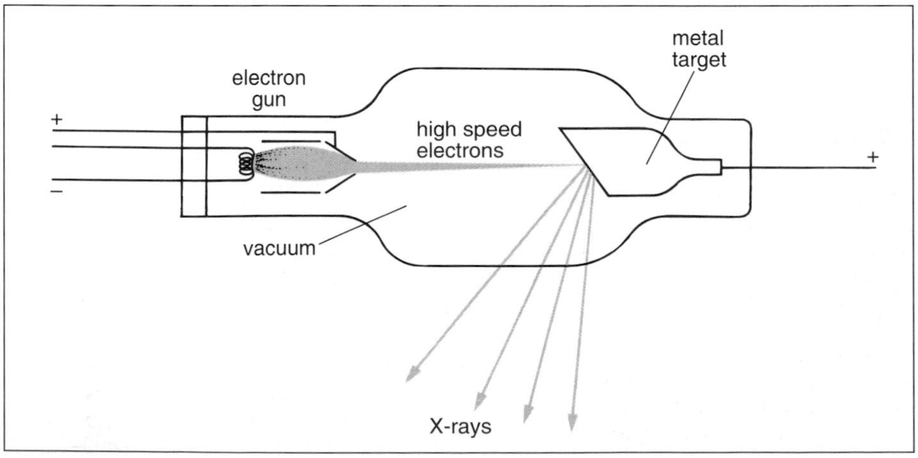

Picture 9 An X-ray tube. The faster the electrons, the more penetrating the X-rays produced.

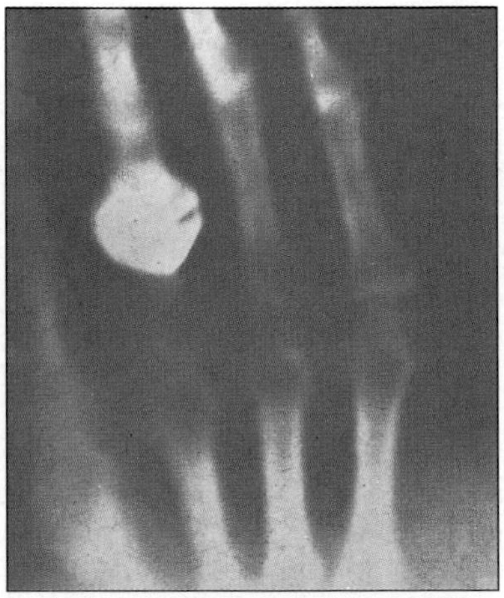

Picture 10 An X-ray shadowgraph of Mrs Röntgen's hand.

damaged lungs. But just as with static electricity 200 years earlier, some people went mad about X-rays. They had 'skeleton pictures' taken of themselves and their families. They tried to use them to cure all kinds of diseases.

It took twenty years for doctors to notice that people who used (and misused) X-ray machines tended to get serious cancers. X-rays are invisible, highly energetic electromagnetic waves. These waves interact with matter and ionise atoms. They thus kill the delicate cells of living matter. But they can also alter the cells, making them turn into cancer cells. All ionising radiation, such as that given out by radioactive materials, can do this.

We know now how to manage X-rays so that the 'dose' given to people is as small as possible. Nurses and technicians who operate the machines are well shielded from them (picture 11). X-rays are only used on people when it is medically necessary, after carefully weighing up the balance between harm and benefit.

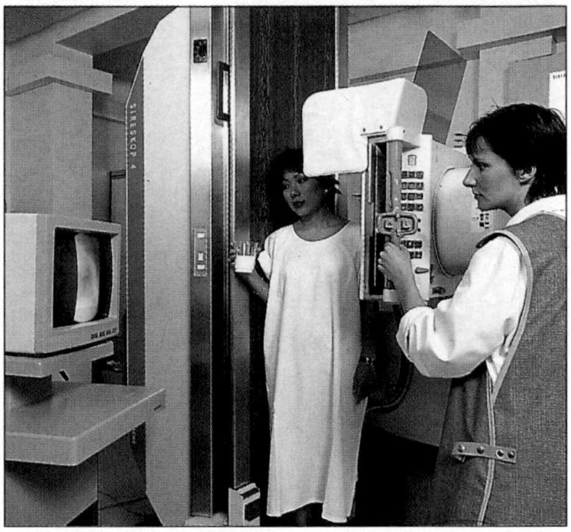

Picture 11 A modern X-ray machine in use.

Activities

A Moving electron streams

Electron streams are used in TV sets and in cathode ray oscilloscopes such as the ones used in your lab. Find out what other devices use electron streams in this kind of way. Write a sentence or two about each device that describes or explains what the device is used for.

B Using a cathode ray oscilloscope

1 Look at the control knobs and switches on the front of the CRO. Find the following: on-off switch, focus, brightness, X shift, Y shift, time-base.

2 *Find the spot!*

Switch on the oscilloscope. The most difficult part now follows – find the spot! If you are lucky you will see a spot or line already on the screen. If not, switch the **time-base** off (or to EXT X), turn the **brightness** to the right to give maximum, and use the X SHIFT and Y SHIFT together to try to get a spot of light in the centre of the screen. Use a combination of FOCUS and BRIGHTNESS control to make the spot small, clear but not too bright. If you can't find it ask for help.

3 *What does a CRO measure?*

Find the Y INPUT. Use the red connection (it may be marked 'dc' or '+') and connect one 1.5 V cell between it and the **earth connection** (marked '–' or '⏚'). If nothing happens to the spot of light try adjusting the control marked Y GAIN (or 'Y amplitude')

What happens when you (a) reverse the cell connections, (b) use more than one cell? What does this investigation tell you about what a CRO measures?

4 Using the time-base

First, remove the batteries you used in part 3 and replace them with an ac supply at about 2 or 3 V. Draw what you see on the screen. Use the X SHIFT to move the spot sideways fairly quickly. Do this once or twice and remember what effect it has. Then find the TIME BASE control and switch it on. Try it at slow, medium and fast. Use the VARIABLE control. The idea is to get a clear, fixed trace of the ac supply on the screen (see picture 8).

5 Try 'looking at' the dc output of the supply. How is it different from the dc from a battery that you looked at in 3?

6 If you have time, connect a microphone to the CRO and talk, whistle, play music or sing into it. You may need to adjust the TIME BASE and/or the Y GAIN to get a clear trace.

Questions

1 What is a **vacuum**? Why does a TV tube need to have a good vacuum inside it?

2 Explain briefly how an 'electron gun' works.

3 Draw diagrams to show how electrons would move in the fields given in picture 12 (look at picture 7 to help you).

4 Picture 13 shows a CRO screen with the voltage of a 50 Hz ac mains supply displayed on it. Draw diagrams to show what the trace on the screen would be like if: (a) the time-base were to be switched off, (b) the time-base speed were to be halved.

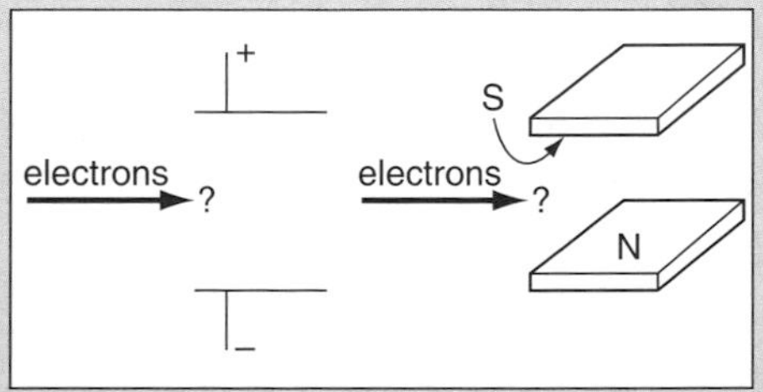

Picture 12

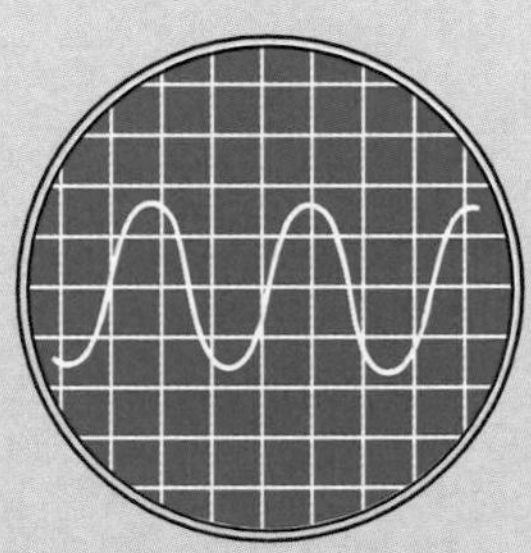

Picture 13

5 Why are X-rays dangerous?

6 X-rays are used in hospitals to look at broken limbs and other parts of the body. Apart from this medical use, what else are X-rays useful for?

F1
The dynamic Earth

The structure of the Earth.

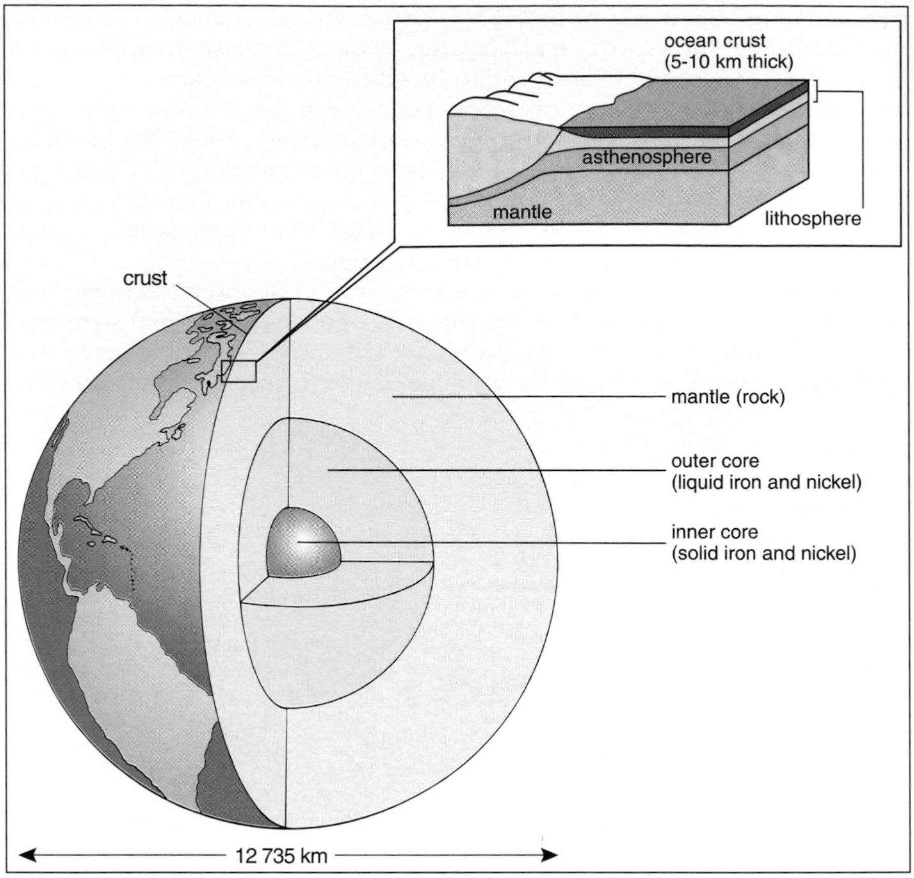

Picture 1 The layered structure of the Earth.

Earthquake waves

The Earth has a layered structure (picture 1). We live on the topmost layer – the **crust** – which is made of solid rock. Compared to the Earth as a whole, the crust is thinner than the skin on an apple. At most it is 70 km thick. Compare this with the diameter of the Earth, which is about 12 735 km. Yet no-one has been able to drill into the crust for more than 14 km – a mere scratch on the surface. So how have scientists been able to discover what lies beneath the crust, to discover the structure of the Earth and what it is made of?

Using earthquake waves

The shock waves from earthquakes are recorded at **seismic stations** all over the world. (Seismic stations are places that detect and measure earthquake waves.) Their records have provided us with the bulk of the clues about the structure of the Earth. These waves are rather like sound waves – and just as

Picture 2

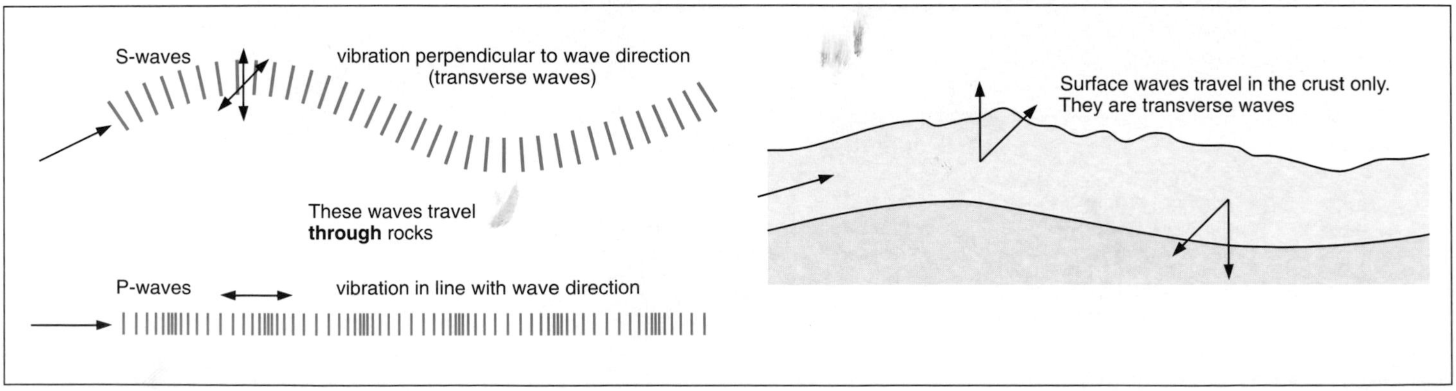

scientists can 'see' what is inside the body with ultrasound, so geologists can 'see' inside the Earth with earthquake waves.

Earthquakes are caused by the movement of rock in the Earth's crust or in the upper part of the mantle. They may occur quite close to the surface or several kilometres below. The nearer an earthquake is to the surface the more damage it is likely to cause. The other main factor is the energy released as the rocks move. The energy is released as shock waves that travel through the rocks. Earthquake damage is caused by the shock waves that reach the part of the Earth's surface closest to the site of the earthquake.

Earthquake waves, called **seismic** waves, are of three types:

- **P-waves** – which are *push–pull* (longitudinal) waves in which rocks vibrate to-and-fro in the direction of travel of the wave,
- **S-waves** – which are *sideways* (transverse) waves in which the rocks move up and down and/or side to side at right angles to the direction of travel,
- **surface waves** – which are more slowly moving waves, consisting of sideways movement of crustal rocks.

Picture 2 shows these three types of wave. Picture 3 shows how these three waves reach a seismic station.

P-waves cause most of the damage to buildings. A tall building can move up and down and still stay in contact with its foundations – think of going up and down in a lift. But a sideways wave can move the foundations more quickly than the building can follow them – think of what happens when you are standing up in a train which suddenly brakes. The building may be torn away from its foundations and collapse.

P- and S-waves travel large distances through rocks, although they rapidly become weaker with distance and can then only be detected by sensitive instruments called **seismometers**. These are very simple instruments in principle, consisting of a large mass of metal suspended on springs. When the Earth below moves, the heavy mass stays still. A pen attached to the mass traces a wavy line on to a sheet of paper which is of course attached to the quaking Earth. The paper is drawn along by a motor so that the sideways motion is drawn out into a wavy line – a *seismogram* (pictures 4 and 5).

The speed of seismic waves has been measured – and indeed can be predicted from the properties of the ordinary rocks in the Earth's crust. P- and S-waves travel at different speeds and the difference in their times of arrival can be used to calculate how far away the earthquake occurred. Thus data from a set of seismographs at different places on the surface can be used to work out the exact site of an earthquake – its **focus**.

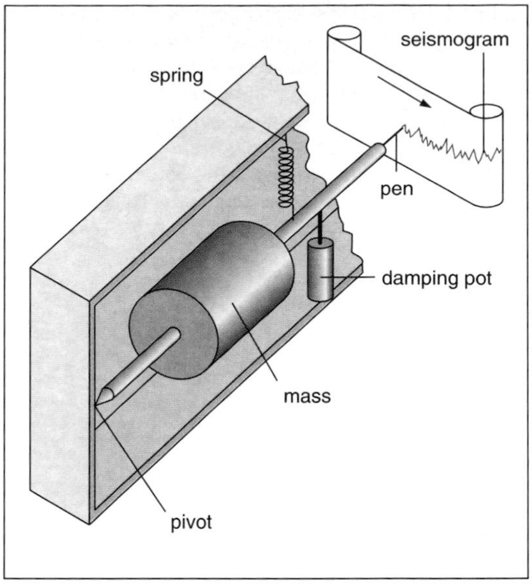

Picture 4 The principle of a seismometer.

Picture 5 A seismogram.

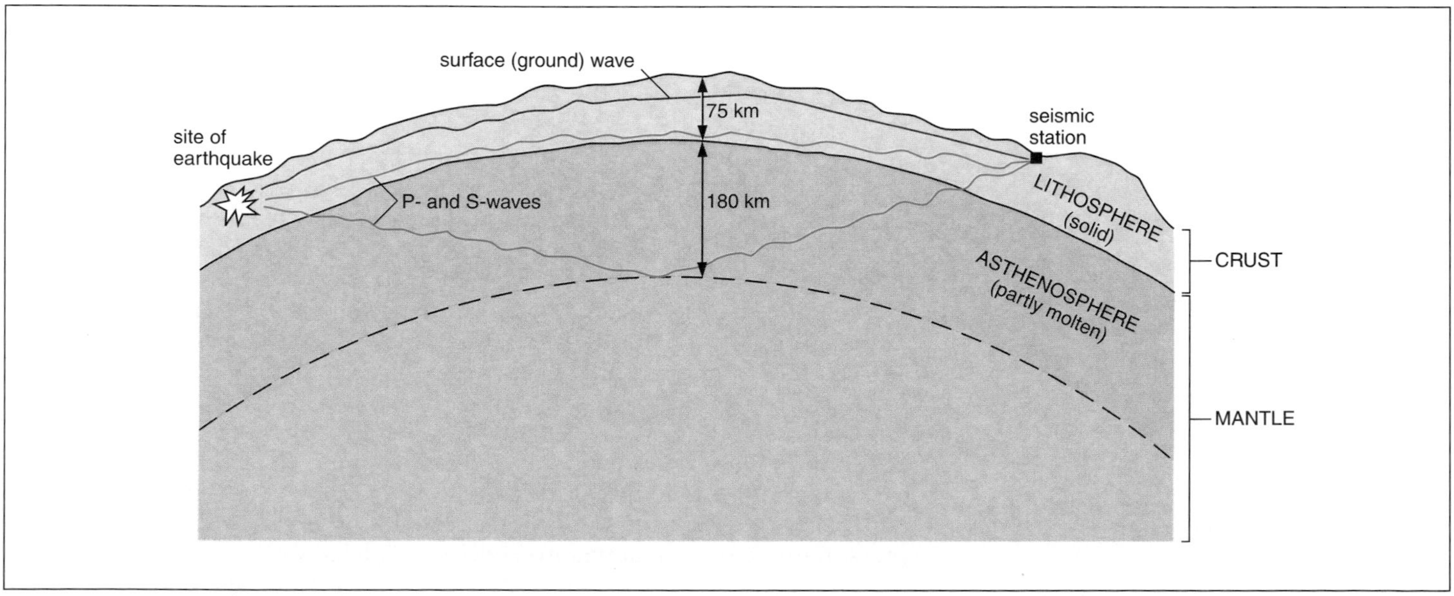

Picture 3 Seismic waves in the crust.

Picture 6 Notice that the waves travel in curved paths. This is because they are being refracted. Waves refract (change direction) when they move into a medium in which they travel at a different speed. (See page 81.) In this case the waves travel more quickly the deeper they go. This is because the deeper rocks are squashed and are therefore more dense.

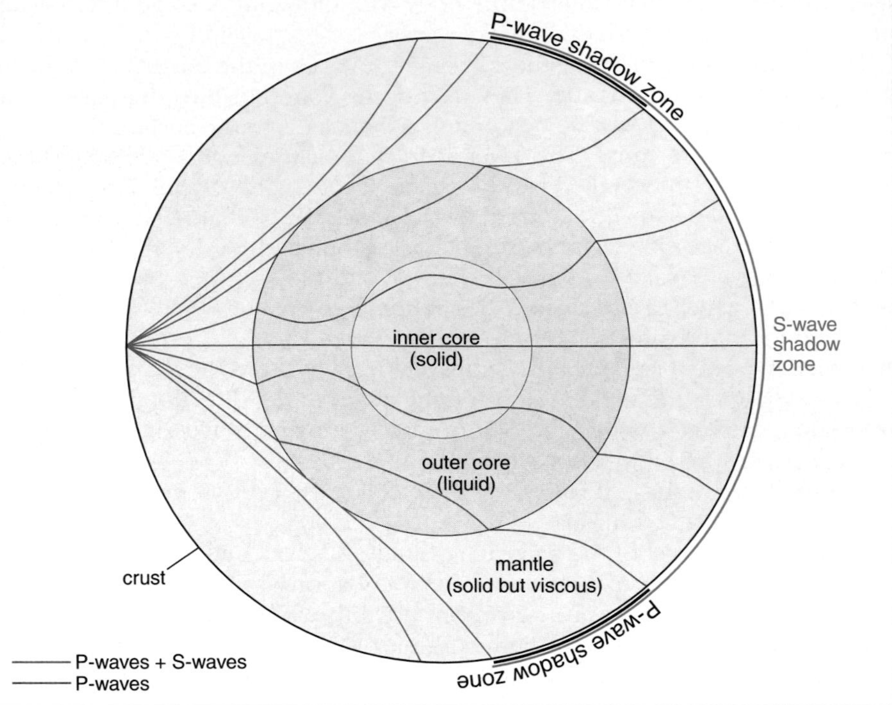

Probing deep Earth with seismic waves

The crust of the Earth is made of solid rocks and varies in thickness from 6 km to about 70 km. It is thickest under the continents. The region below the crust is called the **mantle**, which is 2900 km thick with temperatures ranging from 1500 to 3000 K. The crustal rocks are made of compounds of silicon, aluminium and magnesium with small quantities of other elements. The crust and upper layer of the mantle together form the **lithosphere**, which consists of mostly solid interlocking plates (**tectonic** plates) which move around very slowly on the Earth's surface. The lithosphere is up to 100 km thick. The lower mantle is a solid but is hot enough to behave as a very viscous liquid. This means that slow convection currents occur in the mantle which provide the forces to move the lithosphere plates across the more liquid asthenosphere, which acts as a lubricant (picture 7). Earthquakes occur as moving plates tear past each other, sometimes moving sideways, sometimes one dipping under the other.

Seismometers are sensitive enough to pick up seismic waves that have travelled from one side of the Earth to the other. Picture 5 shows typical paths for P- and S-waves. The waves change direction because they are *refracted*, like light waves going from one medium to another. A great deal of careful analysis was needed to identify the depth at which the waves change speed. These depths show where the properties of the rocks change, and that the Earth is indeed made up of layers as shown in picture 1. The calculations from wave speeds tells us what the various layers are made of.

There is a shadow zone for S-waves directly opposite the earthquake focus. This suggests that the Earth has a liquid centre. P-waves are like sound waves, and can travel through both solids and liquids. But liquids cannot 'bend' – so cannot carry sideways waves. A liquid core would thus stop the S-waves. The temperature in the core is over 6000 K, which is enough to melt iron even at the enormous pressures of over a million times atmospheric pressure. But only the outer core is a liquid. Although the inner core at the very centre of the Earth is hotter than the outer core pressure increases with depth and the pressure there is so great that iron becomes solid again.

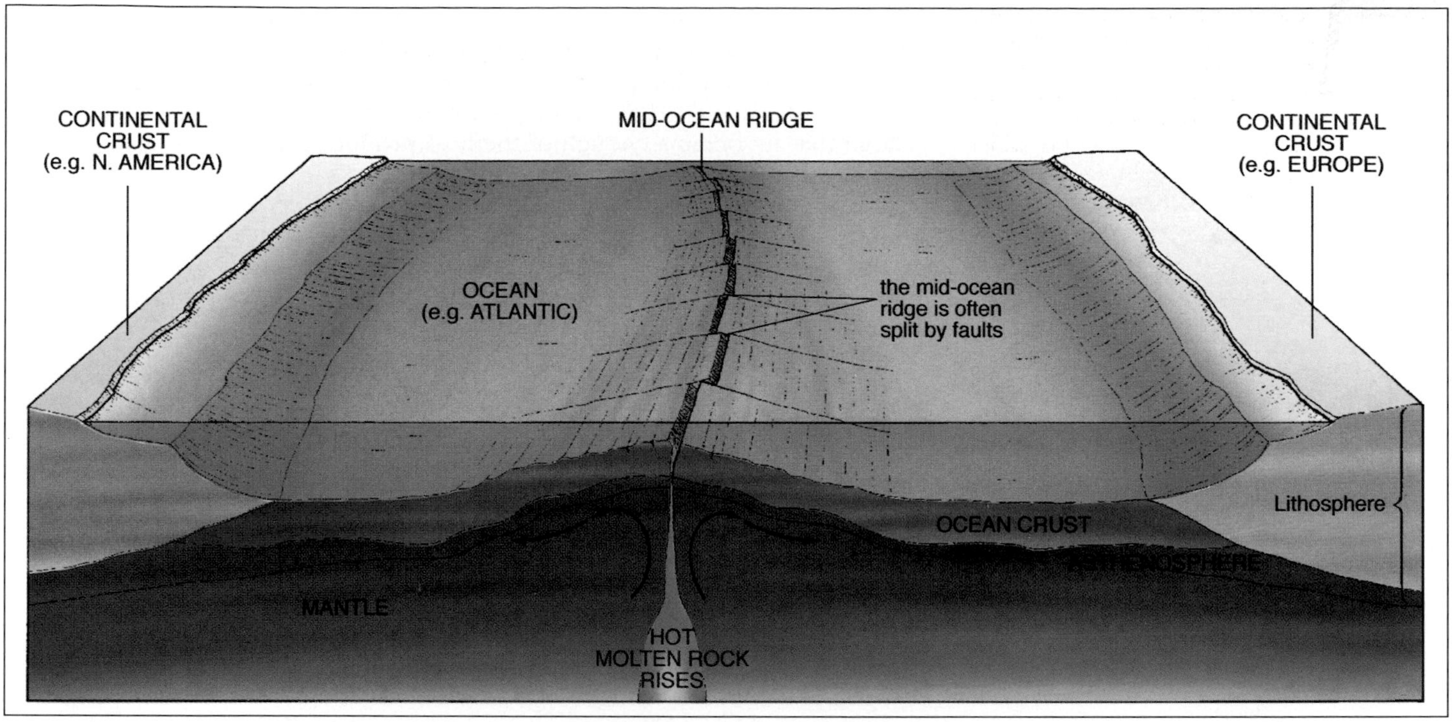

Picture 7 Convection currents and plate motion. The currents are pulling the crust apart at the mid-ocean ridge.

Density

Density measurements also give clues about the Earth's interior. The mass of the Earth has been measured using Newton's Law of Gravity (see page 49). We also know its volume so we can calculate that the mean density of the Earth is 5500 kg/m^3. However, the density of crustal rocks is on average 2800 kg/m^3. The speed of seismic waves depends on the density of the rock they travel through, and the speed measurements show that the mantle has an average density of 4500 kg/m^3 and the core density is as high as 10 720 kg/m^3. With such a high density the core can only be made of metal. The evidence suggests that it is a mixture of iron and nickel. The mantle is a mixture of compounds, mostly metal oxides and silicates.

Evidence from inner and outer space

Lumps of rock

We do have some more direct evidence about what the inside of the Earth is like. Sometimes lumps of rock from deep in the Earth's mantle are found in the lava from volcanoes. Even rocks from space – **meteorites** – give us clues. It is likely that the Earth was formed at the same time as meteorites such as these. (See topic F4.)

The materials of the Earth seem to become denser the deeper you go. So there are light gases in the atmosphere, water in the oceans, relatively light rocks in the crust, dense rocks in the mantle and very dense metals in the core.

Why is the inside of the Earth so hot?

One of the reasons that the deep interior of the Earth is so hot is that the Earth formed at a very high temperature (see topic F4). Because the inside is **insulated** by the outer layers some of this original thermal energy is still 'trapped' inside.

Also, some of the 92 elements of the Earth are unstable. They are the **radioactive** elements (see topic D5). The nuclei of such elements (mainly uranium, thorium and potassium) break up, giving out energy as they change into smaller nuclei. These elements are, in fact, quite rare, but the Earth is so large that it contains enough of them to produce huge quantities of energy. Some of these elements are found in crustal rocks.

This energy keeps the Earth hot inside, and every day 2.5 billion billion joules (or 2.5 exajoules) of energy escape from the Earth's surface to help heat the air. This is about four times as much as the energy used by all the people on the Earth.

Convection currents in the mantle

Energy flows from the hottest part of the Earth, the core, outwards to the surface. This energy travels in two ways: by **conduction** and by **convection**. Convection is by far the most important as it means that semi-molten material rises and falls in the mantle, creating the effects of plate tectonics described next.

Plate tectonics

As a result of the convection currents in the mantle the Earth's crust has been broken up into large areas called **tectonic plates** (picture 8). These plates fit together in a spherical jigsaw pattern but move against each other. It is this movement that is the main cause of earthquakes. Picture 8 shows the main tectonic plates and also the places on Earth where earthquakes occur most often. These are also the places which show the most volcanic activity.

The main zones of seismic and volcanic activity are at the plate boundaries or **margins**.

Picture 8 The Earth's plates showing the position of the continents and areas of major seismic activity.

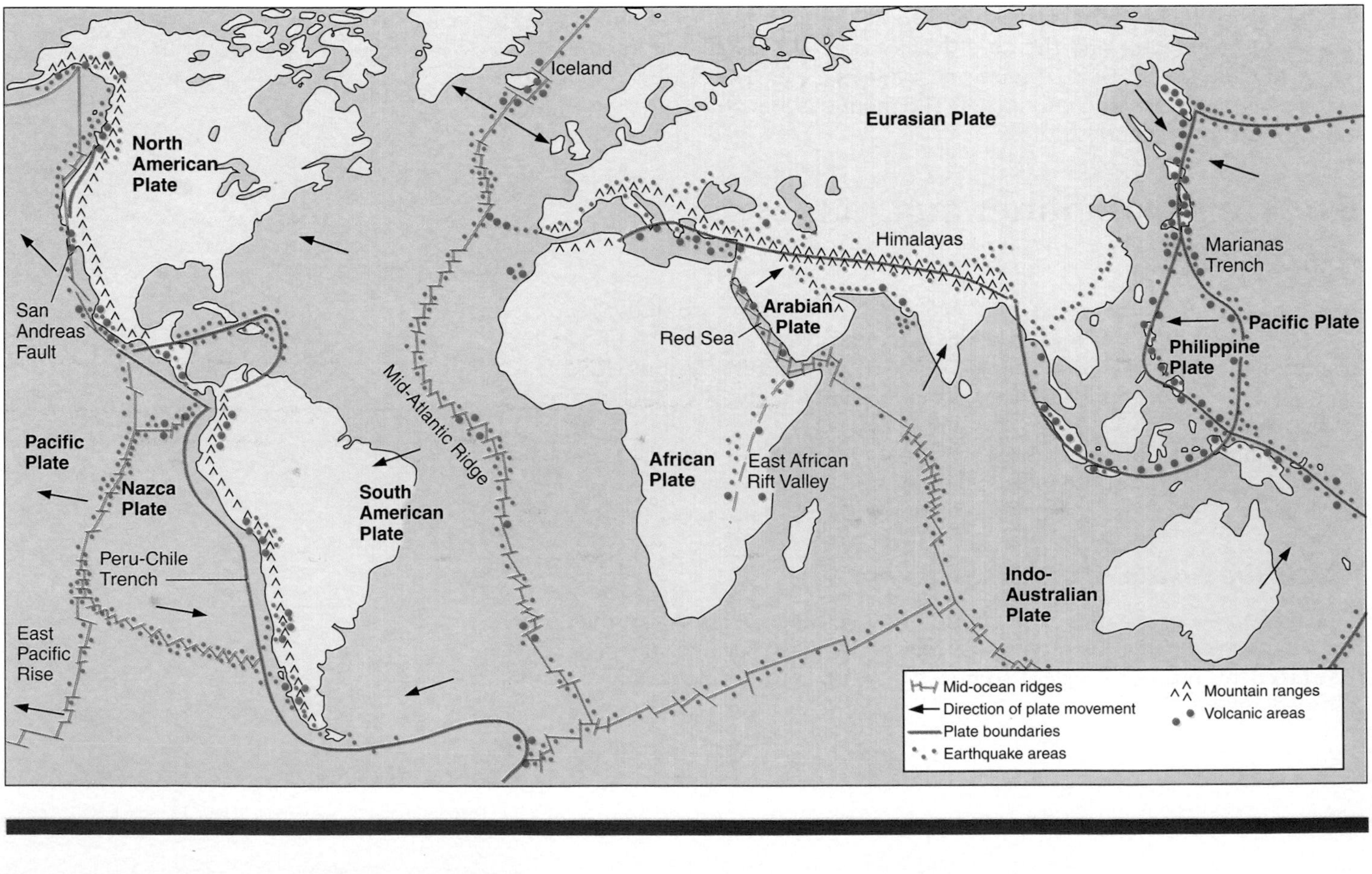

Activities

A Using porridge to model convection currents in the mantle

Fill a beaker with made-up porridge and put it over a bunsen flame. Put a few drops of food colouring in the centre. After a while you should be able to see the colouring being carried round in convection currents. Eventually a skin will form on top – this represents the crust. This crust will be 'subducted' at the edges of the beaker where the current moves downwards.

CARE! Stop heating when this happens and remember that under the crust the porridge will be very hot – just like the Earth.

B How did the Earth become layered?

Put the following in a test tube: about 10 ml cooking oil, 10 ml golden syrup, a couple of spatula-fulls of iron filings. Put a cork in the top and shake vigorously. Leave it to settle. Use the results you observe to make a hypothesis about how the Earth gained its layered structure.

You could then compare what you think with the theories of the Earth's formation outlined in topic F4. How accurate is the model of the layered Earth in this experiment? What are its shortcomings?

Questions

1 No-one has ever been deeper than 14 km into the Earth. How, then, do we seem to know so much about its inside?

2 The diameter of the Earth is 12 735 km. P-waves travel through the Earth at an average speed of 5.6 km/s.

a How long does it take P-waves to travel directly across the Earth to a place directly opposite the earthquake site?

b Why can't S-waves travel the same route as the P-waves in (a)?

c A seismic station records the arrival of P-waves at 12.00 noon. S-waves from the earthquake arrive 16 s later. The mean speeds of P- and S- waves in crustal rocks are 5.6 km/s and 3.6 km/s respectively. Show (i) that the earthquake occurred about 30 s before noon (ii) that the focus was about 160 km from the seismic station.

F2
Sky patterns

The stars are fixed in their constellations. We learn about the Solar System by studying the movements of the Sun, the Moon and the planets against the background of the fixed stars.

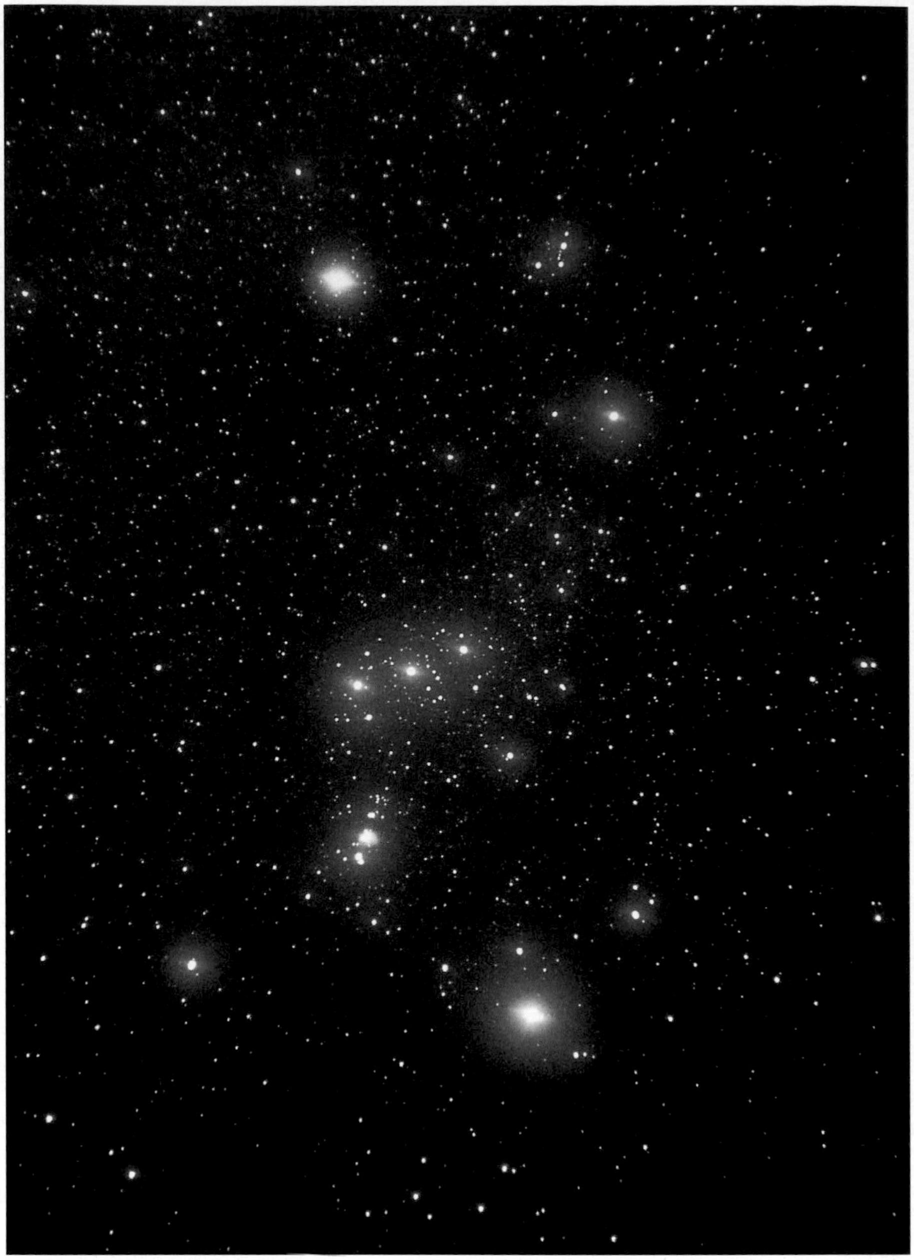

Picture 1 Orion is one of the easiest constellations to find.

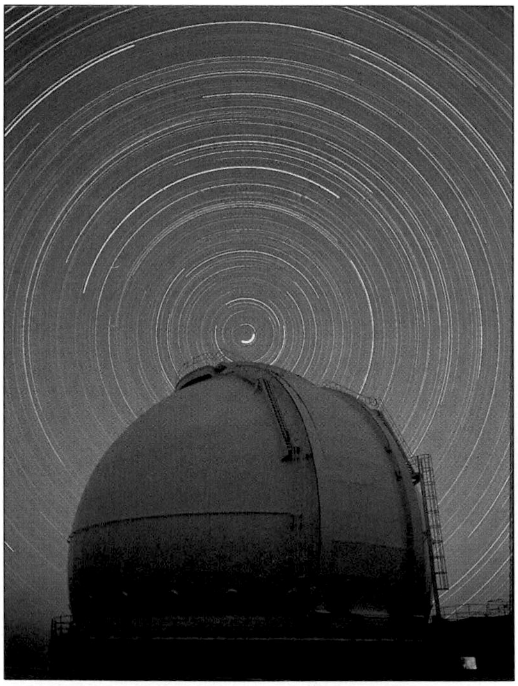

Picture 2 The Pole star makes a circle around the Celestial Pole. This picture was taken over several hours using a camera pointing at the Pole Star.

Star patterns

On a clear starry night you might be able to see 5000 stars, if you have good eyesight. To make sense of them star watchers many years ago arranged them into groups – the **constellations**. Picture 1 shows the constellation called **Orion**. Many of the constellations are named after Ancient Greek heroes or heroines. Orion is named after a Greek hero who was a mighty hunter.

You can see Orion from autumn to spring, in the southern sky. If you look at it every hour or so in the winter you will notice that it moves from east to west. You will see other stars rising in the east, like the Sun, and setting in the west.

All the stars follow this same pattern of movement. But if they are high enough in the sky they never rise or set. Instead they circle around a fixed point in the northern sky (see picture 2). Close to this point is a star, called the **Pole Star**, or **Polaris**. Picture 3 shows how to find this star by using the two 'pointer' stars in the constellation of the **Plough** (**Ursa Major**).

The Pole Star is directly above the North Pole of the Earth, and so it is very useful in navigation. As you may remember from earlier work, this movement

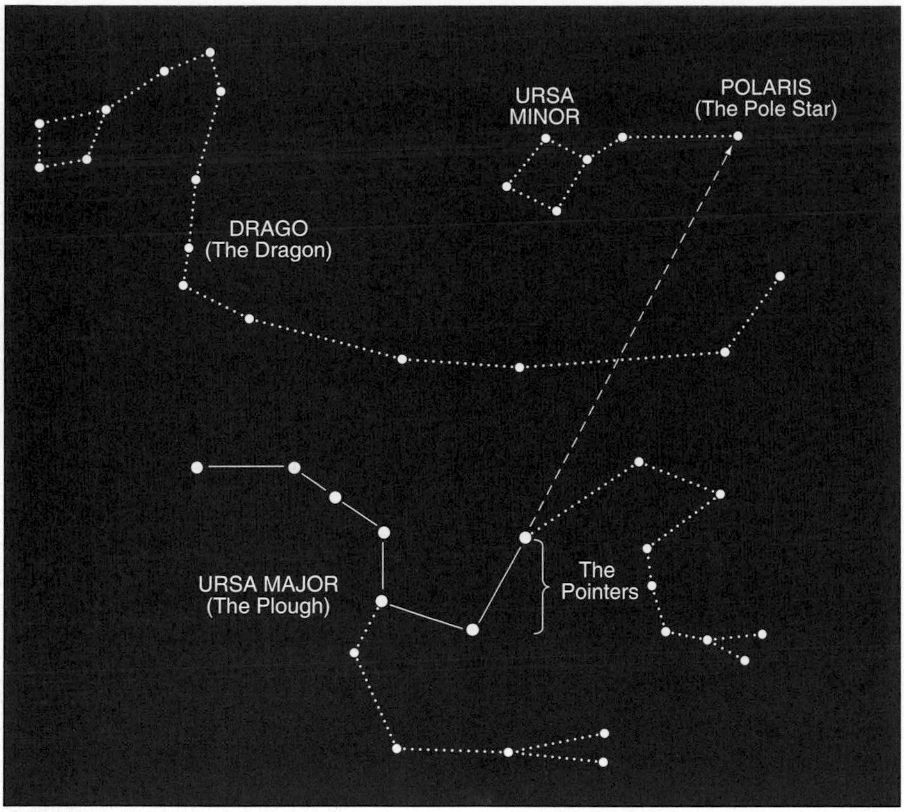

Picture 3 How to find the Pole Star.

Picture 4 The Moon seems to change its shape, 'waxing and waning'.

of the stars across the sky is caused by the fact that the Earth is spinning on its axis.

The Earth spins on its axis once every 24 hours, and as we move under the stars they seem to be passing overhead. It is this spinning of the Earth that causes the Sun to rise and set.

The Moon

The Moon, too, rises and sets. But it also changes shape to give the **phases** of the Moon (picture 4). The rising and setting is because of the spinning of the Earth. Its changing shape is caused by the fact that the Moon actually does move on its own. It is a **satellite** of the Earth. One complete orbit of the Moon around the Earth takes a little over 27 days. As the Earth orbits the Sun at the same time, the time from one full moon to the next is 29.5 days.

This is shown in picture 5, which also explains how its shape appears to change. What we see is only the part of the Moon that is in sunlight.

Because it moves on its own, the Moon doesn't keep pace with the stars. If you look at the Moon at the same time every night you will see it in a slightly different part of the sky each night. It seems to slip back against the constellations.

The stars are further away from us than the Moon is. We can tell this because as the Moon moves through the star patterns it cuts them off. We never see stars in front of the Moon.

But the Moon also moves in front of the Sun. When this happens the sunlight is cut off. We then have an **eclipse** of the Sun, or **solar eclipse**. It can only happen when the Moon is 'new', lying directly between us and the Sun.

Sometimes the full Moon gets dark. This happens when the Moon is in the Earth's shadow, so we have an eclipse of the Moon, or **lunar eclipse**. Picture 6 shows how these eclipses are produced.

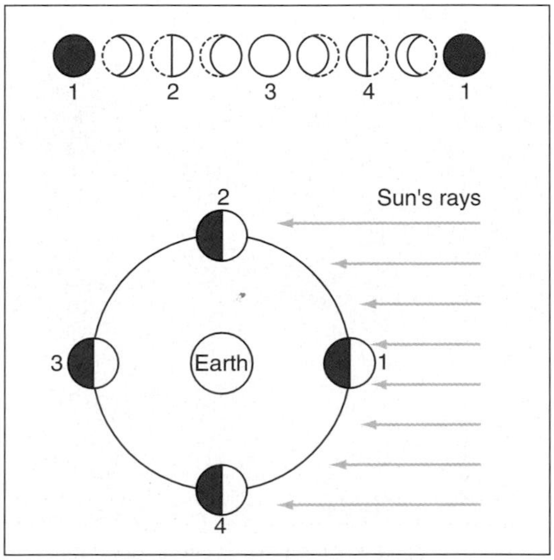

Picture 5 Why the Moon changes its shape: the phases of the Moon.

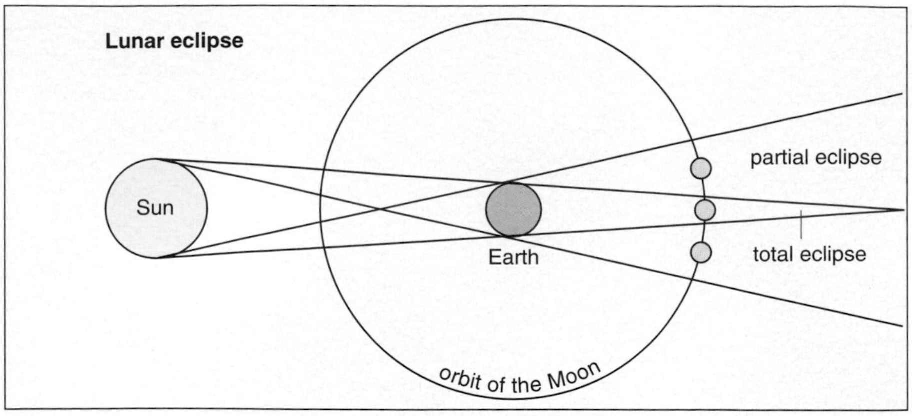

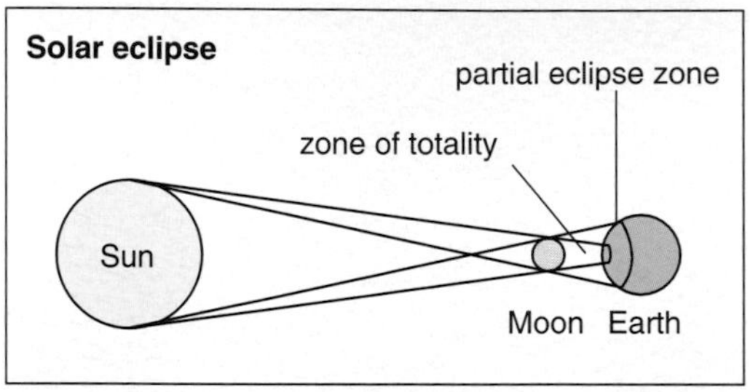

Picture 6 Eclipses of the Sun and the Moon.

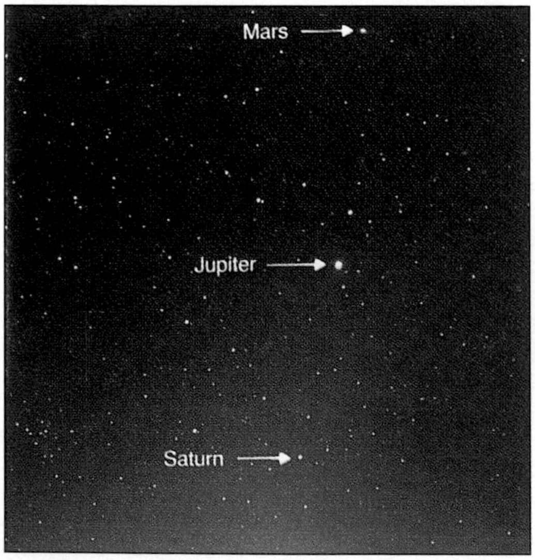

Picture 7 The two planets look close together but Jupiter is much further away from us than Mars.

The planets

The planets look like stars but they are in fact very different. They are much smaller than stars, and do not shine by their own light. We can only see them because they reflect the light of the Sun.

They were first noticed in ancient times. Like the stars, they rise and set. But careful starwatchers picked them out because they also move against the background of the ordinary 'fixed' stars.

The ancient astronomers discovered five of these 'wandering stars'. We still call them by Roman versions of the names given to them by the Ancient Greeks, who named them after their gods: Mercury, Venus, Mars, Jupiter and Saturn.

The easiest ones to see are Jupiter, Venus and Mars. Mars and Venus are easy to see because they are the planets closest to Earth. Jupiter is a lot further away but it is the biggest planet of all. We now know that there are three more planets: Uranus, Neptune and Pluto (which was only discovered in 1934).

Uranus and Neptune are visible to the naked eye, but quite hard to find unless you are an experienced observer. Mercury is very close to the Sun and you can see it best just before dawn – if you know exactly when and where to look.

The zodiac

The Sun, Moon and planets all seem to move across the sky through a belt of stars called the **zodiac**. The stars in the zodiac are grouped into twelve constellations – the 'signs of the zodiac'. You will recognise their names because they are often listed as 'birth signs' in newspapers and magazines in their astrology columns.

Don't confuse *astrologers* with *astronomers*. Astronomers observe and measure the positions and properties of stars and they are very accurate. Astrologers claim that they can predict people's future and personality from the positions of the stars and planets. But they get it wrong about as often as they get it right.

Your 'birth sign' is decided by where in the zodiac the Sun was when you were born. If you were born on 12 June, for example, you are a 'Gemini'. At this time the Sun is between us and the constellation of the **Twins** (**Gemini**). Picture 8 shows the zodiac and the Sun's position at this time.

The Milky Way

The Milky Way is the part of the sky where stars are most crowded together. It can be seen all through the year. It is a wide band of stars that runs through the constellation of Cassiopeia, which never sets. In the winter it is close to Gemini and Orion, and in summer it is a splendid sight as it crosses the sky from Cygnus to Scorpio.

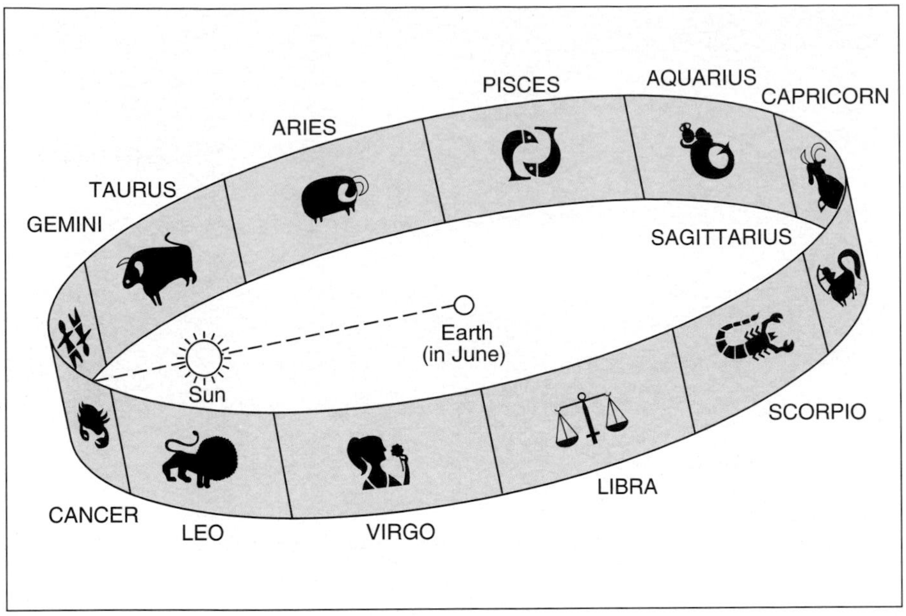

Picture 8 As the Earth goes around the Sun, the Sun appears to move against the background of the stars. The star groups it moves in front of are called the signs of the zodiac.

Look at any part of the Milky Way through a small telescope or pair of binoculars. What to the naked eye looks like a faint whitish blur becomes a mass of stars. Find out more about the Milky Way in topic F5.

Questions

1 Give two differences between stars and planets.

2 Explain what the following words mean:

zodiac, eclipse, orbit, astronomy, astrology, planet, star, lunar, satellite.

3 The Moon goes around the Earth once every 28 days or so. Why don't we get eclipses of the Sun and Moon every month?

4 We don't get eclipses of the Sun when the Moon is a 'half' moon. Explain why not.

5 Your young brother refuses to believe that the Earth is round. 'It looks pretty flat to me', he says.

What would you say to him, or show him, to prove that the Earth isn't 'flat'?

Activities

A Looking for the constellations

Use a simple star map. These are published every month by some newspapers *(The Times, The Guardian, The Daily Telegraph, The Independent)* and you should be able to get a photocopy from your library. The best time of the year is when it gets dark fairly early (autumn to spring). Choose a moonless night. Try to find the following constellations: Plough (Great Bear), Cassiopeia, Gemini, Leo, Cygnus, the Pleiades, Orion, Perseus with Andromeda and the Great Square of Pegasus.

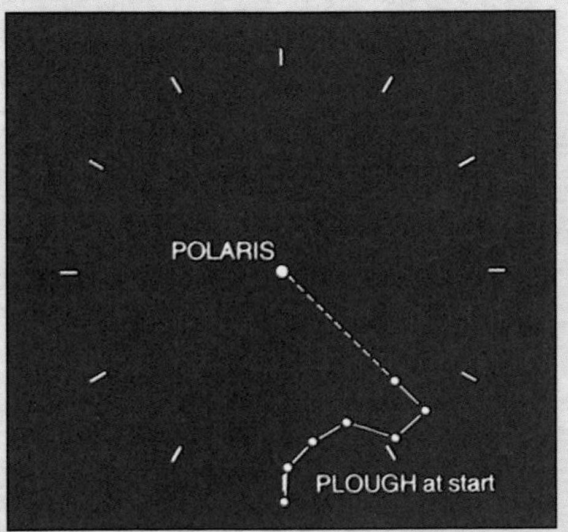

Picture 9 How do the stars move during the night?

B Do the stars move?

Draw or photograph the positions of stars near the Pole Star.

1 Drawing: find the Plough and mark its position on a 'clock diagram' (picture 9) at, say, 7 pm. Mark its position every half hour until 10 pm.

2 Taking a photograph: you need a camera with a 'B' button that lets you keep the shutter open as long as you want. Put the camera on a firm surface pointing at the Pole Star. Open the shutter and leave it open for an hour or so. It is important not to move the camera. Make sure that there aren't any bright lights nearby.

C The Moon

1 Use a telescope or a good pair of binoculars to look at the Moon. The best time is when the Moon is between 'half' and 'full'. Can you see the 'mountains'? Draw what you can see as carefully as possible. A good encyclopaedia will have a 'Moon Map' you can use to identify the main features. Try your school library.

2 Draw the shape and position of the Moon (compared with the star patterns) every night for a week – or every other night for a fortnight.

D Looking for planets

Use a newspaper map (see activity A) to find some planets. Draw where they are compared to nearby stars. Do this for a week or two. Comment on what you notice.

E The Milky Way

Use a small telescope or a pair of binoculars to look at the Milky Way. Describe what you see. What does this tell us about what the Milky Way might be?

F3
Patterns in space

The Sun, Earth and planets are part of a pattern in space called the Solar System.

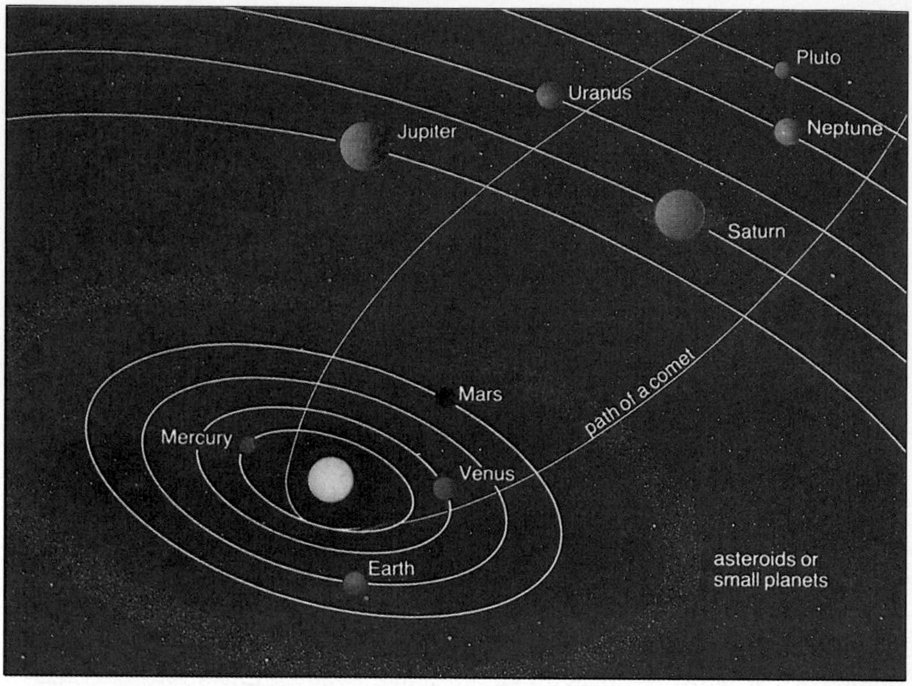

Picture 1 The Solar System. It is not drawn to scale because the outer planets are so far away from the Sun compared with the inner ones.

The Solar System

The Sun is the centre of the Solar System. It contains 99.8% of all the mass in the System, and so produces a huge gravity field that holds the planets in their orbits around it (see topic B6). Picture 1 shows the Sun and the planets, viewed from outside the System. The actual masses and distances of the planets from the Sun are given in table 1.

The Sun

The Sun is a star. It is quite a small one, as stars go, and it isn't very bright. It is the brightest object in the sky because it is so close to us, compared with other stars. The energy it provides supports all life on Earth. This energy comes from the Sun's own mass, which it uses up at a rate of 4 million tonnes per second.

The Sun emits energy at the rate of 400 000 000 000 000 000 000 000 000 watts (4×10^{26} W). Only a tiny fraction of this energy reaches Earth. Most is radiated into empty space.

Question 6 is about using the Einstein equation $\boldsymbol{E = mc^2}$ to check these amazing figures.

The energy is produced by a process called **nuclear fusion** (see topic D7). The Sun is mostly hydrogen. Hydrogen nuclei in the centre of the Sun are

Table 1 Planetary data.

	Mass (Earth=1)	Diameter (km)	Density (tonnes m³)	Surface gravity field (N/kg)	Distance from Sun (10^9 m)	Period 'year'	'Day'
Mercury	0.05	4 880	5.4	3.7	58	88d	59d
Venus	0.81	12 112	5.25	8.9	107.5	224d	243d
Earth	1.0	12 742	5.51	9.8	149.6	365d	23h 56m
Mars	0.11	6 790	3.95	3.8	228	687d	24h 37m
Jupiter	318.0	142 600	1.34	24.9	778	11.9y	9h 50m
Saturn	95.0	120 200	0.70	10.5	1427	29.5y	10h 14m
Uranus	14.6	49 000	1.27	8.8	2870	84.0y	17h 14m
Neptune	17.2	50 000	1.64	11.2	4497	165y	16h 07m
Pluto system	0.003	2 284	2.0	0.6	5900 (variable)	248y	6.4d

under a huge pressure and at a very high temperature. Some of the hydrogen nuclei collide to form helium nuclei. In doing this they lose a tiny fraction of their mass which is converted to the kinetic energy of the particles that are left.

Picture 2 shows the surface of the Sun. The surface is a gas at a temperature of about 5500 °C, and the picture shows a typical 'Sun storm' in which hot gas is hurled far out into space. These storms reach a peak every eleven years. At times of peak activity the Sun sends out far more ionised particles than usual, which affect our atmosphere and so the weather on Earth.

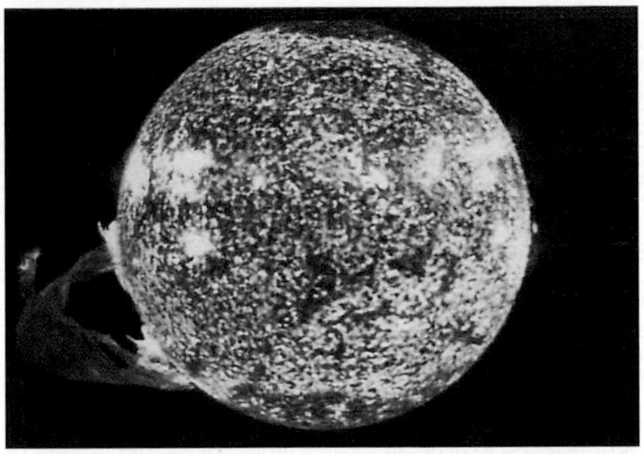

Picture 2 A Sun storm. On the scale of the picture the Earth would be about the size of one of the dark blobs or about half a millimetre across.

The planets

The planets move in orbit around the Sun. They all move in the same direction, which is anticlockwise when viewed from above. The nearer the planet is to the Sun the faster it moves. Thus the orbital speed of Mercury is 55 m/s while Neptune travels at a tenth of that speed, about 5.4 m/s.

Neptune has a larger orbit than Mercury and travels much more slowly. This means that Neptune takes much longer than Mercury to complete its path around the Sun. This orbit time is called the planet's 'year'. A 'year' for Mercury is just over twelve Earth weeks, while Neptune takes 165 Earth years to make one orbit around the Sun.

Mercury is so close to the Sun that its surface is heated up to over 400 °C, which is hot enough to melt tin. It spins on its axis rather slowly, managing to get three spins ('days') for every two orbits ('years') around the sun. It is too small to have an atmosphere.

The next planet out from the Sun is **Venus** (picture 3). It is almost exactly the same size as the Earth and is only a little less massive. You might think it would be a good place to go for a sunshine holiday, but you would be wrong. Its atmosphere is mostly carbon dioxide, so the greenhouse effect is so great that it is even hotter than Mercury, with a surface temperature of 460 °C.

The atmosphere of Venus is very corrosive, containing hydrogen chloride and hydrogen fluoride. No one has seen the surface of Venus, as it is hidden by clouds of concentrated sulphuric acid and particles of pure sulphur. Also, the atmospheric pressure is 95 times what it is on Earth, so that a very well-designed space suit would be needed. When the Russian Venus Probe landed by parachute on the surface of Venus in 1972 it managed to survive for only about 30 minutes in these very nasty conditions.

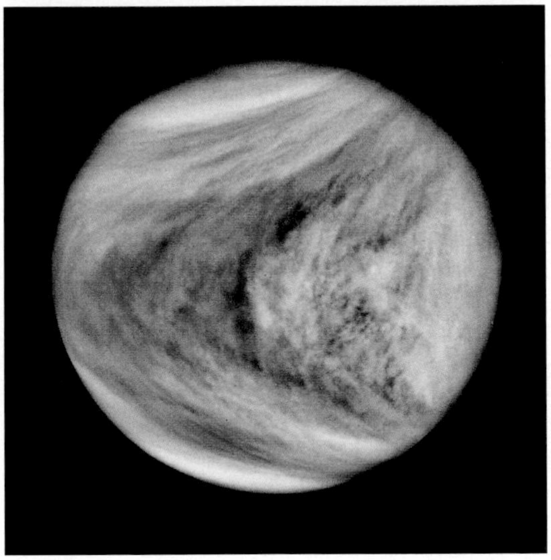

Picture 3 Venus.

Bypassing planet **Earth** we next reach the planet **Mars**. At one time it was thought that Mars could support life. Indeed, a nineteenth-century astronomer was convinced that the markings he could see on its surface were canals. He was wrong; he might have seen lines of craters or dust blown by the wind and used his very vivid imagination!

But spacecraft sent to Mars have taken photographs which seem to show old river beds. It may be that at one time there was enough surface water on Mars to support life. It also looks as if Mars once had volcanoes (picture 4). This suggests an internal source of energy which might have been able to

	Surface temperature (°C)	Number of moons	Atmosphere
Mercury	350	0	None
Venus	460	0	Thick: carbon dioxide, sulphuric acid
Earth	20	1	Nitrogen, oxygen
Mars	−23	2	Thin: carbon dioxide
Jupiter	−120	16, 1 ring	Hydrogen, helium, ammonia, methane
Saturn	−180	17, plus rings	Hydrogen, helium, ammonia, methane
Uranus	−210	15, plus rings	Hydrogen, helium, ammonia, methane
Neptune	−220	8	Hydrogen, helium, methane
Pluto system	−230	1	None – frozen

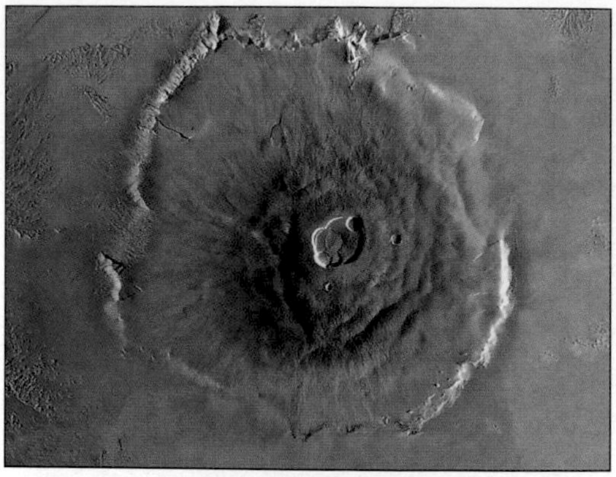

Picture 4 A Martian volcano.

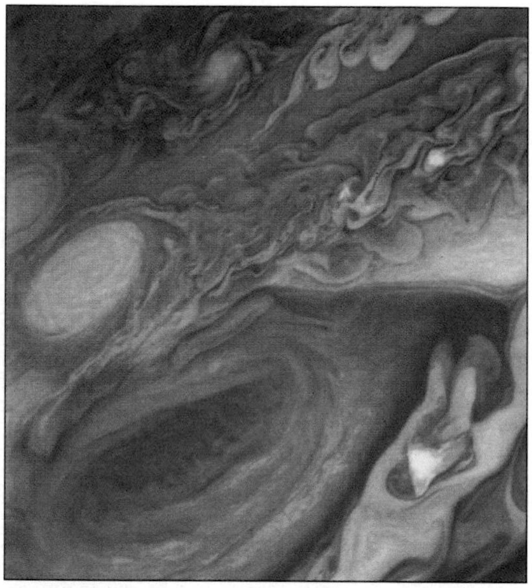

Picture 5 Jupiter's Great Red Spot.

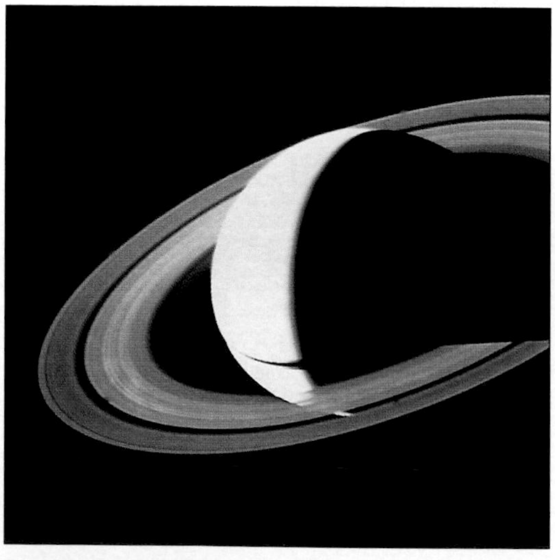

Picture 6 Saturn and its orbiting rings.

support some kind of life. Mars even has an atmosphere, but it is much thinner than the Earth's.

In 1976 the American Viking Spacecraft managed to 'soft-land' probes which were able to take pictures of the Martian surface.

These probes also looked for signs of life. They scooped up some Martian soil and tested it to see if carbon dioxide or any other chemical signs of life were present. The first experiment seemed to give a positive result. But when the experiment was repeated many times no more of the chemicals were detected. Scientists now agree that there is no life on Mars.

Asteroids

Between Mars and the giant planet Jupiter astronomers have discovered hundreds of stony objects. These range in size from the largest (Ceres) which is just over 700 km in diameter to rocks which are less than a few kilometres across. There are probably thousands of others too small to see. These objects should be called *planetoids* (little planets) rather than **asteroids** (little stars).

The asteroids are mostly clustered in their orbits between Mars and Jupiter. But some of them wander away from this region. They climb high above the plane in which the planets move, or have strange orbits which bring them closer to the Sun even than Earth. It is calculated that one of them, Hermes, might one day pass between Earth and the Moon.

The Giant Planets – Jupiter, Saturn, Uranus and Neptune

Beyond the asteroids lies the largest planet, **Jupiter**. It is big enough to hold 1300 Earths. If it was just a little more massive it would turn into a star. As it is, the energy generated as it slowly collapses on itself creates huge storms in its atmosphere. One of these storms, a huge hurricane 48 000 km long by 11 000 km wide, has probably existed for thousands of years. This is the famous Great Red Spot, which you can see in picture 5.

At the visible 'surface', Jupiter's gravity field is 2.6 times stronger than Earth's. But what we see is not the planet's real surface, but the top of its atmosphere. This is made of swirling clouds of hydrogen, methane and ammonia. The bands on its surface are huge **jet streams**. Below the atmosphere is a very deep 'sea' of liquid, metallic hydrogen. This covers a comparatively small solid core. The planet's core is very hot. It might be rocky, or even white hot, solid hydrogen.

Like Jupiter, the next three planets are large and have a low density (see table 1). They are also likely to be made mostly of hydrogen and helium.

Saturn is famous for its 'rings', shown in picture 6. These are made of small rocks, pebbles and grains which orbit the planet, all together in the same plane. The Voyager spacecraft discovered that both **Uranus** and **Neptune** have rings as well. They are not so large or as clearly visible as Saturn's.

All these outer planets have several moons. Some orbit so close to their planet that they are in danger of being pulled apart by its gravity forces. One of the moons of Jupiter, **Io**, is being shaken up so much that it is hot enough inside for volcanoes to exist.

The odd one out

Pluto is the furthest known planet of the Solar System. But it isn't always the furthest – it moves in an orbit that cuts inside the orbit of Neptune.

Pluto is small and very hard to see. It was not discovered until 1930, fourteen years after its existence had been predicted (just as Neptune had been, because of its effect on the movement of the other outer planets).

It seemed to be a very small planet, probably smaller than Earth. We now know that it is a very strange object indeed. It is a 'double planet', with a moon, Charon, almost as big as itself.

Activities

A Holidays in space!

Imagine that it is the year 2020 and you are an advertising agent for holidays on the planets. Make up an advertising slogan and:

- draw a poster, or
- produce a TV commercial, or
- write and record a radio commercial

for 'A Holiday on Mars' (or Venus, or Jupiter, or...).

B Exploring the Solar System

Use a library to find out what you can about the probes that have been sent out to investigate the planets. Examples are: Venera (to Venus); Mariner (to Mercury and Venus); Pioneer (to Venus); Viking (to Mars); Voyager (to the outer planets).

C Looking for planets

At the beginning of each month some newspapers print star maps which show where the planets are in the sky for that month. You should be able to get one of these maps from school or from a public library. Use it to find some planets. Watch them over a few weeks to track their movements against the background of the fixed stars.

Questions

1 Use table 1 on pages 202–3 to answer the following questions.

a Which is the most massive planet?
b Which planet has the greatest gravity field at its surface?
c Which planet has its 'year' shorter than its 'day'?
d Which planet has the shortest day?
e Which planet has the longest day?

2 Why is it hard to get information about:

a Venus?
b Pluto?

3 Four planets have much higher densities than the others (see table 1).

a Which planets have this higher density?
b What is the reason for this high density?
c Get a sheet of paper at least 50 cm long and 5 cm wide. Draw a simple scale diagram of the Solar System to a scale of 100 Mm (megametres) to 1 mm. What does the attempt to do this tell you about the high-density and low-density groups of planets?

4 Use the data in table 1 to plot one or more of the following graphs. Put the name of the planet against its point on your graphs. Comment on each graph you draw.

a Plot the density of the planets against their distance from the Sun.
b Plot the mass of the planets against their distance from the Sun.
c Plot the mass of the planets against their density.
d Plot the orbital period ('year length') of the planets against their distance from the Sun.
e Plot the surface temperature of the planets against their distance from the Sun.

5 Use the data in table 1 to make bar charts of the following:

a the sizes (diameters) of the planets,
b the number of moons of each planet,
c the day lengths of the planets.

6 The Sun radiates 3.9×10^{26} J of energy every second. This energy comes from the conversion of its mass into energy, given by the Einstein equation $\boldsymbol{E = mc^2}$. Use this equation to check that to produce this energy output the Sun has to lose 4 million tonnes (4×10^9 kg) of matter every second.

7 The asteroids are the 'bits' of a planet that was never made. They orbit between Mars and Jupiter. Use the data in table 1, and any other ideas that you have, to answer the following questions.

a What would such a planet be like?
b Suggest its 'planetary data' – day length, size, distance from Sun, temperature, etc.
c Suggest a name for this planet.

F4
How the Earth was made

No one really knows how the Earth, the Sun and the planets were made. Scientists think that it was probably like this...

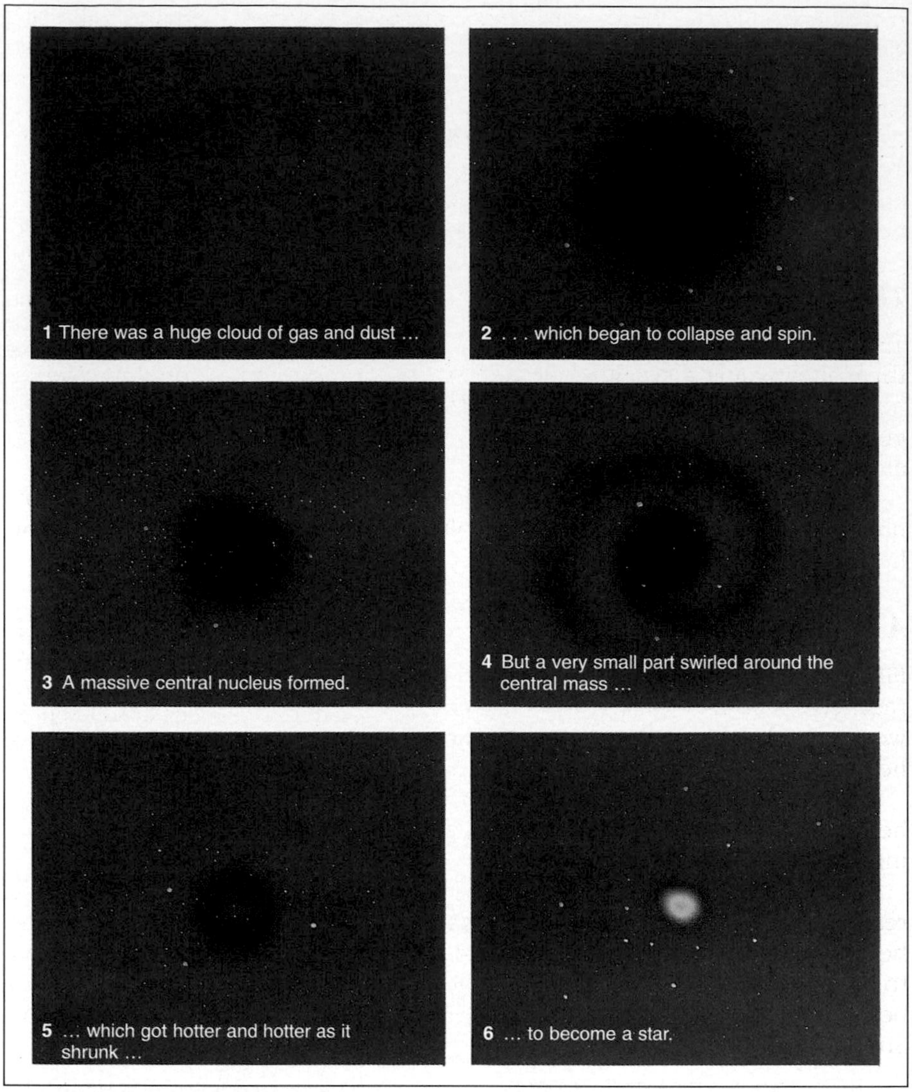

1 There was a huge cloud of gas and dust ...
2 . . . which began to collapse and spin.
3 A massive central nucleus formed.
4 But a very small part swirled around the central mass ...
5 ... which got hotter and hotter as it shrunk ...
6 ... to become a star.

Picture 1 The formation of the Sun.

Making a sun

It would have been about five thousand million years ago. On the outer edge of the Milky Way a thin, invisible cloud of gas and dust was collapsing inward, pulled by the force of its own gravity. The gas was mostly hydrogen, but about a fifth of it was helium. These are the two lightest elements, and make up most of the Universe.

As the cloud fell together it began to spin, and the smaller the cloud got the faster it spun (picture 1). When the cloud reached the size of the present Solar System it began to collapse very quickly. It took just twenty years to reach the size of the Earth's orbit.

At this size the molecules of gas were crowded close enough to smash into each other. As the particles fell they lost gravitational potential energy, and the gas got hotter.

The first glow

As the centre of the cloud became hotter and hotter it gave out radiation. At first the radiation was invisible infra-red radiation. As the temperature rose the cloud began to glow red. It was almost – but not yet – a **star**.

The light did not escape easily from the hot centre. The cloud of hydrogen was not pure. Mixed in with it were particles of other elements, mainly iron, nickel and silicon. There were also compounds: water, methane, silicates. These particles clumped together to make fine dust, or even small 'stones'. The frozen water was mixed with silicates to make lumps of what astronomers call 'dirty ice'. All these stopped most of the visible radiation escaping.

The gas continued to collapse, but much more slowly now that it was so hot. The gas and dust particles were moving very quickly at this temperature. Like any mass of hot gas it was trying to expand. There was a delicate balance between the force of gravity and the tendency of the gas particles to escape.

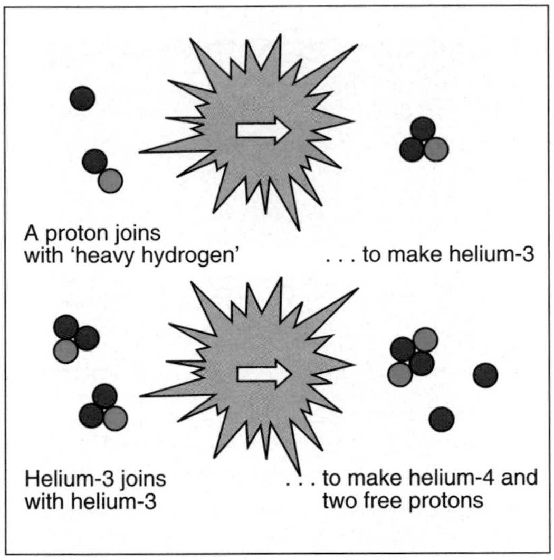

A proton joins with 'heavy hydrogen'
. . . to make helium-3
Helium-3 joins with helium-3
. . . to make helium-4 and two free protons

Picture 2 Nuclear fusion: hydrogen is changed to helium.

The birth of a star

Time went on. The gravitational energy of the gases falling into the centre of the cloud made it hotter and hotter. It went from being red hot to being white hot. In the hottest part the atoms smashed into each other so hard that their electrons were stripped away, leaving the nuclei of the hydrogen and helium atoms quite bare.

The mixture of electrons and nuclei were squashed together even more under the enormous pressure of the collapsing cloud. They became hotter and hotter, moving and colliding with greater and greater energies.

A hydrogen bomb

Fifty million years after the cloud started to collapse the centre of the cloud reached a temperature of ten million degrees Celsius. The hydrogen nuclei were now moving so fast that they began to stick to each other, producing helium nuclei. This is called **nuclear fusion**.

Now one of Einstein's ideas had come into play, the equation $E = mc^2$. The helium nucleus has less mass than the separate hydrogen nuclei, and the lost mass (m) became energy (picture 2).

Nuclear fusion like this is exactly what happens in a hydrogen bomb. The result was a sudden huge release of energy at the centre of the cloud. But the hot centre of the gas cloud did not explode like a bomb – it was far too heavy to be blown apart. It simply kept on working as a giant nuclear reactor, and has been doing so for about five billion years. It had become the star we call the Sun.

The force of light

One of the strangest properties of electromagnetic radiation – including ordinary light – is that it can exert a force when it shines on an object. The force that comes from a torch is very, very small – and you are not in danger of being knocked over by just the headlights of a car. But the Sun was now producing so much radiation that it began to have an important effect.

First, infra-red radiation was absorbed by the frozen water and gases, so that they became hot enough to melt and then evaporate. The fog of 'dirt' and ice became clearer. The radiation reached out to exert its pressure on more distant particles. The lighter material was slowly pushed away, leaving behind the heavier rocky and metallic pieces that were to form the inner planets (picture 3).

Radiation pressure pushed away a lot of the dust and gas. The Sun now contained only a small fraction of the original cloud, but it was still an enormous mass. It was enough for its gravity field to hold all the heavy particles and a lot of the gas molecules in orbit. The steady pressure of its radiation carried on the work of pushing the lightest particles into more distant orbits.

Gravity pulled inwards, radiation pushed outwards. The balance between these forces made the lighter material form a doughnut-shaped cloud, which was mostly hydrogen and helium, with ice and some solid grains of rock left from the original gas cloud.

This doughnut was about a thousand million kilometres away from the Sun

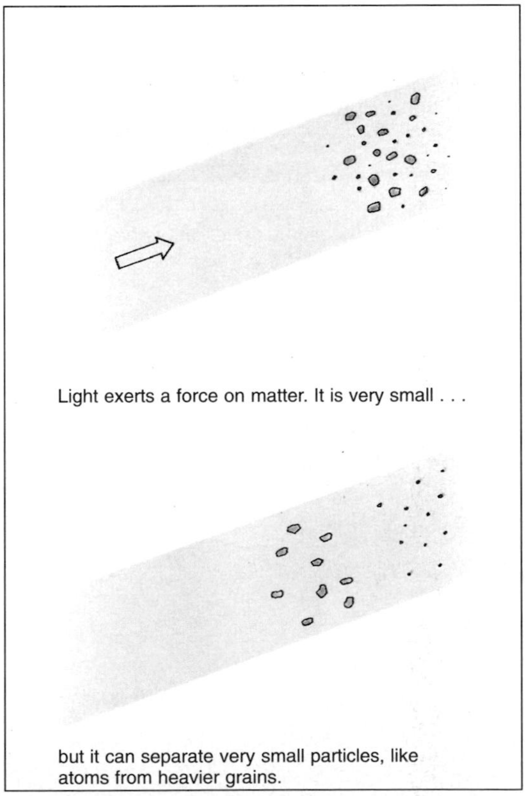

Light exerts a force on matter. It is very small . . .
but it can separate very small particles, like atoms from heavier grains.

Picture 3 Radiation evaporated water and frozen gases, and drove them away from the Sun.

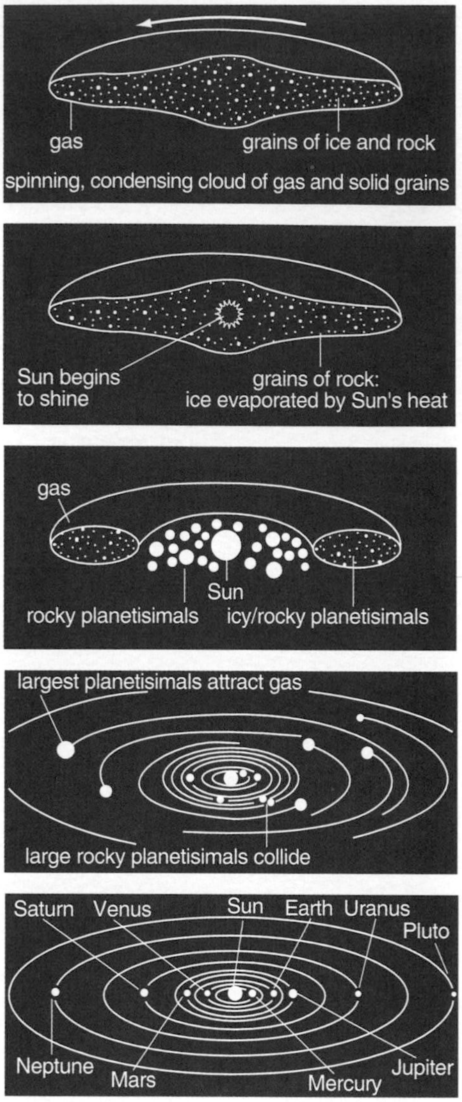

Picture 4 How the planets might have been formed.

(picture 4). Between the doughnut and the Sun was a chaotic crowd of grains and pebbles, each in its separate orbit.

Making the planets

Even the smallest particles produce a gravity force, and sooner or later this caused the countless trillions of particles, grains and pebbles to move closer together. When they collided they stuck together.

The larger lumps had a larger gravity field. The bigger they grew the more they were able to attract the smaller particles. Millions of rocky 'planetoids' grew, but in the end the larger ones swept up the smaller ones to make the **planets**.

Most of the particles – nearly three-quarters of them – eventually formed themselves into one very large lump. This was almost big enough to become a second Sun. But its central temperature never became quite as high as the 10 million degrees needed for a hydrogen-bomb explosion. Instead, it settled down to become the largest planet in the Solar System – Jupiter.

Most of what was left became the giant planets beyond Jupiter: Saturn, Uranus and Neptune (see topic F3). These large planets are mostly made of light materials, hydrogen, helium and methane. The heavier materials closer to the Sun formed the **inner planets**: Mercury, Venus, Earth and Mars. Between Mars and Jupiter is a belt of unsuccessful mini-planets which never quite made it – the **asteroids**. The orbits of the asteroids are being disturbed by the gravity field of their huge neighbour, Jupiter. This seems to stop them collecting together into a planet. It also means that some of them may be made to pass very close to Earth.

Comets

Far out in space, beyond the orbit of Pluto, there still exists the shell of the gas cloud that formed the Solar System. It contains perhaps 100 billion lumps of rocky ice, up to 8 km across. Now and again something disturbs their slow, distant orbits and one of them is propelled along a very long path towards the Sun. As it enters the Solar System the Sun melts the ice. The pressure of the Sun's radiation and the stream of particles it sends out also affect it. A long streamer of gas, ice and dust is formed. The sunlight reflects off this tail and we see a **comet**.

The most famous comet is **Halley's Comet** (see picture 5). It is a comet that has settled into a fixed orbit. It sweeps in a huge ellipse around the Sun, taking 76 years to complete each orbit. New comets appear quite often, for example, Comet Shoemaker–Levy, which actually crashed into Jupiter in July 1994.

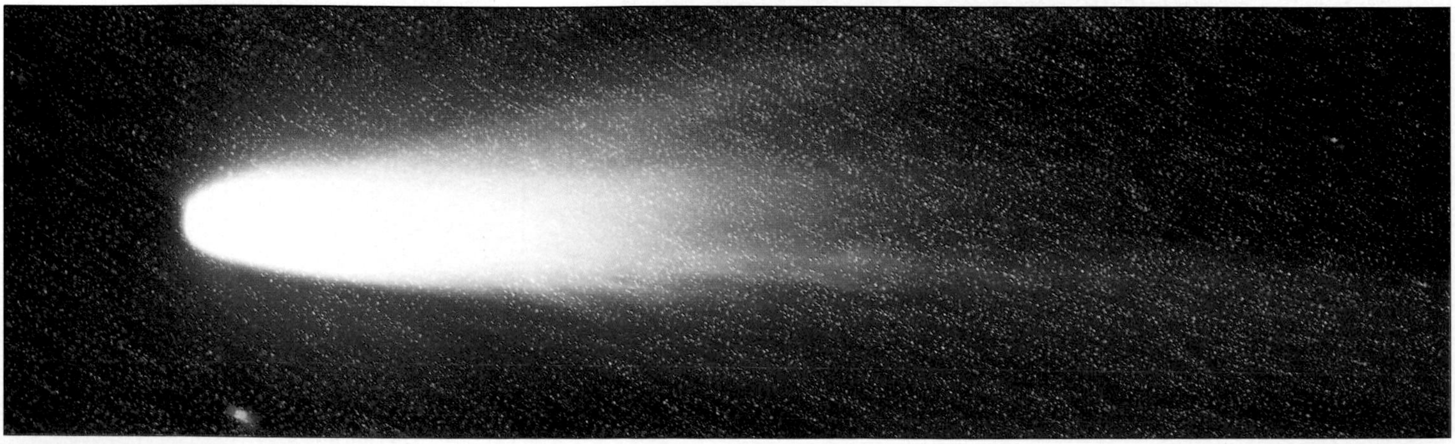

Picture 5 Halley's comet.

The Earth

The Earth is the largest of the inner, dense planets. Even so, its mass is only 0.3% the mass of Jupiter. It finished being formed about 4.5 billion years ago, according to measurements of the age of the oldest rocks.

The Earth can be called an iron planet. Its core is mostly iron, with some nickel mixed in. It has a very thin layer of lighter materials on top, forming the Earth's crust (see topic F1). It is just the right distance from the Sun for life as we know it to exist. It is not too cold – so water doesn't freeze all the time. It is not too hot, so water doesn't boil.

The Earth's crust is amazingly thin, compared with the size of the Earth, and so is the atmosphere. When you trace the outline of a coin with a pencil to represent the Earth, the thickness of the line would cover both crust and atmosphere. It is this crust, and the thin layer of gases surrounding it, which provide the materials that all life on Earth needs.

The surface of the Earth's crust is changed by the action of wind, water, earthquakes and the mysterious upwellings of new rocks from deeper inside the Earth. The energy to move winds and water on the Earth comes from the Sun.

The energy that produces volcanoes and earthquakes comes from deep inside the Earth.

How do we know all this?

The layered structure of the Earth was discovered by the study of earthquake waves. Just as radar waves bounce off different kinds of objects, so the shock waves from earthquakes bounce off the different layers of the Earth. See topic F1 for more details.

Radioactive dating

The best evidence for the age of the Earth comes from measurements of the radioactivity of minerals in rocks. This is also explained in topic D5.

Using this and other methods scientists have worked out that the oldest unmelted rock found on Earth is about four billion years old. The oldest rocks brought back by the American astronauts from the Moon were 4.5 billion years old. The Earth and Moon were probably formed at the same time, but the Earth is so active geologically that we are unlikely to find the oldest rocks still unchanged.

Meteorites

Meteorites are what we call 'shooting stars'. They are bits of dust and rock that enter the Earth's atmosphere from time to time. They travel at high speed and most of them are burnt up by friction before they reach the surface. They are the remains of the original cloud from which the Solar System was formed. Measurements on meteorites that have landed on Earth also give an age of about 4.5 billion years.

The surface of the Moon, and many of the moons of other planets, show the effects of meteorites. In the last stages of the formation of moons and planets meteorites weighing many thousands of tonnes collided with them. They made huge craters. With a good telescope you can see these on the surface of the Moon. They are also shown on page 199.

The oldest parts of the Earth also show large craters, probably formed by huge meteorites. Picture 6 shows Meteor Crater in Arizona. This was made by a large meteorite made of iron 2000 years ago.

Picture 7 on page 210 shows a meteorite burning up in the Earth's atmosphere on August 10, 1972. It was estimated to have a mass of 1000 tonnes, and its trail was large enough to be seen in daylight. Luckily it burnt out before reaching the ground. The Earth was formed by the collisions of planetoids and meteorites like this. It is in fact still growing, at a rate of 400 tonnes a day. Most of this is due to tiny meteorites which burn up in the atmosphere.

Picture 6 The Barringer Meteor Crater in Arizona. It is over a kilometre wide and 200 m deep. The largest we know on Earth is 26 km across.

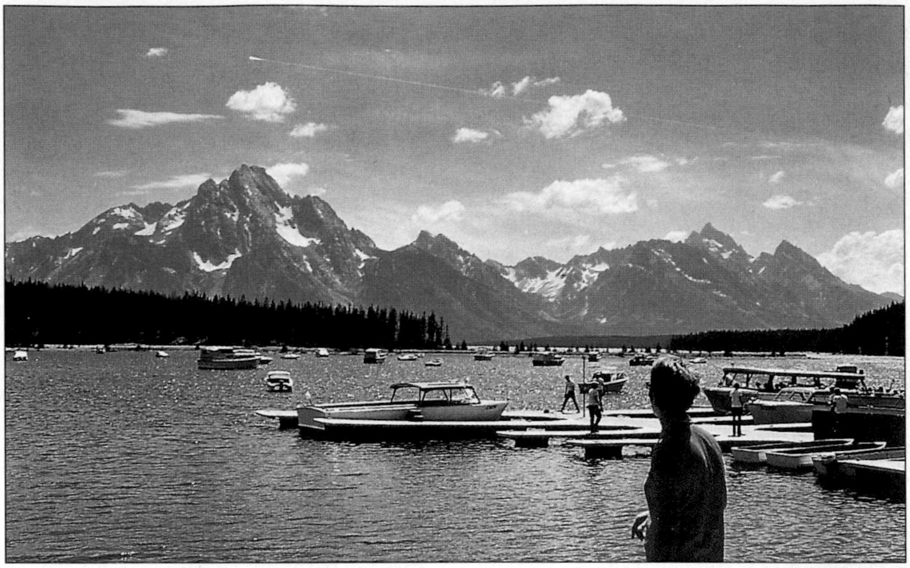

Picture 7 The daytime meteorite of 10 August 1972. It weighed 1000 tonnes and could have destroyed a small village.

The lives and deaths of stars

The Sun is a middle-aged star. It was formed about five billion years ago (5×10^9 years) by the process described above (pages 206–7). Will the Sun shine for ever? Or will it eventually run down and cease to exist as the source of energy that supports life on Earth?

The evidence for the likely future of the Sun comes from careful observations of other stars in the sky. The evidence is fitted into the theories of the **astrophysicists** who apply the laws of physics as we know them on Earth to what is seen in the wider universe. The most obvious things that we can see in the stars is that they are

- **bright** – but some are brighter than others,
- **coloured** – but different stars have different colours.

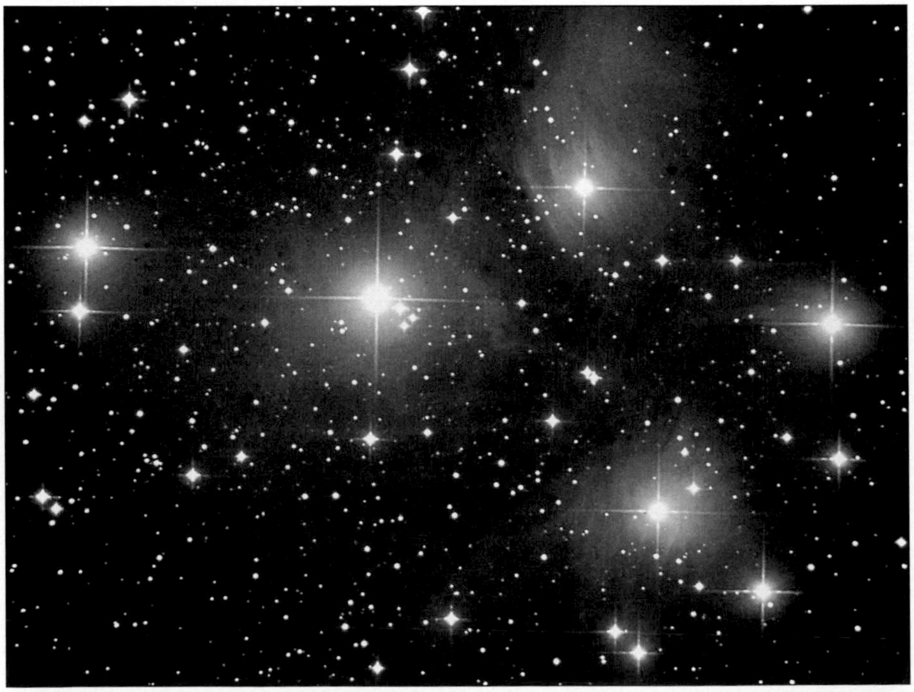

Picture 8 Stars vary in colour and brightness.

Why some stars are brighter than others

The brightness of a star is called its **magnitude**. One star can look brighter than another for two reasons. The first is that it is larger or hotter than normal stars. Or it could simply be an average star that happens to be quite close to the Earth. The brightest star in the sky is Sirius, the 'Dog Star' in the constellation Canis Major. Sirius is close to the Earth at about nine light years' distance. It is also hotter than average. If Sirius were twice as far away it would look just a quarter as bright. To compare the brightness of stars astronomers work out how bright they would look at a *standard* distance from Earth. This gives a standard brightness value called the **absolute magnitude** for the star.

Why are stars coloured?

Imagine heating a piece of steel. When it is too hot to touch it doesn't look any different but it emits invisible infra-red radiation (see page 84) which you can feel with your skin. As it gets hotter it begins to glow a dull red. Hotter still, yellow appears and the steel glows with an orange light. Then it becomes white hot. At a high enough temperature the white light is tinged with blue, but the steel will now be melting. All materials show similar colour changes as they are heated, and the colour balance in the radiation they send out is an accurate measure of their temperature.

When a graph is plotted of the absolute magnitudes of stars against their colours an interesting pattern appears. Picture 9 shows this, plotted on a graph called the **Hertzsprung–Russell Diagram**. The colour axis has also been labelled with the corresponding temperature. This is, of course, the surface temperature – stars are much hotter inside. Most stars fit into a broad curving band called the Main Sequence.

Above and to the right of the Main Sequence we find brighter, redder (so cooler) stars. Although these are cool they are bright because they are very large, and are called **Red Giant** stars. The easiest Red Giant to see is Betelgeuse in Orion (shown in picture 12).

Below and to the left we find dim stars that are quite hot. They are dim because they are small, and are called **White Dwarfs**.

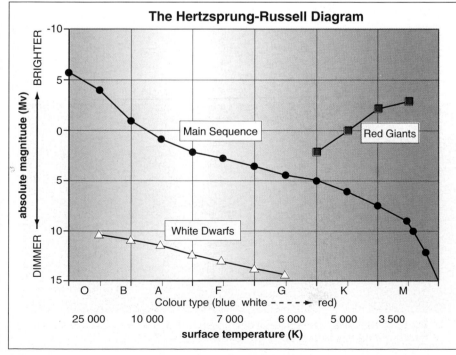

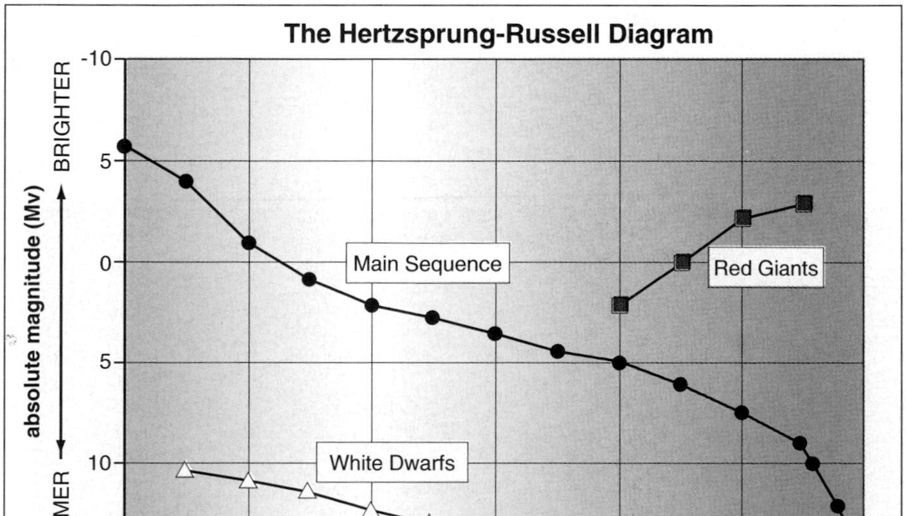

Picture 9

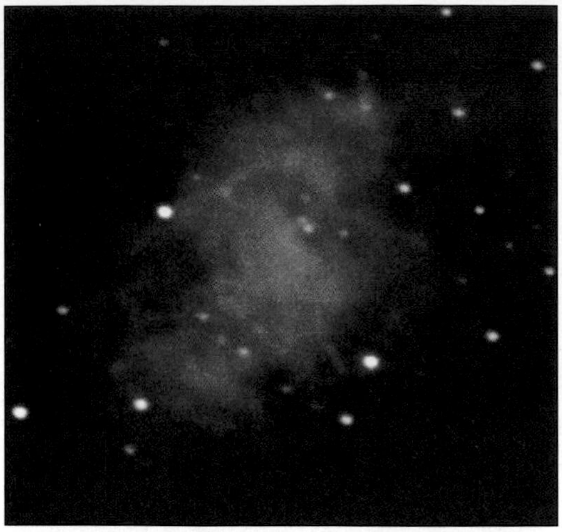

Picture 10 The Crab Nebula is a cloud of hot gas moving away at high speed from a neutron star. It is the remains of a supernova which exploded in 1054, forming a short-lived 'new star' which was bright enough to be seen in daylight.

The life of a star

The Sun is firmly in the Main Sequence. As it formed it began to glow red and would have lain just outside the Main Sequence. It quickly brightened and took its place as a yellowish star but of below average brightness.

A star formed from a much bigger cloud of gas and dust would have become bigger, hotter and much brighter – like Sirius. Sirius emits 30 times as much energy as the Sun. The very bright 'Blue Giant' stars emit as much as 40 000 times as much energy. All the stars on the Main Sequence get their energy by the hydrogen to helium fusion process described on page 207. The energy from fusion keeps the pressure of the nuclei that form the Sun high enough to stop it collapsing under the immense gravitational forces that exist. As time goes on hydrogen is used up. What happens next depends on the size of the star.

In an average size star like the Sun the following happens. When the hydrogen–helium conversion finishes other nuclear conversion processes take over. For example, helium is converted to carbon and carbon to oxygen, neon or magnesium. Some of these energy-releasing processes occur in layers nearer the surface of the star. Here the gravitational pressure is less and the star suddenly expands to many times its original size. The surface cools. It has become a Red Giant. Eventually all possible nuclear reactions are finished. The star cools and collapses to become a dwarf star. But gravitational potential energy is released and the star gets hot enough to become a White Dwarf. It is estimated that the Sun has enough hydrogen to stay as a normal star for another five billion years or so, when it will become a Red Giant, expanding to include the orbits of Earth and Mars. It will later become a **White Dwarf** with a diameter of about 10 000 km, about a hundredth of its present size.

Large stars burn up their nuclear fuel very quickly. They make very large Red Giants. When they collapse the gravitational energy released triggers off violent nuclear reactions. The result may be an exploding star called a **supernova**. Most of the star's mass is ejected into space, with a great release of energy. The core remains as a very small, massive star: a **neutron star** (picture 10). Some very massive stars may collapse to form black holes – matter which is so dense that its gravity field can trap light.

Activities

A Looking for stars

The gas clouds which turn into stars are usually invisible, although they can detected by the radio or infra-red radiation they emit. But a small telescope or pair of binoculars will show you a gas cloud which is glowing brightly with the light of new stars that have just formed. This is the cloud ('nebula') in the constellation of Orion. Picture 11 shows a photograph of this cloud taken with a large telescope, and picture 12 shows where it is.

Picture 11 The Orion Nebula is a huge cloud of dust and gas. New stars were discovered in the Nebula in 1955 that hadn't been there ten years earlier.

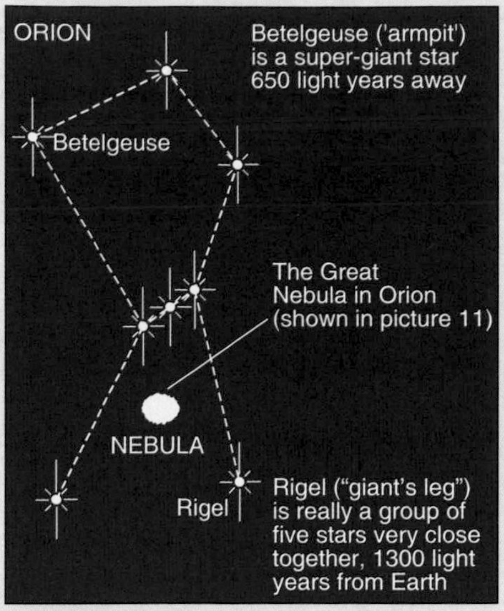
ORION
Betelgeuse ('armpit') is a super-giant star 650 light years away
Betelgeuse
The Great Nebula in Orion (shown in picture 11)
NEBULA
Rigel
Rigel ("giant's leg") is really a group of five stars very close together, 1300 light years from Earth

Picture 12

Use a star map to find Orion. You can get a map from your library, or from the newspapers which publish star maps near the beginning of each month. Use the map to find the Nebula.

B Looking for meteors

Meteors are meteorites that burn up completely in the atmosphere. Most of them are no bigger than grains of sand. They are likely to be the bits that get left behind by comets. Each year the Earth passes through these old comet paths and we get an extra supply of meteors – **meteor showers**.

Try to see some meteors (or 'shooting stars'), during the following periods:

April 12–24: linked with Halley's Comet, best on April 22

July 20–Aug 19: linked with Tuttle's Comet, best on August 11

Oct 11–30: another pass through Halley's trail, best on October 19

Oct 24–Dec 10: linked with Temple's Comet, best on November 13

Dec 5–19: best on December 12

C Catching up

The exploration of the Solar System is still taking place. New theories and evidence are appearing every year. This mostly comes from deep space probes like the Voyager and Galileo spacecraft.

There are plans to send probes, and possibly manned spacecraft, to Mars.

The Hubble Space Telescope is a satellite-based telescope that should revolutionise our understanding of distant galaxies.

Find out all you can about one of these and prepare to make a presentation to your class about it.

Questions

1 What are: (a) comets, (b) asteroids, (c) satellites?

2 The Solar System began as a gas cloud. When the gas cloud collapsed it was squashed together by gravity. It got hotter. Give an example from your own experience where squashing a gas makes it hot.

3 Explain why the 'inner planets' are made of denser material than the outer ones.

4 a A million years is a long time. Were you alive a million *seconds* ago? What were you doing a million minutes ago?
b A billion is a thousand millions. Where were you a billion seconds ago?
c What was the world like a billion days ago?

5 How does the Sun get its energy?

6 Explain, using a diagram, why the energy the Earth gets from the Sun is only a tiny fraction of the energy the Sun emits. (*Hint* the Earth is 150 million km from the Sun.)

7 Two stars at the same temperature radiate the same amount of energy per square metre of surface. Explain why (a) if one star is twice the radius of the other it will radiate four times as much energy in total, (b) both stars would look equally bright if the larger star was twice as far away as the smaller star.

8 Compare the life history (evolution) of the Sun with that of a star twenty times as massive.

Planets, atmospheres and life

This question brings together ideas from a number of topics. The table shows what the atmospheres of three planets are like. It also shows what the atmosphere of Earth was probably like, 4 billion years ago. The figures for the gases are fractions of the atmosphere, in percentages.

	Planet			
Atmosphere	**Venus**	**Young Earth**	**Mars**	**Earth now**
carbon dioxide	98	98	95	0.03
nitrogen	1.9	1.9	1.7	78
oxygen	trace	trace	0.13	21
rare gases	0.1	0.1	2	1
temperature on surface (°C)	477	300	-53	13
surface pressure	90	60	0.064	1

1 What are the main differences between the atmosphere of young Earth as it was and the Earth now?

2 One gas (very important for life!) has been left off the Earth data. What is it?

3 Where do you think the oxygen on the Earth has come from?

4 What has happened to the carbon dioxide that was in the young Earth's atmosphere?

5 Give two reasons why you would not expect to find life on Venus.

6 Would life be possible on Mars? Give some reasons for your answer.

F5
Outer space

When you look up at the night sky you are looking across immense distances. You are also looking back into very ancient times.

Time and distance

On 5 September 1977, a space craft was launched from Cape Canaveral, Florida, by the National Aeronautics and Space Administration (NASA). It left Earth at a speed of over 11 km/s. It needed this high speed to escape the pull of Earth's gravity field.

As it climbed away from Earth it slowed down, just as a ball slows down when you throw it up in the air. But after a few minutes the space craft had left the Earth's atmosphere and thrown away the empty shells of its rockets and fuel tanks. Voyager 2 had begun a journey to infinity.

Since 1977 Voyager 2 has been climbing through the gravity field of the Sun. The NASA space engineers have been clever. They have used the gravity fields of the planets to help Voyager 2 on its way. As it gets closer to a planet the space craft speeds up because of the increased gravity pull. Its approach is carefully angled so that the space craft changes direction, swinging around one planet to move off exactly in the right direction to get to the next one. This is shown in picture 1.

Some of the pictures of the planets in topic F3 were taken by Voyager 2.

After exactly twelve years, Voyager 2 shot past Neptune, the last of the giant gas planets in the Solar System. As it leaves the Solar System, it will miss Pluto, the outermost planet, because it is in a different part of the sky.

Space travel?

Voyager 2 is now moving into outer space. This is a very empty place. By comparison, the Solar System is crowded with planets, comets, meteorites and asteroids. There are also bits of dust and molecules left over from its formation, ten billion years ago.

When will Voyager 2 reach the stars?

When it leaves the Solar System Voyager 2 will be travelling at a speed of about 10 km/s, or 36 000 km/h. It will be moving towards the brightest star in the sky, **Sirius**. This is in the constellation of Canis Major which you can find just off the Milky Way, low in the sky below Orion.

Voyager will take nearly 300 000 years to get there. Barring accidents, it will reach Sirius in the year 296036. Sirius is one of the stars closest to the Solar System.

Picture 1 How Voyager 2 used the planets to move out to Neptune.

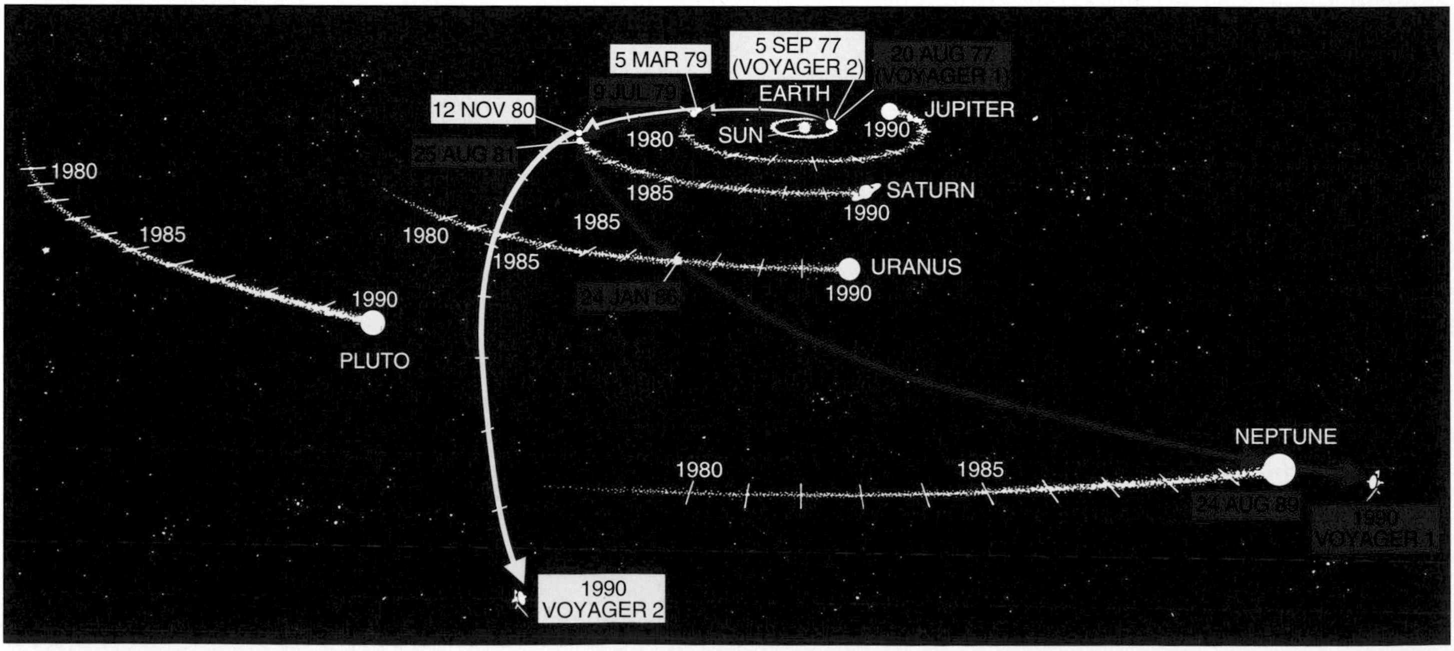

Space travel using rocket engines and space craft as we know them today is possible – but only to nearby planets. Travellers to the nearest stars will not return. If all went well, their descendants would come back, half a million years later.

The signals sent back from the planet Neptune by Voyager 2 took about four hours to reach NASA on Earth. They were of course radio signals, travelling at the speed of light. Signals from our nearest star, **Alpha Centauri**, would take 4.3 years to reach Earth. Messages from Sirius will take 9.7 years to arrive.

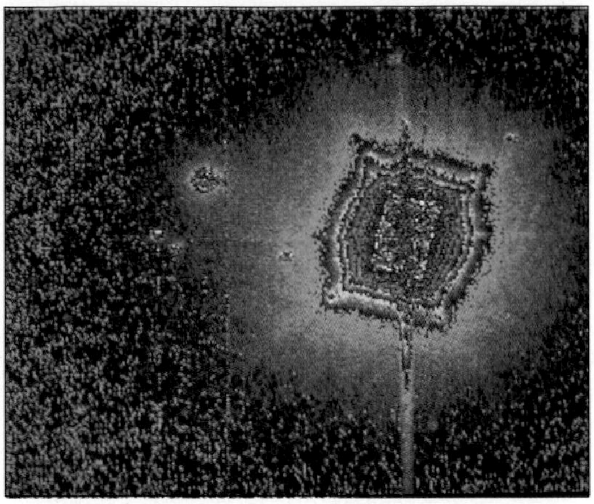

Picture 2 The 'Red Rectangle' star taken in red light with a very sensitive CCD camera similar to a video camera – but better!

Light years

The stars are so far away that astronomers measure their distances in terms of how long light or radio waves take to travel from them to Earth. A **light year** is the distance covered by light in one year. As light travels at a speed of 300 000 000 metres per second (3×10^8 m/s) in empty space, this is a very large distance. It is 9.5 thousand million million kilometres, which we can write as 9 500 000 000 000 000 km, or 9.5×10^{15} km.

Table 1 shows the distances of some well-known stars and galaxies from Earth.

Measuring the universe

We can use quite simple physics to find out what stars are like and what they are made of. We can measure how far away they are using much the same methods as surveyors use to make maps on Earth. The problem is that the stars are so far away, and the Earth is so small, that the work has to be done very carefully and with great accuracy.

Signals from space

Information about stars comes to us at the speed of light. It is carried by electromagnetic waves (see topic C6), and astronomers now use almost the whole range of radiation, from the very short X-rays to the long radio waves, to find out about stars.

When we look through a telescope our eyes can detect only visible radiation – light. Special photography can record invisible radiations, like X-rays, ultra-violet and infra-red. But most radiations from space are now detected and recorded electronically, and displayed on computer screens (see picture 2).

When it arrives on Earth the radiation from a star is all mixed up together. For it to be useful it has to be split up into a **spectrum**. Picture 3 shows a part of the spectrum of visible light from the Sun. Each dark line running across the spectrum is a clue about what elements the Sun contains.

A spectrum is produced when light passes through a **prism**, or through a

Table 1 Distances of stars and galaxies.

Object	Name	Distance from Earth (light-years)	
star	Alpha Centauri	4.3	Nearest star to Earth
star	Sirius	8.7	The brightest star we can see, the 'dog star' in Canis Major
star	Canopus	196	In Carina, used by air navigators
star	Betelgeuse	650	A red supergiant, the brightest star in Orion
star	Polaris	780	The Pole Star, in Ursa Major
galaxy	M31	2 200 000	The Andromeda galaxy, our nearest galaxy
	M81	10 000 000	In Ursa Major (The Plough)
	M87	42 000 000	The Sombrero Galaxy, in Virgo
clusters of galaxies	Virgo	78 000 000	In the constellation Virgo
	Hydra 3	3 960 000 000	In the constellation Hydra

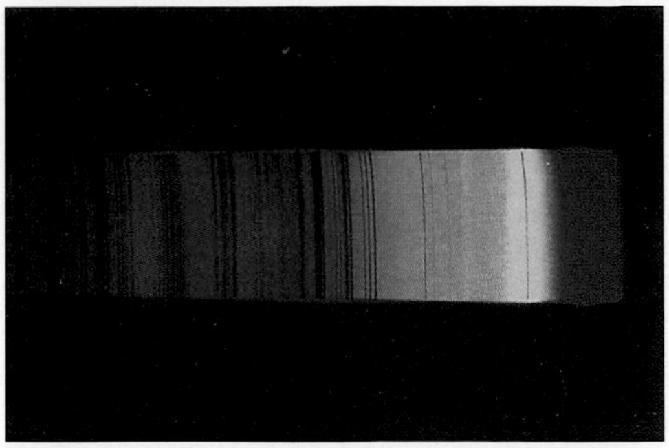

Picture 3 The dark lines in the spectrum of light from the Sun. These lines show what elements are present in the Sun's atmosphere.

diffraction grating. Different wavelengths in the radiation are separated out and so they can be photographed and studied.

Light from stars also shows these spectrum lines, and this is how we know what elements a star contains. Astronomers can also work out how hot the star is, by studying its spectrum. Activity A is about looking at spectra.

Stars also give out radio waves, which are picked up by huge **radio telescopes** (see picture 4). Radio waves tell us a lot about stars and also about the dark material we find in between the stars.

The scale of the universe

Human beings and many other animals are quite good at telling how far away things are. If one object seems to pass in front of another when it moves it must be nearer. This effect can also be seen when you move your head, and one object *appears* to move in front of another. (Just try looking out of the window and moving your head.)

How much the object appears to move gives our brains a good clue as to how far away it is. This effect is called **parallax**, and is used by astronomers to help measure distances of stars using a method called **triangulation**.

Picture 5 shows how triangulation works. Knowing the angles and the length of the baseline, a surveyor can calculate how far away the tree is.

Stars are much further away than trees. So astronomers use the longest baseline they can. This could be the diameter of the Earth, using two telescopes on opposite sides of the Earth. For very distant objects they use the diameter of the Earth's orbit, giving a baseline of 300 million kilometres.

Using this method, astronomers can measure the distances of stars as far away as about 300 light years or so. But this is just a very tiny part of the Universe. There are lots of stars with no measurable parallax which must be even further away.

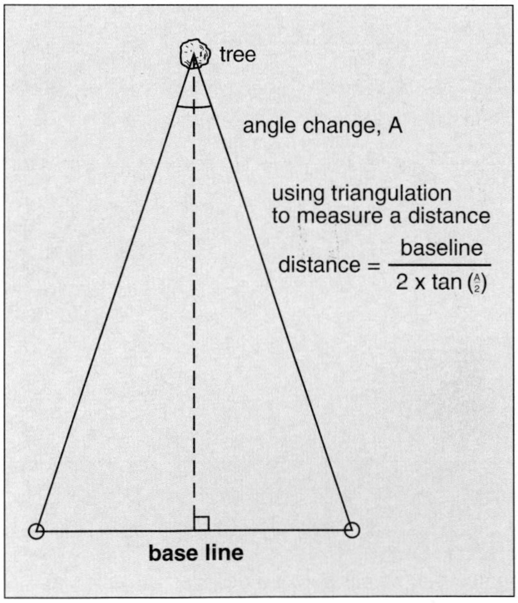

Picture 5 How triangulation works.

Using brightness

Some stars are brighter than others. This might be because they really do give out more light energy – or they might look bright because they are closer to us. The star Sirius, for example, is many times brighter than the Sun. But the Sun looks brighter because it is closer to us.

If we know how bright stars really are we can work out how far away they are. This is where the spectrum of starlight comes in again. Stars of different real brightness have different spectra. By looking at the spectrum of a star we can work out its real brightness, and so its distance from Earth.

Picture 4 The Jodrell Bank radio telescope. Astronomers now use the whole electromagnetic spectrum to observe the Universe. This is the 76 m Lowell telescope.

This method allowed astronomers to take measurements out to nearly all the stars you can see in the night sky.

Galaxies

On a clear night you might be able to see as many as 5000 stars. But if you use a telescope you can see far more stars (picture 6). And some of what you see are not stars at all, they are in fact huge groups of stars – called **galaxies**. The nearest galaxy to Earth is in the constellation of Andromeda. You can see it with the naked eye, on a fine summer night. Picture 7 (below) shows it as seen through a large telescope. To begin with astronomers thought that objects like this were clouds of gas – and called them **nebulae**, from the Latin word for a cloud.

We can now see that each speck of light is a star. Astronomers have discovered many thousands of these groups of stars, and we believe that the Universe contains many millions of them.

Edwin Hubble was an American astronomer who was put in charge of a new telescope at Mount Wilson in California. The first thing Hubble did was look at the Andromeda Nebula. He was the first astronomer to see that the 'cloud' was not a cloud of gas, but was made of millions of stars.

He was amazed to find that the stars in the Andromeda Nebula were further away than any other known object. The Nebula was over two million light years from Earth. He calculated that it contained more than a billion stars.

Galaxies upon galaxies as far as the telescope can see

Since then we have discovered many more galaxies. Some are 'quite close', at about the same distance as the Andromeda Nebula. This is our *Local Group* of galaxies: there are nineteen of them. Some are quite small, with just a few tens of thousands of stars. Others contain a few thousand million stars, like Andromeda and our own galaxy – the **Milky Way**.

We now know that the Universe is made up of many **groups** or **clusters** of galaxies, separated from each other by huge regions of empty space (picture 8). One of these clusters, in the constellation of Coma Berenices, contains 100 000 galaxies.

Picture 6 Star field in the Milky Way.

The expanding universe

After Andromeda, Edwin Hubble then turned his telescope on other nebulae. He measured them to be even further away.

Hubble also discovered something else. The Universe is expanding. In fact, it is expanding in all directions. He found that every galaxy in the Universe is moving away from every other galaxy. And the further apart they are, the faster they are travelling. It looked like the result of a gigantic explosion that took place billions of years before.

Picture 8 The Virgo cluster.

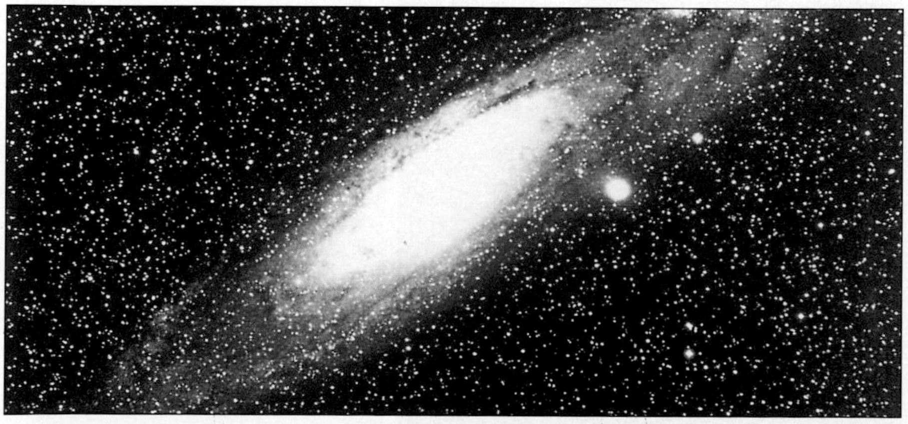

Picture 7 The nearest galaxy to Earth – the Great Nebula in Andromeda.

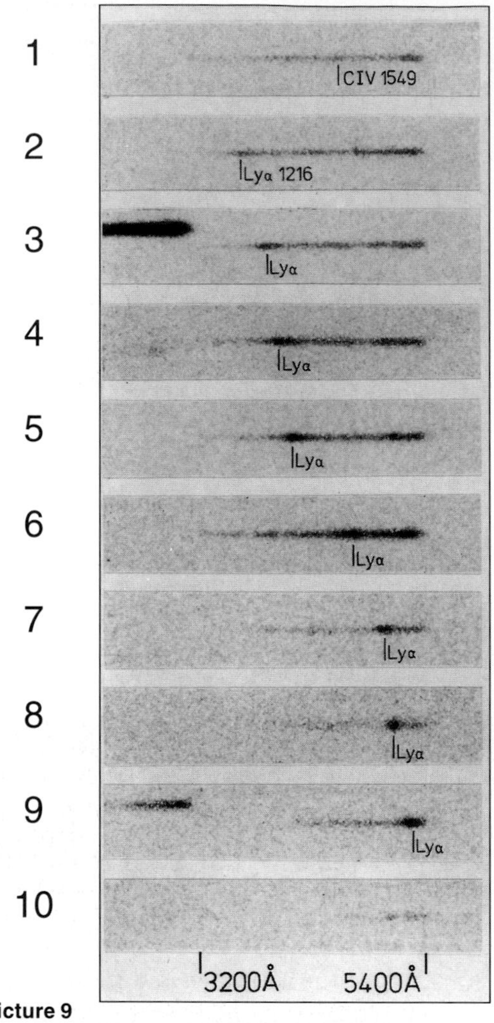

Picture 9

The Red Shift. These photographs show the spectra of very bright 'stars' called quasars. Going from top to bottom (1 to 9), the same spectrum line (Lyα) shifts across. It moves towards the red end of the spectrum – the 'red shift'. Quasars with the largest red shift are thought to be furthest away. The bigger the red shift, the faster they are moving. This fitted in with Hubble's theory of an expanding universe.

The red shift

The evidence for this expansion came from the spectra of the galaxies. But the spectra had all been somehow distorted. The lines did not appear at the same wavelengths as they did in the Sun. They had all shifted towards the red end of the spectrum – the **red shift** (see picture 9).

To an experienced astrophysicist like Hubble this was not a great surprise. He knew that waves from objects change their wavelengths and frequencies if the object is moving. It is the well-known **Doppler Effect** that you hear when ambulances or police cars move past you with the siren sounding. The effect is used in radar speed traps to measure the speeds of cars.

What was a surprise was the size of the change, and what it told astronomers about the distances of these further galaxies.

The size of the universe

With his new telescope and new techniques Hubble measured the distances of some galaxies that were not too far away. They too showed the red shift. He discovered a simple pattern between red shift and distance. It is known as **Hubble's Law**: *The further the galaxy is from Earth, the bigger is its red shift.*

But what did this mean? The red shift is caused by the galaxy's movement, so what his law really said was:

The further the galaxy is from Earth, the faster it is moving.

But this also means:

The faster it is moving, the further away it must be.

This is illustrated in picture 10. Thus objects with a large red shift must be very far away. This is now how we find how far away the most distant objects in the Universe are.

Time and the speed of light

The telescopes focused on these distant galaxies are seeing light that left them nine billion years ago.

We can never find out what they are like now. All the objects in the sky may already have changed! When you look at the Andromeda Nebula you are looking 2.5 million years into the past. Even the sunlight we see has taken eight minutes to reach us. The night sky is a historical museum of what the Universe was like at any time from four years to nine billion years ago.

The beginning – and the end

There is now a lot of evidence to back up the idea that the Universe was all together in one very small atom-sized place about fifteen billion years ago. That was when time started, and also space itself. There was what astronomers call

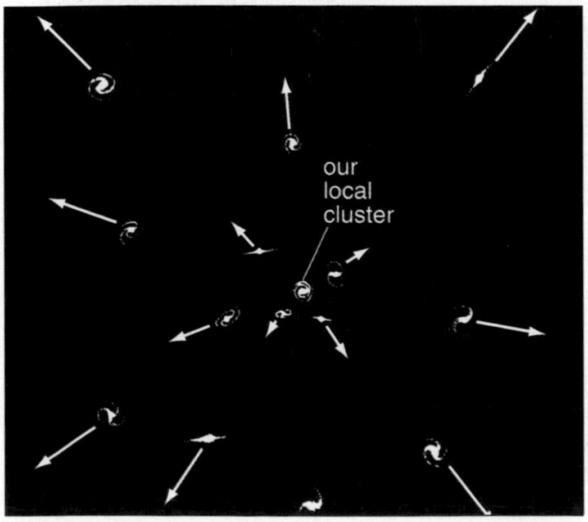

Picture 10 Galaxies are moving away from other galaxies.

the **Big Bang**, and everything started to happen.

Before that there was a kind of unimaginable nothing, not even empty space. But out of this nothing came the vast system of space–matter–energy–time that we now see as the Universe.

So what happens next? For a very long time – nothing much. In the very very distant future, long after the Earth has been swallowed up by an exploding Sun, one of three things might happen.

1 The Universe will reach a steady state and stop expanding.
2 The Universe will keep on expanding for ever and ever.
3 The Universe will stop expanding and start to fall back in on itself.

These options are illustrated in picture 11.

Gravity will decide which of the above actually happens. The Universe is held together by gravitational forces. These are produced by the combined mass of all the stars, dust and gas in all the galaxies and all the spaces in between them.

If there is not enough of this mass, the Universe will keep on expanding. If there is enough mass, its gravity force will stop the expansion and make the Universe collapse again, perhaps producing another Big Bang.

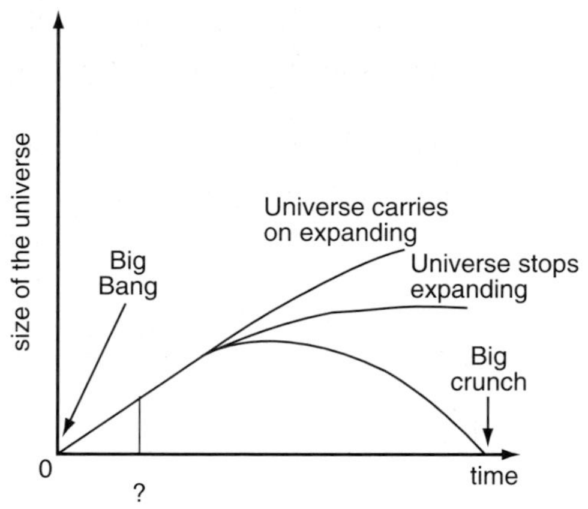

Picture 11 Three possible fates of the Universe.

Activities

A Looking at spectra

For this you need a prism – or better still a *diffraction grating*. You can look through it and see the light from different sources being spread out into a spectrum. Use it to do the following.

1 Look at the light from a 12 V lamp as the voltage applied to it is changed gradually from 2 V to 12 V. Explain how astronomers might be able to use a spectrum to tell the temperature of a star.

2 Look at a lamp that has a straight filament. What do you see when you put different coloured filters in front of the lamp? What do you see when you put a solution of chlorophyll in the way? If your teacher can arrange it, look through a tube of iodine vapour. This should help you understand how scientists can detect different elements by means of an *absorption spectrum*.

3 Look at the light given out by some or all of the following:

a a neon tube,
b a helium tube,
c salt being heated in a bunsen flame,
d other chemicals being heated in a bunsen flame – try salts of copper, potassium and barium.

4 Look at a thin line of sunlight reflected on a sheet of white paper. **CARE! Never look directly at the sun! Sunlight passing through any lens system – camera, telescope, binoculars etc. – can permanently damage your eyes.** You may be able to see the dark lines (Fraunhofer lines) that are shown in picture 3.

B In a different universe

There is a respectable scientific theory that says there may well be many different universes, with different properties. Imagine a universe in which the speed of light was only 1 m/s.

As a group activity, work out some of the effects that this would have. For example, on TV broadcasts, on team games, traffic etc.

C Looking things up

Use a good book on astronomy, or an encyclopaedia, to find out what the following astronomical objects are:

1 a black hole, **2** a pulsar, **3** a neutron star, **4** a quasar, **5** a globular cluster, **6** a radio galaxy.

Questions

1 a The speed of light is 300 000 km/s. How long, in kilometres, are the following distances:
(i) a light second, (ii) a light minute, (iii) a light day?
b Why is the 'light year' a more useful unit for measuring astronomical distances than the metre?

2 Look at table 1, showing the distances of stars from the Earth. Canopus is the second brightest star in the sky, and is just about half as bright as Sirius. Which of these stars has the greater real brightness? Give a reason for your answer.

3 Put the following in order of size, with the smallest first:

star, asteroid, galaxy, planet, meteorite.

4 The energy for the expansion of the Universe probably came from the 'Big Bang'. The rate at which the Universe is expanding is getting less. What could be making it slow down?

5 Russia and America are planning to send astronauts to the planet Mars and back. It is the second nearest planet to Earth.
a What are the problems that they might have to solve so that people could make this journey safely?
b This expedition will be very expensive, costing perhaps billions of dollars. Is it worth it?

6 Design a space ship that could take people to Sirius.

7 'Space: the final frontier!' How far will humans go?

8 Outline the problems of setting up a permanent human settlement on the Moon. Suggest some solutions to these problems.

Appendix
Physics: units, graphs and data

Units

All physical measurements are in units linked to a few basic **SI** (Système International) units. These base units are:
length: **metre**; time: **second**; mass: **kilogram**; electric current: **ampere**; temperature: **kelvin**; luminous intensity: **candela**; amount of substance: **mole**.

For example, **speed** is defined as *distance covered per unit of time*. **Velocity** is speed in a given direction. Thus the unit for speed is metre per second, written as m/s or m s^{-1}. Acceleration is velocity change per second, so its units are m/s^2 or m s^{-2}.

Force is defined in terms of how much a mass is accelerated:

$$\text{force} = \text{mass} \times \text{acceleration}.$$

Thus the units of force are kg m s^{-2}. This unit has its own name the newton (N). You should always quote the units when you write down the value of a physical quantity. The most common units have names chosen from the famous physicists who either invented the concept or investigated it well:

frequency	hertz	(Hz)
force	newton	(N)
current	ampere	(A)
electrical capacitance	farad	(F)
energy	joule	(J)
power	watt	(W)
potential difference	volt	(V)
pressure	pascal	(Pa)
electric charge	coulomb	(C)
resistance	ohm	(Ω)

Large and small

Prefixes are used to multiply units, always in powers of 10. The ones in common use are:

multiplying factor	**power of 10**	**prefix**	**symbol**
one billionth	10^{-9}	nano	n
one millionth	10^{-6}	micro	m
one thousandth	10^{-3}	milli	m
one hundredth	10^{-2}	centi	c
one thousand	10^{3}	kilo	k
one million	10^{6}	mega	M
one billion	10^{9}	giga	G

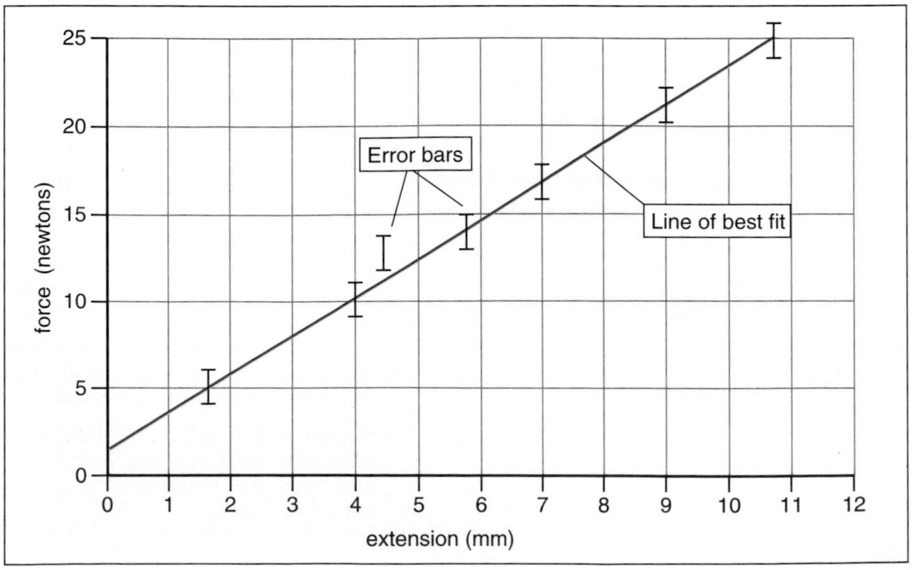

Picture 1 A well-drawn graph.

Fundamental formulae in physics

The fundamental formulae in physics are those that define important ideas in terms of simpler ones, for example, momentum is defined as mass × velocity. There are many other important formulae but they are 'discovered' relationships (like the Hooke Law) or are derived from more fundamental ones (like $s = ut + \frac{1}{2}at^2$). The fundamental formulae you have met in this book are:

speed (velocity): $v = \frac{s}{t}$

acceleration: $a = \frac{v}{t}$

force: $F = ma$

work: $W = Fs$

momentum: $p = mv$

gravitational potential energy: $E = mgh$

kinetic energy: $E = \frac{1}{2}mv^2$

pressure: $p = \frac{F}{A}$

resistance: $R = \frac{V}{I}$

power: $P = \frac{E}{t}$

electric charge: $Q = It$

electric potential difference: $V = \frac{E}{Q} = \frac{P(\text{power})}{I}$

Graphs

Graphs can show us the relationship between quantities, how one thing affects another. We can also make calculations from graphs. Most graphs in physics are line graphs. A useful line graph must have

- a clear, numbered scale, with correct units,
- points clearly plotted showing the data which were used to draw it (with error bars if possible),
- a line of best fit.

These features are illustrated in picture 1.

A **straight line** graph shows that one quantity is proportional to another. The two quantities (say x and y) will be related to each other by the relationship.

$$y = mx + c$$

where m is the slope (gradient) of the graph and c is the intercept on the y axis (picture 2). In this formula the value of y is decided by the value of x. y is thus called a dependent variable. x is the independent variable. As a general rule we use the vertical (y) axis to show what happens to a quantity when we vary another one, plotted on the horizontal (x) axis. The vertical axis is for the dependent variable, the x for the independent one. But this is not a strict rule. It often makes more sense to do it the other way around, as in picture 1.

A graph of two quantities related by a formula such as $y = k/x$ is an inverse relationship. It will be like picture 3, which was obtained by plotting volume

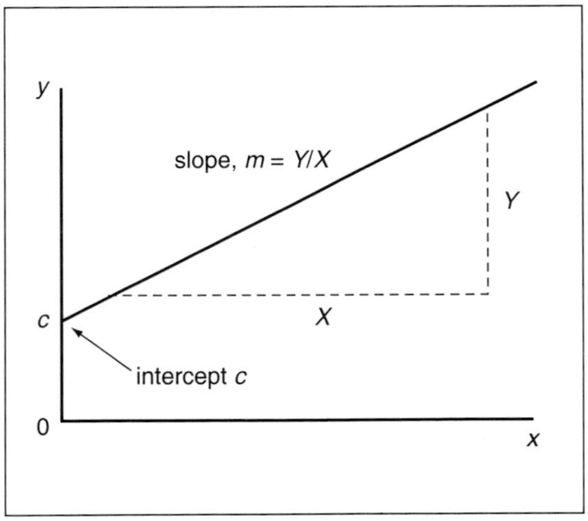

Picture 2 Illustration of linear relationship.

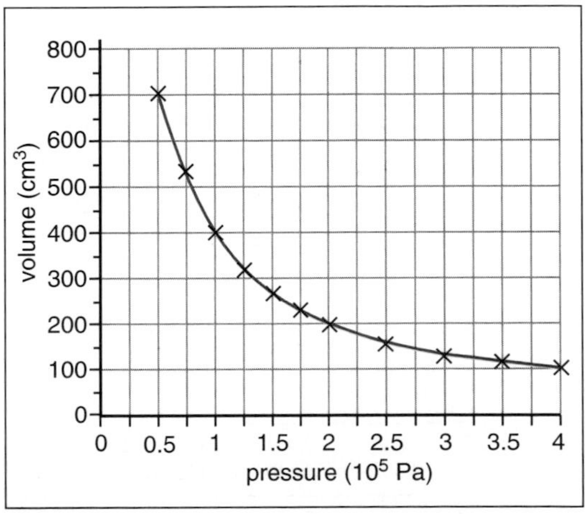

Picture 3

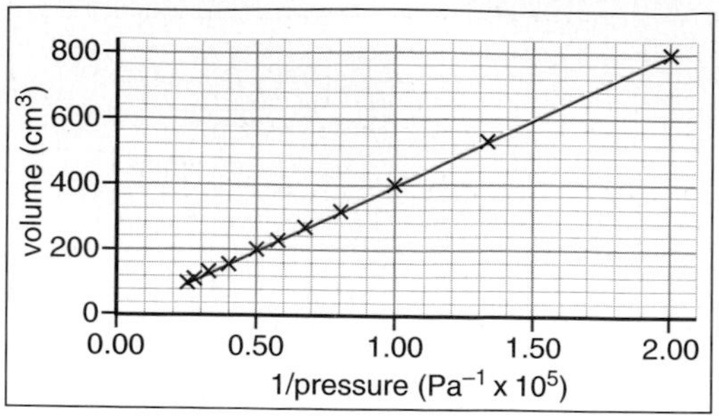

Picture 4

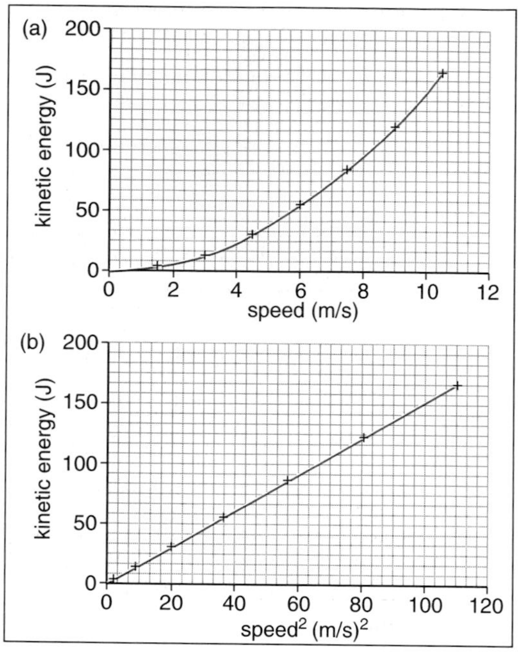

Picture 5 (a) and (b)

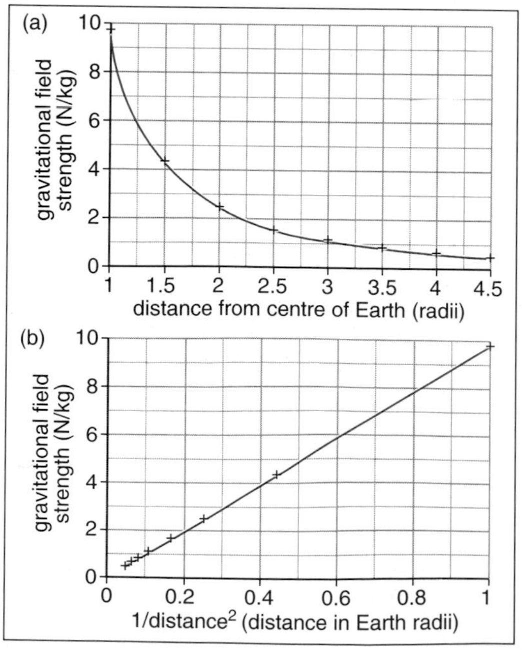

Picture 6

against pressure for a gas (Boyle's Law – page 38). If you suspect a relationship like this you can test it by plotting y against $\frac{1}{x}$. This produces a straight line, as in picture 4, which is based on the same data as the graph in picture 3.

Some relationships involve the square of the independent variable: for example, the kinetic energy (E_k) of a car is proportional to the speed squared. Picture 5(a) shows that E_k increases very rapidly as speed v increases. If you suspect that a set of results show this kind of relationship you can plot the dependent variable against the square of the independent one. This will give a straight line graph if your suspicion is correct (picture 5b).

Another common relationship in physics is an inverse square relationship: e.g. the gravitational law:

$$F = G\frac{Mm}{r^2}$$

This will also give a curved line when you plot F against r. A graph of F against $\frac{1}{r^2}$ will give a straight line (picture 6).

Graphs of growth and decay

Picture 7 shows how the activity (emission rate) of a sample of a radioactive isotope changes with time. The activity falls off with time, at first rapidly and then more slowly. This is typical of radioactive decay (see topic D6). Remember that the nucleus of a radioactive isotope is unstable. It is liable to emit some radiation and become a different nucleus as a result. The activity is always proportional to the number of undecayed nuclei present. The graph is due to a simple physical effect: when radiation is emitted from the first nucleus it stops being radioactive.

Thus the activity is high at the start because there are a lot of radioactive nuclei present. But as time goes on the number of active nuclei gets less, and so does the activity. This process is an example of what is called exponential decay.

Picture 8 shows what might happen to a population of rabbits when a small number are put on an island where there is plenty of food and no predators. The growth of the population is quite small at the start, but then rapidly increases. This is because the number of young rabbits added to the population each season is proportional to the number of mature rabbits present. As the offspring grow up, so they produce even more young rabbits. This is an example of an exponential growth.

Both examples have one thing in common: the change in a variable is proportional to the value of the variable itself at any time. The graphs also have a constant feature related to the time it takes for things to change. In exponential decay there will be a constant half life – this is the time it takes for the dependent variable to fall to half of any given value. In exponential growth we have a constant doubling time – this is the time it takes for the dependent variable to become twice what it was at any given time.

These values are shown on the graphs in pictures 7 and 8.

Using graphs

Graphs can be used to make predictions. For example, we can guess that in picture 9 the value of current at a voltage of 7 V is likely to be 0.29 A. It is unlikely that a well-behaved piece of metal will suddenly do something odd between 6 V and 8 V. We have no real evidence that it does behave well, of course. This trick of guessing a value we haven't actually measured is called interpolation.

We can even predict what should happen if we increased the voltage. If the wire carries on behaving as it did up to 12 V than it should carry a current of 0.67 A at 16 V. This kind of prediction from a graph is called extrapolation.

Both methods usually work well when the graph is linear, but it would be dangerous to rely on them for accurate predictions when the graph is like that in picture 10. Nevertheless predictions were made and later measurements showed them to be correct. This graph was of early results that showed that the universe had an average temperature of about 3 K, and was the main evidence for the Big Bang Theory of the origin of the universe (page 216).

The area under a graph

The area under a graph can give useful information. Picture 11(a) shows force plotted against extension when a spring is stretched. The shaded area under the graph is equal to the work done in stretching the spring. Why? The definition of work done is

$$\text{work} = \text{force} \times \text{distance moved by force}$$

The force increases as the spring extends, so that the work done per mm of extension changes continuously. The maximum force is F, the minimum is zero. Thus the average force is $\frac{F}{2}$

So we can say that the work done = average force × distance moved.

$= \frac{1}{2}Fx$ which is also the geometrical area under the graph.

This rule applies even when the force–distance relationship is not linear (picture 11(b)).

This idea is used on page 30 to derive formulae for distance moved by an accelerating object.

Example

The table shows the results of a test on the performance of a model car.

Time (s)	4	6	8	10	12	14	16	18	20
Speed (ms^{-1})	1.0	1.2	1.4	1.6	1.8	2.0	2.2	2.4	2.6

These results are plotted on a graph (picture 12). By extrapolating backwards the intercept on the speed axis shows us that at time zero the model was travelling at 0.6 ms^{-1}. We might guess that the car would be travelling at 3 m/s 24 seconds after the start of timing (by extrapolating forwards). The slope of the graph gives the acceleration: 0.1 ms^{-2}. The area under the graph gives the distance travelled in the first 20 seconds: 32 m.

Query: would it be sensible to predict by extrapolation that the model car would reach a speed of about 60 ms^{-1} after a total elapsed time of 10 minutes (600 s)?

Useful data

Fundamental physical constants

speed of light in a vacuum, c	3×10^{8} m s^{-1}
charge on electron, proton, e	1.6×10^{-19} C
Universal gravitational constant, G	6.67×10^{-11} N m^2 kg^{-2}
acceleration of free fall, g	9.8 m s^{-2}

Other constants

radius of Earth	6.4×10^{6} m
mass of Earth	6×10^{24} kg
Earth–Sun distance	1.5×10^{11} m
mass of Sun	2×10^{30} kg

Speeds

sound in air	330 m s^{-1}
sound in water	1410 m s^{-1}

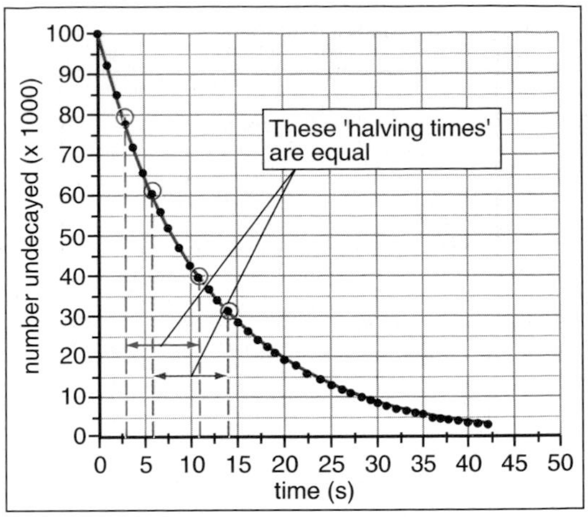

Picture 7 Exponential decay.

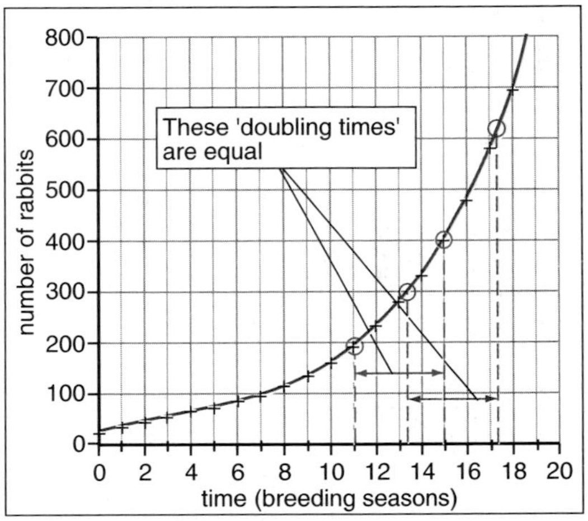

Picture 8 Exponential growth.

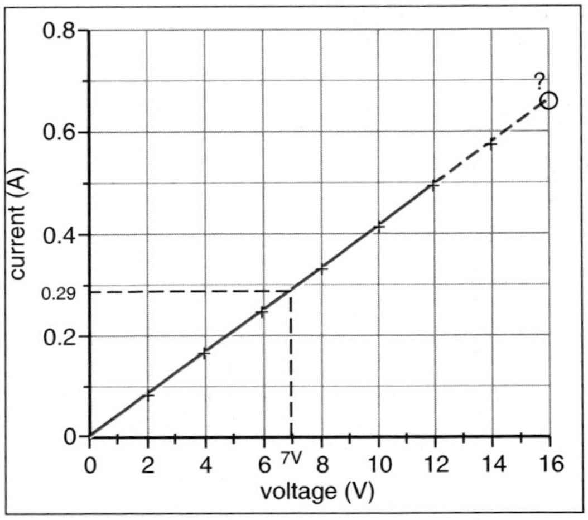

Picture 9

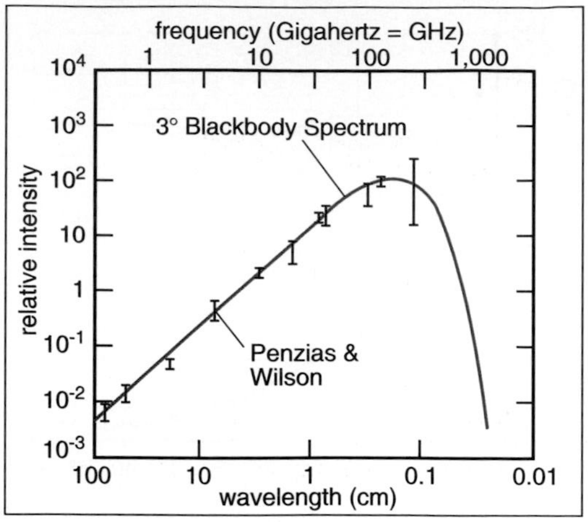

Picture 10 Early graph of 3 K background, with error bars.

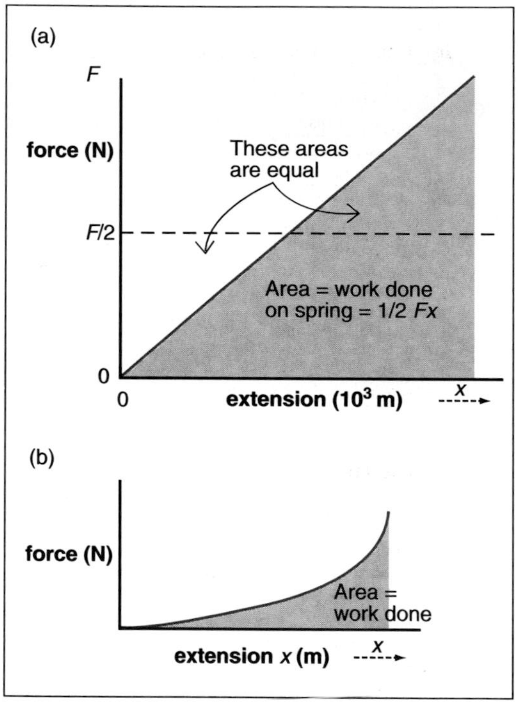

Picture 11

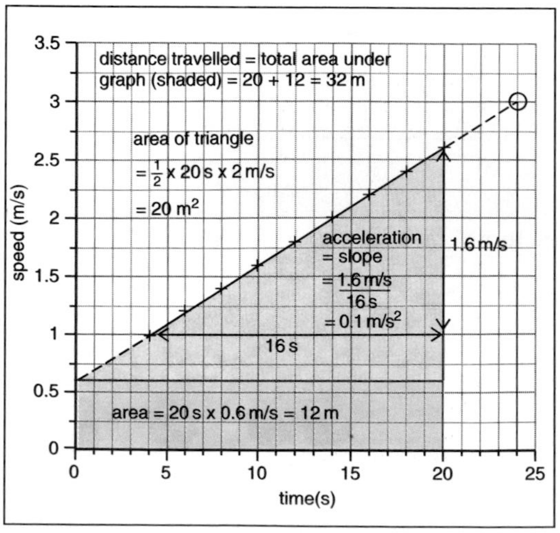

Picture 12

	Specific heat capacities ($J\ kg^{-1}\ K^{-1}$)	Densities ($kg\ m^{-3}$)
aluminium	886	2700
brass	372	8500
copper	380	8930
glass	about 600	about 2500
ice	210	920
rubber	113	920
iron	490	7870
lead	127	11370
marble	880	2700
water	4180	1000
paraffin	2140	800

Useful formulae

$$\textit{pressure} = \frac{\textit{force}}{\textit{area}} \qquad P = \frac{F}{A}$$

$$\textit{speed} = \frac{\textit{distance}}{\textit{time taken}}$$

$$\text{for an ideal gas, } \frac{p_1V_1}{T_1} = \frac{p_2V_2}{T_2}$$

work done = *force* × *distance moved in direction of force*

$$W = Fs$$

$$\textit{power} = \frac{\textit{energy transferred}}{\textit{time taken}} = \frac{\textit{work done}}{\textit{time taken}} \qquad P = \frac{W}{t}$$

electrical energy (in kWh) = *power* (in kW) × *time* (in h)

sum of clockwise moments about any point in a plane = *sum of anticlockwise moments about that point*

moment of a force about a pivot = *force* × *perpendicular distance from force to pivot*

energy = *potential difference* × *current* × *time* $W = VIt$

energy supplied to raise temperature = *mass* × *specific heat capacity* × *temperature change*

force = *mass* × *acceleration* $F = ma$

$$\textit{acceleration} = \frac{\textit{change in velocity}}{\textit{time taken}} \qquad a = \frac{v-u}{t}$$

wave speed = *frequency* × *wavelength* $v = f\lambda$

charge = *current* × *time* $Q = It$

potential difference = *current* × *resistance* $V = IR$

electric power = *potential difference* × *current* $P = VI$

weight = *mass* × *gravitational field strength* $W = mg$

for a body of mass m moving with velocity v, *kinetic energy* = $\frac{1}{2}mv^2$

for a body of mass m raised through a height, h, *increase in gravitational potential energy* = mgh

momentum = *mass* × *velocity*

Index

A
ac generator 182
acceleration 29
  of free fall 41–2, 44
acoustics 73
airbag 38
alpha particles 116–17
alternating curent (ac) 182
amplitude of sound 62–3
amplitude of waves 71
analogue signal 60
analogue-to-digital conversion 60
apparent depth 76
arch 14
Archimedes' Principle 11
atomic number 123
audible range 67
average speed 25

B
background radiation 118, 132
batteries 172–3
beam 14
bending forces 13
beta particles 116
Big Bang 218–19
boiling 109–10
Boyle's Law 38
brittleness 3, 12

C
cantilever 14
carbon fibre 7, 13
cathode ray oscilloscope (CRO) 189
cathode ray tube 188–9
CCD 175
cells, electric 173
centre of mass 16
chain reaction 129
charge and current 137
charge, electric 137, 155–6
charge, laws of 155
circuit breaker 164
circuit symbols 138
circuits 136
codes and coding 58–61
collisions 32
colours 90–91
  and temperatures of stars 211
comets 208
compass, magnetic 140
composite materials 6
compression forces 7, 13
concrete 7
conduction, thermal 106
conductors and insulators, electric 156, 176
conservation of energy law 112
constants, physical 223
constellations 198–9
convection 107
coulomb 137
critical angle 76
current, electric 137

D
data, useful 223
dating, radioactive 248
deafness 68
decay, radioactive 122–6
decibel (dB) 68
density 8
diffraction of light 86
diffraction of sound 72
digital coding 60
diode 151
dispersion 90
dynamo 170

E
ear and hearing 66–8
Earth
  age 209
  magnetic field 141
  origin 206
  structure 192
  'weighing' 49
earth wire 164
earthquake waves 192–4
echoes 64
eclipses, lunar and solar 199–200
efficiency
  of engines 114
  of a machine 20, 114
  of a power station 181
effort 19
Einstein, Albert 56–7
elasticity 3, 12
electric bell 174
electric charge and current 137
electric cooker 147
electric field 154
electric generator 170
electric heating and lighting 160–61
electric motors 169
electric power 162–3
electricity 154
  costing 162
  formulae 139
  generation of 180–81
  nature of 154–6
  and safety 164–6
  transmission 182–3
electrochemical series 173
electrolysis 177–8
electroplating 178
electromagnetic induction 169–70
electromagnetic spectrum 82–5
electromagnetism 142
electron gun 188
electrons 136, 176, 188
electrostatics 154–6
endoscope 77
energy
  costing 104–6
  definition 98
  laws (thermodynamics) 112–13
  measurement and units 101–2, 110
  systems 101
  thermal transfer 106–8
energy sources 96–8
  biomass 186
  from fuels 96
  geothermal 185
  hydroelectric 185
  kinetic 42, 99
  nuclear 128–31
  potential 42, 98
  renewable 184
  solar 96, 135
  tidal 134, 185
  waves 134, 185
  wind 185
equations of motion 25, 29–30
evaporation 110

F
Faraday, Michael 168–9
fibre optics 79
field
  electric 154
  gravitational 40–42
  magnetic 140–42
flotation 9
fluid pressure 21
fluorescent lamps 161
focus 75, 76–7
formulae, useful 221, 224
fossil fuels 96
free fall 41–2, 44
frequency 62
friction 34
fuses and circuit breakers 164–5

G
galaxies 217–18
Galileo 46–8
Galvani, Luigi 172
gamma rays 85, 116, 118
Geiger–Muller tube 117
generator, electric 176, 182
geostationary orbit 52
gravitation 40
gravitational field strength, *g* 40
gravitational potential energy 42–3
graphs of motion 30
graphs in physics 220–23

H
half-life 118
hearing, frequency range of 67
heat pump 113
hertz 62
Hertzsprung–Russell diagram 211
Hooke law 3
Hubble's Law 218
Hubble telescope 175
hydraulics 20
hydrocarbon fuels 96–7

I
images in mirrors 75
incidence, angle of 74
induction, electromagnetic 169–70
infra-red radiation 84, 107
insulation (thermal) 108–9
interference of light 86–7
ionising radiations 116
ions 116, 176–8
isotopes 122

J
joule 100
Joule, James 100

K
kelvin temperature scale 37
kinetic energy 42–3
kilowatt-hour 104, 162

L
latent heat 110
LDR 150

lenses 77
lever principle 18–19
levers 18
light
as wave 86–7
speed 80–81
light year 215
lines of force 140–42, 154
lithosphere 192
load 19
longitudinal waves 71
loudness and amplitude 63

M
machines 18–23
magnetic fields, poles 140–42
magnetism, law of 141
main sequence 211
mains plug 164
mantle 192
mass 33
mass and weight 40
mass number 123
mass spectrometer 120
materials 2
properties 9
meteorites 195
microwaves 84, 106
Milky Way 200, 217
mirrors, curved 74–5
moment of a force 18
momentum 33
and impulse 35
Moon 199
Morse code 59
motion
equations of 25, 29–30
graphs of 30
motor, electric 169
motor effect 168
motor rule 168–9
movement formulae 25, 29

N
National Grid 180–2
neutron star 212
neutrons 122
newton 30
Newton, Sir Isaac 44, 55–6
Newton's Laws of Motion 36
nuclear energy 128–31
nuclear fission 128
nuclear fusion 130
nuclear reactor 128–30
nuclear waste 130, 133
nucleus of atom 122

O
ohm 144
Ohm's Law 146
optical fibres 76, 79

P
parallax 216
parallel circuits 148–9
pendulum 44
period of a wave 70
phases of Moon 199
photons 92
physical constants 223
pitch and frequency 62
planes, sloping 19
planets 200
data 202–3
descriptions 203–4
origin 208
plastic 3
plate margins 196
plate tectonics 196
polarised light 88
potential difference 145
potential divider 145
potential energy, gravitational 42–3
power, definition 102
power, electric 162–3
power stations 180–81
prefixes, multiplying 220
pressure 21
in fluids 21
in gases 37–8
prisms 76, 90
protons 122
pulleys 19

Q
quality and shape of a note 62–3

R
radar 84
radiation as energy transfer 107
radiations, ionising 110
radiators, good and bad 108
radio 83
radioactive dating 120, 209
radioactivity 116–18
dangers of 132–3
detectors 117
Red Giant stars 211–12
red shift 218
reflection of light 74
total internal 76
refraction
of light 76, 81
and light speed 81
of sound 72
refrigerators 113
relative atomic mass 124
relative density 11
renewable energy sources 184
resistance and resistors 144–5, 149
resistance formulae 139, 148–9
resistors in parallel 148–9
resistors in series 148–9
rheostat 145
rockets 38, 51

S
satellites, Earth 50–53
seat belts 36
seismic waves 192–4
seismometer 193
semiconductor 157
series circuits 148–9
shear forces 13
shock, electric 165
SI units 220
signals, digital and analogue 60
Solar System 202–4
sonar 64
sound speeds 62
sounds 62–4
space travel 214
specific heat capacity 109
specific latent heat 110
spectrum
electromagnetic 82–5
of white light 90
speed 24, 25, 40–43
stability 15
stars
colour–magnitude diagram 211
constellations 198–9
distances 215
lives and deaths 210–12
magnitude 211
types 211
state, changes of 109–10
static electricity
uses 158
dangers 158
steam iron 199
stiffness 12
stopping distance of a vehicle 35
strength of a material 12
Sun 202
origin of 206–7
supernova 212
symbols, electric 138
synthetic materials 2

T
tectonic plates 196
telephone 95
tension forces 7, 13, 14
terminal velocity (speed) 42
thermal insulation 108–9
thermistors 150
thermostat 167
thrust 21
ticker-timer 25
torsion forces 13
total internal reflection 76
toughness 6–7
transducers 59
transformers 181, 183
transverse waves 71
triangulation 216
TV tube 188

U
ultrasound 68, 95
ultraviolet 85
'unit' of electricity 162
units of measurement 220
Universe 215
expansion of 217–19
upthrust 9, 11

V
variable resistor 145
volta 172
voltages and volts 145
Voyager spacecraft 214

W
watt 102
wave energy 71
wave speed formula 70
wavelength 70
weight 40
wheel and axle 22
White Dwarf stars 211
wiring, electrical mains 196
work
definition 100
and gravity 43, 101
and machines 18

X
X-rays 85, 190

Y
Young's two-slit experiment 87

Z
zodiac 200–1

Acknowledgements

The publishers are grateful to the following for permission to reproduce photographs. While every effort has been made to trace copyright holders, if any acknowledgement has been inadvertently omitted, the publishers will be pleased to make the necessary arrangements at the first opportunity.

Allsport, 24.1, 33.3/Adrian Murrel, 40.1/Yann, 112.1
Heather Angel, 172.1
David Bamber, 13.6
Barnaby's, 25.5, 32.2, 71.5
BICC, 183.9
Birmingham Symphony Hall, 73.12
Stuart Boreham, 13.7, 17.2, 17.18, 72.7, 108.11, 109.12, 145.3, 146.9
British Cement Association, 6.2
British Steel, 8.6
Carrington Counter Associates, 160.2
J Allan Cash, 7.5(a), 26.7, 42.8, 75.8, 100.1, 144.1, 180.1, 180.3, 216.4
John Urling Clark, 3.4, 13.4, 57.8, 140.1 *right*, 162.7, 165.5, 170.7, 170.9
Bruce Coleman, 14.11, 143.8/Colin Molyneaux, 172.2
Department of Transport, 34.6, 36.7
East Anglian Daily Times, 116.1
Ever Ready, 173.6
Ford, 38.1, 158.2
Griffin & George, 146.6
Hawker Siddley, 8.8
Michael Holford, 46.1, 55.3
Holt Studios, 108.9, 108.10
Hulton-Deutsch, 28.2 *bottom*, 59.5
Hutchison Library/Andre Singer, 98.7
Imperial War Museum, 83.6
Frank Lane Picture Agency/NASA, 52.7
Glynn Millhouse, 88.10
NASA, 203.3, 204.5, 212.11
Pilkington, 6.1
Renewable Energy Enquiries Bureau, 134.2, 134.3, 135.1
Rex, 12.1, 15.15
Richmond College Department of Photography, 86.1, 86.4, 87.7, 91.3
Chris Ridgers, 2.2, 5.1, 7.5(b), 14.1, 15.12 *top*, 18.1, 18.2, 25.3, 41.4, 66.1, 74.4, 76.11, 105.3, 106.5, 113.4, 136.1, 136.2, 137.5, 148.1, 154.2, 161.3, 164.1, 165.6, 166.7, 189.4, 189.6, 190.8
Ann Ronan, 28.2 *top*
Rowenta, 167.1, 167.2
Royal Observatory, 208.5, 217.8, 218.9
Salters, 4.6
Scope Optics, 78.18
Spectrum, 12.2, 20.1, 186.14
Science Photo Library, 2.1, 13.5, 15.12 *bottom*, 15.14, 28.1/NASA, 29.3/NASA, 32.1, 46.2, 50.1/Novosti, 50.2/NASA, 51.4/NASA, 52.8/Earth Satellite Corporation, 54.2, 55.4, 56.5, 56.6, 56.7, 57.9, 78.19, 90.1/David Parker, 92.5/Richard Folwell, 92.6/Ralph Eagle, 94.2/Imperial College, 95.1/J Croyle/Custom Medical, 95.3/Max Planck Institute, 96.2/Barney McGrath, 117.4/Los Alamos, 119.2/James King-Holmes, 131.5/Los Alamos, 132.1/John Heseltine, 132.2/Martin Bond, 149.6/Martin Dhorn, 154.1/J Kiovula, 154.4/James Stevenson, 155.6, 156.11/Gordon Garrad, 161.4/Hank Morgan, 185.12, 185.13, 190.10/Chris Priest, 191.11/Chris Priest, 193.5, 198.1/John Sandford, 198.2/NASA, 199.4 /NASA, 200.6/George East, 200.7/John Sandford, 203.2/NASA, 204.4/NASA, 204.6, 209.6/John Sandford, 210.7/Baker, 210.8, 212.10, 215.2/Royal Greenwich Observatory, 216.3/Imperial College, 217.6/Ronald Royer, 217.9/Max Planck Institute/NASA
TRIP, 178.6
Watford Stadium, 14.8
Wild Leitz(Heersburg), Germany 80.2